156

EMILE MEYERSON

IDENTITY & REALITY

AUTHORIZED TRANSLATION

By

Kate Loewenberg

DOVER PUBLICATIONS, INC.
NEW YORK

This new Dover edition, first published in 1962, is
an unabridged and unaltered republication of the
English translation first published by George Allen
& Unwin Limited in 1930.

This edition is published by special arrangement
with George Allen & Unwin Limited.

Library of Congress Catalog Card Number: 62-53523

Manufactured in the United States of America

Dover Publications, Inc.
180 Varick Street
New York 14, N. Y.

AUTHOR'S PREFACE
TO THE ENGLISH EDITION

FOR many years I have wished that this book might be known to the English-speaking public. The ideas developed in it are not entirely unfamiliar to that public. The very year of the book's appearance (1908) Professor A. Wolf reviewed it sympathetically in the *Hibbert Journal* (October 1908), and summaries of it, as well as of later books of mine, have since appeared. In 1915, A. J. Balfour (now Lord Balfour) concluded a chapter of his book, *Theism and Humanism* (p. 237), by acknowledging his "obligation to the acute and learned work" of the author of *Identity and Reality*. Nevertheless, material obstacles were difficult to overcome, and to render possible this translation there was needed all the disinterested enthusiasm of Mrs. Loewenberg, who devoted four years of effort to this thankless task. Much is due also to Professor Muirhead's very kind and effective help. I hope that they will accept here this expression of my great gratitude. I wish also to thank very heartily Professors Lenzen and Loewenberg (of the University of California) for their very competent and valuable suggestions concerning the translation of many scientific and philosophical terms.

The first edition of the book appeared in 1908; the second, revised and enlarged, in 1912. Since then I have changed nothing in the text. To the third edition, which appeared in 1926 and which has been used in this translation, I have added only a certain number of short notes designed especially to refer the reader to my later publications. The reason for this is, not that I was unaware of the need to introduce other corrections and improvements, but solely because I felt that I should embarrass the reader by a complete remodelling of a work which in the meantime has become somewhat known and is even used as a text in courses of instruction.

To leave the book in its present state has, it is true, this disadvantage: that on certain special points the exposition may not appear to recognize fully the most recent scientific ideas. For this condition I can only plead extenuating circumstances and ask the reader, on the one hand, to take into account the later writings referred to in the notes added to the third edition, and, on the other hand, to return in thought to the time, not so very distant, when the book originated. Moreover, since the object in my research has to do, not with the actual results of the physical sciences, but with the processes of thought by which they have been attained, the observations deduced from a certain phase of scientific knowledge cannot be regarded as useless just because a certain part of a science of a given period may now be judged to have been superseded. It is sufficient, so it seems to me, to invade even superficially the domain of the theory of knowledge to realize that the *form* of reasoning—which is here its essential part—strikes us only in so far as we are not in agreement with its *content*. Indeed from the point of view of the science of our day, form and content tend in some way to fuse inevitably: that which one concludes from the facts appears as flowing directly from them, as if it were there all present in advance. The science which we recognize as ours is like a tunic of Nessus which in vain we would try to shed; the functioning of our mind, in this case, is as imperceptible as is the progress of a boat to one aboard it who does not see the shores. In studying a subject with which we are no longer familiar, we see, on the contrary, the boat passing and we *cannot* be ignorant of its movement. This is the ruling idea which has directed the method of research employed in the present book, and that is why its results seem to me to apply not to the particular phases of this or that science but to scientific knowledge in general.

PARIS   EMILE MEYERSON
July 1929

AUTHOR'S PREFACE
TO THE FRENCH EDITION

THE present book belongs, by reason of its method, to the domain of the philosophy of science or *epistemology*, to use a word sufficiently appropriate and now becoming current. We have, however, in our research been guided by certain conceptions foreign to this domain.

The most important conception is that contained in the following words of Helmholtz: "The more I study phenomena the more I am struck by the uniformity and agreement in the action of mental processes." The context of this passage renders precise what at first sight might appear to be somewhat general and indefinite. The great physicist means that the unconscious psychological processes inseparably accompanying visual perception are identical with those of conscious thought. Those who have perused the *Physiological Optics* know that this is not a random statement but one of the fundamental ideas of that admirable work. It has seemed to us that the application of this principle might be considerably extended, that not only vision but the perception of the external world in general ought to set in motion the processes which nature would disclose, at least in part, if one were to scrutinize those by whose aid conscious thought transforms this image. In other words, we believe that the best way to solve the problems concerning common sense consists in examining the methods followed by science. In so doing we seem to run counter to that fundamental rule which demands that we proceed from the simple to the complex; but this is because the simple, in this case, is not really simple. Berkeley pointed this out before Helmholtz: the process of visual perception, to continue the example chosen, contains a number of condensed reasonings very difficult to follow. We have therefore a greater opportunity, assuming the process to be the same, of tracing the progress of a phenomenon apparently more complicated, but where the different stages will be differentiated.

Moreover, the rule that we have mentioned is dominated by that other more important rule which demands that we proceed from the known to the unknown. But he who speaks of the unconscious speaks of the unknown and of something in its very essence directly unknowable.

It is, however, not at all manifest that because of this the reasoning which we are accustomed to characterize as conscious offers to our mind all desirable clearness. Our reason is competent to scrutinize everything except itself. When I reason I am really powerless to observe the action of my reason. Is it, indeed, by such or such a way that I have arrived at such or such a deduction? As soon as I ask myself the question, doubt overwhelms me, a doubt which I can dispel only by rehearsing to the best of my ability, methodically, the reasoning in question, so that all its phases, which were subconscious while I was reasoning in order to attain the end as quickly as possible, appear on the level of my knowledge. It is thus, as we can readily see, that we proceed, for example, in logic. This procedure is not always free from danger. Reasoning carried on purposely shows us indeed *a* way by which we may arrive at a conclusion; but is it, in fact, *the* way which we have followed? It is certain that we cannot distinguish them directly, since the intermediary stages had not reached the level of our knowledge. Consequently, we resort to indirect means; we say to ourselves, for instance, that *if* we had reasoned in such a manner, such other result would have followed—a result which we are able to verify. But these investigations, direct or indirect, can easily lead us astray. It must not be forgotten, indeed, that research is always dominated by preconceived ideas—that is, by hypotheses; contrary to what Bacon believed, these are indispensable in guiding our advance. We are thus never entirely free from them; if we believe that we are, this simply proves that they have remained subconscious. Let us suppose, what is impossible, that we really have no opinion at the outset of our investigation of a given subject; an opinion will then come into being spontaneously with the first steps in the new field of inquiry, and it will come into being under the influence of dispositions of the mind hidden from ourselves and under the influence of a knowledge apparently quite foreign to the field we are studying. But the hypothesis once in existence will influence our entire later work. When we try afresh the same act of reasoning, we shall unconsciously seek to accommodate it to the idea which we had conceived, and, owing to the many resources which our reason has at its disposal, reason may be plastic enough to yield to the pressure which we involuntarily exercise upon it—and this evidently will falsify our results. We shall partly avoid this danger by turning, not to our own thoughts, expressly called forth for the occasion, but to the thought of others, free from plasticity, since it is embodied in writing and hence unchangeable. Science offers us a summary of these thoughts. But science of to-day is not sufficient. As a matter of fact, what we are looking for is less the result than the method, the way by which we came. Now the scientist on this point does not differ from the ordinary man. He does not see himself in the act of reasoning. He therefore does not know directly the way by which he has come to such or such a conclusion; the motives which have influenced him in adopting it may be very different from those which he himself supposes. That is why it is advisable to control his assertions by turning, not to the individual thought, but to the collective thought, by searching for the genesis, the evolution, of these conceptions in history. Finally, therefore, however devious this way may appear, it is with the help of the history of science that we shall search for the solution of problems concerning common sense. This is a procedure somewhat analogous to that extolled by Auguste Comte, and although we do not think of denying, as he did, the possibility of all introspective psychology, and since, as we shall see later, the results which we have obtained are very different from those promulgated by the founder of positivism, we believe that he merits great praise for proclaiming the fertility of the *a posteriori* method to discover the laws which rule the human mind.

Of course, we do not claim this procedure to be infallible. The principle upon which it rests, the identity of the progress of conscious and unconscious thought, is not at all self-evident, and we have no pretension of demonstrating it *a priori*. It is only a *heuristic* principle, a *working hypothesis*, which we hope the results of this book will tend to confirm to a great extent. In a sense, moreover, one may maintain that this procedure is unique and inevitable. Whatever we do, it is always with our reason that we reason. We do not know and we cannot know any way to establish a bond between concepts other than that followed by our reason, a term which can only signify here "conscious reason." Even when we believe that we most radically deviate from it, it is always with the help of scraps of conscious reasoning that we try to create another which is different.

*   *   *   *   *

The history of science to which we appeal is especially the history of the governing ideas in science. All those who know a little of this domain, know how much there remains to be done. To the best of our ability we ourselves have attempted to fill certain very evident gaps by returning directly to the sources; we dispensed with them each time that it seemed unnecessary to us, when the subject was sufficiently elucidated. Moreover, we have no illusions about the inadequacy of our information relative to certain very important questions.

Historical research being for us not an end but a means, it happens that the genesis of conceptions is not always stated in conformity with chronological order and that considerations relative to the same science, even to the same phase of evolution of some particular science, are scattered in different chapters; for instance, the evolution of chemistry in the eighteenth century before Lavoisier and the genesis of the modern notion of the chemical element are dealt with in Chapter VII and in Chapter X. We did not know how to avoid these inconveniences. It is for the reader to judge whether the results of our work compensate for the additional labour imposed upon him by this procedure.

We also wish to apologize for the multiplicity of quotations and notes. It would have been very difficult to dispense with the former, since the method adopted by us consists precisely in forming deductions by examining the processes of reasoning of scientists; on the other hand, the meaning of a text being determined at bottom only by the context, we believed that the reader would be helped in his verifications by having the opportunity to turn constantly to the book from which the quotation was taken. Moreover, is not the greatest merit of a work of this kind to prepare the way for later researches?

We have made every effort to acknowledge the work of our predecessors. There are certain omissions and we apologize for them in advance. No investigator, especially to-day when intellectual activity is so intense in a realm contiguous to so many different orders of thought, knows exactly how much he owes to the ideas of others. But we wish particularly to acknowledge the influence of Boutroux and Bergson, Poincaré and Duhem. This influence is not limited to the passages where their names are mentioned.

*   *   *   *   *

Here in brief is the general outline of our work. We begin by investigating whether it is true, as Comte and, later on,

Mach affirm, that all science is established only for the purpose of action and prevision. We prove that the principle thus put into play, the principle of lawfulness (*légalité*), is not enough, that science attempts equally to *explain* phenomena, and that this explanation consists in the identification of the antecedent and the consequent (Chapter I). It is from this second principle, the principle of *scientific causality*, that the atomic theories are derived (Chapter II). It enters also into the part of science devoted to law by creating the principles of conservation (Chapters III, IV, and V), and by bringing about the elimination of time (Chapter VI). An extension of this same principle creates the concept of the unity of matter which leads to the assimilation of this latter with space, and from that to the annihilation of the external world (Chapter VII). These conclusions are not a result of science, they come from the *a priori* elements which science conceals; science reacts, and this action is expressed by Carnot's principle (Chapter VIII). After having determined more precisely the limits of causal explanation, to which is opposed the concept of the irrational (Chapter IX), we show that non-mechanical theories are also evolved from the principle of causality (Chapter X). We then state that the world of common sense is created by a process strictly analogous to that which produces scientific theories (Chapter XI). We end with certain conclusions relative to the philosophy of science, during which we again examine, with the help of the results attained, the problem of the relation between the two principles of lawfulness and of causality (Chapter XII).

PARIS   EMILE MEYERSON
June 1907

EDITOR'S PREFACE

I HAVE been asked by the translator to write a short introduction to this book in its English dress, which may also be an introduction, if that is necessary, of Dr. Meyerson to the English-speaking public.

Born in 1859 at Lublin, at that time in Russian Poland, Emile Meyerson was sent, while still very young, to Dresden, thence to Leipsic, and finally to Berlin for the finishing of his school education. On leaving school he studied chemistry, first at Göttingen, then at Heidelberg, where Bunsen was at the height of his reputation, finally again at Berlin. In 1882 he settled in France, where for some years he was engaged in business as a practical chemist. In 1898 he accepted an administrative post in Paris, which he held till 1923.

During all these years his mind was occupied with other things besides the details of business. His interest in the history of chemistry had been aroused by Hermann Kopp's great book on that subject, but it was not confined to the history of chemistry and extended in the end to the history of natural science in all its branches, on which he is perhaps to-day the greatest living authority.

What interested him in the study of the history of science was not the succession of theories, however fascinating the story of these might be, but the principle which seemed to him to underlie all the efforts of the human mind to penetrate below the superficial generalizations of ordinary knowledge, and reach an explanation of phenomena which should satisfy the reason. What impressed him was the impossibility of understanding the various forms which scientific theory has taken, except in the light of a single principle which is bound up with the very nature of the mind itself, and in that sense may be said to be *a priori*.

This he found in the demand for something permanent and self-identical amid spatial and temporal change, and again amid the qualitative variety of elements. It was under the impulse of this demand that the atomic theory took shape in ancient philosophy, and has continued to our own time to assume one or other of its protean forms. It is this that, in physics, explains the rapidity with which the conception of the conservation of matter and energy were accepted on their first enunciation; in chemistry, the persistence of the belief in some one fundamental element into which all others are resolvable; in biology the old belief in preformation, and the general acceptance to-day of the idea of heredity.

The significance of this view becomes clear when we contrast it with such views as that of Comte and, more recently, of Mach, according to which the work of science is limited to finding likenesses in the characters and uniformities in the sequences of things,—in fact, the discovery of laws of phenomena in the interest of their practical application. Meyerson holds to the universality in nature of the principle of conformity to law—what he calls *légalité* ; but this is a conception with which the human mind can never rest content. Science in its essence is only a further stage of the "natural metaphysic," whereby common sense assumes the existence of permanent substances underlying the appearances of things. It is in vain that timidity and scepticism would confine it to the generalizations that are required for practice. Practice is only one of the phases of the life of mind. Going deeper than practice is the craving of the mind to discover rationality in the world, and to find itself at home in what presents itself as a foreign material.

While in this respect Meyerson parts company with the positivism that has formed so large a portion of the French tradition in science and philosophy, there are other respects in which he allies himself with that tradition. He is at one with it in approaching philosophy from the side of natural science, and in finding in Descartes the chief representative of the genius of modern thought. In spite of his admiration of the scholastics, of Newton, of Leibniz, and of Kant, Descartes, Lavoisier, Sadi Carnot are, as Leon Lichtenstein says,[1] his "three great heroes."

But there is a still deeper sense in which his work falls into line with ideas which are characteristic of French philosophy, as we know it to-day in such writers as Emile Boutroux and Henri Bergson. To him, as to them, the aim of science is the discovery of rationality in things, and rationality means the reduction of differences to identity in such a form that they shall be absorbed without remainder—an identity of which the mathematical equation is the type, and the undifferentiated Being of the Eleatic sphere is a picture. With these writers he holds also that this ideal is one that can never be completely achieved owing to the presence of a residual element of irrationality in nature, which in the end defies us. Our results are never either *a posteriori* or *a priori* completely demonstrable but only, to use his own phrase, "plausible." Yet there are degrees of plausibility and, in proportion as the innate and indomitable craving of the mind for rationality is satisfied, we have a right to speak of things as explicable.

The present work, in which Meyerson first expounded this view of the logic of the mind, amounting in reality to a theory of knowledge, was published in 1908. A second edition appeared in 1912, and a third (that from which this translation has been executed) in 1926.[2] It is impossible, except by reading it, to obtain any idea of the extent of learning combined with acute-

[1] See this writer's admirable article on the Philosophy of Emile Meyerson in the *Berichten der mathematisch-physischen Klasse der Sächischen Akademie der Wissenschaften zu Leipsig*, LXXX Band, to which I owe the above biographical details.

[2] Since it first appeared he has also published *L'explication dans le: sciences* (1921) and *La déduction relativiste* (1925).

ness of insight and lucidity of style which the book exhibits. Its importance has been recognized not only in his own country, but in Germany (where a translation of it is about to appear); not only by the general public, but by the leaders of science. In a recent article in *The Times* (February 5, 1929), Einstein referred to Meyerson's "brilliant studies in the theory of knowledge" as reflecting, in contrast to the suspicious attitude of so many physicists, the same spirit of faith in the uniformity of nature and its accessibility to the speculative intellect as has inspired the work of the mathematician.

Much doubtless might be said from the point of view of Logic of the complete validity of a conception of rationality which makes it consist in undifferentiated identity, as contrasted with that which finds it in the discovery of unity of principle in diversity of character, and which, under Hegel's influence, has recently dominated the work of English logicians. But a preface of this kind is a place for acknowledgment, not for criticism.

Besides the debt which we owe to the author himself for the interest he has taken in the translation and the preface he has written for it, and to the translator for the faithfulness of the rendering and the enormous labour that the verification of references to the English works, quoted in the French text, has involved, we have to acknowledge our obligation to Professor Lenzen, of the Physics Department in the University of California, who has read the whole of the translation in manuscript and been of the greatest assistance in securing accuracy in the rendering of technical terms.

J. H. MUIRHEAD

May 1929

CONTENTS

IDENTITY AND REALITY

CHAPTER I

LAW AND CAUSE

WHEN a certain phenomenon strikes our attention, it appears enigmatic at first, but after having studied it, we can explain it and we say that we know its cause.

What do these terms exactly mean? What is a scientific explanation? What is the cause for which we were looking?

A precise answer to this question was given by Berkeley nearly two centuries ago.(1) "For the laws of nature being once ascertained, it remains for the philosopher to show that each thing necessarily follows in conformity with these laws; that is, that every phenomenon necessarily results from these principles. This is to explain and solve the phenomena; that is, to assign the reason why they take place." From the context we see that Berkeley regarded the laws and the principles mentioned in this passage as experimental (*experimentis comprobatae*).

Thus the cause of a phenomenon is the law, the empirical rule, which governs the entire class of analogous phenomena. This rule teaches us that one group of phenomena involves another group. Since we are able to observe only in time, i.e. successively, the empirical law amounts really to a law of succession of phenomena. And consequently Berkeley's formula is equivalent to that enunciated a little later by Hume; namely, that the concept of cause or causality is reducible to succession.(2)

Berkeley's formula has often been revived since. "A stone tends to fall," says Taine, "because all objects tend to fall."(3) Helmholtz writes: "The principle of causality is nothing else than the supposition that all the phenomena of nature are subject to law."(4) Hannequin in the same way declares that "to search for the cause of a fact, is, for a physicist, to search for its law,"(5) and Ostwald formulates the principle of causality as follows: "If we establish the same conditions, phenomena will take place in the same manner,"(6) a statement which, we see, approaches Hume's conceptions.

Here we find a complete assimilation of the two concepts of "cause" and "law," the second entirely absorbing the first. But the opposite tendency has also continued—that is, efforts have been made to include the law in the cause. Thus Lucretius, after having stated what is, as we shall see later on, one of the forms of the principle of causality, declares that if we do not admit it, we are forced to give up establishing any regularity whatsoever in nature. "Nor would the same fruits stay constant to the trees, but all would change : all trees might avail to bear all fruits;"(7) and eighteen centuries later, Jean Bernoulli expresses himself in an identical manner by declaring that if we reject the principle of causality "all nature would fall into disorder".(8)

It seems that this assimilation could be explained only if there were a real logical identity between the two concepts of law and cause, if the two terms were synonymous. Everyone knows that this is not so. Yet it is important to throw some more light on this question.

Let us take up again the formula of Helmholtz, considering it for what it really is—that is, as an expression of the principle, not of causality, but of lawfulness (*légalité*). Although the use of this term is not customary in the sense we are giving to it, yet we believe it is clear: it signifies the supremacy of law. This will permit us to translate with more exactitude the last part of Helmholtz's phrase, which we have cited earlier, where he stipulates literally "the supposition of the lawfulness (*Gesetzlichkeit*) of all the phenomena of nature."(9).

How do we arrive at formulating laws? By the observation and the generalization of phenomena. The human mind's power of generalization has at all times occupied the attention of philosophers; but this is a chapter of logic which we mean to leave here completely aside. We shall consider as an accepted fact that the human mind possesses the faculty of forming, with the aid of the perception of different individuals, the concept *man*, just as it will form the concept *sulphur* with the aid of the perception of different pieces of a matter which is yellow, inflammable, etc. The principle of lawfulness of nature demands evidently the formation of such concepts, otherwise, phenomena being infinitely diverse we should not be able to formulate rules, and having once formulated them, we should not be in the least helped by them without the faculty of generalization.

Helmholtz, we have just seen, characterizes conformity to law as a "presupposition"; but, in certain respects, it is much more than that, it is a real conviction, perhaps the strongest amongst those we are capable of harbouring. In fact, all of our conscious acts are intentional acts—that is, acts performed in view of an end which we foresee; but this foresight would be entirely impossible if we did not have the absolute conviction that nature is well-ordered, that certain antecedents determine and will always determine certain consequences. It is this which Auguste Comte has summed up in the following terms: "Knowledge generates foresight, foresight generates action."(10)

It has sometimes been asserted that this conviction is based solely on experience. But this seems difficult to believe. Without doubt, from the abstract point of view one can completely separate observation from action, construct a type of observation from which every element of action would be absent. But when one thinks of the functioning of our sense organs, of their elementary acts, intentional or semi-intentional, which it pre-supposes, such as turning the eyes or moving the hands, one begins to doubt the possibility of a real separation of that kind; and one doubts especially whether the period of action is or ever has been preceded in nature by a period of observation necessary to establish the conviction that order is the rule of the world. It is indeed certain that primitive man, however near to the animal one may imagine him, must have been imbued with this conviction, since without this conviction he could not have acted at all; and the animal itself, acting as it does, implies, by its action, that its intelligence on this point does not radically differ from our own, unless we suppose, as did Descartes, that it is a simple machine, or that it does everything impelled only by instinct. The dog to whom I throw a piece of meat knows how to catch it in the air: this is because he knows in advance the trajectory that this body will describe in falling. It appears, without doubt, to him no less than to us, as a way of behaving, peculiar to the object thrown under certain circumstances—that is, as a law. Goethe has said: "In the beginning there was action."(11)

But the dog's processes of generalization and investigation are extremely limited. He knows how to foresee only a very limited number of phenomena. Primitive man was already immensely superior to him. His previsions, it is true, based on the belief in regularity, were applied only to a part of nature; a great number of phenomena appeared to him as evading the rule, being subject to the free-will of invisible powers. But however general one may suppose this latter conviction, it has doubtless never embraced more than the smallest part of the ordinary phenomena of life, the far greater number of phenomena having always been conceived as purely conformable to law. As Adam Smith has remarked, no people on earth has ever known a god of gravity.(12)

The progress of science has naturally resulted in limiting more and more the domain of the miraculous. "Science," as H. Poincaré has so well said, "is a rule of action which succeeds,"(13) and there where our ancestors saw only miracles, eluding all prevision, we observe more and more the effect of exact laws. And yet, however marked may be this progress, does it suffice to explain even the modern conviction of the reign of law? The number of phenomena whose rules we know is necessarily minute compared with the phenomena comprising *all* nature, the first being finite and the second infinite; every general conclusion on the basis of known phenomena, extending to nature in its entirety, would thus seem logically questionable. This probably explains why certain philosophers, who emphasize this point of view, have appeared to doubt the absolute sway of laws in nature. The most striking example of this is Auguste Comte. He believed that "the natural laws, the true object of our research, could not remain rigorously compatible in any case with a too detailed investigation."(14) Comte does not question the validity of a certain particular law which we are required to maintain provisionally for lack of a better one, even though knowing it to be only approximate, he questions the validity of the very occurrence of law—that is, of the conformity of nature to law in general. Comte does not believe that beneath this law a better one may exist, perhaps more complicated, but adapting itself more closely to the phenomena; he is convinced that a too detailed investigation would lead us to the knowledge of phenomena evading all law, all rule. And so he rejects very severely all research of this kind; piling up terms of reprobation, he declares that the investigations in which too precise measuring instruments are used "are incoherent or sterile," proceeding from a curiosity that is always "vain and seriously disturbing," from a "childish curiosity stimulated by vain ambition"; he protests strongly against the "abuse of microscopic research and the exaggerated merit still too often accorded to a means of investigation so dubious," and he does not hesitate to invoke against "the active disorganization" by which the system of positive knowledge seems to him menaced because of these endeavours, the secular arm of "the veritable speculative rule" of the future.(15)

We shall discover later on the source of these opinions of Comte's. To understand fully how far they are foreign to the principles which really guide the advance of science, it is perhaps not sufficient to prove, as has already been done very justly, that science has since followed a direction diametrically opposed to that indicated by the founder of positivism. It has tirelessly sought for phenomena more and more minute, measures more and more precise, and its constant care has been to perfect its instruments of investigation, amongst others, the thermometer and the microscope so obnoxious to Comte, far beyond the limits of accuracy at that time.(16) We must still add that in spite of the celebrity of Comte's work and the prestige which his writings enjoy, no scientist, in the course of his studies, has ever tried to follow the principles laid down by positivism. Without doubt, confronted by a multiplicity of phenomena, a scientist may ask himself whether the data which he possesses and which his means of investigation will permit him to acquire, will be sufficient to bring to light the particular laws which govern them; but never has any physicist, chemist, or astronomer asked himself whether the phenomena which he was about to investigate, no matter what their nature might be, were conformable to law. Never has any scientist worthy of the name doubted that nature, even in its most intimate recesses, was entirely subject to law. A single doubt in this respect would have been sufficient, as G. Léchalas has justly said,(17) to put a stop to all research.

Might this be, as has sometimes been intimated, a manner of thinking peculiar to the scientist or to the modern man trained in his school? We have seen that, on the contrary, it could not be acquired by experience, that, even to-day, experience does not justify it; and it appears that wherever they find themselves confronted with dead nature alone, in which they suppose that no intervention of the will of a living being occurs, primitive men, and even the animals, have opinions on this subject entirely analogous to our own. What, then, is the source of this conviction? How does it happen that we have an absolute faith in the validity of laws, that we infer their existence, even when we have not yet learned how to formulate them?

To understand it we have only to recall that foresight is indispensable for action. Now action for any organism of the animal kingdom is an absolute necessity. Surrounded by hostile nature it must act, it must foresee, if it wishes to live. "All life, all action," says Fouillée, "is a conscious or an unconscious divining. Divine or you will be devoured."(18) Therefore, I have not the choice of believing in prevision (that is, in science), or of not believing in it. If I want to live, I must believe in it. Consequently, it is not astonishing that this conviction based directly on the most powerful of the organism's instincts, that of conservation, should manifest itself with such unusual force.

In defining science in terms of utility from the point of view of action, have we not diminished its domain? At all times the scientist who is not busy with researches immediately applicable has been a subject of ridicule to the man in the street, and surely at the present moment many physicists, chemists, geologists, etc., are occupied with problems the solution of which does not seem to admit of practical consequences. Are these investigations illegitimate?

Auguste Comte believed that there was, indeed, also a limit on that side; certain speculations were radically useless, and, moreover, doomed to sterility, such as, for instance, studies of the physical constitution of the stars. In the following terms Comte states the existence of this limit: "There exists in all kinds of research, in all important relations, a harmony that is constant and necessary between the study of our real intellectual needs and the actual range, present or future, of our real knowledge. This harmony . . . springs simply from this evident necessity: we need only know what can act upon us in a more or less direct manner, and, on the other hand, just because such an influence exists, it becomes sooner or later a sure means of knowledge for us."(19)

It is quite permissible to doubt whether Comte's deduction is of any value, even from the point of view of his definition of science. There is, indeed, at the base of his reasoning a postulate: that by some means or other we are able to distinguish in advance that which can act upon us more or less directly (that is, *useful* knowledge) from that which can never render us any service. Indeed, if it were not so, the distinction established by Comte would be meaningless, for it would not permit us to trace any limit. Now, it is easy to see that this postulate cannot be upheld. The universe from the point of view of its relations to us is a whole. All of its parts must act upon one another, and all of them may, directly or indirectly, react upon us. A part of the universe which had no possible relation to us would be something, not "that we should not need to know," as Comte says, but which we simply would not know, whose existence would be inconceivable—in other words, something not existing.

Le Dantec, trying to determine the exact meaning of Comte's statement, hit upon a very apt example, namely, of worlds placed in a ball of ether, separated from our universe by a substance incapable of transmitting light.(20) Assuming that this medium transmitted no other form of action, not even gravitation, it is certain that we could never conceive of the existence of the worlds in question.

In the precise case cited by Comte of the physical constitution of the stars we know that he was mistaken about the facts. The spectral analysis discovered a few decades after the publication of the *Cours de philosophie positive* has absolutely contradicted him on this point. But is it true even that this knowledge must necessarily remain sterile from the point of view of practical utility? What do we know about it? May it not reveal to us data concerning the genesis of the heavenly bodies which will permit us to draw conclusions about phenomena, taking place in the interior of the sun or even of the earth, where it is impossible for us to make direct observation, but where we have nevertheless an interest in knowing what is going on in regard to the future? Is it inconceivable that we should unearth some facts about the constitution of matter? Indeed, suppositions of this kind have already been formulated and no one may say whether they are not destined to revolutionize the science of to-morrow. Such and such phenomena which at this time seem to us to be infinitely remote, to-morrow may reveal to us relations, acquaintance with which would be of the most immediate usefulness.

Comte, himself better advised than he was at the time when he formulated and justified the restriction to which we have alluded, has given a striking example of his deeper insight by showing that, according to Condorcet, the sailor of to-day making astronomical observations profits by the mathematical discoveries about cones due to Greek geometers who lived twenty centuries ago;(21) now it is quite certain that the latter could not foresee any utilization of this kind.

Thus starting from the utilitarian concept of science, one can nevertheless justify science, in its entirety, including even research about the physical nature of stars, only, of course, in so far as science has for its aim to learn the relations between phenomena, the rules and the laws which govern them. Such seems to be, moreover, the almost unanimous opinion of all those, philosophers or scientists, who define science in accordance with Comte's conception. No one, it seems, would now be disposed to renew an injunction such as has just been mentioned.

While extending its domain science becomes more and more compact and the same causes explain this evolution.

A ray of light passes through water; we notice that it changes direction and we are able to recognize that for the same angle of incidence the angle of refraction is identical, but that for different angles, it is different. We must therefore draw up a table whose principal points of reference at least we must keep in mind if we are interested in this part of science; the more exactly we want to calculate the more detailed the table will have to be until it becomes impossible to keep it in mind. But now the law of refraction sums up all of these observations. Knowing that $\frac{\sin i}{\sin r} = n$, we no longer need a table; we no longer even need to remember the points of reference. We have therefore diminished our effort, and in so doing we have obeyed the natural and general tendency of every organized being. Moreover, the facts of nature are infinite, and infinite is their variety. Our desire is to grasp all of them in order to be able to foresee all of them. Doubtless, we shall never succeed, but at least we must know the greatest number possible. Now the more the effort is diminished for each particular case, the more we shall be able to extend it. This is what Comte has defined by saying that "the utility of laws" is "to dispense, as much as the different phenomena allow, with all direct observation, by permitting the deduction of the greatest possible number of results from the smallest number of immediate data."(22) In other words, laws have for their end an "economy" of effort or of thought. We borrow this expression, not being Comte's own, but nevertheless summing up exactly his ideas, from the writings of a modern thinker of great note, E. Mach, whose conceptions have influenced and still do influence science considerably.

Does science embrace the totality of the phenomena of nature? There are some facts which do not appear to me to be entirely determined. They are those which have to do with my will. Am I really free? What is certain is that, at this moment, and within certain limits, I feel that I am free to act, and that retrospectively I feel myself responsible for the deeds I have done.

Is the feeling only an illusion and an epiphenomenon, as the determinists would have it? At any rate, we seem to be grappling here with one of the most serious questions that has ever perplexed the human mind. Shall we be forced to solve it before proceeding farther? It seems to be essentially insoluble, being one of the antinomies through which the unknowable shows itself. But, happily, we can eliminate it here, and this procedure conforms entirely to the methods followed by science. Science, we have just seen, has an end, prevision. Its domain will thus include all that is capable of being foreseen, all of the facts subject to rules. Where there is no law, there is no science. Free will, supposing that it exists, is certainly outside this domain.

It is evident that the limit thus established can only be quite indeterminate: this results from the hypothetical import involved in the proposition of "free will." According as we admit or deny free will or as we assign to it a domain more or less vast, that of science will grow smaller or grow greater. The same act, according as we consider it as emanating either from the moral individual supposedly responsible or from the environment of which he is the natural product, will appear to us now as free and now as determined, as something possible to have been foreseen if we had known and properly appreciated the circumstances by which it was surrounded. Since the name of psychology has been coined and since this name does not in itself seem absurd to us, we apparently believe it possible to formulate rules on the subject of the phenomena of the will; for psychology, according to the just remark of Fouillée, is essentially "the study of the will."(23) When we study the psychology of the people who surround us, whether we try to know why they have acted or how they will act, we tacitly suppose that their actions are determined.(24) Do we mean by that to deny their free will? Assuredly not, since we consider them as responsible for their acts. But in trying to foresee we are working scientifically, and whoever speaks of science speaks of predetermination. And thus the lack of precision in determining limits does not really present here the inconveniences which we might expect from it. Lange asserted that science, if it is not to relinquish its task, must explain the motion proceeding from reason (vernünftig) as a special case of the general laws of motion.(25) The truth is that science, if it treats of this particular motion, is forced to consider it as determined. But it does not, it indeed could not, affirm that it is so. To suppose the existence of free phenomena entirely detached from the domination of law and from our prevision in no way assails the principle of science. Nor is it contrary to its conclusions, for determinism being a fundamental postulate of science and science limiting in advance its activity to what is capable of being foreseen, it is certain that, whatever results may come of it, they can teach us nothing about what, by previous agreement, has been omitted from the domain of our investigations.

In order to indicate better the importance of this thesis we need only leave momentarily the realm of science to enter that of religion. All religions, taking the term in its most generally accepted sense, tend to show us the intervention in the course of

the world of a superior will placed outside of nature. This is all
the truer the more we consider a primitive theological state.
In the beginning man often symbolizes the power of hostile
nature surrounding him under the form of invisible but active
beings.(26) These beings act like men though with an increased
power. No one indeed can doubt the anthropomorphic character
of the concept of divinity, especially before the transformation it
was forced to undergo by the more or less absolute monotheism
which has become the religion of an important part of humanity.
God, then, just like man, has his free will. The believer can
influence his will by prayers, just as on the human level every
man may influence the will of another man. But in both cases
all absolute constraint is impossible. To affirm the contrary,
to believe that by determined acts it is possible to coerce
divinity, is no longer religion but magic, and magic in so far
as it is belief in the absolute efficacy of its practices literally
establishes a law—that is to say, transforms itself into an experimental science; this explains why alchemy, having retained
to the very end such intimate connection with magic, was able
to develop normally into chemistry.

But in religion, strictly speaking, the acts of God remain
quite free—that is to say, they are not determined, or at least not
completely so; just as, in respect to my own acts or those of my
fellow-men, I suppose generally that they are partly determined
by antecedents of different kinds, and partly free; so the
believer considers the acts of the divinity toward him as
partly motivated by the merit or lack of merit of the supplicant,
by his prayers, etc., and in part free. On the other hand, these
acts determine events which in turn give birth to others and
so on without end. If tracing back a chain of events we find
an act of free will of a divinity, the whole or a part of the chain
will stop right there, and this will be what Renouvier has called
an "absolute beginning."(27) The act there appears as not
determined by its antecedents, but as a departure from laws.
This is commonly styled a miracle.

It is sometimes said that science repudiates miracles; this
is inexactly expressed. As it progresses, we have seen, science
tends to restrict the domain of miracles. Many of the phenomena
which appeared to primitive man as miracles, for us enter the
domain of science. One can say, in this sense, that science

verifies the postulate of conformity to law, but it must be understood that this confirmation cannot be absolute. As to the miraculous, like every other act of free will, it remains necessarily outside the realm of science and separated from it by an impassable wall. Indeed, in all times the devout have experienced the quite natural desire of showing by experiments the efficacy of their divinity's intervention. One may boldly say that in a way perhaps no other experiment has been so frequently tried. Yet the demonstration has never succeeded: it is essentially impossible. If the water of the grotto at Lourdes invariably healed all the paralytics who were plunged therein, it would be a law, and we should certainly begin to look in the composition of the water for some characteristic explaining this action. If needed, we should be forced to invent a hypothetical element or an unknown form of energy. If the sacerdotal ceremonies constituted a necessary and sufficient aid, the act would leave the domain of religion to enter into that of magic, for there would be a determined act of the divinity. But it is a religious act because the divinity remains free. The phenomenon cannot be foreseen, nor reproduced at will—that is to say, it is essentially beyond the control of science. One can invalidate a miracle—that is, show that the phenomenon in question is really consistent with the laws that we know; but one cannot demonstrate a miracle scientifically. The most one can do is to show that the phenomenon, if it had been ruled by certain laws, would have had to follow a different course. But the incredulous will always have plenty of opportunity to insist that there were circumstances and laws remaining unknown.

It is a little more difficult to disengage the concept of causality, precisely because of the confusion already mentioned. However, we find a very clear expression of it in the writings of Leibniz, who calls it "the principle of determining reason" or "sufficient reason." "One must consider," says Leibniz, "that there are two great principles in our reasoning: one is the principle of contradiction, which states that of two contradictory propositions one is true and the other false; the other principle is that of sufficient reason—that nothing happens without there being a determining cause or at least a determining reason, that is to say something which can serve to explain, *a priori*, why this exists in this rather than in any other fashion." And he adds: "This great principle takes place in all events and no contrary example will ever be given; and although most often these reasons are not sufficiently known, we do nevertheless catch a glimpse of their existence."(28) Plato had already stated the same postulate, saying: "Any beginning without cause is impossible";(29) and Aristotle: "Nature is no wanton or random creator."(30) Schopenhauer, in his treatise *On the Fourfold Root*, adopted the same formula, saying with Wolf, *Nihil est sine ratione cur potius sit quam non sit,*(31) which is, we see, the literal statement of Leibniz.

But in other passages Leibniz has explained with greater precision what he means by the cause or sufficient reason. In the treatise *De legibus naturae et vera aestimatione virium motricium* (it is a question of demonstrating by the method of *reductio ad absurdum*, the principle of the conservation of *vis viva*), we read: "It would follow that the cause could not be entirely restored nor substituted for its effect, which is, one easily understands, entirely contrary to the habits of nature and the reasons for things";(32) and in the *Dynamica* (proposition 5) he writes: "The whole effect can reproduce the entire cause or its like."(33) He again expresses the same idea in his *Essai de Dynamique* (here also the principle of *vis viva* is in question): "For if this *vis viva* could ever increase, there would exist an effect more powerful than its cause, or else perpetual mechanical motion—that is to say, something which could reproduce its cause and something more, which is absurd. But if the force were able to decrease it would come to nothing in the end, for never being able to increase and always being able to decrease, it would always diminish more and more, which is without doubt contrary to the order of things."(34) Finally we see that the principle of Leibniz comes back to the well-known formula of the scholastics, *causa aequat effectum.*

Jean Bernoulli, to whom we have referred previously, uses the same statement: it is the equality between causes and effects which seems to him to be the indispensable guarantee of order in nature. Lucretius writes, *Nil posse creari de nihilo,*(35) which is evidently the formula of Anaxagoras, "Nothing comes into being and nothing passes away," a formula which has often been attributed to more modern authors, even to Lavoisier. It is clear, moreover, that this formula is immediately deducible from the preceding one, for all nature being, by postulate, only a chain of causes and effects, and the sum of the second being always equal to the whole of the first, there is nowhere any room for creation or for disappearance.

On the other hand, it is apparent that the postulate of causality is in no way identical with that of conformity to law. A more profound analysis will but confirm this.

In positing the existence of rules we postulate that they are knowable. A law of nature of which we are ignorant does not exist in the strictest sense of the term. Certainly, nature seems to us ordered. Each new discovery, each realized anticipation, confirms this opinion in us. So much so that nature itself seems to proclaim its own orderliness; this idea appears to enter our minds from the outside, as it were, without our doing anything but receive it passively; in the end the orderliness appears to us as a purely empirical fact, and the laws formulated by us appear as something belonging to nature, as the "laws of nature," independent of our intelligence. This is to forget that we were convinced in advance of this orderliness, of the existence of these laws. All the acts of our daily life witness to it. This is to forget also how we arrived at these laws. We have observed some peculiar and strictly unique phenomena. We have formed general and abstract concepts of them, and our laws, as a matter of fact, apply only to these latter. The law which governs the action of the lever considers only the "mathematical lever"; but we know very well that we shall never encounter anything like it in nature. In the same way we shall never encounter the ideal gases of physics nor the crystals of which we possess crystallographic models. But even when we affirm that sulphur has such and such properties we are not thinking of some particular piece of the well-known yellow substance. Sometimes what we affirm applies to a sort of average of the pieces we are apt to encounter in industry, and sometimes even (when we speak of "pure sulphur") it applies to an ideal matter to which we can approach only after many experiments; the qualities of a piece of sulphur taken at random may differ widely from those of the substance in question. We know of the formidable amount of work to which Stas had to devote himself in order to obtain silver approximately chemically pure. We know, moreover, that he chose this substance as the starting-point of his determinations because it appeared to him to offer the greatest facilities, and we know also that the silver obtained by him was not really pure, so that it has since become necessary to rectify the results which he had obtained. We can see from this typical example how much the substratum even of the law, the generalized concept, is a thing of our thought. For it will in no way help to affirm that, silver being a definite element, the pure substance must necessarily exist in the piece of metal which I am holding, which I call by the same name, but which I know to be impure. The existence of the silver-element is only an hypothesis which is obtained after many deductions; and pure silver, like the mathematical lever, the ideal gas, or the perfect crystal are abstractions created by a theory. It is, as Duhem has justly said,(36) impossible to understand the law, impossible to apply it, without performing the work of scientific abstraction, without knowing the theories which it presupposes.

If we sometimes have the illusion that the laws formulated by us apply directly to reality it is solely because of the clumsiness of our senses and our imperfect means of investigation, which do not permit us to perceive all that differentiates particular phenomena from one another. Poincaré has observed that these circumstances have favoured the discovery of certain laws and that it may be a disadvantage for a science to be conceived at a time when measuring instruments permit very detailed investigations.(37)

In fact, we only attain laws by violating nature, by isolating more or less artificially a phenomenon from the whole, by checking those influences which would have *falsified* the observation. Thus the law cannot directly express reality. The phenomenon as it is envisaged by it, the "pure" phenomenon, is rarely observed without our intervention, and even with this it remains imperfect, disturbed by accessory phenomena. Experiments performed in academic lectures designed to illustrate certain laws, claim sometimes to show us this pure phenomenon. We know with what minute care these experiments must be previously regulated in order to succeed. Even then they make the impression upon the spectator of something profoundly artificial; the professor appears as a sort of prestidigitator.(38) Whoever has worked in a laboratory recalls how difficult it is to carry on the most simple experiments indicated in manuals. In time the habit is formed; precautions are taken with less and less consciousness, and we begin to believe that the experiments of verification are accomplished all by themselves without our having to coerce nature. In the same way the astronomer, after having observed and calculated the movement of the stars, succeeds in actually *seeing* that the moon is falling upon the earth. This does not prevent the unprejudiced observer from viewing the two bodies as remaining at about the same distance. In respect to the phenomenon directly observed the law is only more or less approximate; with the aid of successive corrections we try to adapt progressively the whole series of laws more and more closely to the real course of nature. But it must be observed that these new contributions unceasingly modify existing science. "Physics does not progress like geometry, which adds new propositions to the definitive and indisputable ones which it already possesses; it progresses because experiments bring unceasingly to light new disagreements between laws and facts."(39) The law is an ideal construction which expresses, not what happens, but what would happen if certain conditions were to be realized. Doubtless, if nature were not ordered, if it did not present us with similar objects, capable of furnishing generalized concepts, we could not formulate laws. But these laws in themselves are only the image of this ordering; they correspond to it only in the measure that a projection can correspond to a body of n dimensions. They can only express it in so far as a written word expresses the thing, for in both cases we must pass through the medium of our intelligence.

Since time passes unceasingly (this is the *unique independent variable* of Newton), laws if they are to be knowable can only be so as a function of the changing of time. It will suffice then, strictly speaking, for nature to seem ordered to us, that we know the form of this function—that is to say, that we know how laws are modified as time advances.

Yet it is certain that in our conception of laws we simplify their relations to time by affirming that this latter is homogeneous in relation to them. If sulphur, that is to say, a piece of substance which is known to us by means of a whole aggregate of physical properties, at this moment gives birth by combustion to a quite characteristic gas which is called sulphurous anhydride, we affirm that it behaved in the same manner in the most distant geological ages, and that it will always do so.

In order to understand why this simplification imposes itself it is sufficient to consider that a modification of laws in time, in order to be knowable, would imply a knowledge of time independent of laws. But this knowledge is impossible. There are two antagonistic opinions regarding the principles upon which the measure of time rests. Certain modern scientists propose to deduce it from uniform motion in a straight line—that is to say, from inertial motion. This theory was formulated, it seems, for the first time by C. Neumann (40), who has been followed, amongst others, by Ludwig Lange (41) in Germany, Hannequin (42) and E. Le Roy (43) in France. But supposing this conception to be valid for the present era, it certainly was not so in the past, for the principle of inertia is a quite modern creation. Now there is no doubt that humanity has always had a distinct consciousness of the uniform flow of time, and even for long centuries it has known how to measure it. Moreover, one need only examine the means by the aid of which this measuring has been accomplished to recognize its foundation. For many centuries we have made use of the pendulum; before that men used water or sand flowing through an opening, or even candles of uniform size. At a still previous epoch, before they knew how to construct any sort of measuring instrument men measured time by the visible motion of the sun or of the stars and by the seasons—that is, by the rotation and the revolution of the earth, measures which even to-day serve as a check. Now all of these means spring from the same principle, to wit, that change in nature is of uniform character, that similar effects take place during similar time-intervals. This is the definition of the measure of time formulated by d'Alembert (44), and after him by Poisson, (45) and now we are able to employ such phenomena as have only a very remote relation to motion, and where consequently the concept of inertia counts for nothing; we can, for instance, take as a starting-point the speed of a chemical reaction; let us say, to be precise, the transformation of white sulphur into red sulphur, (46) or, better still, the diminution of the radio-activity of the emanation of radium, proposed by Curie, and which appears, in fact, capable of furnishing a precise unit. (47)

Moreover, whatever the phenomenon which we take as a starting-point, provided it be properly chosen, so that we can determine sufficiently the conditions under which it must take place and observe its progress with necessary precision, we shall find all the other phenomena being regulated by it. Starting with the vibration of a pendulum, the flowing of water or of sand between two fillings of the water-clock or of the hour-glass, the burning of a candle of uniform size, the production of a given proportion of red sulphur or a given diminution in the radio-activity of the emanation of radium, all these will last each time that we reproduce these phenomena under favourable conditions as long as a determined number of vibrations of the pendulum. One could say because there is agreement between these different phenomena that we succeed in conceiving that time flows uniformly. Yet this agreement amongst phenomena, in so far, at least, as we shall be able directly to observe them, will never be absolute. The best clock which we can construct will need regulating from time to time, and it is supposed that the rotation of the earth, conceived primarily as the change the duration of which must regulate that of all others, does not always strictly possess the same value; it lengthens, whence an apparent acceleration of the moon's motion. We are in a position to explain this anomaly by saying that the duration of the earth's rotation is modified by the influence of two factors: the continual shrinking of the earthly globe and the action of the tides; these two causes act inversely, but the second is predominant, and the difference between the two actions brings about precisely the result which we have stated. However, the very fact that the agreement is not immediately perfect, that we make it such, that this lengthening of the year appears to us as an anomaly having need of explanation, warns us that the concept of the absolute uniformity of the passage of time cannot be entirely due to the observation of phenomena, that it must bring into play a higher principle. Now this principle evidently is none other than the one designated by us as the principle of the reign of law. We have only to take up again the formula of d'Alembert, that what takes place during similar time-intervals has similar effects, and to compare

it with that of Ostwald (p. 18): "If we establish the same
conditions, the phenomena will take place in the same manner."
It is clear that the first is included in the second, for the expression "in the same manner" forcibly indicates that the phenomenon must take place in an identical lapse of time.(48)
Moreover, since, as we have seen, laws have prediction as their
end, it is just as interesting for us to know *when* things will take
place as to know *what* takes place. If the dog to whom I throw
a piece of meat wants to catch it, he must be able to calculate
at what precise moment the morsel will attain the height of his
jaws. Thus it is our conviction of nature's regularity which
intervenes; nature lends itself to it, this is incontestable, but
this conviction, as we have noted, exceeds the limits of direct
observation; it is absolute and guarantees the future.(49)

And so time-measurement depends, in the last analysis, on
the existence of laws in nature, and consequently time appears
to us, as we have said, to be homogeneous in respect to laws.
On the contrary, the postulate of conformity to law in no way
implies that objects themselves remain immutable in time.
Here it is really sufficient to know the form of the function—
that is, the manner in which the objects change with the time.
In stating it we formulate a law. One can even affirm that
this form of the law is its primitive form, since it corresponds
best with its aim. Indeed, since we wish to predict, to know
the future, and since we know how to measure time, the simplest
thing would be to determine how objects in the external world
are modified as a function of the time.(50) If this proposition
does not seem evident to us at the first glance, it is because of
the peculiar nature of the concept of displacement. This
concept is ambiguous; a displaced object appears to us to have
undergone a modification and at the same time to have conserved its identity. We shall have occasion to come back to
this subject at greater length. For the moment let us be content
to remark that, putting aside the difficulty which this concept
is apt to add to the question which is occupying us, we need
only have recourse to the phenomena already mentioned,
which do not directly conjure up in our minds the image of
motion. Thus, in affirming that in t seconds from a solution
of white phosphorus in tribromure of phosphorus of a given
concentration a determined proportion will be transformed

into red phosphorus, or again, that after t days the emanation of radium will lose the nth part of its radio-activity, we are certainly formulating laws. It is, moreover, easy to see that particularly the sciences of living nature are full of laws of this kind, as, for example: after n months of existence the caterpillar becomes a butterfly; or, during their nth month tadpoles lose their gills.

The analysis to which we have just devoted ourselves in regard to time is in a certain measure applicable to space. Here also it would be sufficient, strictly speaking, so that there may be order in nature, to know laws as a function of changes in space. But here also we simplify by affirming that the modification of the function is nil, that laws remain immutable throughout space. It will perhaps not be entirely useless to emphasize the fact that this homogeneity of space with respect to laws is independent of what we call its relativity. One might suppose, indeed, that we were forced to believe in the indifference of place, because real place is unknown to us. It is certain that in this respect we are constantly undergoing a change. The earth turns around its axis and also around the sun, which in its turn progresses in space at a considerable speed. The probability that we ever come back to the spot which we have occupied for a moment is very small. If we can formulate abstract laws while in the act of changing place with such great rapidity, apparently the changing of place is indifferent to these laws. This reasoning would seem valid for the present state of science. But it is a comparatively recent state. During an incalculable series of centuries humanity firmly believed that the earth was a motionless table-land, that places marked by certain objects of considerable height, such as mountains and high buildings, were really places in absolute space, and that one could come back to the same "spot" by marking its position in relation to these landmarks. It believed also that space had two real directions, distinct from others, height and depth. Were we to scrutinize our own beliefs we should discover that we ourselves are not entirely free from these conceptions; we always experience some difficulty in picturing to ourselves the antipodes which, whatever we may do, seem to us "head downwards." But even when they believed that the earth was below and the heavens above, men were firmly

convinced of the homogeneity of space. To establish this it is
enough to recall that it is this idea which constitutes the basis
of geometry. If a Greek had been asked at what depth within
the earth such and such a proposition of Euclid ceased to be
true, the question would certainly have appeared as paradoxical
to him as it is to us.

But geometry proves to us equally that our belief in the
homogeneity of space implies something more than the persistence of laws. We are, indeed, convinced that not only laws—
that is, the relations between things—but even things themselves
are not modified by their displacement in space. This is what
geometry plainly postulates. And one of the masters of contemporary scientific thought has very aptly said that geometry
would not exist if there were no solids displacing themselves
without modifications.(51) Now it is very essential to state
that geometry (and in general those sciences which we include
under the term of "pure mathematics"), though dealing with
the abstract concepts of thought, enjoys evidently the advantage
of application to reality in an absolute manner. We shall later
consider a science which at first sight seems strongly to resemble
geometry, namely rational mechanics. It also is concerned
with abstract concepts, but it does not enjoy the same advantage as pure mathematics, since we can (and even must, as
we shall see later on) conceive that reality does not entirely
comply with it. We shall not here inquire to what is due this
privilege of pure mathematics; that is a chapter in the philosophy of mathematical sciences which is foreign to the subject
of this book. Let us state only that the fact itself cannot be
contested and that it is impossible to doubt seriously that a
geometric deduction is verified by experience.(52)

What precedes shows us that it would be vain to attempt for
space the deduction which we have carried out for time. The
postulate of lawfulness alone will not suffice, for, as we have
just seen, we attribute to space more uniformity than lawfulness
would strictly demand for it. This proves that a particular
principle or postulate is here at stake, that of "free mobility."
Russell thinks that a "denial of this axiom would involve logical
and philosophical absurdities, so that it must be classed as
wholly *a priori*."(53) What is certain is that it is an integral
part of our concept of space. It is clear, moreover, that time

admits of no such statement. It appears to us as flowing uniformly in the same direction; the supposition that we could move about freely in it, voyaging in the past and in the future, implies at least as many absurdities as the contrary supposition for space.(54)

On this point, then, there is not a complete analogy between time and space. This dog, just born, I know will be grown in two years, decrepit in twenty, and dead in thirty years at the very latest; but if I carry him into another part of space he will remain what he is. Without doubt, if I place him on the summit of Mont Blanc, he will be very uncomfortable, and if I keep him at the bottom of a pond he will be drowned, but this will be so because the visible physical conditions of the surroundings will have changed and not because of a simple change of place. Objects are not modified by the action of space as they are changed by the action of time; the very expression seems paradoxical, startling in the first case, trite in the second. Space (the same thing has been affirmed for time, but wrongly) is really a "pure form" void of all content.(55)

All the postulates which are here enumerated and which are indispensable for the formulating of laws are needed when we speak of causes, yet something else is added. Indeed, if there is always complete equality between causes and effects, if nothing begins and nothing ends, it is because not only laws but also things persist throughout time. It is this principle that Aristotle formulated, applying it, it is true, to "substances" alone: "That substances properly so-called, and in general all beings which exist absolutely, come from a prior cause is clearly seen. There is always a being previously existing whence is born that which is born and becomes."(56) Lucretius states in a quite general manner: *Eadem sunt omnia semper*, and it is this same idea which Cournot expresses with much precision: "Every time that we deal with phenomena of the physical order, if these phenomena appear in the first place to depend on forces or causes which vary with time, it is inherent in the nature of our mind not to regard the phenomenon as accounted for until it has been brought back to depend on permanent causes, immutable in time, the effects of which alone vary from a certain given moment in consequence of the dispositions which the world, or parts of the world, presented at that moment

—dispositions which our mind accepts not as laws but as facts."(57) Helmholtz, who, we have seen, has tried to reduce causality to lawfulness, has declared in another passage that the final aim of science is "to bring back the phenomena of nature to the invariable forces of attraction and repulsion, the intensity of which depends on distance," and that it is only on that condition that nature can be rendered completely comprehensible.(58)

In summing up what we have just stated, we may say that the principle of causality demands the application to time of a postulate, which, under the rule of lawfulness alone, is only applied to space.

Before proceeding farther we must remove certain difficulties.

Were we right in speaking simply of "geometry"? Would it not have been better to speak of Euclidean geometry? We know, indeed, that since the speculations of Lobatschewsky, of Riemann, and of Bolyai science has had to envisage the hypothesis of a space in which the axiom of parallel lines would cease to be valid. We know also that these hypotheses have not remained confined to the domain of mathematics, since not only Lobatschewsky (59) and Riemann,(60) but even Helmholtz (61) have expressly claimed their verification by astronomical measurements. Tait has formulated the supposition that the solar system, and with it our earth, might some day enter a region of space in which the *curvature* of the latter would be modified.(62) On this hypothesis space would no longer be entirely homogeneous, and we could be led to relate, by an empirical rule, the modification of the properties of bodies to their displacement in space. Poincaré (63) has admirably shown why these suppositions are inadmissible. What we call a straight line in astronomy is the path of the light ray, and if we were to happen to discover anomalies such as Helmholtz has foreseen, we should certainly attribute them to the nature of light and not to that of space.(64)

Another difficulty is of rather a logical order. The reasoning which precedes is based evidently on a distinction between objects and laws. Now, is an object anything but a group of phenomena? And since these phenomena are all ruled by laws, is not what we call an object simply a group of relations conformable to law? One can immediately render obvious the truth of this proposition by observing that we only know an object by its properties, and that each property in particular can be so formulated that the statement is a law. What is sulphur? It is a solid substance, yellow, melting at 114° C., boiling at 448° C., producing by combustion a gas well known under the name of sulphurous anhydride, etc. Now in saying: Sulphur is yellow in colour, sulphur melts at 114° C., etc., I incontestably state laws. How does it happen that I stipulate the immutability of laws in time and not that of objects?

Let us look a little more closely at our statement about the properties of sulphur. In saying that it is a solid and yellow substance, did we mean to affirm that it is always so? Assuredly not. We know very well that it can also be a brownish liquid, and that, even when solid, if precipitated in a solution of potassium pentasulphide, it will appear as an almost white powder; moreover, if we illumine a piece of sulphur with green monochromatic light, it will appear green. In fact, then, for each property which we stated certain conditions were presupposed. If we have been able not to specify them expressly in certain cases it is because we supposed what one calls *ordinary conditions*—that is, those which we notice in the immense majority of cases in the world surrounding us. Thus a temperature at which sulphur remains solid, and illumination by the light of the sun or of an incandescent substance, are a part of the ordinary conditions; and, in the same way, sulphur being found in industry especially under the aspect of a compact substance, we can, if necessary, in enumerating its qualities, omit this condition. But for several of the properties indicated above we cannot proceed in this way. When I say that sulphur melts at 114° C., that it boils at 448° C., or that it is combustible, it is clear that these are phenomena which cannot be observed unless the temperature is high—that is to say, they cannot be observed if the ordinary conditions cease to exist. Without doubt we indeed assume that to this phenomenon which will only be produced under determined circumstances, there corresponds, even in sulphur at an ordinary temperature, *something*—a thing badly defined, however—not showing itself constantly, but being apt to show itself, as is plainly indicated by the grammatical form of the terms when we say that sulphur is *fusible* or *combustible*. It is not, then, an actual quality, but a *faculty*, and, if we refer to what has been said previously, it is clear that all the properties which we attribute to substances are only faculties of this kind, all manifesting themselves only under determined conditions and apt to be modified if these conditions happen to change.

We thus see clearly where, in this respect, the difference between the purely lawful conception of nature and the causal conception is found. The law states simply that, conditions happening to be modified in a determined manner, the actual properties of the substance must undergo an equally determined modification; whereas according to the causal principle there must be equality between causes and effects— that is, the original properties plus the change of conditions must equal the transformed properties. We shall see later how the difficulty, purely specious, which we have just discussed, has been productive of error.(65)

What is the origin of the causal postulate? It is clear in the first place that the instinct of preservation has nothing to do with it. Provided I can foresee the course of events, I find myself in possession of all the knowledge which I need for action. The assurance of equality between causes and effects does not, in itself, bring me any information useful from that point of view, or, rather, it will only bring me information to the extent that I shall be able with its help to make predictions— that is, to obtain rules of experience. It is just as evident that the principle of causality is not, like that of lawfulness, confirmed unceasingly by our sensations; it is even contradicted by them. All the objects we know are unceasingly modified in time, and we have the very distinct feeling that our own individuality obeys this same rule. When we speak of things eternally immutable, we know very well—unless we speak of purely ideal things—that we are expressing ourselves inexactly. The very planet upon which we live and the entire system to which it belongs seem to us to be changing continually.(66)

To discover the real source of the principle it is enough to recall the name which Leibniz and many others after him have given it. It is the principle of the determining reason or sufficient reason. Wherever we establish it the phenomenon becomes rational, adequate to our reason: we understand it and we can explain it. This thirst for knowledge, for understanding, is felt by each one of us. Comte, without denying it absolutely, believed, however, that this bent was one of the least imperative of our nature. This assertion, it seems, is emphatically contradicted by the immediate feeling of all those who are immersed in the work of science, all those who investigate nature. Great scientists have often recognized in themselves the force of this tendency, and H. Poincaré notably declares, not only that we do not easily resign ourselves "to ignoring the foundation of things,"(67) but that in his opinion this feeling is stronger than the one which impels us to act. He says: "In my view knowledge is the end, and action is the means."(68) Mach himself admits that scientific thought "creates its own ends, seeks to satisfy itself by suppressing all intellectual uneasiness."(69) Aristotle had already said: "All men by nature are actuated by the desire for knowledge;"(70) and Spinoza declared: "The mind judges only that to be of use to itself which leads to understanding."(71)

Moreover, if this tendency is abstracted from the human mind, the evolution of science becomes an enigma. We have seen, it is true, that *all* learning is, or will certainly be, useful from the point of view of prediction. But this is a truth which is far from being immediately evident; it would have appeared rather as a paradox in the days when the physical sciences were but little developed. How explain the very great ardour of which humanity has given evidence in the acquisition of a knowledge "the object of which could be neither pleasure nor need," according to Aristotle, who expressly places the mathematical sciences in this category?(72) In the Alexandrine period, what conception was there of the possible utilization of conics? Is it quite certain that the physical doctrines of the ancient atomists or those of Aristotle permitted of practical application from the point of view of prevision? One could object, it is true, that this was not science but metaphysics. Then let us say immediately that that branch of human knowledge alone would suffice, if need were, to establish the existence of the tendency of which we are speaking. Indeed, however convinced one may be of the sterility of these researches, one cannot ignore that humanity, as a matter of fact, has devoted to it an enormous amount of effort, and that the most vigorous minds have made of it their most cherished work. Now metaphysics, according to its own avowal, aims at knowing, at understanding the essence of things, and this without any utilitarian end, as Aristotle had already shown. Therefore this desire must be very strong in us; and if it is true that the end is inaccessible, the sterility of efforts constantly repeated is but one more proof of the strength with which humanity strives toward it.

It is, moreover, easy to establish the union between the notion of the rational and that of the persistent throughout time. The principle of identity is the true essence of logic, the real mould into which man pours his thought. "I agree," says Condillac in the *Langue des Calculs*,(73) "that in this language, as in all others, one only makes identical propositions when the propositions are true," and in his *Logique* (74) he affirms that "the evidence of reason consists solely in identity."

To affirm, however, that an object is identical with itself seems to be a proposition of pure logic and, moreover, a simple tautology, or, if you prefer, an analytical judgment, according to the terminology of Kant. But as soon as the consideration of time is added, the concept becomes twofold, so to speak, for beside the analytical sense, it acquires a synthetical sense, as Spir excellently says. It is analytical "when it expresses simply the result of an analysis of the concept; synthetic, on the other hand, when it is understood as an affirmation relative to the nature of real objects."(75) But this relation between the principle of sufficient reason and that of identity was already perfectly clear to Leibniz, as one can see by Couturat's exposition,(76) and, moreover, as is indicated by the manner in which Leibniz places the two principles on the same level in the passage which we have already cited (p. 28).

Thus the principle of causality is none other than the principle of identity applied to the existence of objects in time. We have been looking, according to the expression of Leibniz, for "something which can be used to justify why this exists in this rather than in any other fashion." What can be the determining reason for that which is conditioned in time? One only is possible: that of pre-existence. Things are thus because they were already previously thus.

It is clearly shown from what precedes that the principle of causality is profoundly different from that of lawfulness. But an error so great in its consequences as the confusion of these two principles, so generally shared by many great minds, can only be considered as removed if we are in a position to explain it. Above all, it seems due to the lack of precision with which we generally employ this term *cause*. Not that we really use it falsely; but constantly, of necessity, and most often unconsciously, in speaking of causes, we use the trope which the Greeks called synecdoche—that is to say, we replace the whole by a part.

I missed my train this morning. What was the cause of it? My watch was slow. Assuredly if my watch had been exact I should have risen earlier or dressed more quickly and I should have been able to arrive in time. But if I had not lived so far from the station I should have arrived equally well; and also if carriages in Paris had better horses or if the train had been a few minutes late, etc.—I could continue thus indefinitely.

What, then, do I designate originally by the term *cause?* It is one of the conditions determining the phenomenon. But do I mean to affirm that it is the only one? In no way. It simply appeared to me for the moment as the most *remarkable*, and one sees immediately that there may be many reasons for this: it is the condition the least known to my interlocutor; it is also the least stable, and that which appears to me the easiest to modify. I have no influence over the trains or carriages of Paris, and it would be a great undertaking to change my residence in order to live nearer the station; but had I possessed a better-regulated watch or had I examined its state the evening before, the event which I regret would not have taken place.(77) And yet I have never ceased to be convinced that the conditions determining the event were many, and that each one of them was determined by a host of others going far back into the past. For, in the last analysis, in order to miss my train because of my watch, it was necessary in the first place that there should be railroads and watches with springs and balance-wheels, two modern inventions which are certainly the very direct consequences of that great spiritual movement called the Renaissance, which took up and continued the admirable work accomplished by the Hellenic mind twenty centuries ago. Thus, in pushing the analysis to its very end, I find myself convinced that if I missed my train this morning Marathon and Salamis had something to do with it, since those two battles prevented Persian despotism from crushing Greek culture in its embryo. As Mill said, "the real Cause is the whole of these antecedents."(78)

About all of that we have a vague feeling. But precisely because we feel that here is a chain of events in which we risk losing ourselves, we simplify. We set aside all the conditions, however essential they may be, for the benefit of one alone which we desire to accentuate. I have omitted to speak of the invention of railroads and of watches, and I have rid myself in that way of all temptation to go back to the battle of Marathon, and likewise I have omitted a host of other circumstances, because I believed they were without interest to my interlocutor.

And so to go back to the causes, whatever be the phenomenon, constitutes an impossible task. We must limit it; we must be satisfied with a partial success. For this reason, in speaking of causes, we all resemble children satisfied with the most immediate answers to the questions they put, or rather we resemble that confiding Hindoo to whom the Brahmins explained that the earth rests upon the back of an elephant, which is standing upon a tortoise, which is perched upon a whale. Whatever seems a step in the way of explanation is invested by us with the name of "cause." We are not surprised, then, that this term is employed where really there is a question of a law. The search for the law is included in that of the cause. Indeed, all the conditions which lawfulness imposes upon us, in whatever concerns time and space, these also causality demands; and it adds another exigency, that of the identity of objects in time; from which it follows that as long as the lawful bond does not exist, there can be no question of establishing the causal bond. Conversely, the establishment of the first is always a step in the way which leads to the second. We say, for example, that the low boiling-point of gasoline is the cause of the disappearance in a short time of a spot made with this liquid. We have thus connected the disappearance of the spot with the phenomena of boiling. If these latter phenomena (as we understand them) could be explained, if we knew their causes, those of the disappearance of the spot would be determined at the same time.

Moreover, we proceed in the same way outside the proper domain of the physical sciences. When we speak of explaining a phenomenon, of searching for its causes, we are trying to know either its pre-existence in time, which is really applying the postulate of causality, or the empirical rule determining its change in time, which amounts to applying only the postulate of conformity to law provisionally while waiting for something better. And since we have to do with phenomena which appear to us to be, from the strictly scientific point of view, of very great complexity—and it is for this very reason that their study does not fall within the field of physical sciences strictly speaking—their solution in accordance with the postulate of causality seems to us to lie in an almost infinite future. Thus cause and law seem to be synonyms here, almost coinciding. When a historian, in order to explain the decadence of the Roman Empire, refers to analogous facts which have taken place in the history of other peoples, when the psychological novelist analyses his hero to show us that his actions, however peculiar they may appear to us, are nevertheless determined by motives which we recognize very well in the men about us and in ourselves, the historian and the novelist make an appeal to lawfulness. But, of course, whenever possible, they will take care to conform to the postulate of causality. The historian will show us that the progress of Christianity was due to a previous mystic tendency of the ancient world, and the psychological novelist will make us see that the fatal blindness of the hero was, at bottom, the consequence of his passionate temperament, although its manifestations had been repressed previously by his active life. Law or identity in time is fundamental in all our explanations, even outside the physical sciences, sometimes the one, sometimes the other, more often the one and the other combined, though the combination of them may never be perceived by us.

In addition to what we have stated another circumstance obscures our knowledge of the rôle of causality. It is the lack of precision in the term *cause*. The meaning which we have just set forth does not exhaust its contents. To make sure of this, it is enough to think of an act emanating from free will. When, by an act of volition, I produce an external change, or when the believer attributes a phenomenon to the intervention of God (we have previously shown that these are associated concepts), it is certain that one does not hesitate to speak of cause and effect. But here no identity is possible, and, what is more, I have the immediate intuition of it. Not for a single moment can I nourish the illusion that my will is something analogous to the movement which it produces; here, then, is a concept of causality fundamentally different from that which we have just stated and which is based on identity. In order to mark the distinction we shall designate the latter concept as that of scientific causality, and we shall apply to the first the term theological causality, since, as we have just seen, the supposition of God's intervention in natural events makes use of it. Is it not astonishing that two concepts so different, so antagonistic, as scientific causality and theological causality, can be designated by the same term? We see clearly their common ground: the cause is what produces—what must produce—the effect. In one of the two cases the conviction of the bond which unites cause and effect will come to me because I shall have shown the fundamental identity of the two terms: it will rest upon reasoning; in the other case I shall obtain it from my act of volition, which constitutes, as Schopenhauer has shown, the essence of the self. The concept of cause is, then, really double, belonging in part to the world of reason and in part to that of will. It may well be that this latter idea is, from the psychological point of view, prior to the first— that is, that the idea of the tie came to me primarily because I feel myself able, according to my will, to perform an action, identity coming to graft itself on this primitive concept in the presence of the need of understanding and the impossibility of attributing to things a volition analogous to mine. However we may dispose of this problem of metaphysical psychology, it is certain that what prevails in science is the second concept, that of causality derived from identity, and hence to be called scientific causality.(79)

We have just recognized that the savage and even the animal make use of the principle of lawfulness. Does the same hold true of the principle of causality? It is difficult to affirm it as regards the animal. The desire to understand, the philosophical instinct, "wonder at one's own existence," as Schopenhauer says,(80) seems to us to be a privilege of man; we shall see, however, a little later that in a certain sense we are indeed forced to attribute causal deductions to animals. At any rate, we could not imagine a human intelligence, however untutored we may suppose it, without attributing to it deductions of this kind. The child, as soon as it knows how to express itself, formulates so many *whys* that one is tempted to believe that the causal tendency existed within it, however obscurely, anterior to speech.

In the pages which follow we shall study the rôle played by the postulate of causality in the physical sciences. We hope to show that this rôle is of fundamental importance, and that neither the evolution of science in the past nor its present condition can be explained if we exclude it.

It is in the attempt to understand a phenomenon that we apply the principle of causality. It is therefore in that portion of science devoted to explanations that we ought to see it play a most conspicuous part.

Does this part exist? It is evident, at any rate, that from the point of view of the opinions of Berkeley, Taine, and Helmholtz it constitutes an anomaly; if law explains the phenomenon it would seem useless to go beyond it. It is enough, moreover, in order to banish from science the study of "explanation" proper, to declare that the aim assigned by us previously to the empirical part of science, defined as the totality of laws, is that of all science. This opinion has been most clearly formulated by Auguste Comte.(81) It appears, indeed, from the context of the passage previously quoted (page 25) that what he defines as the "use of laws" seems to him equally to be the aim of "all science." Comte rigorously condemns all attempt to know anything beyond the law. He repeats on several occasions that injunction, which constitutes, we know, one of the corner-stones of his philosophy: "We evidently cannot know what at bottom this mutual action of the heavenly bodies and this weight of the terrestrial bodies are; any attempt in that direction would be necessarily profoundly disillusioning as well as perfectly useless. Only minds entirely alien to scientific studies can occupy themselves with it to-day."(82) "All *scientists* admit to-day that our real search is strictly limited to the analysis of phenomena in order to discover their effective laws—that is, their constant relations of succession or of similitude, and that it in no way can be concerned with their intimate nature, nor their first or their final cause, nor their essential mode of production."(83) Even if we are called upon to formulate suppositions or hypotheses they must have as their sole object a still unknown empirical rule: "Every physical hypothesis, to be really legitimate, must deal exclusively with the laws of phenomena and never with their mode of production."(84)

To Mach also "the economy of thought" seems to be the sole and definite aim of science. He has applied this principle with much rigour in the exposition of certain chapters on physics, and he has particularly insisted upon the idea that science can only be descriptive. Independently of him, one of the greatest physicists of the nineteenth century, Kirchhoff, has maintained the same idea. Both, moreover, appear to have ignored Comte, who we have just seen expresses very analogous ideas.(85)

Comte's attitude in regard to explanatory theories necessitates withdrawing them entirely from science. The founder of positivism has not hesitated before this consequence. Starting from this point of view, he arrives at the denial that the undulatory theory, so magnificently developed by his great contemporary, Fresnel, has exercised any influence whatsoever upon the development of optics.(86) But this radical solution is inconveniently in contradiction with the facts. A glance at the evolution of science is sufficient to convince us that the experience of scientists has been quite different. Newton in his *Principia* expresses himself in these terms: "Hitherto we have explained the phenomena of the heavens and of our sea by the power of gravity";(87) and farther on: "I have not been able to discover the cause of those properties of gravity from phenomena, and I frame no hypotheses."(88) An attempt has sometimes been made to make of this *hypotheses non fingo* a sort of profession of faith, as if Newton had declared the search for the explicative hypothesis illegitimate. It has even been fancied that Newton had made possible the execution of this programme. "All hypotheses are banished," Musschenbroek affirms in 1731,(89) at the moment when Newton's authority was at its zenith, and he utters this cry in expounding the theories of the Newtonian School on action at a distance— theories the hypothetical character of which is quite evident.

Moreover, Newton himself, toward the end of his life, seemed a little inclined to attribute to his famous statement a rather pretentious meaning.(90) Now the text of the very passages which we have just cited proves very clearly that Newton had sought for an hypothesis without finding it. We shall see later on (p. 78) that the *Opticks* has preserved traces of these investigations.(91) On this point all the contemporaries of Newton were substantially in agreement with him. Some supposed the existence of forces operating at a distance, whereas others devised extremely complicated theories reducing this apparent action at a distance to action by contact. But whether they were partisans or adversaries of what were called the Newtonian conceptions, they were in agreement in thinking that the phenomena of gravitation demanded explanation. Now, what they were searching for is not easy to imagine if one wishes to remain in the domain of pure conformity to law. Newton's law is of a marvellous simplicity; it is, moreover, absolutely general, since it embraces the totality of *matter*. Doubtless one can conceive of still more general laws, and the contemporaries of Newton were able to foresee that the phenomena of gravitation would some day be connected by a common rule with such or such a series of phenomena. What seems strange is that unanimously and imperatively they demanded this explanation *hic et nunc*—that is, something going beyond the law —and it is almost superfluous to say that everyone, beginning with Newton himself, used the terms *cause* or *reason* to indicate the object of these researches. We can characterize it more nearly by remarking that Leibniz, Huygens, and many others after them were seeking for a mechanical theory of gravitation, and that, without a doubt, if a valid one could have been produced, the partisans of action at a distance would have been forced immediately to accept it.

Is the example cited an exceptional one? It is, on the contrary, entirely typical. Everyone knows that science is full of these mechanical theories or hypotheses. Doubtless there exist scientific treatises and even books dealing with whole departments of science which contain only laws or assumptions relative to laws. But how many others differ on this point! The works of the most illustrious protagonists of science—we may choose between those of Laplace, of Lagrange, of Lavoisier, of Fresnel—are full of hypotheses, and more recently Maxwell, Lord Kelvin, Hertz, Cornu, H. Poincaré, to mention only a small number of illustrious names, have devoted an important part of their works to these theories.

As a matter of fact, Comte's solution is not the only possible one in this case. Instead of brutally suppressing theories one can try to make them enter the realm of science—that is (according to Comte and to Mach) the realm of laws, by assimilating them.

Laws establish relations between elements of fact which can be directly observed and controlled. When I say that benzene boils at 80°C., or that, subjected to the action of bromine under fixed conditions, it produces a substance which boils at 154°C., I am only affirming a series of facts which every physicist and every chemist can verify. If there is no mistake about what I call benzene, and if I have properly explained the conditions of the experiment, anyone who will reproduce it in the laboratory will arrive at the same result.

Now here is an hypothesis: the molecule of benzene contains six atoms of carbon, forming a hexagon attached alternately by simple and double bonds. All direct verification is evidently impossible. No one has ever seen either a molecule, an atom, or an atomic bond, and still less has anyone ever seen this hexagon of which we are speaking, nor doubtless will any one ever see them.

And yet, if we have been led to assume these things, it is because they seem to correspond to a whole series of facts which are known to us by experience. It is these latter, connected by more or less convincing reasons, which I summarize in speaking of the hexagon. To use a figure familiar to the mathematician, we have introduced an imaginary term which eventually will be eliminated.

Therefore, according to this conception, theories have no value, no virtue in themselves. They only serve to bind laws together in a provisional manner. Their hypothetical elements have no more existence than the mathematical expression which we use in the statement of certain laws. Thus when, in order to formulate the law of refraction, I say that the quotient of the two sines must be equal to a constant quantity, I seem to suppose the existence of this function. But it is only an appearance. At bottom I am perfectly convinced that angle and sine are only concepts which I have created for convenience. I have not supposed for a moment that nature calculated with the aid of a table of logarithms. In the same way, molecules, atoms, forces, and ether, of which we speak so frequently, are only pure concepts, like the angles, the sines, and other abstractions.(92) Hypotheses, then, are no longer assumptions about real happenings of nature, about their mode of production, so energetically outlawed by Comte. They are simple figurative representations, destined to serve as mementoes, to fix ideas, as we say in mathematics. If I assert that benzene contains six atoms of carbon forming a hexagon, I am expressing myself inexactly; what I want really to affirm is that benzene acts in certain respects as if it were thus constituted. So, contrary to appearance, I do not affirm the existence of the hexagon. I use it as a convenient term, because it would be too complicated to establish a direct relation between different elements which, however, are all elements of fact. "Mathematical theories," says Poincaré, speaking of the undulatory theory, "have not as their object to reveal to us the true nature of things; that would be an irrational pretension. Their sole end is to co-ordinate the physical laws which experience makes known to us, but which, without the help of mathematics, we could not even state."(93) Duhem affirms in the same way that the physical theory is not an explanation, but a system of mathematical propositions;(94) it classifies laws.(95)

One can, indeed, with the aid of devices of this kind, assimilate hypotheses to laws, the latter being expressed by formulae analogous to those which we have used for the former. We can say, therefore, that the celestial bodies move as if they were mutually attracted in proportion to their masses and inversely to the square of the distances, and also that the light ray acts as if the sines of the angles of incidence and of refraction must observe a certain proportion. But it will be noticed that this manner of expression seems natural for the law of gravitation (which, moreover, was expressed by Newton in about this same form) and not for that of the sines. That is because Newton's law really contains an hypothesis, an assumption about the real happenings of things, whereas for angles and sines it is only a question of concepts of our imagination; consequently the precaution seems to us entirely superfluous here.

In other words, the assimilation which we have just tried is purely artificial. There is a real chasm between physical concepts and mathematical abstractions. To declare that the atom of carbon is the limit of a series of concepts like the point, the line, or the infinitely small quantity, is really to do violence to our intelligence.

Moreover, there cannot be the slightest doubt about the opinion of the scientists of the past concerning hypotheses. Duhem, whose very great authority in these matters is reinforced by the fact that his own ideas are diametrically opposed to this manner of thinking, writes: "It is not at all doubtful that several of the geniuses to whom we owe modern physics have constructed their theories in the hope of giving an explanation of natural phenomena, that some have even believed themselves to have realized this explanation."(96) He states also that the great scientific theories, notably the doctrines of the peripatetics, of the atomists, of Descartes, of Boscovich, were entirely dominated by metaphysical conceptions, and, in fact, were only the prolongation of philosophical systems,(97) an evident proof that both had the same aim, to wit, the explanation of reality. But, even in perusing the works of those who actually use these hypothetical concepts, without excepting the most cautious amongst them, one feels that they attribute to them quite another degree of reality than to a purely mathematical concept. Without doubt the explicit affirmations about reality have become a little less frequent recently. The anathemas of Comte and of Mach have had much to do with it, as have also certain critical works, such as those of Stallo and of Hannequin, of whom we shall speak later, but the principal reason lies probably in the fact that scientific hypotheses themselves are even now in the act of undergoing a profound transformation, of "moulting," if one dares to use this term. This does not prevent scientists, as soon as they bring into play atoms and ether, from reasoning implicitly as if they were not concepts but real things—nay, even the only real things, since they must explain all reality.(98) Far from limiting science to laws or from considering hypotheses as provisional substitutes for future laws, the scientists manifestly and constantly subordinate

the second to the first. Duhem furnishes us with excellent
examples of this subordination.(99) Thus when optics classifies
the phenomena of the prism and of the rainbow in the same
category, while Newton's rings are classed with the interference fringes of Young and of Fresnel, or when biology
treats the swimming bladders of fish as homologous to the
lungs of mammals, both of these sciences yield to the considerations of pure theory and to hypothetical conceptions. The
physicist, whether he brings everything back to mechanics,
or whether, adopting a more recent way of thinking, he
considers, on the contrary, electrical phenomena as fundamental, has implicitly the pretension of *explaining* nature to
us with the help of his theory. And the most flagrant anomaly
which one can discover in the application of a law (for example,
the phenomenon of Gouy in respect to the impossibility of
perpetual motion) appears *to be explained* as soon as the theory
takes account of it.

Such is, incontestably, the practice of scientists. But does it
follow that it is accurate? We are accustomed to treat as
erroneous the ways which science has followed at certain
epochs—for instance, when it tried to explain phenomena
with the aid of substantial qualities. May it not be that there
is in this tendency of science to erect explanatory theories—
a tendency of which we cannot deny the reality—a vicious
propensity from which it would be wise to keep science as free
as possible? We have seen that this was Comte's opinion.
Mach, at bottom, is not far from agreeing with him. Duhem
also believes that scientists have been, and still are, the victims
of an illusion like that which made the Spanish explorers
catch glimpses of the fabulous Eldorado. The search for the
explanation is not Ariadne's thread, capable of guiding us in
the labyrinth of phenomena; the explanatory part of science
is only a parasitic growth.(100)

To try to settle this question, let us examine, in the first
place, scientific theories in themselves. The accomplishment of
this task is greatly facilitated by the remarkable works which
have been devoted to this subject, amongst which we shall
here mention especially the works of Lange, Stallo, Hannequin
and Duhem.(101)

But before entering into the heart of the subject, let us

formulate one restriction: we shall at the very outset exclude from the chapter which follows the most recent phase of theoretical conceptions—that of electrical theories—and we shall be content to envisage the entirety of the hypotheses about the constitution of matter as they appeared to dominate science but a few years ago. Our principal reason for proceeding thus is that the new theories of electricity, being still in a great measure in the process of elaboration, offer for that very reason, from our point of view, a less propitious subject of study than their elders, mechanical theories, more advanced as to their evolution. Moreover, it is only with evident exaggeration that one can treat this phase of science as belonging entirely to the past. Many physicists, amongst those of the greatest authority, would protest doubtless against such a pretension. Some because they do not accept these new ideas or because they accept them only incompletely; others because, although adopting these theories, they consider them more or less consciously as a simple stage. For the moment one may reduce to electricity all the diversity of natural phenomena, including even those of mechanics, but later on electricity itself will be explained by a still undetermined modification in the hypothetical medium, a sort of local tension which evidently one would like to have appear as purely mechanical.

It is only after having studied the purely mechanical theories that we shall pass to the examination of the electrical hypothesis, an examination which, we hope, will tend to confirm the results already reached.

NOTES

1. BERKELEY: *De motu. Works*, ed. Fraser. Oxford, 1871, Vol. III, § 37: *Nam inventis semel naturae legibus, deinceps monstrandum est philosopho, ex constanti harum legum observatione, hoc est, ex iis principiis phenomenon quodvis necessario consequi: id quod est phaenomena explicare et solvere, causamque, id est rationem cur fiant, assignare.* This is not an isolated passage of Berkeley's; over and over again he comes back to this question. Cf. especially *A Treatise concerning the Principles of Human Knowledge. Works*, Vol. I, § 62, 105.

2. HUME: *Essay on the Human Understanding*. London, 1739, p. 76.

3. TAINE: *De l'intelligence*. Paris, 1869, Vol. II, pp. 403-404.

4. HELMHOLTZ: *Ueber die Erhaltung der Kraft* (*Wissenschaftliche Abhandlungen.* Leipzig, 1882), p. 68: *Ich habe mir erst spaeter klargemacht, dass das Prinzip der Causalitaet nichts anderes sei als die Voraussetzung der Gesetzlichkeit aller Naturerscheinungen.*

5. HANNEQUIN: *Essai critique sur l'hypothèse des atomes dans la science contemporaine.* Paris, 1895, p. 8.

6. OSTWALD: *Vorlesungen ueber Naturphilosophie.* Leipzig, 1902, p. 302.

7. LUCRETIUS: *De rerum natura*, trans. Bailey. Book I, line 160 and ff.

8. JEAN BERNOULLI: *Discours sur les lois de la communication du mouvement. Œuvres.* Lausanne and Geneva, 1742, Vol. III, p. 58. We also find this deduction expressed with much precision with respect to the principle of the conservation of matter by Kozlowski, Bibliothèque du Congrès de Philosophie. Paris, 1901, Vol. III, p. 536; cf. later, p. 445, n. 96.

9. What we here call lawfulness (*légalité*), a term which we borrow from Helmholtz, but of which he has badly defined the import, corresponds very nearly to what Kroman (*Unsere Naturerkenntnis*, trans. Fischer Benzon, Copenhagen, 1883) designates as *causality*, just as our concept of *scientific causality* approaches that of *identity* of the same author. And yet Kroman seems at times to underestimate the true limits of the first of these two concepts (cf., for example, p. 204, where he confuses it, just as Helmholtz does, with the postulate of comprehensibility; p. 211 and ff., where he would like to derive from it the existence of the noumenon (cf. also pp. 22, 195–196, 199, 250), and deduces the second from the first, because of an error analogous to that in Helmholtz and in Hertz (cf. later pp. 201, 219). The concepts of *empirical causality* and of *rational causality* formulated by Kozlowski (*Revue philosophique*, 1905, p. 250) differ still more from those defined by us, since that author, on the one hand, uses the term *rational* to designate what is simply conformable to the rule—that is, in accordance with our terminology, conformable to law (cf. *Psychologiczne zrodla.* Warsaw, 1899, p. 11; *Revue philosophique*, October 1906, p. 407), and on the other hand his concept of causality implies that of irreversible becoming (*Przeglad filozoficzny*, 1906, pp. 200, 204).

10. COMTE: *Cours de philosophie positive*, 4th ed. Paris, 1877, Vol. I, p. 51.

11. GOETHE: *Faust*, 1 *Theil. Studirzimmer.*

12. COMTE, we know, often used this example, which is indeed admirably chosen. Cf. LÉVY-BRUHL, *La Philosophie d'Auguste Comte*, 2nd. ed. Paris, F. Alcan, 1905, p. 49.

13. POINCARÉ: *La valeur objective de la science. Revue de Métaphysique*, Vol. X, 1902, p. 265.

14. COMTE: *l.c.*, Vol. VI, pp. 637–638.

15. Cf. also *ib.*, Vol. III, p. 369; Vol. VI, p. 596. The researches which seemed particularly condemnable to Comte were those of the biologists which resulted in recognizing the importance of the cell (Comte describes it, with scorn, as the "true organic monad") and those of Regnault on the anomalies in Mariotte's law. Lévy-Bruhl (*l.c.*, p. 111) believes that Comte nevertheless conceived these phenomena as subject to laws, but that he supposed these laws accessible only to minds more powerful than ours. One indeed finds passages which seem to admit of this interpretation

(cf., for example, *Cours*, Vol. VI, p. 640). At any rate, since Comte sets limits, not temporary, but permanent, springing from the very nature of the human mind, this conception is tantamount to the one which we are expressing in the text. The law being certainly a subjective construction, to say that it exists but that it will remain eternally inaccessible to us is equivalent to denying its existence. Later Comte, acquainted with the discoveries of Schwann, came to a more just appreciation of the work on the cell (*Politique positive*, Vol. I, p. 649). On the other hand, it is curious to remark that even in 1878—that is, at a time when the usefulness of Regnault's researches had been evident for a long time—P. Laffite, the authorized disciple of Comte, renewed his master's anathemas, alluding to Regnault as "an academic factionist" (*Revue occidentale*, Vol. I, 1878, p. 288).

16. As an example of the concern for exactness which dominates modern science we may cite as one of thousands the results of Stas on atomic weights, with their minute precautions; and yet these precautions have seemed insufficient to the chemists of following generations, who have constantly amended Stas's figures, as may be seen by the work of special commissions engaged in the task of controlling these measures. Two articles at the *Congrès international de physique de 1900*, that of Benoit on *Précision dans la détermination de longueur en métrologie* and that of Rubens on the *Spectre infra-rouge*, give an excellent idea of the precision obtained and the constant concern of physicists for it. Naturally, new results have been obtained since that date.

17. G. Léchalas: *Les confins de la science et de la philosophie. Revue des questions scientifiques*, XIX, 1901, p. 505. It is hardly necessary to recall that in Kant (cf. especially *Kritik der reinen Vernunft*, ed. Kirchmann, pp. 215, 229) the concept of experience presupposes a strict order in the domain of phenomena.

18. A. Fouillée: *Les origines de notre structure*, etc. *Revue Phil.*, XXXII, 1891, p. 576.

19. Comte: *Cours*, Vol. II, p. 11. Cf. *ib.*, pp. 6–8.

20. F. le Dantec: *Les limites du connaissable*. Paris, F. Alcan, 1903, pp. 98–99.

21. Comte: *l.c.*, Vol. I, p. 53. Lévy-Bruhl, although elsewhere he attempts to defend the unity of Comte's doctrine (*l.c.*, p. 12), recognizes that Comte changed his opinion on this question and that this change was due "to the increasing subordination of the scientific to other interests," which he believed "superior" (*ib.*, pp. 173–175). This evolution continued after the publication of the *Cours*, and in the *Politique positive* (1851) Comte succeeded in limiting astronomy to the solar system (Vol. I, p. 510) and in ridiculing the "supposed discovery" of Le Verrier, "which, even if it had been real, would only have been of interest to the inhabitants of Uranus."

22. Id., *Cours*, Vol. I, p. 99.

23. A. Fouillée: *Le problème psychologique. Revue Phil.*, XXXII, 1891, p. 235.

24. *Man kann also einraeumen, dass wenn es fuer uns moeglich waere, in eines Menschen Denkungsart, so wie sie sich durch innere sowohl als aeussere Handlungen zeigt, so tiefe Einsicht zu haben, dass jede, auch die mindeste Triebfeder dazu uns*

bekannt wuerde, imgleichen alle auf diese wirkenden aeusseren Veranlassungen, man eines Menschen Verhalten auf die Zukunft mit Gewissheit, so wie eine Mond und Sonnenfinsternis, ausrechnen koennte. Kant, *Kritik der praktischen Vernunft*, ed. Rosenkranz and Schubert. Leipzig. 1838, p. 230.

25. F. A. LANGE: *Geschichte des Materialismus*, 4th ed. Iserlohn, 1882, p. 20.

26. This reasoning may be compared with that by the aid of which Lucretius infers the materiality of air (see later, p. 306); it is the same which compels us to suppose the existence of the ether. The gods exist, for they act. To say that the gods are not interested in the world is atheistic, as if one were to deny mass to the ether: it would immediately become useless, inexistent.

27. RENOUVIER: *Critique philosophique*, Vol. VII, 1878, p. 186.

28. LEIBNIZ: *Opera philosophica*, ed. Erdmann. Berlin, 1840, p. 515.

29. PLATO: *Timaeus*, trans. Jowett. New York, 1892, § 28.

30. ARISTOTLE: *De Caelo*, trans. J. L. Stocks. Oxford, 1922. Bk. II, Chap. XI, § 2.

31. SCHOPENHAUER: *Saemmtliche Werke*, ed. Frauenstaedt. Leipzig, 1877, p. 5.

32. LEIBNIZ: *Mathematische Schriften*, ed. Gerhardt. Halle. 1860, Vol. VI, p. 206. *Sequeretur etiam causam non posse iterum restitui suoque effectui surrogari quod quantum abhorret a more naturae et rerum rationibus facile intelligitur.*

33. *Ib.*, p. 439. *Effectus integer causam plenam vel ejus gemellum reproducere potest.*

34. *Ib.*, p. 219.

35. LUCRETIUS: *l.c.*, Book I, line 156.

36. DUHEM: *La théorie physique*. Paris, 1906, p. 272.

37. H. POINCARÉ: *La science et l'hypothèse*. Paris, s.d., pp. 211–212.

38. Cf. the amusing exposition of the difficulties of class experiments and the lack of agreement between their results and those described in books, in WELLS' *The New Machiavelli*. Leipzig, 1911, Vol. I, p. 33.

39. DUHEM: *l.c.*, p. 290.

40. C. NEUMANN: *Ueber die Principien der Galileit-Newton'schen Theorie*. Leipzig, 1870.

41. LUDW. LANGE: *Ueber die wissenschaftliche Fassung*, etc. *Wundt's philosophische Studien*, Vol. II. Leipzig, 1883. Id., *Nochmals ueber das Beharrungsgesetz*, ib. Id., *Ueber das Beharrungsgesetz, Kgl. Saechs. Ges. der Wissenschaften*, Vol. XXXVII. Leipzig, 1885, p. 336 and ff. Id., *Die geschichtliche Entwicklung des Bewegungsbegriffs*. Leipzig, 1886. Id., *Das Inertialsystem, Wundt's phil. Studien*, Vol. XX. Leipzig, 1902.

42. HANNEQUIN: *Essai critique*. Paris, F. Alcan, 1895, p. 79.

43. E. LE ROY: *La science positive et la liberté. Congrès international de philosophie*. Paris, 1900, Vol. I, p. 331.

44. D'ALEMBERT: *Traité de dynamique*, 2nd ed. Paris, 1758, pp. 13–14.

45. POISSON: *Traité de mécanique*. 2nd ed. Paris, 1833, p. 204 and ff. In Streintz's book, *Die physikalischen Grundlagen der Mechanik*. Leipzig, 1883, p. 81 and ff., there is found an excellent discussion of the two principles of the measure of time.

46. See on this subject R. Schenck, *Ueber den rothen Phosphor, Berichte der deutschen chemischen Gesellschaft*, XXXV, 1905, p. 352 and ff.

47. The importance which the measure of the diminution of radio-activity in time had in this part of physics is well known. It is considered as the most characteristic property of radio-active bodies, that according to which their identity or non-identity is decided. Cf. Rutherford. *Radio-Activity*, 2nd ed. Cambridge, 1905, pp. 223–32, 411, 412, and Madame Curie, *Revue scientifique*, November 17, 1906, p. 654.

48. LUCRETIUS, while trying to prove that nature obeys the law, insists also on the condition of duration (Book II, v. 175 and ff.).

49. PAINLEVÉ : *Bulletin de la Société française de philosophie*, 1905, pp. 64–65, asserts that the notion of the homogeneity of time and space with respect to laws exists in man prior to any science, as it also does in the animal.

50. HENRI POINCARÉ very justly deduces this form of the law directly from the "scientific conception" of the world—that is, according to our terminology, from the principle of lawfulness (*légalité*). Cf. *Cournot et le calcul infinitésimal. Revue de métaphysique*, XIII, 1905, p. 295.

51. HENRI POINCARÉ : *L'espace et la géométrie. Revue de métaphysique*, 1895, p. 638. Cf. id., *La géométrie non-euclidienne. Revue générale des sciences*, 1891, p. 772.

52. Cf. on the manner with which this relation between geometrical deduction and physical statements is found to be modified in recent conceptions, *La Déduction Relativiste*, especially paragraphs 86, 98, 156.

53. BERTRAND RUSSELL : *An Essay on the Foundations of Geometry*, pp. 150–151.

54. Cf. p. 216. It is easy to understand that the recent theory of "local time," so profoundly revolutionary in many respects, has, however, in spite of appearances, respected this fundamental distinction between time and space. Minkowski's formula, according to which space and time must blend into a more general notion, that of the Universe (cf. P. Langevin, *L'Evolution de l'espace et du temps. Revue de métaphysique et de morale*, July 1911, p. 459) might, in truth, give rise to some doubt. But Einstein's fundamental argument, which consists in showing that one cannot "telegraph into the past," is enough for us to see that in this respect nothing is modified (*ib.*, p. 463). The new theory leads, however, to an assimilation of the notions of time and space from a definite point of view (cf. later, p. 257, n. 73), and it results from this that two observers who move differently do not appreciate the time elapsed in an identical manner. One may, therefore, imagine, as Langevin proves by a pleasant and ingenious fiction, an observer leaving the earth and finding it again after two centuries, whereas he himself would only have lived two years (*ib.*, p. 466). But this fiction in no way contradicts what we said about the impossibility of a voyage into the future, since having once succeeded in traversing the space of two centuries, the traveller could no longer by any means retrace his steps. This invention therefore is to be classed with romantic anecdotes, where a cessation of animal life is supposed, as in About's *l'Homme à l'oreille cassée* or in Wells' *Sleeper*, inventions which do not shock too greatly our sense of possibility.

55. SPIR, who had a very genuine feeling for diversity between space and time, did not always indicate exactly the difference between the two concepts. What he says about the impossibility of conceiving an empty time (*Denken und Wirklichkeit.* trans. *Pensée et réalité.* Paris, 1876, pp. 327–328) is just as applicable to the space which would be marked by nothing. The example which he uses as a basis, that of man who would have slept, finds its analogy in the man, who with the world would have been carried through empty space.

56. ARISTOTLE: *Physics*, Book I, Chap. VIII.

57. COURNOT: *Traité de l'enchainement,* etc. Paris, 1861, p. 276.

58. HELMHOLTZ: *Wissenschaftliche Abhandlungen.* Leipzig, 1880, p. 16.

59. LOBATSCHEWSKY: *Etudes géométriques sur la théorie des parallèles,* trans. Houel, *Mémoires de Bordeaux,* Vol. IV, 1866, p. 120.

60. RIEMANN: *Ueber die Hypothesen,* etc. *Abhandlungen der Kgl. Gesellschaft zu Goettingen,* Vol. XIII (1854), p. 148.

61. HELMHOLTZ: *Ueber den Ursprung,* etc. *Populaere Vortraege,* Brunswick, 1876, pp. 42–43, and *Ueber den Ursprung,* etc., *Wissenschaftliche Abhandlungen,* Leipzig, 1882, p. 954.

62. P.-G. TAIT: *Conférence sur quelques-uns des progrès récents de la physique,* trans. Krouchkoll. Paris, 1886, p. 12 and ff.

63. H. POINCARÉ: *Les géométries non-euclidiennes. Revue générale des sciences,* II, 1891, p. 774. *La science et l'hypothèse,* p. 93. *La valeur de la science,* p. 109. This argument had already been proposed by Lotze. Cf. Bertrand Russell: *An Essay on the Foundations of Geometry.* Cambridge, 1897, p. 100.

64. We are obliged to recognize that Poincaré's prevision which we had followed in this matter has not been confirmed by the later progress of science. Cf. on this subject *La Déduction Relativiste,* § 121.

65. See p. 219 and ff.

66. SPIR (cf. amongst others *Pensée et Réalite,* p. 128) greatly insisted on this disagreement between the postulate of identity and reality, and saw in it justly a direct proof of the *a priori* character of this postulate. Wundt had already pointed out (*Die physikalischen Axiome und ihre Beziehung zum Causalprincip.* Erlangen, 1866, p. 125) that at the time of a change "intuition (*Anschauung*) compels us to posit two things, whereas the concept would allow the subsistence of only one thing." And yet he declares in another place that this conception of something which remains through change is not *a priori,* but is, on the contrary, suggested by the phenomena themselves (*ib.,* cf. 2nd ed., Stuttgart, 1910, p. 178, the somewhat modified and more precise expression of the same thought).

67. H. POINCARÉ: *La science et l'hypothèse,* p. 258.

68. Id., *Sur la valeur objective de la science. Revue de métaph.,* 1902, p. 266.

69. E. MACH: *Erkenntnis und Irrtum.* trans. *La connaissance et l'erreur,* Dufour. Paris, 1908, p. 13.

70. ARISTOTLE: *Metaphysics*, Book I, Chap. I.

71. SPINOZA: *Ethics,* Part IV, Prop. 27.

72. ARISTOTLE: *l.c.,* Plato had already pointed out that geometry, in spite of appearances, pursues no practical end, and "knowledge is the real

object of the whole science." *Republic*, Book VIII, trans. Jowett. New York, 1892; Vol. III, p. 229.

73. CONDILLAC: *La langue des calculs*. Paris, an VI, p. 60.

74. Id., *Logique*. Paris, an VI, p. 177.

75. SPIR: *l.c.*, p. 192.

76. L. COUTURAT: *La logique de Leibniz*. Paris, F. Alcan, 1901, pp. 186, 209 and ff.; see also the exposition made by the same author at the *Société française de philosophie*. Bulletin 2nd year, 1902, February 27th. This is also Cassirer's opinion (*Leibniz's System in seinen wissenschaftlichen Grundlagen*. Berlin, 1902, p. 325). And yet the principle of the equality of cause and effect appears more often in Leibniz as independent and sometimes even has the appearance of a statement deduced from experience. Cf. *Mathematische Schriften*, ed. Gerhardt, Vol. II, p. 308.

77. "In the purely physical order no necessary condition is at bottom the cause more than another." RENOUVIER, *La Méthode phénoméniste. Année philosophique*, 1890, p. 20.

78. JOHN STUART MILL: *A System of Logic*. London, 1884, p. 340.

79. We shall show (p. 308) that within very restricted limits science is equally forced to make use of a concept derived directly from that of theological causality.

80. SCHOPENHAUER: *Die Welt als Wille und Vorstellung*, ed. Frauenstaedt, Vol. II, p. 175.

81. Did Comte share at bottom the opinion expressed later by Taine, and did he confuse law and cause? One would be tempted to believe it, seeing that identity between the weight of terrestrial objects and the attractions of the planets appears to him to constitute the true mutual explanation of the two orders of phenomena (*Cours*, Vol. II, p. 169). And yet we shall see later that Comte conceives one cause "first or last" distinct from law, although he condemns the search for it.

82. COMTE: *ib.*, Vol. II, p. 169.

83. *Ib.*, Vol. II, p. 298.

84. *Ib.*, Vol. II, p. 312.

85. The analogy between the opinions of Comte on the one hand and of Kirchhoff and Mach on the other has been brought to light by Kozlowski (*Psychologiczne Zrodla*. Warsaw, 1899, p. 30; *Przeglad filozoficzny*. Warsaw, 1906, p. 193).

86. COMTE: *Cours*, Vol. II, p. 442. In other circumstances, however, Comte formulated less decided opinions. Thus, if he rejects the ether, he admits the corpuscular theory of matter, which he calls a "good hypothesis" (*ib.*, IV, p. 641). It is probable that in this case Comte has yielded less to his principles and more to his powerful scientific instinct. His conception then draws markedly nearer that which tends to consider these hypotheses as instruments devised to fix our thought.

87. NEWTON: *Principia*, Book III, p. 506.

88. *Ib.*, p. 179.

89. Cf. ROSENBERGER: *Geschichte der Physik*. Braunschweig, 1884, Vol. III, p. 3.

90. Cf. especially in Eddleston, *Correspondence of Sir Isaac Newton*, etc.

London, 1850, Cote's letter of February 18, 1713, and Newton's replies of March 28th and 31st (pp. 151–156).

91. There is also in the *Opticks* a complete exposition of the principles of the atomic theory (cf. later on, p. 424). It is known, moreover, that in this work the theory of emission—that is to say, an hypothesis with the best characterizations on the mode of production—plays a considerable part. Cf., on the real sense of Newton's declaration, Appendix I, p. 454.

92. BERKELEY (*De motu. Works*. Fraser. Oxford, 1871, Vol. III, § 39) formulates with great precision this analogy between mathematical concepts and physical concepts.

93. H. POINCARÉ: *Leçons sur la théorie mathématique de la lumière*. Paris, 1889, p. 1.

94. P. DUHEM: *La théorie physique*. Paris, 1906, p. 26.

95. *Ib.*, p. 33.

96. P. DUHEM: *La théorie physique*. Paris, 1906, p. 46. Planck is still more affirmative; he states that "all the great physicists have believed in the reality of the image of the world" (*Die Einheit des physikalischen Weltbildes*. Leipzig, 1909, p. 36). Wundt compares the theories of "economy" and of "convention" to "legal fictions" which abound in the history of law; these are attempts which aim at establishing the genesis of knowledge independently of all real history; even the most determined partisan of these conceptions is forced to recognize that the principles of science have not really been created in this way (*Die Prinzipien der mechanischen Naturlehre*. Stuttgart, 1910, pp. 7–8).

97. Id., *l.c.*, p. 11 and ff.

98. PLANCK expressly affirms that atoms or electrons are as real as the heavenly bodies or the objects which surround us and that contemporary physicists "speak the language of realism and not that of Mach" (*l.c.*, pp. 33–37). Henri Poincaré declares in the same way (*Science et Méthode*. Paris, 1908, p. 186) that in the physical sciences the term "existence" has not the same meaning as in mathematics; "it no longer signifies absence of contradiction; it signifies objective existence."

99. P. DUHEM: *l.c.*, pp. 33, 35. In a recent article Planck has pointed out to what a degree this procedure is general and characterizes the true direction of the evolution of science. Thus we now classify acoustics with mechanics, and, on the other hand, magnetism and optics with electrodynamics. What used to be called the physics of heat is now divided; radiant heat is ranked with optics (and electro-dynamics), whereas the rest is dealt with in connection with mechanics and kinetic theory (*l.c.*, p. 6).

100. Id., *l.c.*, pp. 46–47.

101. J. B. STALLO: *The Concepts and Theories of Modern Physics*. New York, 1882. We have already cited the titles of other works.

CHAPTER II

MECHANISM

IN perusing a book of popular science or materialistic philosophy (let us take as an example *The Riddle of the Universe*, by Ernst Haeckel,(1) the celebrated biologist), one gains the impression that the mechanical theory is a logical conception, complete and finished, directly applicable if not to the totality, at least to the great majority of natural phenomena. But looking more closely it is easy to see that this is an illusion. That all the phenomena of organic matter should be explained by those of inorganic matter has always been postulated by a great number of thinkers. "I suppose," says Descartes, "that the body (of man) is nothing but a statue or a machine made of earth."(2) Leibniz writes: "All that takes place in the body of a man or of any animal is as mechanical as that which takes place in a watch,"(3) and, in the nineteenth century, Claude Bernard affirms in the same way that there can be no barrier "between the science of living bodies and that of inorganic bodies."(4) But in reality these are simple postulates, and every impartial observer is obliged to recognize that, if some progress has been made in this direction, thanks to the conceptions of Lamarck and Darwin, and if, on the other hand, thanks to certain works of Jagadis-Chunder Bose,(5) Traube, A. L. Herrera, Stéphane Leduc,(6) we are beginning to catch glimpses of vague analogies between brute matter and living matter, what has been done is extremely little compared to what remains to be done. Indeed, one can scarcely discover in modern physiological doctrines the faintest traces of mechanical explanation. Let us reflect: here are two germs between which the most minute microscopic examination is incapable of finding the slightest difference; and yet one is the germ of a man and the other the germ of a cat. Still, there must be differences. In two men, each of whom will resemble his father, all the peculiarities of their final evolution, the infinitely slender differences which distinguish them from each other, must be explained by some mechanical arrangements in these germs.

These difficulties have been shown many times, and E. von Hartmann, in one of his last memoirs, has given an admirable summary of them.(7) But even in inorganic science is there not much that is illogical? To be sure, in almost every treatise there is talk of atoms and molecules. But it would be a mistake to believe that, under these names, there is a question of identical or even very analogous conceptions. Chemistry, for instance, since Dalton and Avogadro, seems at first sight to be the chosen field of atomic theories. It refers incessantly to these atoms and molecules and even to formulae of "constitution," pretending to show their arrangement in space. But this is pure appearance. The chemical atom, with its multiple and mysterious qualities, which just as mysteriously engender still others in the molecule, has little in common, apart from the name, with the atom of the mechanical theory, whose essential characteristic is to possess but one unique property, mass, and to know but one unique mode of action. The most recent works connected with Svante Arrhenius's theory of *ions* hint but slightly at the possibility of a transition (not to speak of a conciliation) between these antagonistic concepts.(8) This contrast is so shocking that a theorist of chemistry and a most distinguished one,(9) after long and fruitless attempts, despaired publicly of any hope of success in this order of studies and looked for solutions in an entirely different direction.

In physics there exists in fact only a mechanical theory relevant to phenomena in a gaseous state,(10) a theory to which recent results permit the assimilation, from certain points of view, of those phenomena produced in dilute solutions. As for the different forms of energy, their unification has made an immense progress through the work of Hertz, confirming the very penetrating ideas of Maxwell on the identity of electricity and of light. But we are still very far from the possibility of reducing different forms of energy to mechanical motion. There has incontestably been a backward step in this respect. Indeed, according to the theory of Fresnel, light was reduced to undulations of the ether, a motion undetermined in certain respects in a medium still less determined, but a motion whose nature was postulated as purely mechanical. Yet at the present moment light is an electric phenomenon. But at no time since electric phenomena have become a part of science has any formula been devised which might in any way pass as a mechanical theory consistent with these phenomena. Nor is this for want of searching. One of the greatest scientific theorists of all time, Clerk Maxwell, as we know, devoted incessant efforts to this task. He took infinite pains to establish in each case the *possibility* of a mechanical explanation. But in this endeavour he very often had to stay his efforts, and when, on the contrary, he attempted to render his ideas precise, his efforts only resulted in contradictory images. Poincaré, who among contemporaries is doubtless the most competent judge of such matters, has clearly shown, in spite of his profound admiration for Maxwell, the hesitation which every logical mind necessarily feels toward that part of the great theorist's work.(11) Moreover, one has only to open a more recent book, such as that of Sir Oliver Lodge, (12) and consider the extremely ingenious, mechanical models, proposed by that eminent physicist, in order to realize that the question has not progressed much since that time.(13) It is, let us remark in passing, this evident retrogression of the mechanical theory which explains in great part the birth of the opposite tendency, that which seeks to reduce mechanical phenomena to those exemplified by electricity.

But setting aside this evolution and considering the still recent past, we easily perceive that even in the great heyday of Fresnel's theory there could be no question at bottom of a complete mechanical reduction. That is because, if the undulation, the motion, furnished a sufficiently clear image to the mind, the substratum of this motion, the ether, remained enveloped in the thickest of shadows. We believe it useless to emphasize the difficulties and contradictions confronting all those who have tried to form a somewhat precise idea of this "medium" which one is forced to conceive of as sometimes continuous and sometimes composed of tiny particles, or again as an extremely rarefied gas and as a solid infinitely more rigid than steel.(14) One particular difficulty which for some years has occupied many physicists is the difficulty resulting from the work of Michelson and Morley; this cannot be reconciled with Bradley's theory of aberration, so that it is now possible to say that we cannot imagine the ether which surrounds us as being either at rest or as following the earth in its motion, or rather that we are forced to accept each supposition alterna·tively. If, on the contrary, we consider this strange anomaly as a definitely established fact, we are forced to make it the base of a theory embracing all of the phenomena of the visible world, thus destroying entirely the foundations of mechanism as Maxwell conceived of it.(15)

The difficulties just mentioned, whose enumeration can be prolonged indefinitely, are quite impressive. But it certainly would be wrong to exaggerate their importance. Are they absolutely insoluble? This has often been affirmed, but without sufficiently valid proof, and it does not seem unlikely that "negative dogmatism" in this question has often been pushed too far. Thus Spir has denied that the mechanical theory can ever embrace not only organic phenomena, but also the diversity of chemical substances.(16) Hannequin has declared that a specific ether would always be necessary for each class of phenomena, the properties of these different media "being profoundly opposed and distinctly irreconcilable,"(17) and he has rejected in particular the electro-magnetic theory of light;(18) according to him, in descending to the atom the theory simply creates "a microcosm where are assembled all the essential traits which its mission is to explain"; one "always surprises it, in one way or another, transferring to the atom and to the individual the qualities required by the whole which it composes."(19) We shall see later on that there is a partial truth in these negations if we understand by the term quality its *quid proprium* considered as sensation. But, if taken literally, they are certainly inexact. If scientific theories were as sterile as this they would not even have a value of apparent explanation, and, for the same reason, they would be useless from the point of view of establishing relations between laws; one could not really understand why humanity should have lingered, and should linger still, over such vain occupations, its very illusion becoming quite inexplicable.

As a matter of fact it is quite impossible to place limits to scientific explanation in this realm of ideas. Many obstacles which appeared almost insuperable at some given moment have been overcome or altered. The differences existing between classes of phenomena are being gradually diminished by the patient research of scientists who refuse to accept them as ultimate. It is certain that the electro-magnetic theory of light has been an immense step in this direction; so also the theory of *ions*, which seems to show the way by which the specificity of chemical phenomena may be made to disappear; and so also, finally, the electric theory of mass, which connects mechanical with electric phenomena. To mention another particular instance: the purely mechanical theory of the ether has for some years been more or less abandoned because of the predominance of electrical theories; but we can see from a paper presented by Lord Kelvin at the International Congress of Physics in 1900 (20) that the opposition between diverse properties, so discordant in appearance, of this hypothetical medium had already been quite noticeably diminished. If some day favour is again accorded to purely mechanical theories—and this, after all, is quite possible—it is not at all certain that there will not be found a way of more or less conciliating these divergences. At any rate, this hope is not denied us because, once again, no one has proved that the task is impossible.

But if one penetrates to the very foundations of mechanical theories there appears an obstacle of a nature different from those which we have just dealt with.

All mechanical hypotheses present the common trait of trying to explain the phenomena of nature by the aid of motion; that is why they are sometimes designated by the word *kinetic*, which, however, has more often been applied to a particular theory concerning the gaseous state. In addition to motion these theories make use of the concepts of mass and of force, sometimes one of the two only, at other times both together. For our analysis it is wise to distinguish between these three classes. We shall designate as *corpuscular* (a term invented by Boyle (21), which seems to characterize them well enough) those which only employ mass and motion, and we shall call *dynamic* those which use only force and motion. This term has sometimes been used in a very different sense, (22) but it suffices to fix its signification. Finally, we do not know any special term applicable to the theories which at once use the concepts of force and of mass.

The corpuscular hypotheses are those which have always appeared the most satisfactory from the theoretical point of view. Many theorists of science firmly believed, during a certain period, in the possibility of reducing all phenomena to the simple terms of mass and motion. Some have even believed this reduction to be quite near. The attempts of those great physicists, Lord Kelvin and Hertz, show to what an extent scientists wish to rid themselves of the concept of force, a concept which seems to some of them nothing short of scandalous.

It is easy to realize whence difficulties arise. The corpuscular theories—one sees this clearly in the kinetic theory of gases, which is the only part of the system really completed—assume the existence of separate particles, atoms or molecules. We have intentionally used this vague expression of *particles*, whereas very often that of *particles of matter* is employed. Matter is a complex concept. It has temperature, colour, sometimes even flavour. Corpuscles are stripped of all these properties. Of matter they have kept only a few characteristics, the most important of which is mass. That is essential to them, since it is inevitable that they should act upon one another.

This action can occur only in impact. This is clearly seen in the kinetic theory of gases. But, although the *Hydrodynamica* of Daniel Bernoulli, where this theory was outlined for the first time, appeared only in 1738, one will not be surprised to notice that the problem had been raised by Leibniz and by Huygens long before that time; we have just seen, indeed, that action by impact constitutes the essential element not only for the theory of gases but for every corpuscular theory. In studying the writings of these great thinkers we are easily convinced that the question has not made much progress since their time.

But for the moment let us remain in the domain of the theory of gases more familiar to our contemporaries. We know that pressure is here represented as resulting from the impact of manifold particles against one another and against the sides of the vessel enclosing them. Since we know from experience that the pressure exerted by a gas in a tightly closed receptacle of impermeable material does not diminish with time (unless, of course, there is chemical reaction between the gas and the sides), it follows that, in spite of impacts being extremely numerous between molecules, the kinetic energy must have remained constant.

We know of bodies which act in about the same way; we call them elastic. Let us say, then, that the molecules of gas must be considered as completely elastic bodies,(23) resembling very perfect billiard balls; moreover, it is of billiard balls that physicists are accustomed to think when speaking of the impacts of atoms. How does the elasticity of a billiard ball show itself? Let us see what happens when one ball hits the other ball or the side of the table. At first the side yields and the ball flattens itself a little; then side and ball come back to their original form and the rejection of the ball is a consequence. But why do these deformations, once produced, not persist?

Attempts have been made to avoid the necessity of an explanation of this point. During the collision of imperfectly elastic bodies, a part of the kinetic energy disappears, or rather is transformed, so that it manifests itself in the deformation of the bodies and the increase of their temperature. But, by definition, molecules are indeformable and, moreover, they cannot become warm, since it is precisely their motion that constitutes heat. Consequently, we are told, granting that energy must remain and that, in this particular instance, it cannot transform itself into anything else, we ought necessarily, after the impact, to find it again as kinetic energy.(24)

But in truth this is an illegitimate way of solving the problem. Conservation of energy, we shall see, is not an axiom, and no one can pretend that its disappearance is unimaginable. If pressure is the result of molecular impacts, the kinetic energy must be preserved. To make this affirmation is simply to state that the pressure of the gas is maintained—that is, to state a law and formulate the problem whose solution is in question, and not to furnish a solution. What we should ask for is a theory telling us *how* this can be accomplished mechanically without the need of endowing the molecules with a special elastic force.

This problem may be approached from still another side. We can imagine elastic bodies which, during impact, deform themselves less and less. In the end there will be no deformation, and the substance, perfectly elastic, will conserve during the impact all of its kinetic energy. But, on the other hand, since the body in question is not deformed, we can consider it as absolutely inelastic, and therefore, during the central impact of two molecules of equal and opposite velocity, this velocity will be simply neutralized and the molecules will remain at rest. That is, from a purely rational point of view, every time that two molecules encounter each other there will be absolute indecision as to the consequences. This is evidently inconsistent with determinism, which is the base of all science.

It is curious to see from a passage in Newton's *Opticks* that arguments analogous to those drawn from the conservation of energy had been set forth even in his time. Only those will be astonished at this for whom the history of the principle of conservation of energy begins with Mayer and Joule; but, in reality, since Huygens and Leibniz, the principle of the conservation of *vis viva* served the same purpose many times. "If two equal Bodies," says Newton, "meet directly *in vacuo*, they will, by the laws of Motion, stop where they meet and lose all their motion and remain in rest, unless they be elastic and receive new motion from their Spring. . . . If it be said, that they can lose no motion but what they communicate to other Bodies, the consequence is, that *in vacuo* they even lose no motion, but when they meet must go on and penetrate one another's Dimensions."(25)

We see that Newton does not treat very seriously the postulate which considers the conservation of *vis viva* as axiomatic; evidently this principle had not acquired the authority which the conservation of energy enjoys in our day. But what is especially remarkable in these few lines is that they establish the fact that not only the elasticity but also the hardness of substances require explanation. We shall return to this point.

As long as it is only a question of billiard balls it is not too difficult, if not to solve the problem, at least to defer its solution. We can suppose that the tendency toward the return to the original form shown by the ball and the side is only an appearance; in reality it is due to molecular motions which we leave undetermined. But when it is a question of the impact of molecules themselves we no longer have that resource. If we suppose that their elasticity is due to motions of a more tenuous medium, since we shall have to explain in its turn the elasticity of this medium, we shall have to imagine another more tenuous still, and so on without end. This is a consequence which Leibniz clearly perceived; yet it did not cause him to withdraw from his position, as we can see from a passage in his *Essai de Dynamique*.(26) But modern physicists will certainly refuse to follow him in this path.

Cannot the elasticity of molecules be due to the movements of ponderable masses themselves? Many attempts have been made in that direction. Thus A. Secchi believed that he was able to establish an explanation based upon a proposition of Poinsot, and that theory, which, in fact, rested only upon a simple misapprehension by the Italian astronomer,(27) has since had a little merited success amongst philosophers.(28) The attempts of Lord Kelvin and of Hertz are much more remarkable. But as soon as one pursues the problem closely, enormous difficulties are encountered, as Boltzmann has stated,(29) in the sense that complication of auxiliary hypotheses and of construction becomes enormous without representing in a satisfactory manner even the simplest phenomena. Now the complication here constitutes a radical defect. We feel sure that if it is to explain something, the atom must be simple. To attribute to atoms a structure and complicated motions is, in fact, to impute to them differentiated parts, to postulate solidarity and cohesion of these parts. When one speaks to me of atoms I do not conceive of them distinctly, and I attribute to them a sort of unity quite ideal. Then their rigidity baffles me less, although, at bottom, the difficulty is the same. But here I feel it immediately, and I realize that the hard atom demands an explanation as much as the elastic one.

We have just seen that the corpuscular atom is analogous to the substances which we know; like them it has mass. It resembles them also, or rather it resembles a determined class of substances, called solids, in that it must have shape. Very often, it is true, physicists or chemists, in speaking of the atom, leave this point undetermined, attributing to it, at most, a shape vaguely spherical.(30) This is simply because the theories are not yet very far advanced and the lack of precision on this point is not an inconvenience. But there is no doubt that in corpuscular theories the atom is really a small solid, and even an ultra-solid. "These primitive Particles," says Newton, "being Solids, are incomparably harder than any porous Bodies compounded of them; even so very hard, as never to wear out or break in pieces."(31) These little solids, certainly, must have a

shape and occupy a strictly limited part of space. This makes
Lasswitz (32) say that the atom is, above all, a "mobile part
of space whose geometrical parts are relatively at rest each
toward the other." Considered from this point of view, there
can no longer be question of that vague ideal unity which we
just postulated. Space, within the corpuscle, has parts; how
does it happen that they are dependent one upon the other?
Why are they not detached in impact? Why cannot a foreign
substance penetrate these parts?

Descartes' theory was not, properly speaking, corpuscular.
And yet since for him the essence of substance consisted in its
spatial extension, this problem presented itself to him in quite
an analogous manner. He solved it by supposing that this
cohesion of parts was the simple consequence of their being
mutually at rest.(33) This solution was hardly satisfactory,
and Leibniz recognized clearly that in order to act mechanically
the corpuscle had to be endowed with a special principle of
action.(34) Newton also, as we have just seen (p. 70), understood
that, deprived of a special principle of action, the corpuscle
was incapable of acting during impact. There have been,
however, some attempts at an explanation. The most remarkable, doubtless, is that of Denis Papin, who in a letter to
Huygens formulates the hypothesis that "matter itself has
no linkage of parts and that the hardness which is experienced
in certain substances comes only from the motion of the
surrounding liquids which press against the parts the least disturbed by one another."(35) The theory thus outlined is analogous to that of Leibniz on elasticity—that is, it ends in the
indefinite multiplication of media. Apparently none of these
"explanations" has remained in science, since in opening a
manual of physics we find the active principle of Leibniz
admitted under the name of *impenetrability*.

Thus we shall not gain much in substituting hard bodies
for elastic ones, for in the end we cannot represent to ourselves
the resistance which a body opposes to the penetration of
another except under the aspect of a mysterious "principle of
action."

Finally, here is an argument drawn directly from experience.
The corpuscular theory rests upon action by contact. But there
is no real contact between two bodies. When one body has

collided with another it seems to have touched it, but this is an appearance. In reality, at the moment of the impact the particles nearest to one another have remained separated by quite appreciable distances. We know the phenomenon called Newton's rings, occurring when a lens is pressed against a level sheet. The colour of these rings permits us to calculate the thickness of the intermediary layer. In the centre, where this thickness is least diminished, a black spot is produced. It is "optical contact," yet it is not a real contact. The two bodies may be brought more closely together, but then there is adhesion.(36)

These difficulties, we have just seen, have been known for the most part since the time of Leibniz and Huygens. And so when Newton had established the law of universal gravitation a quite different theory of matter arose—a theory which, based upon the existence of forces acting at a distance, tended in the first place, as Poincaré aptly remarked, to transform the substances into something analogous to a stellar system, thus disclosing that it had its origin in celestial mechanics. This theory was clearly formulated by the English physicist Cotes in the preface to the second edition of Newton's *Principia*, which appeared in 1713. Newton never committed himself definitely in that respect, but it seems probable that he was in agreement with his disciples regarding it.(37) In the beginning of the nineteenth century the theory seemed to receive confirmation in Lagrange's *Mécanique Analytique* (38) and in the experimental results of Coulomb,(39) which seemed definitely to assimilate gravitation with other forces acting at a distance, more especially electricity. But still earlier the hypothesis had already found a theorist, who developed it to its logical conclusion. This was the Jesuit Boscovich, whose principal work appeared in 1759.(40)

Boscovich supposes that atoms are not corpuscles but geometrical points absolutely divested of space. Each of these points is a centre of forces, or rather of a single force identical with itself at equal distances round the point but varying according to the distance. At a very slight distance it is repulsive and increases in intensity indefinitely as one approaches the centre, so that it is susceptible of resisting, no matter what the impulsion is, and so that no two centres can ever coincide.

If one withdraws, the repulsive force diminishes, and at a given distance becomes nil, so that there is neither repulsion nor attraction. If one departs still more from the centre, the force becomes attractive, increases, reaches a maximum, and decreases in such a way as to become nil at a given distance; after which it becomes repulsive, in order to increase, decrease, and become nil again. This happens several times until at a certain distance, the force having become definitely attractive, diminishes in proportion to the square of its distance to infinity or "at least to distances greatly surpassing those of all the planets and comets."(41) Boscovich represents the variations of this force by a curve the two extreme parts of which are the arcs of an hyperbola, having for their asymptotes, one the axis of the distances and the other that of the forces, while the middle part cuts the axis of the distances several times.

Boscovich's system has rarely been applied in its entirety by scientists. We hear very little said of his unique curve of forces. In the nineteenth century Saint Venant (42) resuscitated and simplified his hypothesis. Saint Venant's curve is still asymptotic to the two axes, but it cuts but once that of the distances. It is rather doubtful whether a single curve of this kind can take account of the different molecular and atomic actions which one is obliged to suppose in order to explain all the phenomena observed. However, the simple force of Saint Venant has not had much greater success than that of his predecessor. And yet Boscovich's ideas have had considerable influence upon science because he was the first resolutely to strip the atom of extension. In this sense all the physicists who since then have used atom-points are following in his footsteps. Boscovich, moreover, did not fail to establish his system on a criticism of the corpuscular theory based upon considerations relative to the transmission of motion. "*Quid autem est impenetrabilitas ista? Unde fit ut idem spatium bina corpora occupare non possint?*"(43) This impenetrability can be but a force, and all transmission of the motion must be effected by the intermediary of a force: "*nullam mutationem motus fieri per impulsionem sed semper per vires agentes in aliqua distantia,*" and, of course, in this system the absolute elasticity of the atoms and the molecules offers no further difficulty.

It is easy to understand why Boscovich's "unique force" had

so little success; it is really too baffling for our imagination. Why does it change at a determined distance? And how can it transform itself at a given point from repulsion to attraction and vice versa? If the single force is to be conceived as the force related to the central force emanating from the centre, we necessarily imagine that near the origin, at a very small distance from the centre, it must have the same character as at a greater distance—that is, it should always be either attractive or repulsive. But it is, of course, absolutely impossible to construct the world with the aid of either of these two suppositions. Boscovich's force doubtless is always, either as attractive force or as repulsive force, directed toward the centre, but it does not appear to emanate from it.

It may be contended that that modification of force is the consequence of a law. This argument, which seems to have been suggested by Boscovich himself, as is shown by the title of his principal work (*Theoria . . . redacta ad unicam legem . . .*), is as little acceptable as that which aims at explaining the elastic collision of corpuscles by the conservation of energy. It is really a question here of an hypothesis about the mode of production, and not of a simple artifice of arithmetic, such as the introduction of the sines in the statement of the law of refraction. The manner in which Boscovich expounds his theory leaves us no doubt in this respect, and his argument against impenetrability would have no sense were it otherwise. We have here, therefore, nothing to do with a law.

And so it is not surprising that the dynamicists have generally preferred to surround their point-atom with many forces, varying according to different laws. Such amongst others was Kant's view.(44) Thus modified, the conception becomes less logical; it lacks that fine unity which Boscovich had given to it without becoming any more acceptable. How admit that the same point-atom emits simultaneously rays of attractive and repulsive force?

But there are objections applicable to all purely dynamical systems. It is not at all certain that all the forces whose existence one is obliged to postulate can be considered as central. This is at least doubtful for molecular forces. It seems, indeed, that the exclusive action of central forces would demand certain relations between the different forms of the resistance of bodies—

relations whose existence is denied by experience. In the same way one cannot explain permanent deformation by supposing only central forces. The phenomena of crystallization also seem to demand that the action of molecules be not exclusively exerted along the straight line which joins their centres of gravity; they should be able to exercise a rotating action one upon the other.

The following objection is still more fundamental, since it is the very concept of purely dynamic atoms which is at stake. Let us penetrate the forces which surround this atom. The centre of these forces is a point which is, properly speaking, empty (since the point is a geometrical abstraction). All objects of our knowledge located in the external world have extension. Can we imagine the existence in space of that which is unextended? We admit, if necessary, the radiating force of the centre; we represent it to ourselves as a straight line. But when it comes in contact with another atom, upon what does it act, since it finds it empty? How can this *nothing* resist motion? How, once in motion, can it preserve it? How, in a word, can it possess a mass, manifest inertia? "No arrangement of centres of forces, however complicated, could explain this fact," says Maxwell; and he adds: "No part of this mass can be due to the existence of the supposed centres of force."(45) Let us observe that we have here to do not simply with what one usually calls an occult quality—that is, a quality which is not explained by those which define the centre of forces. No, it is a property which our imagination refuses to join to the mental image which we possess—a property which clashes with that image. After all, the difficulty here is analogous to that which we encountered with respect to the corpuscular atom. If this latter appears unable to act, we do not understand how the dynamic atom can be acted upon. So that of these two systems, one represents only the passive side, and the other only the active side of a phenomenon, which, of course, can only be conceived as bilateral.

From the point of view of our imagination the dynamic representation is even incontestably inferior to the corpuscular representation. To convince ourselves of this we have only to think of motion, which is, after all, the essential function of the atom, the only modification of which it is susceptible. As to the dynamic atom, we have as much difficulty in representing to ourselves the displacement of that "nothing" which constitutes its nucleus as in representing that of the forces which surround it, and which, in fact, we figure to ourselves necessarily as a sort of gigantic spider's web, which in each atom embraces the entire universe. "Can a force be moved and displaced from one place to another?", asks Spir with much propriety.(46) The concept of displacement seems natural when applied to the corpuscle, limited in its extension, but it seems paradoxical applied to the dynamic atom. We are compelled to consider as more simple and more logical a direct variation of the dynamic force as a function of the time, which is, we shall see later on, a sure sign that the theory has failed.

And so we must not be astonished that the physicists have generally preferred less absolute solutions, departing still farther from rigorous logic, but offering more of a hold on our imagination. We preserve the corpuscular atom; we surround it with forces acting at a distance. This composite system is evidently exposed to a number of the objections formulated against the two extreme conceptions. It meets, moreover, with difficulties which belong to it particularly. How can the atom, an existence supposedly simple, be constituted by the union of two components as heterogeneous as a corpuscle and forces? What can be the bond between them? And then— and this is but another side of the same problem—the force emanating from an atom, when it comes in contact with another atom, easily finds a nucleus upon which it can act. But how can it act? The only picture we can form to ourselves of a force is that of a straight line. Between this picture and that of the corpuscle which it is supposed to influence we can find no connection. Nor shall we discover any between the concept of force and that of motion. When I see a body set in motion by impact I have the illusion of understanding, because in appearance the motion springs from another motion, but here the motion must be born from force—that is, from something absolutely heterogeneous to it.

But does not the idea of forces acting at a distance, common to all the systems which deviate from the strict corpuscular hypothesis, seem really quite paradoxical? Doubtless, even before Newton, a tendency of bodies toward a determined motion had been many times supposed—in fact, an "appetence" of bodies each for the others. It is thus that Aristotle supposed that among the four elements, two, earth and water, had a natural tendency toward a lower level, whereas the other two tended toward a higher level.(47) Galileo (48) and Kepler (49) supposed that all terrestrial objects had an appetence for the earth. But these were rather substantial forms, qualities more or less occult, with which the schools had been so unsparing. It is not apparent that there had been any question before Newton of something transmitting itself instantaneously across space like the Newtonian attraction. Descartes protested vigorously against all supposition of action at a distance, which seemed to him to culminate in endowing material particles with knowledge, to the point of making them "truly divine, so that they may know without any intermediary that which happens in places far away from them and exercise their actions upon them."(50)

When the hypothesis of universal gravitation was formulated, in spite of the enormous progress which the law discovered by Newton had made in celestial physics, it met with very strong resistance on the part of its contemporaries. Leibniz especially was very emphatic upon this point.(51) Huygens also declared that to attribute gravitation to some interior and inherent quality is "to formulate obscure and unintelligible principles."(52) He, moreover, took great pains to construct a mechanical theory of gravitation, but he arrived at no very satisfactory result. Newton himself seems, at least at the beginning of his work, to have envisaged the possibility of reducing gravitation to the action of the medium.(53)

The new idea seemed to flow directly from the law established by Newton, and that law dominated absolutely one of the most important parts of physics, the development of which had been the most rapid and the most complete. In other parts it permitted important simplifications of calculation, and it promised, we know, to furnish the basis of a general theory of matter. It was natural, then, that it should triumph. What is apt to surprise is, on the contrary, the resistance which it encountered. Doubtless one can attribute the first resistance to the influence of Descartes, who had entirely remade science and philosophy, dominating minds even as powerful as those of

Leibniz and Huygens. But if we examine what happened afterwards we see that there had always been in science a strong current of opposition to the conception of action at a distance. D'Alembert in 1755 calls forces, considered as efficient causes, existences "obscure and metaphysical, which are only capable of spreading shadows upon a science clear in itself."(54) A little later Euler states that, in supposing action at a distance, we place ourselves in contradiction with the declaration of the principle of inertia, according to which a body must modify its motion only by impact against another.(55) In 1771 Aepinus states that forces are still considered as occult qualities.(56) Even after Lagrange and Coulomb, although using unscrupulously "central forces," many physicists did not cease to see in the conception of an instantaneous action across space a kind of stumbling-block for physics nothing short of scandalous. In Stallo (57) there is to be found a long list of very convincing citations to this effect, borrowed exclusively from the physicists in the nineteenth century. The list might be prolonged almost indefinitely. Let us be content to add to it as particularly significant the declaration of Sir William Thompson (Lord Kelvin), who thinks that the hypothesis of action at a distance is "the most fantastic of paradoxes."(58) It is perhaps still more curious that physicists whose theoretical convictions were less pronounced have not ceased on every propitious occasion to give evidence of their desire to rid themselves of action at a distance. Thus Gauss (who, however, calls himself a Newtonian) believes (when nothing from the experimental point of view justified such a proposition) that for electricity the notion of a propagation in time would be much preferable to that of an instantaneous propagation.(59) Faraday, also, though pretending to follow in theory the ideas of Boscovich, felt a great repugnance to the conception of forces acting far from their base and without physical connection with their source.(60) Maxwell declares that were a scientific theory able, with some probability, to lead to an explanation of gravitation men of science would gladly devote the rest of their lives to its study.(61) Helmholtz, who had established his demonstration of the principle of conservation of energy on the hypothesis of central forces, is of the same opinion.(62)

Thus J. J. Thomson simply sums up the actual situation by declaring that action at a distance, although the facilities it offers to calculation have made it plausible to many mathematicians, is a concept which the greatest physicists have never been able to accept.(63) They have made numberless efforts to free themselves from it. Hooke, Varignon, Fatio de Duillier, Redeker, Euler, Challis, Guyot, Schellbach, Guthrie, Thomson,(64) and many others, have made the attempt after Huygens. The theory which has had the greatest success is indisputably that of Le Sage.(65) Maxwell was of the opinion that it was the only consistent theory of gravitation which had ever been formulated.(66) It is well known that Le Sage's hypothesis consists in supposing that gravitation is the result of the impacts of an enormous number of ultramundane corpuscles with respect to which the celestial bodies mutually become screens. The difficulties raised by this theory are enormous. It is not only necessary to suppose that a body of the density of the earth is almost translucent in respect to the corpuscles in question, but again it is almost impossible, as Maxwell stated,(67) to make this theory or any other mechanical hypothesis agree with the principle of conservation of energy. Moreover, Laplace had indicated as the lower limit of the velocity of propagation of gravity, a velocity 100 million, or at least 50 million, times greater than that of light.(68) That is, one was obliged to suppose this velocity, and, in consequence, that of the ultramundane corpuscles, almost infinite. It is extremely significant that all these difficulties have not prevented renowned physicists from devoting serious efforts to the examination and the development of this theory. Consequently we are obliged to suppose that the profound dislike for the hypothesis of action at a distance must have acted upon their minds with great intensity.

It must be remarked that in this matter the physicists could in no way count on the help of the philosophers, who, on the contrary, seemed to get along perfectly well with action at a distance. Kant in his *Metaphysische Anfangsgründe* expressly postulates it and makes it the corner-stone of his theory of matter. If, later on, in his posthumous work, *Vom Uebergange von den metaphysischen Anfangsgründen der Naturwissenschaft zur Physik*, he became less positive in this respect, he, nevertheless, never denied the concept in question.(69) Schopenhauer is, if possible, still more positive; force appears to him as something primordial, whose rationality it would be vain to look for.(70) In the same way the *Naturphilosophen* have operated incessantly with forces. This tradition persisted, and the concept of action at a distance became current in German metaphysics, as may be seen in Hartmann.(71) In France, Auguste Comte considered the concept of gravitation as above all dispute, and reproached astronomers of the past with having been "almost always dominated by contemporaneous prejudices concerning the vain search for causes."(72) In England, John Stuart Mill spoke of the "prejudice" against action at a distance and congratulated his contemporaries on being free from it.(73) Herbert Spencer made use of the concept of force without any hesitation after the fashion of the German *Naturphilosophen*.(74)

The attitude of physicists on this question has forcibly struck Stallo,(75) a witness all the less questionable since their resistance appeared to him, as to John Stuart Mill, based upon simple prejudice, having its sole source in the fact that we ourselves act upon bodies only by contact. It is to be observed, moreover, that the adversaries of action at a distance have generally adopted an analogous point of view. We shall have occasion to return to these considerations later on. But the real reasons for the resistance of scientists to the assumption of action at a distance seem to us to be much more profound.

When we try to render intelligible the action of gravitation, we certainly have recourse to the procedure which was often used to make plausible the concept of forces radiating from a centre in general. We represent to ourselves surfaces placed, normally to the radius, at different distances from the centre, and we easily come to the conviction that (to use light as an example) the same light is spread over a greater surface the farther it is removed from the centre, and in proportion to the square of the distance. We then see for gravitation the same force expand, so to speak, like a fluid over spherical surfaces of increasing diameter, which furnishes an apparently satisfactory spatial image. One can well ask with Lotze what produces the continual flux of this pseudo-fluid and what happens to it if it encounters nothing upon its path.(76) One can be equally astonished that this flux does not rather repel the bodies which it is supposed to attract. But what is most essential to note is that the spatial image itself is only a decoy and that the concept of action at a distance is certainly in reality anti-spatial.

We know matter only by its effects. This is true by definition. The conception of a material body which would be really and absolutely inert, neither acting upon our senses nor upon other bodies and not reacted to by them, is, indeed, contradictory; such a material body could not exist, existing and acting in this case being terms strictly synonymous. "Its being," says Schopenhauer, in speaking of matter, "is its action; one could not conceive of a manner of being other than that."(77) It follows that a material body which is supposed to exercise a simultaneous action in entire space exists simultaneously, strictly speaking, in the entire universe. This is what one clearly sees in the purely dynamical theory: the atom of Boscovich is anywhere rather than in its "centre." In order to reply to this objection, the dynamicists have made every effort to establish the necessity for the assumption that a material body acts where it is not. According to Kant, "everything in space reacts upon something else only in a place where the acting body is not. For if it had to react in the place where it is itself, the thing upon which it reacts would not then be outside of itself. Even if the earth and the moon were to touch each other the point of contact would still be a place in which there would be neither earth nor moon."(78) In reasoning in this way one neglects completely the continuity of space. This is clearly seen if time is substituted for space. The hypothesis of action at a distance consists in supposing that one phenomenon is the condition of another and that nothing happens in the intermediary space. Assuredly it will be affirmed that that intermediary space is traversed by force. But the two phenomena being simultaneous, force does not cross space; it leaps over it, if we dare to express it thus. Can we admit something analogous for time? Can one phenomenon be the cause of another through time without anything being modified during the intermediary moments? Apparently not. Doubtless we often express ourselves as if an event were the consequence of a distant past. But that is only a manner of speaking. We know very well that there must have been modifications during the intervening epochs, although they have escaped notice. We are not attempting here to decide the question whether time and space are or are not really continuous. What is certain is that in order to picture to ourselves action we are forced to suppose them such.(79) It is thus natural to postulate that each part of space is influenced only by the active principle of the part immediately contiguous to it, just as every moment is conditioned by the preceding moment and in turn conditions the moment immediately posterior. So if this restriction is abandoned in regard to space, if a body can really act, produce a modification in a part of space without modifying anything in the intermediary spaces, why can it not equally well appear in a far distant place without passing through the spaces which separate the two positions? Why, since it acts simultaneously everywhere, could it not appear simultaneously in two different places?(80) Ideas of this kind, however extravagant they appear, were formulated as early as the eighteenth century by Prémontval; one can see in the curious little work in which they are contained (81) that they are very directly connected with the concept of action at a distance. It is significant in this connection that a recent author, in a book of genuine interest,(82) has connected the action of gravitation with the hypothesis of the fourth dimension. It is upon this same assumption that the idealists base those ideas whose relationship with Prémontval's cannot be denied. It is well known that Zoellner (83) made use of them for an analogous purpose. As a matter of fact, action at a distance is destructive of the idea of space. It goes on, as a celebrated philosopher, himself a partisan of action at a distance, has picturesquely said, "behind the back of space."(84) The conception is anti-spatial, or at least non-spatial.

The resistance of physicists is therefore justified. Science has always unwillingly accepted action at a distance, and only very reluctantly does it preserve it. This will always be necessary as long as it remains understood that the motions of celestial bodies cannot be explained without the assumption of an instantaneous action of gravitation. But as soon as that hypothesis is no longer absolutely indispensable, as soon as one can attribute a finite velocity to gravitational action, it is quite certain that this idea will disappear for ever, for no one has ever admitted, nor ever probably will admit, a leap in time analogous to the leap in space, which the notion of action at a distance postulates. This, moreover, has happened for the forces at a distance which have successively been reduced ,to a step by step action as soon as it was ascertained that their propagation required time. Hertz in his famous work on the *Relation of Light to Electricity* (85) had already brought out this evolution and foretold that gravitation would undergo it. It seems that this prophecy is about to be accomplished, especially by the work of Lorentz, the illustrious Dutch physicist, of Wien, and of still others. Laplace, we have seen, believed that there should be assigned to gravitation a prodigious velocity of propagation, as a lower limit. This was, Wien tells us, an error of principle. In order that calculations of this kind could be valid, one would have to be able to increase or diminish the force of the gravitational attraction of a body and to observe the disturbances to which these modifications would give rise. But we are completely powerless to modify in any way the gravitation of a body; it remains absolutely constant, therefore there can only be a question of changes initiated by the motion of celestial bodies. Now these changes are, as Lorentz points out, of very slight importance: they are of the second order of magnitude. Henceforth nothing precludes the acceptance for gravitation of a finite speed of propagation identical, for example, with that of electricity and of light.(86) This theory does not seem yet to be generally accepted by physicists, but it has numerous partisans amongst them; the names we have just cited are enough to show to what a point it merits attention. If it succeeds in establishing itself, it is clear that the concept of action at a distance will be definitely eliminated, for in the whole domain of science there will be no longer a single fact imposed upon us by that "extravagance," to use Lord Kelvin's words.(87)

To sum up in a few words the results of this rapid examination, mechanical theories show themselves to be at once very complicated and irremediably contradictory. Does this conclusion not seem to support those who would either exclude them completely from science or keep them only as a help to the memory?

Yet if one tries to take in at a glance the physical theories of all the centuries, one must be struck with the common character of the elements composing them. Sometimes, especially in scientific books of a popular nature, atomism is represented as the last word of science, being a result at which science has arrived with great difficulty. Since the great antiquity of atomic systems can scarcely be denied, some have tried to make a distinction between the ancient and the modern systems, declaring that the first were arbitrary, speculative conceptions, whereas the second are genuine discoveries of science. Lange in his *History of Materialism* has already refuted this allegation of Büchner.(88) As a matter of fact, the likeness between the two is complete.

However fragmentary our knowledge about the beginnings of human knowledge, it permits us to ascertain that atomism under one form or another appears at the very dawn of science. In India atomism is complete from the twelfth century B.C.; it was, as its historian Mabilleau states, "not only the first, but the most constant and almost the only form of the philosophy of nature."(89) We find two principal systems of atomistic philosophy; the first chronologically, that of Kanada, resembles the ideas of Anaxagoras in the sense that he admits of atoms qualitatively different from one another. The atoms of Kanada are inextended; they are endowed with a kind of faculty or power (which is singularly like the antitypy of Leibniz, if we may judge from the fragments of the text which we find in Mabilleau's book), and also with gravity, the cause of their fall. It goes without saying (for we have here the essential foundation of every mechanical theory) that every material fact reduces itself to local displacement.(90) The Jainas, contrary to Kanada, do not recognize different elements from a qualitative point of view, but homogeneous atoms, like those of Leucippus and Democritus.(91) It is their system especially which seems to have prevailed later with the Hindoos. In Greece atomism is generally dated from the time of Leucippus. We know but little of the relation between Leucippus and Democritus,(92) nor do we exactly know the contribution of each to the system more commonly presented under the name of the second but belonging certainly in great part to the first, anterior in date. All that one can say about this system, and assuredly the least one can affirm, is that it is absolutely complete. As it came from the hands of the Greeks of the fifth century B.C., so we see it reappear almost without change or with insignificant additions in the writings of philosophers and scientists until the end of the nineteenth century—that is to say, until the appearance of the electrical theories of matter. To summarize this system it is sufficient to cite some of the admirable but, alas, very rare fragments which have come down to us from Democritus. "There are two kinds of knowledge: real knowledge and obscure knowledge. To obscure knowledge belong all things of sight, sound, odour, taste, and touch; real knowledge is distinct from this." "Sweet and bitter, heat and cold, and colour are only opinions; there is nothing true but atoms and the void." "We perceive nothing true in what concerns the thing itself, unless it is that which is modified from the point of view of the position of the body and the things which fall upon or resist us."(93) The atomism of Epicurus, which differs little from that of Democritus (we are not even very sure of the nature of these differences), (94) was one of the dominating philosophies of antiquity and produced in the Latin world that imperishable masterpiece, the *De rerum natura* of Lucretius. The works of Hero of Alexandria and of Vitruvius (95) show that the physicists were accustomed to take atomic conceptions as a foundation, but sometimes fused them with conceptions borrowed from philosophers who made "quality" predominant. Even in medicine a corpuscular theory was very common, as we see from the book of Caelius Aurelianus,(96) which had great authority. The early Christians willingly quoted from Lucretius; even after the definite victory of Christianity, and while combating the doctrines of Epicurus, Saint Ambrose and Saint Hieronymus preserved his physics.(97) In the eighth century Rabanus Maurus voiced opinions distinctly atomistic which he seems to have borrowed from Lucretius.(98) About this same time a school of Jewish atomists sprang up; we know of it from the refutations of Saadia,(99) a philosopher of the eleventh century. The movement is continued in the Orient by the Arabian school of Motekallim or Motekallemin; and Maimonides, who rejected their opinions, has left us a summary which leaves no doubt as to the real character of their doctrines. "They maintained that the entire universe—that is, each of the bodies which it encloses—is composed of very little particles which because of their subtility cannot be divided. Each one of these particles is absolutely without quantity, but when they are reunited this whole has quantity and is then a body. All of these particles are similar and equal to one another, and there is between them no kind of difference. It is impossible, they say, for any body to exist which is not composed of like particles by juxtaposition, so that for them birth is reunion and destruction is separation."(100)

In the West, after Rabanus Maurus, atomism suffered an eclipse because of the domination of peripatetic theories. And yet we know from recent investigations that the oblivion was less complete than we had been led to suppose until now. There was, it seems, almost constantly a kind of undercurrent distinctly atomistic, of whose protagonists we know only little, but whose power we can appreciate somewhat indirectly by the refutations of great scholastics, such as Roger Bacon, Duns Scotus, Occam, Albert of Saxony. Beginning with the first part of the fourteenth century, we can cite the following names : Gerard Odon and Robert Holkot, whose atomism seems to have been especially geometrical; Egidius de Colonna, who admits, on the contrary, the infinite divisibility of geometrical magnitude, but denies it of material magnitude, so that, if one were to divide a minimum volume of water, one would transform it into a different substance;(101) and finally Nicholas of Autricuria, or Ultricuria, (102) who is only known because he was forced in 1348 at Paris publicly to renounce certain doctrines formerly professed by him, amongst which was found the thesis that all phenomena of nature are reducible to motions of union and separation of atoms. But the broken chain was definitely resumed at the Renaissance. Prepared by Giordano Bruno, Fernel, Gorlaeus, Sennert, Basso, Maquedus, the atomism of Democritus and of Epicurus was rigorously formulated by Gassendi. In the meantime Galileo and Descartes had transformed physics, definitely putting aside the Aristolelian conceptions. Both were mechanists, and Descartes especially, with incomparable brilliancy and authority, proclaimed that every phenomenon must be reduced in the last analysis to a mechanical change. It is useless to follow this analysis farther. Until the end of the nineteenth century the principles of Descartes have dominated science in the most absolute fashion. No scientist of renown can be cited who has consciously set them aside.

Doubtless in our rapid survey we have only mentioned the outlines of the theory, thus neglecting the less important details. The atomism of the Motekallemin, resolving space into points and time into indivisible instants, necessitating incessant acts of creation by God, approaches the conceptions of the Hindoos but differs distinctly from the corpuscular atomism of Democritus. Neither Galileo nor Descartes are atomists in the strict sense of the term,(103) and amongst later physicists, many, even those who assert that they adhere to this doctrine, formulate its principles in a very different way, often with inexactness, and, in practice, frequently straying from it. Yet it is certain that one can unite all the conceptions under the term *mechanical* and that their common characteristics are of considerable importance.(104) On the whole, it does not seem too bold to affirm that the mechanical hypotheses had their birth with science and have formed one body with it during all the epochs in which it has really advanced; likewise the period when science ignored these hypotheses was an epoch of very slow progress.(105) Does this coincidence not astonish us? Stallo himself, who is a determined adversary of mechanism, considering it as prejudicial to the progress of science, as a vestige of the realism of the Middle Ages (106) (a curious opinion, as can be seen from the above exposition), is nevertheless forced to agree that the atomic theory has "held its ground more persistently than any other tenet of science or philosophy."(107)

The historians of atomism have generally supposed an affiliation between these ideas. That is not at all impossible. However different the atomism of Leucippus and Democritus from that of Kanada and of the Jainas, it may well be that some germs of the Oriental ideas penetrated Hellenic philosophy in the beginning.(108) The Jews were certainly inspired by the Greeks. The Motekallemin may have been influenced by Hindoo conceptions, by Jewish writings, and also by atomic theories as they were expounded by certain medical books, such as that of Caelius Aurelianus. Finally, the modern renaissance of mechanical theories is certainly due to the renewal of classical studies. Yet this perennial character of mechanical conceptions is somewhat strange. Must it not be true that the ground where they flourished was of a particularly favourable nature, since germs often minute soon led to such prodigious results?

Finally, during the last few years we are witnessing an impressive sight. The rapid strides of science seem to shake its most solid foundations. And yet in this universal upheaval certain conceptions, allied to mechanical or atomic theories, give proof of a singular stability. Impartial observers are struck by it. Thus Henri Poincaré declares that the greater part of Fresnel's conclusions, although they are founded upon a molecular hypothesis, remain without change when one adopts the electro-magnetic theory of light.(109) Etard, while expressing doubts about the existence of atoms and molecules, shows that all of the most recent investigations may without difficulty be fitted into S. Arrhenius's theory of *ions*, which itself is but a form of the kinetic theory, so that in the end general chemistry "fuses with the atomic theory taken in its widest sense."(110) Sir E. Rutherford, summing up the conceptions which dominate the science of to-day, to the development of which he has contributed so much, declares that they confirm "the old theory of the discontinuous or atomic structure of matter."(111) Larmor believes that the development of electrical theories tends constantly toward atomism,(112) whereas during the greater part of the nineteenth century the theories prevailing in that phase of science appear to be founded on very different assumptions.(113) J. Perrin, too, declares that the atomic hypothesis, which he qualifies as happy, "more and more, and in spite of all the astonishment which one may feel, seems well to merit the name of exact."(114) Lucien Poincaré, while examining the progress of modern physics, notes with surprise that kinetic hypotheses are about to gain new conquests. "Is the history of physics, like the history of peoples, but an eternal recommencement, and must we periodically come back to the conceptions which philosophers have imagined since antiquity? The progress of thermo-dynamics gave birth to other hopes; it alone seemed able to guide us into the domain of physics, while laying emphasis only on the reasonings and the principles formed by the natural generalization of certain experimental laws. Must we always have recourse to imagery, to mechanical interpretations, doubtlessly resembling nature but little?"(115) This physicist, we see, shows no enthusiasm for the theories in question, which gives additional value to his words.

What must be particularly noted in this recent phase of the history of atomism is that it is not a question of a simple renaissance, but of a true and an enormous progress. This progress has worked in two directions. On the one hand, atomism, it seems, has definitely conquered the immense domain of electrical phenomena (this aspect of the theory interests us particularly, and we shall have opportunity of returning to it), but, on the other hand, it has become definite to an extent that a generation ago would doubtless have seemed unbelievable, even to the most determined partisan of these conceptions. Indeed, even quite recently, when one spoke of the size or the weight of molecules, it was well understood that the figures indicated could have only a relative value : that, for instance, the molecule of water must weigh eighteen times more than an atom of hydrogen, but that all speculation on the absolute value of this weight was out of the question. Now it is no longer so. By methods of an extreme ingenuity physicists have arrived at determining definitely the weight in question. This seems so astonishing that at first sight one is almost tempted to ask whether these investigators have not been victims of an illusion in this case, if they have not succumbed to an unconscious trick of their own minds. But to be entirely free from this doubt it is enough to look at a table summing up the results reached in this domain of ideas, such, for example, as the one presented by Perrin.(116) Indeed, the data obtained in ways that were different and entirely independent of one another are all of the same order of magnitude and the more often (this is the case with six of the fifteen results cited by Perrin, and they are those which proceed from the surest methods) converge in the most astonishing way toward one single and identical numerical datum: 7×10^{23} for the number of molecules contained in a gramme-molecule (for instance, in 2 grammes of hydrogen).

Let us notice also that this evolution did not take place with constant progression, but by fits and starts, a sort of flux and reflux. During a part of the nineteenth century atomic theories

were somewhat discarded, discredited at least in appearance.
Ostwald proclaimed the "defeat of atomism."(117) Duhem
wished to direct science toward a return to peripateticism.
It is certain that at the present moment these two thinkers,
in spite of their great authority, are no longer followed as
regards this question, save by an extremely small part of
scientific thought; scientific thought on the whole has manifested, as we have just said, a very strong leaning toward
atomistic doctrines.

Cournot had already foreseen that the success of mechanical
theories must have profound causes. "No ideas of antiquity,"
he said, "have had a greater or even a like fortune. The inventors
of the atomistic doctrine must have fallen immediately upon
either the very key to natural phenomena or upon a conception
inevitably suggested to the human mind."(118)

Cournot was right, and we can now pursue the question more
closely than has been done. Let us establish in the first place
this essential point: kinetic theories are explicative. Our mind
often imperatively demands them, and is always satisfied when
it recognizes them as valid or as having even a chance of
appearing as such. We have already seen that this clearly
follows from the experience of scientists. But, moreover, some
of these latter have expressly affirmed it. Leibniz, in a passage
frequently cited, states rather ironically this peculiar character
of atomic theories.(119) But his irony was directed only toward
the concept of the atom. As to the principle according to which
every phenomenon must be reduced to a mechanism, Leibniz,
we have seen, proclaimed it as firmly as Descartes, and he
noted with perfect clearness that this reduction appeared
to be necessary in order to render phenomena intelligible. His
great contemporary, Huygens, after having defined the "true
Philosophy" as being that "in which one conceives of the
cause of all natural effects in terms of mechanical reasons,"
adds: "This must be done, in my opinion, or else all hope
of ever understanding anything about Physics must be
renounced."(120) Modern scientists have been, if possible,
still more explicit. E. Du Bois-Reymond, in a passage which
recalls strangely that of Huygens, defines science as "the
action by which we reduce modifications in the physical
universe to the mechanics of atoms," and continues: "It is a

psychological fact that where this reduction is successful our need of causality is satisfied for the moment."(121) Lord Kelvin writes: "It seems to me that the test of *'Do we or not understand a particular subject in physics?'* is *'Can we make a mechanical model of it?'* "(122) In another place he expresses himself in these terms: "I never satisfy myself until I can make a mechanical model of a thing. If I can make a mechanical model, I can understand it. As long as I cannot make a mechanical model all the way through, I cannot understand it."(123) Maxwell begins by declaring that "when a certain phenomenon is susceptible of being described as an example of a general principle applicable to other phenomena, this phenomenon may be said to be explained," which seems to conform to the opinion of Comte and Mach. But he also adds: "On the other hand, when a physical phenomenon can be completely described as a change in the configuration and motion of a material system, the dynamical explanation of this phenomenon is said to be complete. We cannot conceive any further explanation to be either necessary, desirable, or possible."(124) For Maxwell, we see, the explanation by law is not as complete as that by mechanics. It is this latter alone which seems *ultimate*.

If the analysis, which we have made concerning the principle of causality, is correct, if this principle consists essentially in the application to the object in time of a postulate which, in science limited to lawfulness, is only applicable to the object in space, we ought here to see the proof of it; atomic or mechanical theories, at least as far as their essential and durable traits are concerned, must be capable of being reduced to this principle. It is easy to verify the truth of this.

The external world, nature, appears to us as infinitely changing, becoming incessantly modified in time. Yet the principle of causality postulates the contrary: we must needs understand, and yet we cannot do so except by supposing identity in time. It follows that change is only apparent; it must necessarily disclose an identity which alone is real. Yet there seems to be a contradiction there. How can I *conceive* as identical that which I *perceive* to be different? There does exist, however, a way, a single means, of conciliating to a certain extent what appears at first sight to be irreconcilable. I can suppose that the elements of things have remained the same, but that their arrangement has altered; consequently with the same elements I can create different manifolds just as with the aid of the same letters one can compose a tragedy or a comedy (the metaphor is Aristotle's).(125) I thus can conceive that "the production and the destruction of things are only the union and the dissolution of their elements"; it is Leucippus himself who in these terms stated the foundation of his system; but before him Anaxagoras and Empedocles had said analogous things.(126)

The possibility of this conciliation depends evidently upon the particular nature of our concept of displacement. Displacement is and is not a change. When a body is displaced it undergoes a modification, and yet it appears to me to be identical to itself. That comes, we have seen, from the very essence of our concept of space, such as we find it at bottom, not only in physical sciences, even when reduced solely to their essentially lawful nature, but also in geometry.

Displacement, then, appears to me as the only intelligible change. If I wish to explain modifications—that is, to reduce them to identity—I shall be forced to have recourse to it. Here is a body, which a moment ago gave me a sensation of cold and which, brought close to another body, reduced its volume. Now it burns me if I touch it, and produces, on the contrary, an increase of the volume of contiguous bodies. This is because, (1) either to the substance of this body was added another invisible one, but one which existed before, or else (2) the arrangement or the movement of parts of the body itself has changed. These two explanations have dominated science by turns. The first has given birth to the hypothesis of fluids, whereas the second is the foundation of mechanical theories, but they both come from the same principle.

Let us set aside, for a moment, the first alternative; we shall come back to it later on. Our deduction being quite general, what we have established for the thermal phenomenon applies to any phenomenon whatsoever. We shall then necessarily reduce all changes of bodies to arrangements, to modifications in space, to displacement of parts.

By the aid of reasoning I have inferred the existence of those parts whose displacement will be the essential phenomenon of reality, the only real phenomenon; but it goes without saying that I cannot directly perceive them; they must, then, be very small. These parts or particles always remain self-identical, eternal, unchanging; this is also a direct consequence of the fundamental postulate. And since they must be displaced without undergoing any modification, and since this manner of displacement is, in the material world, the privilege of solid bodies, the particles will necessarily be unmodifiable ultra-solids, consequently unable to break or be divided mechanically —that is, they must be atoms.

We are now at the end of our deduction; later on we shall show that another distinctive feature of atomic theories, the unity of matter, which they presuppose, can be explained in an analogous manner. But our exposition is sufficient to establish what is the true foundation of the "psychological fact" of which E. Du Bois-Reymond speaks: the explanatory force of the theories resides essentially in the application of the postulate of identity in time. It is also clearly seen that it is in virtue of this postulate that physical theories arc dominated by the concept of discrete particles. It is this which differentiates them from mathematical conceptions, where the infinitely small, the indivisible, appears only momentarily to lose itself again in the continuum.(127) This difference has its source in the fact that in pure mathematics we are not preoccupied with change in time.(128) But in physical sciences, where there is question of this latter, since change in time must be explained and since the identity of the whole cannot be postulated, we are forced to fall back upon the parts, and these, required to be unchanging, can only be conceived as discrete individuals, limited in space.

Evidently the mental process which we have just traced must be mainly an unconscious process. Consequently it may seem rather vain *a priori* to expect to discover in the individual scientist, creator or follower of a mechanical theory, the motives actuating him, since those motives, not having come directly to his knowledge, would only have been revealed to him if he had been capable of applying himself to an introspective analysis of his thought—an arduous task, and one for which the scientist is in no way especially qualified.(129) But we have already shown that there are cases where the quest for the genesis of collective thought may in a certain measure correct the limitations presented by individual thought; the question now occupying our attention is, we believe, capable of furnishing a particularly striking example of the efficiency of this method. It so happens that, at least once in history, atomism arose under known conditions—conditions noted with admirable precision by an observer of a truly unique character—namely Aristotle—and the evolution which he has retraced is that from which was born the doctrine of Leucippus and Democritus. The dominant feature of this evolution upon which Aristotle lays the most emphasis is that the atomic conception sprang from the notion of the Eleatics, who assumed that being was one, permanent, and immovable. It was a theory consistent with itself but in disagreement with the facts attested by the senses, which show us the production and the destruction, the motion and the plurality of beings. To save the reality of these phenomena, Leucippus supposes, contrary to the Eleatics, that being is not one but composed of an infinite number of elements, invisible because of their great tenuity. In a word, as Zeller has summed it up, in drawing attention to the great importance of this exposition of Aristotle, "the only difference that there is under all conditions between the atomic theory of being and that of the Eleatics is that the former transfers to the particular multiple substance what Parmenides had said of the universal substance or of the whole of the world."(130) It would seem unnecessary to set forth to what extent the genesis of the atomic theory retraced by Aristotle confirms the deduction attempted by us.

The fact that the postulate of identity in time is an integral part of our reason explains the spontaneity with which these theories arise and the ease with which they develop. We understand, likewise, why there is in science not one atomic doctrine, but a multiplicity of doctrines, which, though having certain fundamental and common features, differ widely, and even often contradict one another. This is because these are the conceptions created more or less independently under the influence of one and the same tendency, through the consideration of a determined group of phenomena; they are not, as one might believe, derivations of a single theory. From this arises also the illusion, so frequent amongst scientists and even amongst a few philosophers, who pretend to distinguish the atomic conception peculiar to one part of science as "experimental truth" from the general atomic theory qualified as "hypothetical"(131)—nay, even all of the modern atomic theories from those of the ancients;(132) whereas it is easy to see that really all these conceptions hold together, that there is amongst them a genuine sameness of foundation. This sameness continues in spite of what appears at first sight to be a fundamental diversity of the starting-point. What differs more from the corpuscle of Lucretius, Gassendi, and Boyle than the point-atom of Boscovich or the electron of contemporary theories? And yet we feel instinctively that the elements common to these conceptions are far more important than their distinctive traits. They are "atomic theories": we may on the whole think of them as being such without specifying the nature of the atom—in fact, physicists have frequently built up atomic theories leaving this question undecided.

Having firmly adhered to a particular form of the atomic theory, scientists and philosophers have taken great pains to find the motive for what appeared to them as its essential foundation. They tried to establish that their conception of the atom was logical and (what was infinitely easier) that the opposite conception harboured irretrievable contradictions.(133) At other times they have sought to disengage the foundations of the theory by a psychological analysis of the sensory elements which contribute to create the concepts forming the ultimate terms of the reduction, such as those of the atom or of force.(134) It is certain that we try to make our theories as little illogical as possible. It cannot be denied, on the other hand, that the concept of the corpuscular atom comes from our tactile sensation, just as that of the dynamic atom issues from the sensation of effort. We shall try to specify in a later chapter the manner in which these conceptions were introduced into science. But it clearly appears that neither the logical nor the psychological factor has nearly as much authority as is attributed to them. We repeat: the explanatory force of the theories comes solely from the principle of identity in time which these theories attempt to make predominant, in other words, from the principle which accounts for the persistence in time of something, the inherent nature of the thing which persists being quite secondary.

The exposition of atomic theories in conformity with a logical system can be reduced to the following reasoning. The phenomena which we perceive appear inexplicable to us with the exception of one alone: the impact of two bodies. This latter is entirely clear and intelligible; if we suppose it fundamental, if we succeed in reducing the others to it, all will be explained. Now we have seen that this reasoning is defective at the very outset. No one has ever understood either the impact of two bodies or action at a distance, and no one ever will. Shall we say, following the psychological system, that we had the illusion of understanding? Doubtless. But how could this illusion, so easy to recognize, which, moreover, has been so clearly exposed by philosophers, come into existence? How does it persist with such vigour? How can it serve as a basis for our conception of science? And how does it happen that this conception satisfies us to such a degree? Reverse the terms and the enigma is explained. It is not because we understand the corpuscle that we choose it as the starting-point. What we postulate is the persistence of something. Among the things whose persistence we can postulate, the least incomprehensible, the nearest to our immediate sensation, or rather to the common sense which creates the external world, is the material corpuscle; it is from this that we start out. It is incomprehensible at bottom, you say? I agree with you, but can you offer a more solid starting-point? If not, we shall keep to this one, for we must at any price have something which persists in time, and, neglecting entirely what it contains that is at bottom inexplicable and contradictory, we shall try to explain with its aid the sensible world. It is only in case this last operation fails that we shall think of modifying our starting-point; then we shall substitute for the corpuscle a centre of force, or the atom which is at the same time corpuscle and a centre of force—concepts still less comprehensible than the corpuscle itself but whose contradictions will embarrass us no more than that of the corpuscle.

If a more direct proof were necessary that such indeed is the unconscious logical process by which atomic theories are constituted, this proof would be furnished us by the aggregate of the conceptions designated as "electric" or "electronic" theory of matter, and these are more especially associated with the illustrious name of J. J. Thomson. It can be affirmed without exaggeration that at the present time this theory is triumphing, that it dominates entirely all of the physical sciences; perhaps in the history of science no general theory has so rapidly obtained such sway. Let us hasten to recognize that the theory by its essential merits explains and fully justifies this enthusiasm. It is marvellously general, penetrating to the very depths of phenomena, not only of the science of electricity and of optics (indissolubly interdependent since the time of Maxwell and Hertz), but of all other branches of physics and of chemistry. It seems definitely to vindicate the old principle of the unity of matter which was the "secret postulate" of the atomic theory, though chemists who pretended to adhere to this theory constantly denied it.(135) It explains also without effort those mysterious phenomena of radio-active bodies which seemed at first to threaten the most fundamental conceptions of science. Finally, though so general and so abstract, since it resolves what is the very heart of our sensible representation —namely *matter*—into something which no longer is anything material, this theory is at the same time astonishingly concrete. Indeed, this last element, this component of the atom, whose size in relation to the latter is of about the same order as that of a planet in relation to the whole of the solar system, this mysterious electron is made palpable, so to speak, by this theory. Thanks to the observation of Wilson, we can surprise it at the instant when it serves as a nucleus round which a drop of water is condensed. We also know that in combining the results of this experiment with the formula of Sir George Stokes, relating the speed with which small spheres fall in the air to the size of these spheres, J. J. Thomson has succeeded in measuring this minimum charge of electricity which we call an electron, and has found it to be identical in chemically different gases.(136)

We have indicated some of the characteristic data of the theory. Let us, however, retrace the principal features, following especially the masterly exposition of J. J. Thomson.

The simplest being which science has envisaged to this day, the chemical atom, is in this new theory conceived as a structure of great complexity. Prout believed that the atoms of all chemical elements were composed of atoms of hydrogen, and J. B. Dumas envisaged the possibility of reconstituting them with the help of half or quarter atoms of hydrogen; the new theory presupposes a unit which about equals 1/1800 of an atom of hydrogen. What we call an atom becomes a sort of nebula without sun, formed of a great number of equal bodies possessing inertia and subject to mutual electrical forces of attraction and of repulsion of a very considerable magnitude.(137) Theorists treat this nebula according to the usual procedure in astronomy, calculate the disturbances and apply Kepler's laws.(138) Chemical atoms differ from one another in the number of these corpuscles (according to the terminology of J. J. Thomson) of which they are composed, but especially in the manner by which these latter are arranged; and one can see how by an ingenious conception, in using the experiments of Mayer on the spontaneous arrangement of little magnets floating on water, J. J. Thomson is able to explain the periodic properties of the elements as being due to the analogous arrangements reappearing from time to time as the atomic weight of the elements increases.(139)

But what is this fundamental element, this *corpuscle*, which constitutes the chemical atom and consequently all that common sense qualifies as matter? J. J. Thomson tells us that it is a unit of electricity.(140) Thus matter becomes an electrical phenomenon. Perhaps we shall see more closely the consequence of this conception if we consider in this connection the concept of mass. The atomic theory, taken in its most general sense, and excepting, of course, the theories at once atomic and qualitative (which we shall take up later on), deprives the atom of any quality save the property of displacement and that of occasioning motion either by contact or by action at a distance. The second of these essential properties we call mass, and mass thus becomes the essence of materiality in general.(141) In explaining matter by electricity, the new theory must certainly hold mass to be an electric phenomenon. This bold hypothesis has been reached very gradually. It was recognized at first that electricity could produce phenomena which made it appear as if the mass of bodies was increased by it. The apparent inertia which the body thus manifested on account of the electric charge was called "electric inertia," to distinguish it from the inertia in the strict sense of the term which it possessed in virtue of its mechanical mass, the action of the two inertias appearing, moreover, as entirely analogous: a charged body which is displaced "simulates exactly the familiar mechanical inertia of a lump of ordinary matter."(142) Later on it was seen that what in the first place had appeared as accessory might very well be the principal; that the electric inertia of the elementary particle, which was calculated from precise experimental data, would easily outweigh the mechanical inertia. Finally, it appeared that there was no longer any room, so to speak, for this latter, that all the apparent inertia of the element might be of electric origin. From that to declaring that it was so was but a step, and this was cheerfully taken. Thus by a process of evolution the mechanical element finally is absorbed, so to speak, in the electric element; the mechanical atom resolves itself into corpuscles which are pure electric phenomena, having no mechanical mass—that is, nothing material. This supposition evidently constitutes the essential feature of the theory, and that is why Kaufmann's experiment, from which it follows, is really, according to H. Poincaré's (143) expression, the "knot" of the whole system.

In thus summing up the theory, we have perhaps represented it as more absolute than it appears to many physicists; they sometimes express themselves as if they supposed that *behind* the electric phenomenon there must be a mechanical phenomenon—in other words, as if, after having reduced the apparent mechanical phenomenon to an electric phenomenon, this latter in its turn must be reduced to a still more fundamental mechanical phenomenon, which evidently seems not very logical. It is not only Lord Kelvin (who may be considered as a belated partisan of the old order of things) who speaks in this way; in the writings of the most pronounced founders and adherents of the new doctrine a number of passages where this conception is held can be easily found. But that is due for the most part, it seems, to the novelty of the theory; time must be granted it to gain strength, so that even those who employ it may entirely assimilate this new kind of thought and clearly perceive all its consequences. Yet it can hardly be contested that the principles of the new conceptions are defined with sufficient clearness; the electric phenomenon is really conceived as serving as a term of reduction for all the others. Hence it is very characteristic that, as Langevin has remarked in the preface to the translation of Lodge's *Electrons*,(144) the very ingenious mechanical constructions, which filled a preceding work of the celebrated physicist, should have entirely disappeared in the more recent book.

Therefore the fundamental phenomenon is no longer the impact of two corpuscles, nor is it the action of two centres of mechanical force; it is that of two electrons. We know the laws that govern this action; they are experimental laws. But who can say that he understands *how* this action is exerted, that he understands the mechanism of it? To do this it would be necessary, as the synonym we have just employed indicates, to furnish a mechanical theory of it; but this hope has been denied us if the electric phenomenon is *ultimate*. Thus even the illusion of understanding, which the corpuscular hypothesis aroused in us, and to a less degree the dynamic hypothesis, disappears; that which is laid down as a fundamental phenomenon in the electric hypothesis is an X, a phenomenon clearly unexplained and which is even declared unexplainable by the very fact that it is laid down as the last term of the reduction. And it is to this X, to this unexplainable thing, that the phenomena which we believed we understood must be reduced. In seeing the action of two masses we had thought that we grasped what was happening; without doubt it was only an illusion, since, we have seen, neither impact nor action at a distance is really explainable. But this time we cannot even preserve the illusion, for the mechanical action which we thought we saw is only an appearance; the mechanical mass does not exist; it is only a function of the electric mass. It is also clear that the electron has nothing to do with our sensation. We have no special organ sensitive to that form of energy—which explains, moreover, why it has remained unknown for such a long time—and we shall have to make long detours if we wish to describe these phenomena in terms borrowed from common sense.(145)

This is not the place to examine the merits of the electric theory from the experimental point of view. It has already rendered enormous service, and it is almost certain that it is capable of rendering still greater service in the future. But the fact that a theory of this kind has been able to spring up, that it has been immediately welcomed with extreme favour, and that in such a short lapse of time it has dominated all science, proves clearly that neither the logical nor the psychological bases ordinarily attributed to theories (p. 96), play a really important rôle in their genesis. It is not from such bases that hypotheses derive their explicative forces, but almost entirely from the considerations of time and of space, above all from persistence of identity in time. Something, as we have said, must persist, the question of knowing what persists being relatively of little importance. Our mind, conscious (unconsciously conscious, if we may be permitted this apparent paradox) of the difficulty involved in the causal explanation, is, so to speak, resigned in advance and consents to accept almost anything, even something unexplained and radically unexplainable, if only the tendency to persistence in time is satisfied.

At the same time one must admit that, since it is a question of an eternal and invincible tendency of the human mind, nothing will be gained by opposing to it artificial barriers. Science, even if it wished, could not rid itself completely of kinetic theories, expressing as they do a necessary form of our understanding.

Moreover, in supposing this elimination possible, what would remain of science would not conform to any greater extent to the programme laid down by Comte and by Mach. In what precedes we have sometimes expressed ourselves as if there really existed a part of science depending solely on the principle of law; but this was pure fiction. Science, really, even in the part appealing apparently purely to law, is profoundly impregnated with the search for causality. This is what we propose to attempt now to establish.

In science there exist several statements whose nature seems somewhat ambiguous. They are designated sometimes as principles, sometimes as laws; some attribute to them an origin purely empirical, others consider them *a priori* in nature.

Sometimes scientists admit their embarrassment. "In the opinion of many physicists," says Hertz, "it will appear as inconceivable that the most remote experience can ever change anything in the immovable principles of mechanics; and yet what comes from experience can always be rectified by experience."(146) It is especially because this ambiguity seemed to him to taint with obscurity the entire foundation of mechanics that Kirchhoff felt that he must limit the task of that science to the simple description of motion.(147) And although, as we shall see later, more accurate opinions have been expressed for a long time, they do not seem to have prevailed till now.

One can include the statements of which we speak under the common name of principles of constancy or of conservation, the conservation of velocity or the principle of inertia, the conservation of mass, the conservation of energy. These principles or laws are, as we see, among the most vast and the most important generalizations to which the human mind has attained to this day. We propose to show that in their genesis the search for identity in time has played a preponderant rôle, and that this origin influences the nature and the import of these propositions.

NOTES

1. ERNST HAECKEL: *The Riddle of the Universe*, trans. Joseph McCabe. New York, 1905.

2. DESCARTES: *L'Homme, Oeuvres*, ed. Adam et Tannery. Paris, 1909, Vol. XI, p. 120.

3. LEIBNIZ: *Opera*, ed. Erdmann, p. 777.

4. CLAUDE BERNARD: *Leçons sur les phénomènes de la vie*. Paris, 1879, Vol. II, p. 401.

5. JAGADIS-CHUNDER BOSE: *De la généralite des phénomènes moléculaires*, etc. *Congrès international de Physique*. Paris, 1900, Vol. III, p. 584 and ff.

6. STÉPHANE LEDUC: *Les lois de la biogenèse*. *Revue scientifique*, February 24 and March 3, 1906.

7. ED. V. HARTMANN: *Mechanismus und Vitalismus in der modernen Biologie*. *Archiv fuer systematische Philosophie*, IX, 1903.

8. Because of the theories following those of which we speak in the text, and especially because of the theory of the atom of Sir Ernest Rutherford and of Bohr and Sommerfeld, the gap which formerly existed between the concepts of the elementary particle in the two sciences seems now about to be bridged. But the reader will be convinced, in glancing at an exposition by the present writer of these conceptions (*La Déduction Relativiste*, § 127 and ff.), of the difficulties which must be adjusted in this case.

9. OSTWALD: *Lettre sur l'énergétique*. *Revue générale des sciences*, December 30, 1895, p. 1071.

10. PLANCK has quite recently declared that if we wish to be sincere we ought to admit that a satisfactory mechanical theory of polyatomic

gases has not yet been found, so that we still do not know what place in the system of theoretical physics we ought to assign to intramolecular phenomena. (*Acht Vorlesungen ueber theoretische Physik*. Leipzig, 1910, p. 66.)

11. H. POINCARÉ: *Electricité et Optique*. Paris, 1901, p. 111 and ff.

12. OLIVER LODGE: *Modern Theories of Electricity*.

13. In recent works (*Ueber den gegenwaertigen Stand der Frage nach einer mechanischen Erklaerung der elektrischen Erscheinungen*, Berlin, 1906, and *Weitere Untersuchungen*, etc., *Annalen der Physik*, 4th series, Vol. XXVI, Leipzig, 1908) Hans Witte has endeavoured to examine methodically the question of the possibility of a mechanical explanation of electrical phenomena. He states that there exist in all nine classes of explanation. He shows in the first place the impossibility of action at a distance (classes 1 and 2) and of emission (class 3). Six classes remain which admit the existence of an ether. The author establishes that if one supposes the ether continuous, each one of these six systems ends in contradictions which make it inadmissible. On the hypothesis of a discontinuous ether, a demonstration of this kind is not possible, but one can show that all the systems of explanation then become extrememly complicated. Physicists would only have the right to be concerned about them if phenomena, entirely unsuspected at the moment, were to come and force them to posit discontinuities in space deprived of matter and of electrons.

14. An exposition of these difficulties will be found in Stallo, *l.c.*, especially p. 119 and ff., and in Hannequin, *l.c.*, pp. 178–224. Cf. also on this subject Stewart and Tait, *The Unseen Universe, L'univers invisible*, Paris 1883, p. 194 and ff., and H. Bouasse, *De la nature des explications*, etc., *Revue de métaphysique*, Vol. II, 1894, p. 312 and ff. Men of science, moreover, have themselves recognized the contradictory character of these assumptions. Cf. Maxwell, *On the Dynamical Evidence*, etc. *Scientific Papers*, Cambridge, 1890, Vol. II, p. 433 and ff., and *On the Dynamical Theory*, ib. p. 26. Hertz, *Ueber die Beziehungen zwischen Licht und Elektrizitaet. Gesammelte Werke*. Leipzig, 1896, Vol. I, p. 341. H. Poincaré, *Electricité et Optique*, Paris, 1890. Vol. I, p. 88 and ff. *La science et l'hypothèse*. Paris, s.d., p. 198 and ff.

15. Cf. later, p. 136.

16. SPIR: *Pensée et réalité*, p. 416. Paris, F. Alcan.

17. HANNEQUIN, *l.c.*, p. 227.

18. *Ib.*, pp. 217, 222, 223. The elasticity of two media (electricity and light) indicates "a profound and probably irreducible difference." This is a "fundamental and probably definite opposition."

19. *Ib.*, pp. 231, 237.

20. LORD KELVIN: *On the motion of an elastic solid*, etc. *International Congress of Physics of* 1900, Vol. II, especially pp. 21–22.

21. BOYLE: *Works*, London, 1772, Vol. III, p. 5. It is certainly to be regretted, from the point of view of clearness of nomenclature, that the creators of the electric theory of matter felt that they must employ the term corpuscle to designate the ultimate element postulated by them. But we may guess the motives, very likely unconscious, which guided them. This element, being a purely electrical phenomenon, has no longer anything really material and therefore is no longer attached by anything to our sensation.

(Cf. pp. 99 and 307.) The name by which it is designated creates at least a factitious bond where any other connection is lacking.

22. Cf. HERTZ: *Gesammelte Werke*, Vol. III, p. 31.

23. This condition of perfect elasticity was clearly postulated by Leibniz, *Essay de Dynamique. Mathematische Schriften*, ed. Gerhardt, Halle, 1860, Vol. VI, p. 228: "Now this elasticity of bodies is necessary in nature to obtain the execution of the great and beautiful laws which its infinitely wise author has proposed." One will find in Stallo, *l.c.*, p. 42, a whole collection of passages from Kroenig, Clausius, Clerk Maxwell, and Lord Kelvin, showing that these creators of the theory of gases were also obliged to insist upon the same postulate.

24. A theory of this kind was formulated amongst others by Lasswitz, *Geschichte der Atomistik*. Hamburg, 1890, Vol. II, p. 368 and ff. Kozlowski (*Zasady*, p. 188) appears partisan of it, Kroman (*Unsere Naturerkenntnis*. Copenhagen, 1883, p. 310 and ff.), and Hannequin (*l.c.*, pp. 133–134) have justly refuted it.

25. NEWTON: *Opticks*, 3rd ed. London, 1721, p. 373. "If two equal Bodies meet directly *in vacuo*, they will by the laws of Motion stop where they meet and lose all their Motion and remain in rest, unless they be elastick and receive new Motion from their Spring. . . . If it be said that they can lose no Motion but what they communicate to other Bodies, the consequence is that *in vacuo* they can lose no Motion, but when they meet they must go on and penetrate one another's Dimensions."

26. LEIBNIZ: *Mathematische Schriften*, ed. Gerhardt, Vol. VI, p. 228. "I shall add but one remark which is that many distinguish between hard and soft bodies and the hard into elastic or not and establish thereon different rules. But one can take bodies naturally as Hard-Elastic, without denying, however, that the Elasticity must always come from a more subtle and penetrating fluid the motion of which is disturbed by tension or by change of the Elastic. And, since this fluid must itself be composed in its turn of little solid elastic bodies, one clearly sees that this Duplication of Solids and of Fluids continues to infinity."

27. Cf. on this subject, Stallo, *l.c.*, p. 46 and ff.

28. Cf. ALFRED FOUILLÉE: *Le mouvement idéaliste*. Paris, F. Alcan, 1896, p. 118; *Le mouvement positiviste*, Paris. F. Alcan, 1896, p. 136.

29. BOLTZMANN: *Anfrage, die Hertz'sche Mechanik betreffend. Wiedemann's Annalen*, Suppl. 1889; id., *Die Druckkraefte in der Hydrodynamik*, ib., 1900; id., *Leçons sur la théorie des gaz*, trans. Galotti, Vol. I, Paris, 1902, p. 3. It is also known that the *Mechanik* of Hertz, a remarkable effort in its ingenuity, has remained to this day almost sterile, in spite of the great authority of its author's name. On Lord Kelvin's attempt, cf. his communication in the *Comptes rendus de l'Académie des sciences*, Vol. CIX, p. 454. *Sur une constitution gyrostatique adynamique pour l'éther.*

30. Of course, physicists and chemists have sometimes made precise tatements, rather in self-defence, so really difficult has this question seemed to them. It is scarcely necessary to recall here the speculations on the tetrahedron of carbon.

31. NEWTON: *Opticks*. Cf. the more complete quotation, later on, p. 424.

32. LASSWITZ: *Zur Rechtfertigung der kinetischen Atomistik. Vierteljahrsschrift fuer wissenschaftliche Philosophie*, Vol. IX, 1885, p. 151.

33. DESCARTES: *Principes. Œuvres*, ed. Adam et Tannery, Paris, 1904, Vol. IX, 2nd Part, Chap. LV, title: "That there is nothing which joins the parts of hard bodies, unless (*it be the fact that*) they are at rest with respect to each other."

34. Cf. Appendix I, p. 447 and ff.

35. HUYGENS: *Œuvres complètes*, Vol. IX. The Hague, 1901, p. 429.

36. MAXWELL: *On Action at a Distance. Scientific Papers*, Cambridge, 1890, Vol. II, p. 314.

37. Cf. Appendix I, p. 452 and ff.

38. LAGRANGE's opinions have been admirably summarized by Duhem: *L'évolution de la Mécanique*. Paris, 1903, pp. 43–45 and 71–72.

39. Concerning Coulomb's influence, cf. Rosenberger, *l.c.*, p. 371.

40. P. ROGERIUS JOSEPHUS BOSCOVICH: *Philosophiae naturalis theoria redacta ad unicam legem virium in natura existentium*. Vienna, 1759. In the introduction of this work there will be found a list of the previous studies of Boscovich on this same matter. Priestley, who was a convinced adherent of dynamism, affirms (*Disquisitions relating to Matter and Spirit*. London, 1777, p. 19) that a theory analogous to that of Boscovich had been formulated simultaneously and independently by the astronomer John Michell.

41. BOSCOVICH, *l.c.*, p. 6.

42. DE SAINT-VENANT: *Mémoire sur la question de savoir s'il existe des masses continues*, etc. Paris 1844, p. 9. Saint-Venant changed his opinion later and tried to put aside completely the notion of force. Cf. Padé, *Revue générale des sciences*, 1905, p. 765.

43. BOSCOVICH: *De Viribus vivis dissertatio*. Rome, 1745, p. 33.

44. KANT was hostile to the hypothesis of atoms (*Vom Uebergange*, ed. Krause, Frankfort, 1888, pp. 96–97, 111–112, 164). Nevertheless, his scientific explanations in the *Met. Anfangsgründe*, etc., are entirely dynamical, in the meaning which we give to this term. Later, in the *Vom Uebergange*, he leans a little more toward explanations by motion.

45. MAXWELL: *Theory of Heat*. London, 1875, p. 86.

46. SPIR: *l.c.*, p. 407.

47. Cf. p. 159.

48. GALILEO: *Due massimi sistemi. Opere*. Florence, 1842, Vol. I, giorn. I, p. 40. There is an excellent account of the concept of gravitation in Duhem: *La Théorie physique*. Paris, 1906, p. 367 and ff.

49. KEPLER: *Opera Omnia*, ed. Frisch. Frankfort, 1870, Vol. III, p. 151. In Kepler this appetency was mutual as in Newton: *Gravitas est affectio corporea mutua inter cognata corpora ad unitionem seu conjunctionem*. . . .

50. DESCARTES: ed. Adam et Tannery, Vol. IV, p. 396. Cf. Duhem, *l.c.*, p. 19.

51. On LEIBNIZ, cf. Appendix I, p. 447 and ff.

52. *Traité de la lumière, où sont expliquées les Causes*, etc. *Avec un Discours de la Cause de la Pesanteur*. By C. H. D. Z. Leyden, 1690, p. 93.

53. NEWTON: *Opticks*, 3rd ed. London, 1721. Question XXI, and especially the 2nd Advertisement to this question. Cf. Appendix I, p. 455 and ff.

54. D'ALEMBERT: *Traité de dynamique*, 2nd ed. Paris, 1758, p. 16.

55. EULER: *Theoria motus*. Rostock, 1765, p. 51.

56. ROSENBERGER: *Die moderne Entwicklung der elektrischen Prinzipien*. Leipzig, 1898, p. 43.

57. STALLO, *l.c.*, p. 53 and ff.

58. WILLIAM THOMSON: *Papers on Electrostatics*. London, 1872, p. 318.

59. Cf. on Gauss, LARMOR: *Aether and Matter*, Cambridge, 1900, p. 72, and Rosenberger, *Die Moderne Entwicklung*, etc., pp. 70–71.

60. Cf. MAXWELL, *Scientific Papers*. Cambridge, 1890, Vol. II, pp. 155 and ff., 311.

61. *Ib.*, Vol. II, p. 341.

62. HERTZ: *Gesammelte Werke*, Vol. III. Introduction by Helmholtz, p. 18.

63. J. J. THOMSON: *Electricity and Matter*. New York, 1904, p. 7.

64. Writings previous to Le Sage have been enumerated in Prevost's Preface to the *Traité de Physique* of the latter, Paris, 1818, pp. 24–33. Certain details on the later writings will be found in Maxwell, *Encyclopedia Britannica*, 9th ed., article *Attraction*, p. 74, and in Stallo, *l.c.*, p. 53 and ff. On Euler's attempt, cf. *Opuscula*, Berlin, 1745, p. 287.

65. LE SAGE has shown the chief features of his theory in *Lucrèce Newtonien. Mem. de l'Ac. de Berlin*, 1872. The *Traité de Physique*, Paris, 1818, edited by Prevost in conformity with the notes of Le Sage contains a more detailed exposition.

66. MAXWELL: *Encyclopedia Britannica*, 9th ed., article *Atom*, p. 47.

67. MAXWELL: *Encyclopedia Britannica*, article *Attraction*, p. 65.

68. The first of these indications is found in the *Œuvres*, Paris, 1880, Vol. IV, p. 327; the second *ib.*, Vol. VI, p. 471.

69. Cf. p. 176 and ff.

70. SCHOPENHAUER: *Die Welt als Wille und Vorstellung*, ed. Frauenstaedt, Vol. I, p. 45 and ff.

71. ED. V. HARTMANN: *Das Grundproblem der Erkenntnistheorie*. Leipzig, *s.d.*, pp. 16, 18, 20.

72. COMTE: *Politique positive*, Vol. I, p. 501.

73. Cf. STALLO: *l.c.*, p. 53 and ff.

74. Cf., for example, SPENCER, *First Principles*, Vol. I, pp. 54, 231, 248, 251–254.

75. STALLO: *ib.*, p. 53 and ff.

76. LOTZE: *Grundzuege der Naturphilosophie*, 2nd ed. Leipzig, 1889, pp. 27–28. It is to be noted that Lotze esteems these reasons sufficient to declare that the picture of an emanation in spherical surfaces must be abandoned: "One should speak only of a linear relation between two elements." Kepler, in examining in what manner the action of the sun on the planets must be modifiable with distance, comes to the conclusion that it would be in inverse proportion to the distance (*Opera omnia*, ed. Frisch. Frankfort, 1870, Vol. VI, p. 349), proof that the picture of spherical emanation did not arise in his mind.

77. *Ihr Seyn ist ihr Wirken. Kein Anderes Seyn ist auch nur zu denken moeglich.* SCHOPENHAUER: *Die Welt als Wille und Vorstellung*, ed. Frauenstaedt. Leipzig, 1877, Vol. I, p. 10.

78. Kant: *Met. Anfangsgründe*, etc.

79. One may see the continuation of the passage from Sir J. Thomson which we have already quoted, p. 80, that he feels very clearly that the real source of the difficulty is to be found there, and it seems that Faraday also felt this.

80. "And since many philosophers have judged that even in a natural order, a body can act immediately at a distance upon several bodies all removed from one another, they believe, rightly, that nothing can prevent divine power from legislating that one body be present to several bodies at once, there being no great distance from immediate action to presence, and one, perchance, depending upon the other." Leibniz: *Théodicée*, § 19, ed. Erdmann, p. 485.

81. De Prémontval: *Vues philosophiques*. Berlin, 1761, pp. 212–237.

82. Maurice Boucher: *Essai sur l'hyperespace*. Paris, F. Alcan, 1903, p. 158 and ff.

83. I. C. F. Zoellner: *Principien einer elektrodynamischen Theorie der Materie*. Leipzig, 1876, p. 72 and ff.

84. Lotze: *l.c.*, p. 26.

85. Hertz: *Ueber die Beziehungen zwischen Licht und Elektrizitaet. Gesammelte Werke*, Vol. I, p. 353.

86. W. Wien: *Ueber die Moeglichkeit einer elektromagnetischen Begruendung der Mechanik. Wiedemann's Annalen*, 1901, p. 501 and ff.

87. This point of view seems indeed to have since almost completely triumphed amongst authoritative physicists. The conception of gravitation which constitutes the basis of Einstein's theory of generalized relativity necessarily presupposes it.

88. F. Lange: *History of Materialism*, etc., trans. E. C. Thomas, 4th ed. Boston, 1880, Vol. II, p. 351.

89. Mabilleau: *Histoire de la philosophie atomistique*. Paris, F. Alcan, 1896, p. 14.

90. *Ib.*, pp. 28–33.

91. *Ib.*, p. 29. We have followed, in the text, Mabilleau's indications concerning Hindoo atomism. But it seems that more recent studies than those used by the author of *L'Histoire de la philosophie atomistique* are of a character to modify these data. Contemporary Hindoo philology seems less and less given to moving back the date of sources. It states that we know but little about India before the time of Alexander. Yet the most important document we possess about the Jainas, dated from Asoka about 250 B.C., shows that they were already an important order (Guérinot, *Essai de bibliographie Jaïna*. Paris, 1905, p. xxviii), and it is supposed that the fundamental features of the doctrine date from the time of the founder, Mahavira, who must have lived at the beginning of the sixth century before our era (*ib.*, p. 5). But if, on the contrary, Hindoo atomism is considered to be more recent in date than that of the Greeks, the relations between the two will be simply reversed and the conclusions, whether an entire independence of the two doctrines is supposed or whether an affiliation between them is admitted, will remain as we developed them on page 88. Let us state, also, that, according to certain texts (cf. especially H. Jacobi: *Eine*

Jaina-Dogmatik, *Zeitschrift der deutschen morgenlaendischen Gesellschaft*, Bd. 60, Heft 2, Leipzig, 1906, p. 515 and ff.; WARREN, *Les idées philosophiques et religieuses des Jainas*. *Annales du Musée Guimet*, X, 1887, p. 361), it seems at least doubtful whether the Jainas conceived atoms as devoid of qualities.

92. MABILLEAU: *l.c.*, p. 214.

93. MULLOCH: *Fragmenta philosophorum graecorum*. Paris, 1860, p. 357 and ff.

94. MABILLEAU: *l.c.*, pp. 194–200, 272.

95. Cf. LASSWITZ: *Geschichte der Atomistik*. Hamburg and Leipzig, 1890, pp. 214–218.

96. *Ib.*, p. 214.

97. J. PHILIPPE: *Lucrèce dans la théologie chretienne*. Paris, F. Alcan, 1895, pp. 9, 11, 13.

98. *Ib.*, p. 42 and ff.

99. Cf. PICAVET: *Esquisse d'une histoire des philosophies médiévales*, 2nd ed. Paris, F. Alcan, 1907, pp. 37, 163.

100. MOISE BEN MAIMOUN: *Le guide des égarés*, trans. MUNK. Paris, 1856–66, Vol. I, p. 377.

101. DUHEM: *Etudes sur Léonard de Vinci*, 2nd Series. Paris, 1909, p. 7 and ff.

102. Cf. LASSWITZ: *l.c.*, p. 257 and ff.

103. Let us note, however, that Cassirer, who is an excellent judge in this matter, considers that Galileo was an atomist at bottom (*Das Erkenntnis-problem in der Philosophie und Wissenschaft der neueren Zeit*. Berlin, 1906–7, Vol. I, p. 298).

104. Not only the philosophers and historians of atomism, such as Lange, Lasswitz, and Mabilleau, but even many physicists have the distinct notion of this continuity. Cf., for instance, Larmor, *Aether and Matter*. Cambridge, 1900, p. 25.

105. The opinion we express in the text has its opponents. Comte had already undertaken the defence of the mediaeval centuries, "a memorable period, unjustly qualified as dark by critical metaphysics of which the foremost organ was protestantism." (*Cours*, V, p. 317: cf. VI, p. 81.) As MILHAUD very justly points out (*Nouvelles études sur l'histoire de la pensée scientifique*. Paris, 1911, p. 18), the law of the three stages would necessarily lead Comte to reduce the science of the Greeks to nothing or nearly nothing. Moreover, Comte's opinions, here as elsewhere, are explained by the fact that he subordinated strictly scientific interests to those foreign to this domain. Duhem, in works whose importance from the point of view of the history and the philosophy of science cannot be too highly estimated, tries to show that our science is attached, by direct affiliation, to that of the Middle Ages and that the so-called renaissances "were only reactions frequently unjust and sterile." We believe that all that can be thus proved is that (as one might expect) the long centuries of the Middle Ages were not *entirely* unproductive and that the rupture at the Renaissance was not complete. It is none the less true that the acquired knowledge of those ten centuries, in comparison with that of the Hellenic mind, is extremely small, and that this very slow advance underwent a marvellous acceleration at

the Renaissance to such a degree that modern science appears, in Milhaud's words (*Etudes sur la pensée scientifique chez les Grecs et chez les modernes*. Paris, 1906, p. 2), as "the natural sequence after centuries of rest of Greek science itself." The Renaissance assuredly remains the most important fact in the whole history of science.

106. STALLO: *l.c.*, p. 134.

107. *Ib.*, p. 84.

108. Cf. p. 108, Note 91.

109. H. POINCARÉ: *Leçons sur la théorie mathématique de la lumière*. Paris, 1889, p. 111.

110. A. ETARD: *Les nouvelles théories chimiques*, 3rd ed. Paris, s.d., pp. 8, 30, 35, 44.

111. E. RUTHERFORD: *Radio-Activity*, 2nd. ed. Cambridge, 1905, p. 1.

112. LARMOR: *Aether and Matter*. Cambridge, 1900, p. 25. The advance of science since Larmor formulated this opinion tends to confirm it. At the present moment the atomic structure of electricity appears certainly to the majority of physicists the indubitable basis of all the theoretical edifice of that part of science. Cf. J. J. THOMSON, *Electricity and Matter*, Cambridge, 1905, p. 41 and ff., and MADAME CURIE, *Revue Scientifique*, November 17, 1906, p. 609.

113. LARMOR: *l.c.*, p. 71.

114. *Bulletin de la Société française de philosophie*, 6th year, 1906, p. 85.

115. LUCIEN POINCARÉ: *Revue annuelle de physique*. *Revue générale des sciences*, Vol. IX, 1898, p. 429.

116. *Bulletin de la Société française de philosophie*, 10th year, p. 98 (meeting of January 27, 1910).

117. OSTWALD: *La déroute de l'atomisme contemporain*. *Revue générale des sciences*, 1895, p. 953 and ff. Naturally the theory of electrons, at the time of its appearance, was treated by the energists as "reactionary" (cf. HŒFLER, *Zur gegenwaertigen Naturphilosophie*. Berlin, 1906, p. 112).

118. COURNOT: *Traité de l'enchainement des idées fondamentales dans la science et dans l'histoire*. Paris, 1861, p. 245.

119. LEIBNIZ: Ed. Erdmann, p. 758. "When I was a young boy I indulged also in the void and in atoms; but reason brought me back. The idea was encouraging. Here research found its limit; meditation was steadied as with a nail; one thought to have discovered the first elements, a *non plus ultra*. We wished that Nature might go no farther, that it were final, as our mind. . . ."

120. HUYGENS: *Traité de la lumière*. Leyden, 1690, Chap. I, p. 5.

121. E. DU BOIS-REYMOND: *Reden*. Leipzig, 1886–87, pp. 105–106.

122. W. THOMSON: *Notes of Lectures on Molecular Dynamics*, etc. Baltimore, 1884, p. 132.

123. W. THOMSON: *Conférences scientifiques et allocutions*, trans. Lugol and Brillouin. Paris, 1894.

124. MAXWELL: *Scientific Papers*, 1890, Vol. II, p. 418. Cf. id., *Theory of Heat*. London, 1875. "When we have acquired the notion of matter in motion, and know what is meant by the energy of that motion, we are unable to conceive that any possible addition to our knowledge could

explain the energy of motion, or give us a more perfect knowledge of it than we have already."

125. ARISTOTLE: *De Generatione et Corruptione*, Book I, Chap. II, § 5. The context would almost make us believe that this metaphor had been borrowed from an atomist, although as we shall see later it also agrees with peripatetic theories. It is also found in Lucretius, Book II, line 668 and ff.

126. ROSENBERGER: *Geschichte*, Vol. I, pp. 11–12.

127. HANNEQUIN was greatly impressed by the problem caused by this difference, and tried to solve it (*l.c.*, p. 92), without success, in our opinion. He seemed to have the firm conviction that mechanism and the principles of conservation are kindred ideas; but, in consequence of the preconceived idea according to which discontinuity was introduced into physics by mathematics, he deduced atomism from the concept of rectilinear and uniform motion—that is, from the principle of inertia (*l.c.*, p. 74 and ff.). This is evidently an anomaly from the historical point of view, for modern atomism is then separated from that of the Greeks, of the Hindoos, of the Jews, and of the Arabs. Spir, we think, was the first (among the moderns, naturally, for the deduction would have appeared trite to a Greek after Aristotle's exposition) to deduce atomism, a little confusedly, it is true, from the principle of identity in time (*l.c.*, pp. 424–425). The first edition of *Denken und Wirklichkeit* appeared in 1873. Hannequin seems to have been unaware of that deduction; the *Essai Critique* appeared in 1895, one year before the French translation of Spir's work. It is extremely curious to notice that Auguste Comte, with the penetration of which he so often gives evidence when his social preoccupations are not in question, compared the rôle of corpuscular hypothesis in physics to that of the principle of inertia in mechanics (*Politique positive*, Vol. I, pp. 520, 555).

128. As a proof of this idea, one may remark that the indivisible only appears in mathematics even momentarily in regard to questions relative to motion—that is, to time. It is because the assumed motion has nothing real about it, because the image of it is eliminated as soon as the curve is traced, that the latter becoming again, as in synthetic geometry, a concept formed outside of time, becomes continuous, at the same stroke. It seems that Hannequin at a certain moment realized something of this relationship.

129. Cf. later on, Chap. XII, p. 387.

130. ZELLER: *Philosophie der Griechen*, trans. Boutroux. Paris, 1877, Vol. II, p. 292. It will perhaps not be useless in view of the particular interest offered by this argument to give to the reader the texts themselves of Aristotle. (*De Generatione et Corruptione*, Book I, Chap. VIII, § 2. Trans. J. H. Stocks, Oxford, 1922.) "The most systematic and consistent theory, however, and one that applied to all bodies, was advanced by Leucippus and Democritus: and in maintaining it they took as their starting-point what naturally comes first. For some of the older philosophers thought that 'what is' must of necessity be 'one' and immovable. The void, they argue, 'is not': but unless there is a void with a separate being of its own, 'what is' cannot be moved—nor again can it be 'many,' since there is nothing to keep things apart." § 5. Leucippus, however, thought he had theories

which harmonized with sense-perception and would not abolish either coming-to-be and passing-away or motion and the multiplicity of things. He made these concessions to the facts of perception: on the other hand, he conceded to the Monists that there could be no motion without a void. The result is a theory which he states as follows: "The void is a 'not being,' and no part of 'what is' is a 'not being'; for 'what is' in the strict sense of the term is an absolute *plenum*. This *plenum*, however, is not 'one'; on the contrary, it is a 'many' infinite in number and invisible owing to the minuteness of their bulk." For the sake of clearness we have thought it preferable to summarize these passages in the text; we have put aside what had to do with the question of the void and of the plenum, which, we know, particularly interested Aristotle, but which might confuse the reader here (cf. for this side of the Eleatic doctrine, pp. 234, 252). But otherwise we have tried to use only expressions characteristic of Aristotle. In saying that Leucippus tried to "save" the reality of the phenomena we borrowed an expression (certainly conformable to the Stagirite's thought) from Zeller's analysis (*l.c.*, p. 282). After Zeller, HERMANN COHEN (*Logik der reinen Erkenntnis*, Berlin, 1902, p. 29. Cf. *ib.*, pp. 40, 187, 272) and CASSIRER (*Das Erkenntnisproblem*. Berlin, 1906, Vol. I, p. 31) have spoken of this affiliation of Greek atomism.

131. Chemists especially are very prone to this illusion. Cf., for example, SCHUTZENBERGER: *Traité de chimie générale*. Paris, 1880, Vol. I, p. vii.

132. Cf. p. 87. HIRN: *Conséquences philosophiques et métaphysiques de la Thermodynamique*. Paris, 1868, p. 209: "The existence of the material atom, finite and indivisible, is *to-day* a fact as well proven as any of those which the scientist accepts, as it were, as axioms."

133. "Each one of these sects, when it does no more than attack, triumphs, ruins, lays low; but in its turn it is laid low and destroyed when it is on the defensive." BAYLE: *Dictionnaire*. Amsterdam, 1734, Vol. V, article *Zeno*, remark G., p. 599.

134. A very remarkable attempt of this kind is that of KOZLOWSKI: *Psychologiczne zrodla*, etc. Warsaw, 1899, pp. 51, 68; *Szkice filozofizne*. Warsaw, 1900, p. 86; *Zasady przyrodoznawstwa*. Warsaw, 1903, pp. 95, 245, 264 and ff., 287.

135. Cf. later, p. 236 and ff.

136. J. J. THOMSON: *Electricity and Matter*. New York, 1904, p. 74 and ff.

137. SIR OLIVER LODGE: *Electrons*. London, 1906, Chap. XV, § 5.

138. *Ib.*, Chap. IX.

139. J. J. THOMSON: *l.c.*, p. 114 and ff.

140. *Ib.*, p. 87.

141. Cf. later, p. 179 and ff.

142. LODGE: *l.c.*, p. 13.

143. H. POINCARÉ: *Science et méthode*, Paris, 1908, p. 271.

144. LODGE: *l.c.*, p. 9.

145. Cf. later, p. 367 and ff.

146. Cf. POINCARÉ: *La science et l'hypothèse*. Paris, s.d., p. 127.

147. KIRCHHOFF: *Vorlesungen ueber mathematische Physik*, 3rd ed. Leipzig, 1883–91, Vol. I, preface.

CHAPTER III

THE PRINCIPLE OF INERTIA

IT is sometimes asserted that this principle was known to antiquity.(1) It is certain that in following the exposition of a Greek atomic system, such as that of Democritus, through the refutations of Aristotle, or that of Epicurus in *De Rerum Natura*, a modern reader is almost without fail led to believe that these philosophers implicitly postulated inertia. We do not, however, believe that such was the case. Nowhere, either in an atomistic philosopher or even in any ancient writer, does there appear any allusion to a belief in an indefinite motion in a straight line by virtue of an impetus received and without the continued action of a force. It is probable that an ancient atomist, if asked the reason for the continuous motion of particles, would have replied that they fall or move in virtue of a force inherent in them. This is plainly seen in Lucretius; and Democritus seems to have been of the same opinion.(2) At the most he would have referred to the example of some known persistent motion, such as that of the top or of the vibrating cord,(3) rather than the motion of a projectile which would appear to him doubtless as a motion toward an object and thus necessarily limited. Had it been otherwise, Aristotle, in expounding his theory of the natural circular motion of celestial bodies, would have been constrained to allude to it. We well know that he takes great pains to refute the opinions of the atomists. Now, his exposition seems to prove, on the contrary, that he had no adverse opinion to combat on that point.(4) It might be objected that this argument is not absolutely convincing as regards terrestrial bodies: for Aristotle, indeed, the two kinds of motion are very different, and, strictly speaking, they might have been so also (although this is little likely) for the atomists. But another passage of the *Physics* seems decisive in this respect. Aristotle uses the impossibility of continuous motion in a straight line as a proof by *reductio ad absurdum;* this impossibility seems so evident to him that he does not even suppose that there can be a difference of opinion on this point.(5) He certainly would have expressed himself quite differently if the principle of inertia had been asserted even implicitly, especially if it had been formulated by Democritus.

In the same context of ideas a passage from Pappus, a mathematician of the third century A.D., proves to what extent the conception of an indefinite persistence of a rectilinear motion was foreign to the ancients. Pappus supposes a moving body of a given weight placed upon a horizontal plane and needing a given force (δύναμις) in order to be moved; he asks that the force necessary to move the weight if the plane is inclined at a given angle be calculated.(6) This passage admits, it seems, of but one interpretation. Pappus did not know that the force necessary to displace a moving body upon a horizontal plane has no relation to the force which is demanded by the displacement of the same moving body on an inclined plane; he believed that if a moving body on a horizontal plane is given a certain velocity, this latter would diminish of itself in time. This opinion is evidently quite consistent with the data of immediate experience: in nature one does see, in fact, rectilinear motion prolonging itself for some time while diminishing and then ceasing rapidly.

Some have believed to see the affirmation of inertia in a passage of Plutarch's *Moralia*. He there states that "the moon has, for a help to preserve her from falling (on the earth), her motion and the impetuosity of her revolution. For every body is carried according to its natural motion, unless it be diverted by some other intervening cause. Wherefore the moon does not move according to the motion of her weight, her inclination being stopped and hindered by the violence of a circular revolution."(7) Certainly to a modern reader these sentences seem to imply that the author supposed a composition of rectilinear motion impressed on the moon and the attraction exerted by the earth. But in truth the idea that the moon could have two motions at the same time was certainly unknown to him. What he meant to say was that the naturally circular motion of the moon, being stronger than the attraction of the earth, prevented this attraction from manifesting itself; for to illustrate his explanation he adds: "Thus projectiles placed in a sling are retained by the circular motion which is given to them." It is, indeed, the circular motion itself, and not a superimposed rectilinear motion, which manifests its influence.

About the persistence of the rectilinear motion, antiquity seems to have been divided between two conceptions. One is that of Aristotle, who supposes that a body can only be moved by another which touches it continually, as if, for example, it were "carried on a chariot." Under ordinary conditions this phenomenon is concealed from our eyes, because in throwing a body we communicate at the same time a certain motion to the air, and this latter continues afterwards to act upon the thrown body: this is the "environmental reaction." But in the void the phenomenon would not take place.(8)

The other theory is attached to the name of Hipparchus. We know it principally from a passage in Simplicius's Commentary on Aristotle's *De Caelo*.(9) The thrown body receives an impulse which remains with it even when the body which communicated the motion to it has ceased to touch it. The motion is rectilinear but not uniform; it diminishes of itself as time advances, and finally disappears. We should say, in modern language, that when the body is once thrown, a sort of negative acceleration intervenes to stop it; but this would not exactly translate the thought of the ancients: they were far from thinking that the velocity could of itself be maintained, and what did maintain this rectilinear and decreasing motion appeared to them under the aspect of a force, δύναμις; the expression is the same as in Pappus, who seems equally to have been guided by a theory of this kind. It is also found in Themistius,(10) another commentator of Aristotle, who compares this impulse to the heat which is communicated to a body, and this is particularly important for the reason that the concept of motion is thus allied to that of a *state*. But this state, as we see from the context, was certainly conceived as ceasing of itself, just as the heated body returns little by little to its initial temperature. Themistius adds to δύναμις the qualifying ἐνδυθεῖσα; and this, it seems, is the origin of the expression *vis impressa* or *impetus impressus* which has played an important rôle in the genesis of the principle of inertia; we shall see that the import of this term for the precursors of Galileo corresponds entirely to Hipparchus's conception.

We find, moreover, in ancient authors considerations which, according to our knowledge, are closely allied to the principle of inertia, and which we shall see have played a certain part in its genesis, but from which these authors did not draw any of the consequences which they seem to us to entail. These considerations are of two kinds. In the first place, ancient physicists well knew the persistence of circular motion, and we sometimes notice in the explanations concerning this motion expressions which seem to have a certain resemblance to those which we employ concerning inertial motion. Thus in the *Quaestiones mechanicae*, attributed to Aristotle, it is said: "Some affirm that the circular line is continually in motion as that which persists because it offers resistance."(11)

The considerations of the second kind have to do with the conception which we now designate as that of the *relativity of motion*. Sextus Empiricus imagines a boat moving at a certain speed, while a man holding a pole moves upon this boat with the same speed but in the opposite direction.(12) As a result of this double displacement, it happens that the pole in relation to the water and the air has not moved at all (Sextus's words are: "It remains in the same perpendicular line of the air and of the water").(13) Since, moreover, the motions spoken of are evidently conceived as rectilinear and uniform, one would be led to conclude that Sextus considered them, for that reason, as relative, which is the very essence of the principle of inertia. But as a matter of fact this idea was certainly unknown to him. Nothing indicates that he had meant to establish a difference between rectilinear displacement and other kinds of motion; on the contrary, this exposition is followed in his work by passages where, with the help of considerations of a very different order, he attempts to demonstrate the contradictory nature of the concept of the motion of rotation. Indeed, the celebrated sceptic tries to demolish the concept of displacement in general, and the considerations about the boat only serve him to draw this conclusion that a thing "may move in being displaced, while neither the thing as a whole nor its parts leave the place where they are."(14) It is certain, on the other hand, that this idea of relativity must have been in a certain sense quite familiar to the ancients, and that precisely with respect to curvilinear motions. This conception, as Wundt (15) has justly remarked, is necessarily at the bottom of all astronomical theories, especially the theory of epicycles.

Toward the end of the Middle Ages, when, very slowly at

first, scientific thought was reappearing in the West, we frequently find traces of one order or the other of the thoughts which we have just mentioned, sometimes incorporated in the prevailing peripateticism, sometimes in manifest opposition to it. This last position was especially that of the theorists of the *impetus impressus*. They knew Hipparchus's ideas not only from the Commentary of Simplicius, translated into Latin in the thirteenth century, but also from a passage of his contemporary, the Alexandrian Joannes Philoponus, a passage which had been summarized by the Arabic astronomer, Al Bitragi (Alpetragius), whose work was made accessible to Europeans by the translation of Michael Scot at about the same time. The merit of having developed Hipparchus's ideas is due especially, it seems, to Albert of Saxony, one of the most renowned masters of the University of Paris in the fourteenth century. This doctrine, characterized sometimes as "Parisian," was propagated in Germany by Marsilius of Inghen and Sunczel, and in Italy (where at first it met with violent opposition) by Gaetan de Tiene; in Paris itself it was continued toward 1500 by John Dullaert of Ghent.(16)

In the same way the conception of the *relativity of motion* was not entirely forgotten. The argument from the man on the boat, more or less modified, appears in high favour. It is true that we know less about those who maintained these opinions than about those who refuted them. But the very energy which Albertus Magnus, Saint Thomas, Campanus of Novara, and Albert of Saxony, employ to expound the arguments of Ptolemy (17) proves that they were fighting a theory which did not lack adherents.

In the first half of the fifteenth century the relativity of motion is clearly affirmed by Nicolas of Cusa. The learned cardinal, who, as we well know, was one of the precursors of Copernicus, while trying to show that the earth can move without our perceiving it, makes use also of the example of the boat which, even though it is progressing rapidly, may seem motionless to us if we do not see the shores.(18)

But in Cusa himself we see that this conception of the relativity of motion, although the principle of inertia seems to us to be derived from it, was not sufficient to give birth to this notion. It is, indeed, curious that Cusa should have affirmed indefinite motion in a straight line, but restricted to a particular case, and basing it on entirely different considerations. His exposition deserves a closer examination, as it seems to have exercised a considerable influence on the progress of science and notably on the genesis of the conception of inertia in Galileo.(19)

Cusa in explaining a kind of game, where it was a question apparently of projecting a ball upon a plane, states that if the ball were absolutely round and the floor perfectly smooth the first would touch the second at only one point (Cusa says: *in atomo*). But the ball, projected upon the plane, rolls—that is, it turns.(20) This turning motion, if it were natural, would continue eternally, as does that of the "ultimate sphere" of the heavens, "without violence, and without fatigue." (This is, indeed, Aristotle's doctrine of the natural circular motion.) For—and it is in this comparison that the boldness of Cusa's theory properly consists—the motion of the celestial sphere and that of the perfect ball thrown by the hand of man upon an absolutely smooth plane are strictly comparable. "This sphere is moved by God the creator or by the spirit of God, just as the ball is moved by thee." Indeed the perpetuity of the rotation results solely from the perfection of the rotundity, "the form of the rotundity is very fit for the perpetuity of the motion." The rounder the thing, the more it moves with facility. "That is why, if the roundness were at a maximum such that it could not be greater, it would move as if by itself, and would be at the same time mover and mobile." Moreover, that which moves could not cease to move unless it behaved differently at a given moment from that of the preceding moment. "Consequently the sphere upon a level and equal surface, since it always behaves the same, once put into motion will move perpetually."(21)

While preserving as faithfully as possible the expressions of Cusa, we have somewhat inverted the order of the sentences; but the progress of the deduction is such as we have indicated. There are evidently in this exposition some ideas which approach our concept of inertia—for example, in the sentence where it is a question of the cessation of motion; in another sentence, which we have omitted, Cusa says that the ball moves from the impulse which exists in itself (*impetum in ipsum faciendo: quo durante moretur*). But that treats only of rotation, and it is in the last analysis solely by the persistence of the motion of rotation, and not, as with us, by that of the motion of translation, that Cusa succeeds in conceiving the perpetual motion of a ball upon a plane.

The idea of relativity of motion was evidently indispensable to the Copernican theory of the earth's motion. However, we see that Copernicus himself was far removed from supposing a general principle of inertia. Indeed, he attributes to the celestial bodies, just as Aristotle did, a naturally circular motion, while clearly indicating that this motion could not give rise to the appearance of a centrifugal force.(22) Such was also the opinion of Telesius.(23) Kepler, on the contrary, believed that the motions of the planets were due to an emanation of the sun, and that each one of them would stop immediately at any point whatsoever of its trajectory if the sun were to cease its action;(24) this was, if possible, still farther removed from the conception of inertia than the natural circular motion of Aristotle and of Copernicus.

In the seventeenth century, we find Carpentarius, who, however, in many respects had freed himself from the influence of scholastic philosophy, using an argument against Aristotle, in order to establish the gravity of the air, wherein it is said that the air, if it pushed upward, would not move toward any centre; the motion would then be infinite, which, of course, the author considers as absurd.(25)

Yet in the sixteenth century the ideas of Hipparchus, taken up again and developed by Albert of Saxony and the "Parisian school" of the fourteenth century, find more and more adherents in Italy. Cardanus, refuting Aristotle's idea of the motion of impulsion, says: "And when one supposes that all which is moved is moved by something, this is very true: but that which moves is an acquired impetus, as heat in water."(26)

It is this example, as we have seen, which Themistius used. Yet Cardanus did not have the boldness to free himself entirely from peripatetic ideas; he supposes that a projectile leaving the apparatus which sends it forth continues for a while to increase its velocity, and this because of the reaction of the air, quite like Aristotle.

Benedetti, toward the end of the sixteenth century, states

precisely the ideas of Cardanus.(27) Benedetti, moreover, had the merit of attempting an explanation of the trajectory of a projectile by the resolution of the motion. Benedetti explains that a body thrown from a sling has the tendency to follow a straight line, tangential to the circle described by the sling, but since gravity happens to act upon it, the composition of the two motions creates a curved trajectory.(28) This was a serious innovation. The composition of a curved motion by the aid of two motions in a straight line had been known from antiquity. A deduction of this kind is found in Aristotle, who held that a motion in a circle is the result of two motions in a straight line, of which the one is constant and the other variable, decreasing continually.(29) We shall see presently that this deduction must have particularly suited Benedetti. But where this latter completely departs from peripateticism is when he supposes that a violent motion, that which one communicates to a body in throwing it, may be compounded in a continuous manner with a natural motion, that of a falling body. Tartaglia had expressly denied the possibility of such a composition, and this conviction was so widely spread that in 1561 Santbeck dared to affirm, contrary to the most manifest evidence, that the trajectory of a ball was composed of two straight lines, the first prolonging itself as long as the violent motion dominated, and the second beginning as soon as the natural motion prevailed.(30)

Of course, Benedetti supposes that the impulse communicated to the body decreases continually with time,(31) and it is exactly in connection with this decomposition of the motion of projectiles that we see to what a point this conception was, so to speak, necessary. Indeed, Benedetti, like his predecessors, had no idea of a force whose effects accumulated, as we admit in the case of gravitation. The effect of this latter must have appeared to him as simply constant, and so, in order to explain how it succeeded in prevailing with time, he had to resort to a diminution of the other component.

Benedetti appears to have been the most direct inspirer of Galileo. In the *Sermones*,(32) Galileo maintains a theory, which is based, as in Benedetti, on the diminution of the *vis impressa;* and yet at the epoch to which the most ancient part of this treatise belongs (1590), Galileo had already discovered the law of distances in falling. It was about 1610 that Galileo seems to have conceived the idea of compounding the trajectory with the aid of the horizontal motion and that of falling.(33) But the diminution of the *vis impressa* is found again in the *Dialogue upon two Sciences* (1638), as the opinion of one of his interlocutors, without the other refuting it. It is true that the same work contains also an affirmation of inertia in every direction; but as Wohlwill has justly emphasized, far from being proclaimed as a universal principle, it only occupies a little "corner" of the treatise.(34) Galileo, moreover, never ceased to consider the circular motion of celestial bodies as "natural," as did the ancients and Copernicus. As regards the genesis of the concept of inertia in Galileo, it is particularly important to notice that he began by affirming the perpetuity of motion in a horizontal direction and that he had a predilection for the use of this particular form of the principle.(35) He proved it by the example of the ball rolling on a plane(36), and it seems at least probable that this deduction is closely associated with the conceptions of Cusa as expounded earlier.

It may be that Descartes discovered the principle of inertia independently of Galileo; yet, at the epoch when he formulated it for the first time (toward 1620), different works of Galileo, which contained, at least implicitly, the principle in question, had already been published, others were certainly disseminated by different means, and it is more probable that Descartes with his powerful logic only expanded the propositions which he found in his predecessor. We know, moreover, that Descartes did not often mention his predecessors, even when his borrowings were very evident—a habit which was quite general at that time.(37) At any rate, Descartes cannot be denied the honour of having been the first to formulate a complete and logical theory of the conservation of velocity in a straight line and to proclaim the primordial importance of this principle for the theory of motion in general.(38)

The principle of inertia is generally stated in a formula in a certain sense bipartite, the first part applying to the body at rest and the second to the body in motion. A formula of this kind is found in Descartes.(39) We shall cite here the formula given by d'Alembert which appears the most often, with few variations, in later authors. First law: "A body at rest will

remain so unless a foreign cause forces it from it." Second law:
"A body set in motion by whatsoever cause must always persist
in it uniformly and in a straight line, as long as a new cause,
different from that which has set it in motion, does not act
upon it; that is, unless a foreign cause and one different from
the impelling force acts upon it, it will move perpetually in a
straight line and will travel over equal spaces in equal
times."(40)

D'Alembert follows up the statement of this double law with
a very curious demonstration. After having formulated the
first part, he continues: "For a body cannot of itself determine
to move, since there is no reason why it should move to one
side rather than to another. *Corollary:* From this it follows that if
a body receives a motion for any cause whatever, it cannot of
itself accelerate nor retard this motion."

The second part is demonstrated in these terms: "For,
either the indivisible and instantaneous action of the impelling
cause at the beginning of the motion is sufficient to make the
body cover a certain space, or the body needs, in order to
make it move, the continuous action of the impelling force.
In the first case it is clear that the space covered can only be a
straight line uniformly traced by the moved body. For (*hypothesis*) the first instant passed, the action of the impelling cause
no longer exists, and yet the motion still exists: it will then
necessarily be uniform, since (*corollary*) it cannot accelerate
or retard its motion of itself. Moreover, there is no reason why
the body should deviate to the right rather than to the left.
Therefore, in this first case, where we suppose it to be capable
of moving of itself during a certain time, independently of the
impelling cause, it will move of itself during this time uniformly
and in a straight line. Now a body which can move of itself
uniformly and in a straight line, during a certain time must
continue to move perpetually in the same manner, if nothing
hinders it. For let us suppose the body leaving A and capable
of covering of itself the line A B; on this line let there be
taken any two points C, D, between A and B. The body being
at D is precisely in the same state as when it was at C, except
that it is in another place. Therefore, the same thing must
happen to this body as when it is at C. Now, being at C, it can
(*hypothesis*) move of itself uniformly as far as B. Therefore, being

at D, it will be able to move of itself uniformly as far as the point G, so that D G = C B, and so on. Therefore, if the first and instantaneous action of the impelling cause is capable of moving the body, it will be moved uniformly and in a straight line, as long as no new cause hinders it. *In the second case*, since it is supposed that no cause foreign to and different from the impelling force acts upon the body, nothing, therefore, occasions the impelling cause to augment or to diminish; from which it follows that its continuous action will be uniform and constant, and that thus, during the time that it acts, the body will move in a straight line and uniformly. Now the same reason which makes the impelling force act constantly and uniformly during a certain time, continuing always unless something opposes itself to this action, it is clear that this action must remain continually the same and produce constantly the same effect. Therefore," etc.

D'Alembert's "second case" refers evidently to some Aristotelian ideas of which one still found traces in France at this epoch. It must be remarked that d'Alembert attempts no refutation, but tries rather to give to the principle of inertia an appearance of Aristotelianism.

But the demonstration of the "first case" merits our further attention. It is found in later authors, notably in Lotze, who, with less precision than d'Alembert, and transposing it from mathematical to philosophic language, formulates it in about these terms: If the motion were not to last indefinitely, it would cease at the very instant when the impulse ceased; but this latter lasts but an instant, an infinitesimal space of time. Therefore, there would be no motion at all. Consequently, inertia follows from the very concept of motion; it is an "integral part of this concept."(41)

It is certainly curious to compare this demonstration with that found in the fourth book of Aristotle's *Physics*. Aristotle observes, just as d'Alembert and Lotze do, that if the motion were to last beyond the impulse itself, it would no longer have any reason for ever ceasing. This proposition appears to him absurd, and so he proves that, in the void, no motion could take place except by the action of a continuous cause, "such as the burden which a chariot carries." But, of course, for the *plenum*—that is, for the real world (Aristotle denying, we know,

the existence of the void)—impulse suffices, for the air and
other surrounding bodies help to maintain the motion.(42)

D'Alembert's demonstration is pure deduction. It borrows
from experience only the very existence of motion. In this sense
the principle of motion would therefore be *a priori*. But what
exactly is the value of this demonstration?

Aristotle's deduction just cited is certainly of a nature to
shake our confidence. Can it be, we ask ourselves, that the
Greek philosopher was able to use the same argument to arrive
at the opposite conclusion? A more minute analysis will confirm
this impression.

In admitting the possibility of arriving at the notion of inertia
by a purely deductive method, a difficulty is raised which was
clearly seen by Herbert Spencer. Spencer is a strong partisan
of the *a priori* point of view in all these questions; for to him
inertia, which he formulates, moreover, in a somewhat vague
manner (immediately allying to it the conservation of energy)
under the name of "continuity of motion," is a directly axiomatic truth, of which the contrary could not be mentally
realized. But how does it happen that it appears so late
in the history of science? "The axiomatic character of the
Truth that Motion is continuous is recognized only after the
discipline of exact science has given precision to the conception.
Aboriginal men, our uneducated population, even most of the
so-called educated, think in an extremely indefinite manner.
From careless observations they pass by careless reasoning to
conclusions of which they do not contemplate the implications
—conclusions which they never develop for the purpose of
seeing whether they are consistent. Accepting without criticism
the dicta of unaided perception to the effect that surrounding
bodies when put in motion soon return to rest, the great
majority tacitly assume that the motion is actually lost. They
do not consider whether the phenomenon can be otherwise
considered; or whether the interpretation they put on it can
be mentally realized."(43) In other words, as Spencer says
concerning the conservation of matter, these people think that
they believe what they really could not believe. This is not in
itself inconceivable. Geometry is composed of deductions,
and yet its propositions have only become known little by
little. A man who has the notion of the rectangular triangle

will certainly believe, if he does not know the proposition of
Pythagoras, that it is possible to construct one in which the
square of the hypotenuse is not the sum of the squares of the
two sides.

Yes, but that implies ignorance of the deduction. Suppose
yourself opposite a man who is trying to construct the triangle
in question and show him the demonstration of Pythagoras.
What will you say if he persists in his first opinion and continues his search? You will think that he has not understood
your demonstration or that he is totally lacking in logic.
But certainly neither the one nor the other is the case with
Aristotle; one evidently cannot class him with the multitude of
aboriginal men, etc., about whom Spencer expresses himself so
severely. It is allowable to affirm, doubtless, that he might have
been able, by the analysis of the facts which he knew, to come
upon the knowledge of the principle of inertia; one may find
especially that his explanation of the motion of projectiles is
insufficient and that he ought to have perceived it. But in
itself the idea of a *plenum*, where nothing moves unless pushed
in consequence of a large motion of the initial mover, has
nothing that is contradictory or at least is not more so than
a great number of incomprehensible notions which we are
nevertheless obliged to accept. In weighing the pros and the
cons we come to assent to Paul Tannery's opinion that the
system of Aristotle at that moment "conformed much more to
the immediate observation of facts than ours."(44) Such was
also the opinion of Duhem, who formulates in these terms the
fundamental propositions of this mechanics: I. A body subject
to a uniform power moves with a uniform velocity; II. A
body which is not subject to any power remains immobile.(45)
The hypothesis of the action of the medium or of the "environmental reaction," as Aristotle calls it, has since continued to
have partisans,(46) and who knows whether electric theories
are not going to bring us back to it?

But we can go still farther: Even where Aristotle and
d'Alembert seem to be in agreement, the demonstration is far
from having the import that both of them attribute to it.
We need only think of Hipparchus and Benedetti. Why would
it be absurd to suppose, as these latter did, and, we have just
seen, Galileo also at the outset, that impulse diminishes with

time? This supposition would necessitate evidently the introduction of a constant, but we are quite willing to have one for the action of gravitation. Doubtless, it is preferable to do without it where it is possible, and from this point of view the subsequent method of Galileo, the resolution of the trajectory into a motion constant in time and another uniformly accelerated motion, is certainly better. But, finally, this would be a demonstration based upon experiments, and even experiments difficult to carry out because of frictions, the resistance of the air, etc., and not an *a priori* deduction. Otherwise, if we wish to maintain this latter, we shall be obliged to reject Benedetti's theory because it supposed the variation of a phenomenon in time; we will say that it is a variation "without reason." What does that mean? We hardly need to explain it: it is an evident application of the postulate of causality, of identity in time, and we see that this postulate forms the true basis of d'Alembert's demonstration, so rigorous in appearance.

The demonstration of the principle of inertia has been attempted by another method still, although it, too, is by deduction. This has been done by starting from what has generally been called the "relativity" of motion or of space, a very ancient conception, since it is found in Sextus Empiricus and in Nicolas of Cusa.(47) The most complete demonstration of this type is that expounded by Kant in his *Metaphysische Anfangsgründe*, etc. "Every motion," he says, "in so far as it is the object of a possible experience can be considered at will, either as the motion of a body in a space at rest, or, on the contrary, as the motion of space in the opposite direction and with an equal velocity, the body being at rest."(48) This is the consequence of the fact that an absolute motion—that is, a motion which cannot be conceived in relation to material bodies placed in space (Kant writes: "In reference to a non-material space")—is not capable of becoming an object of experience, and, consequently, "is a nonentity for us," absolute space being "nothing in itself" and not being "an object."(49) Now, matter is inert, "all change of matter has an external cause."(50) And, Kant says, "this is the only law which ought to bear the name of law of inertia." Indeed, combined with what precedes it amounts to d'Alembert's formula; for, on the one hand, matter is incapable of emerging from rest, except under the action of a force, and, on the other hand, motion in a straight line is assimilated to rest. Thus Kant was able to continue the general statement just cited with this parenthesis: "every body persists in its state of rest or of motion, in the same direction and with the same velocity, unless it is forced by an external cause to leave that state"—showing that he considered the two formulae as absolutely equivalent. It is the demonstration of Sextus Empiricus, but reversed. The Greek sceptic used the consequences of the principle of inertia to show that motion in space could not exist in itself; Kant, having arrived at this last idea by a different way, on the contrary, bases his reasoning on it to establish inertia.

Maxwell (51) gave a demonstration combining that of d'Alembert with that of Kant. Maxwell supposes that motion could gradually cease. This would be in a way a negative acceleration, and it would change into positive if we considered motion in relation to a body to which we would lend an appropriate motion. This demonstration seems to unite the inconveniences of the two systems. Inasmuch as it resembles that of d'Alembert, it rests, just as this latter does, on the principle of causality, and, for what remains, it is evidently based upon the notion of the relativity of motion, as that of Kant. With many contemporary physicists this notion of the relativity of motion or of space, stripped, however, of all metaphysical trappings, appears as a sort of axiom (although contrary opinions are not wanting, as we shall see later on); and it is certainly astonishing that, this conception being admitted, it is not used to establish the principle of inertia.

But just what is the "relativity of space"?(52)

To understand the true character of this notion it may not be amiss to distinguish at the outset between the relativity and the homogeneity of space. Homogeneity is the characteristic resulting from the principle of free mobility, which we have recognized as fundamental from the point of view of our concept of space. Space seems to us therefore absolutely identical in all places; from the fact alone that an object has changed place, or has been displaced, no other modification could result. But, and this is very essential, it does not follow that the object *in the act* of displacement, the object in motion, is identical with the object at rest. Our innermost feeling, fortified

by a long experience, protests against such an affirmation.
To take an example: I know very well that this cannon-ball,
to whatever part of space I carry it, will present the same
essential properties. But when it has been fired from the cannon's
mouth, and is in the act of travelling through space with a
velocity of several hundred metres a second, its essential
properties will be considerably modified, and I shall be careful
not to touch it as I do when it is at rest. Descartes, long after
he had proclaimed the principle of inertia and had recognized
its importance, still persisted in believing that a force must
act differently upon a body in motion and upon a body at
rest, and that its action must even depend on the velocity
with which the body was being displaced.(53)

But is it correct to say that motion, as Descartes puts it, "in
its proper signification is only related to the bodies which touch
that which is said to move"?

We cannot doubt that Descartes sometimes applied this
principle to the motion of rotation as well as to that of translation. According to his theory the earth is surrounded by
"celestial matter," and he proves that if the two had the same
rotary motion, the earth would have to be considered as
"a body which has no motion," and on which, consequently,
the effects of centrifugal force could not make themselves
felt.(54)

Let us suppose two bodies absolutely isolated in the universe
and endowed with a uniform motion in a straight line. Their
motions appear to us as relative, for we can indifferently
consider one of them as immobile while attributing to the
other an appropriate velocity. Let us suppose, now, that of
these two bodies one remains fixed and the other describes
a circle around the first; the result would be the same as if
the first had turned around its axis in the opposite direction.
But can we really replace the first motion by the second?
To affirm it is to state that the fixed stellar body would undergo,
if it were liquid, in consequence of the motion of the immobile
body, a flattening identical with that which would have been
produced by a rotation around its axis, and it is certain
that this inference seems hardly admissible. This problem was
admirably studied by Newton in the following passage of the
Principia: "If a vessel, hung by a long cord, is so often turned

about that the cord is strongly twisted, then filled with water, and held at rest together with the water; after, by the sudden action of another force, it is whirled about the contrary way, and while the cord is untwisting itself, the vessel continues for some time in this motion; the surface of the water will at first be plain, as before the vessel began to move; but the vessel, by gradually communicating its motion to the water, will make it begin sensibly to revolve, and recede little by little from the middle, and ascend to the sides of the vessel, forming itself into a concave figure (as I have experienced), and the swifter the motion becomes, the higher will the water rise, till at last performing its revolutions in the same times with the vessel, it becomes relatively at rest in it. This ascent of the water shows its endeavour to recede from the axis of its motion; and the true and absolute circular motion of the water, which is here directly contrary to the relative, discovers itself, and may be measured by this endeavour. At first, when the relative motion of the water in the vessel was greatest, it produced no endeavour to recede from the axis; the water showed no tendency to the circumference nor any ascent towards the sides of the vessel, but remained of a plain surface, and therefore its true circular motion had not yet begun. But afterwards, when the relative motion of the water had decreased, the ascent thereof towards the sides of the vessel proved its endeavour to recede from the axis; and this endeavour showed the real circular motion of the water perpetually increasing, till it had acquired its greatest quantity when the water rested relatively in the vessel. And therefore this endeavour does not depend upon any translation of the water in respect of the ambient bodies, nor can true circular motion be defined by such translation."(55) These are, according to Newton, "the effects by which we distinguish absolute from relative motion," and the exposition which precedes serves as a support to this affirmation, whose clearness leaves nothing to be desired: "Absolute space, without regard to anything external, remains always similar and immovable."(56) It is, we see, the exact counterpart of the ideas held by Descartes and Kant.

But from the point of view of what now occupies our attention Newton's exposition is really decisive, in the sense that it enlightens us as to the motives of the hesitation which we have felt about the relativity of rotary motion; at the same time we also see the true source of our certainty concerning the relativity of rectilinear motion. We had hoped to deduce it from abstract considerations about space, which we had artificially emptied of all physical content, capable of determining points of reference. In reality our memory had preserved the image of space such as we see it—physical space, filled with bodies—and if we declared without hesitation for rectilinear motion, it was because in physical space that motion is really relative. The extremely rapid motion with which the earth is displaced in space remains absolutely without influence on the motion of ponderable terrestrial masses; this is precisely the reason why the first of these motions is so difficult to determine. But the motion of daily rotation, infinitely slower, can be very easily made perceivable by terrestrial phenomena, such as Foucault's pendulum. It is in no way relative to the solar system nor to any other limited system which we can specify. It is relative to the *celestial vault*—that is, to the totality of the bodies of the universe in their spatial arrangements; that is to say again, to absolute space, as Newton well said. It is clear, moreover, that even rectilinear motion cannot always be considered as relative. It is only truly so if it is uniform. If the earth, in its motion of translation, were to undergo an acceleration, even though this latter were infinitesimal compared to the velocity which we generally attribute to the celestial bodies, we should not fail to perceive it.

Let us remark, however, that in speaking of absolute space we have thought of physical space—space filled with body. It is important, indeed, to dissociate completely the considerations we have just expounded from the metaphysical conceptions about the existence or the non-existence of space. This is not a useless precaution. We have seen that Sextus Empiricus had already used the relativity of motion in a straight line to establish (if we may express his ideas in modern language) that space does not exist in itself. This argument is completely destroyed by Newton's demonstration. Must we conclude that the opposite metaphysical thesis is henceforth established? Newton himself probably thought so,(57) and in any case philosophers have often given this sense to his declarations. And yet there is no logically necessary connection there.

We may even dispense with examining whether, supposing that bodies which indicate the orientation of the system of co-ordinates simply play the rôle of points of reference, the thesis of the existence of space could avail itself of Newton's argument. Nor is it necessary in speaking of absolute motion to conceive of it from a philosophic point of view and to attribute to the moving body, according to Bergson's apt expression, "a soul, and as it were a condition of mind."(58) This is because we can attribute the essential qualities of space filled with matter, not to space, but to body. This interpretation, already found in Berkeley,(59) is the foundation of Mach's argument against Newton's ideas. The fact that the rotary motion of the water is relative to the substances of the celestial vault and not to the wall of the vessel, this thinker tells us, might very well be due to the fact that the walls possess only the smallest mass compared to that of celestial bodies. "No one could say what the experiment might have proved if the wall of the vessel had been made so thick and so massive that it had a thickness of several miles."(60) From the experimental point of view one might object that no experiment permits us to conclude as to the influence of the thickness of the walls upon the rotary motion of the water in a vessel. Thus Mach's argument could in no way weaken Newton's demonstration. But in our opinion it clearly shows that this demonstration may be completely dissociated from any metaphysical idea about space.(61)

On the other hand, we see now that deductions of the kind attempted earlier, proceeding from space emptied of bodies, could not be of any help for the demonstration of the principle of inertia. In space, stripped of points of reference, every motion will obviously appear as relative. Whatever may be the trajectories which the two bodies describe, we can always replace them by a motion of one of them. But we know that if we pass into physical space the motion of rotation will become absolute. In two bodies which approach each other we can attribute motion indifferently to one or to the other; but a top which is turning upon a table will remain upright; it would fall were we to try to keep it immobile by giving to the table a motion of opposite rotation. This difference between motion in a straight line and rotation is an integral part of the principle of inertia, and it is unexplainable by considerations drawn from empty space.(62)

It is very curious that Newton's conception, in spite of the great authority of his name, never succeeded in completely establishing itself in science. It is true that it was eventually adopted by many scientists, such as Euler (who expounded it vigorously in his *Theoria motus*),(63) Poinsot,(64) Neumann (65) (to cite only a few illustrious names), and we find it sometimes formulated by our contemporaries.(66) Yet the conception of the relativity of space is much more widespread;(67) it is, so to speak, quite current in the exposition of the principles of science. But it certainly is not easy to adhere to it strictly. To be convinced of this it is sufficient to examine the formula of the principle of inertia as we have quoted it from d'Alembert. What is the body at rest of which it is a question in the first part? All the bodies we know are in motion, including fixed stars; the statement thus becomes inapplicable and hence useless. The second part of the principle, guaranteeing the continuation of uniform motion in a straight line—that is to say, of apparent rest—should now render us the service which we hoped for from the first, and it would be necessary to add to it a formula concerning the composition of motions to replace the present second part. The terms "rest" and "motion" in the present statement of the principle could therefore signify nothing but apparent rest and motion, relative to neighbouring bodies. But we find this relativistic formula in partisans of absolute space, and even in Newton.(68) Moreover, side by side with these terms, seemingly implying the relativity of motion, the same statement of d'Alembert contains another in a contrary sense. What is, indeed, the straight line in which the body will move, according to d'Alembert's expression? How shall one set about to determine it, in relation to what object or to what collection of objects? A motion which, seen from the earth, would seem in a straight line, seen from the sun would appear curvilinear, as Neumann has justly remarked.(69) In fact, no one doubts that a motion made in virtue of inertia is entirely independent of the motion of the celestial body in whose vicinity it is produced, and that this straight line is oriented by points of reference related to the "celestial vault"; space seems to us in this respect to be filled with an infinity of systems of absolutely rigid co-ordinates.(70)

One can in a certain measure preserve the appearances of relativity by stipulating that motion shall be rectilinear with respect to another motion or to a system of motions which should take place in virtue of inertia. Formulae of this kind were proposed by Streintz(71) and Ludwig Lange,(72) and we see from the *Theoria motus* of Euler that he also conceived an analogous idea.(73) Streintz calls "fundamental body" any body which can be considered as independent of the bodies surrounding it and which is not in the act of executing a motion of rotation. One can be assured of this last fact by direct experiments, with the aid, for instance, of Foucault's pendulum or gyroscope,(74) instruments which, we know, indicate the absolute velocity of the motion of rotation and not only, as is the case when we consider rectilinear velocities, modifications of velocity. The principle of inertia consists in this case in affirming that in respect to such a fundamental body or to a system of co-ordinates which are connected with it and which Streintz designates as a "fundamental system of co-ordinates," any other body, if it is not subject to influences from without, will move in a straight line and with a uniform velocity. Ludwig Lange considers the motions of three "material points" upon three straight lines which meet in a point, and relates the motions of all the other bodies to this "inertial system." The supposition that these three original points follow a uniform motion in a straight line is a convention; if it is accepted, the analogous statement for other bodies can be considered as a truth proved by experiment. Streintz's system has the great advantage of being somewhat in conformity with the manner in which we do actually proceed. To calculate motions on the earth, we most often use co-ordinates attached to this latter, without taking account of rotation, as we know from experience that the motion of a point of the terrestrial surface can be considered, in these cases, as inertial, because of the small angular velocity. For astronomical measures we use co-ordinates oriented by points of reference of the celestial vault; this has the advantage of permitting a very rigorous determination. But that is because we have the conviction, confirmed by the experiment of Foucault, that it is these

co-ordinates which regulate the planes of rotation. But let
us suppose a planet having a very rapid motion of rotation,
whose atmosphere is charged with vapour, so that the inhabitants could not perceive the sky; the pendulum and the gyroscope could furnish them with systems of invariable co-ordinates.
Lange's conception, on the other hand, seems somewhat
artificial: these three material points are entirely ideal.(75)
But neither of these two systems in any way invalidates Newton's demonstration; the "fundamental body" of Streintz or
the "inertial system" of Lange are at bottom, as Mach
recognized,(76) only substitutions for the system of co-ordinates
connected with the fixed stars. If we affirm, as does Lange,
that for the first three points considered there is nothing but
convention, then either we refuse to take account of the fact
that the orientation of the system of co-ordinates remains
invariable in relation to certain points of the celestial vault,
which circumstance deprives it of this conventional character,
or else we are using the term "convention" in a particular
sense. Nothing prevents us, indeed, from conceiving that the
celestial vault—that is, the whole visible universe—performs
some kind of a motion in empty space except the fact that
such a supposition would be altogether trivial and that it would
be a transgression of the essential law of thought which is the
basis of the celebrated maxim by which Occam forbids "the
creation of entities without necessity." And without doubt
each time that we obey this fundamental principle and abstain
from introducing useless complications into our conceptions
it may be affirmed that we are creating a convention. But
this convention is then a general law of our thought, and it is
at the basis of all universal propositions. It is obviously implied,
but there is no need to emphasize its use in a case like this one.

A proposition very different from that of Streintz and Ludwig
Lange had been previously presented by Carl Neumann.(77)
Neumann admits the existence of a body which he calls Alpha
and which, situated somewhere in space, remains completely
immobile. Every motion having to do with this body becomes
by this fact really absolute, even if it is accomplished uniformly
and in a straight line. An analogous conception had been formulated by Euler,(78) who called this body A, and still earlier
by Newton,(79) who had rejected it after examination. He

clearly indicated his reasons: Assuming that this immobile body exists, such a body, since it is inaccessible to us, can render us no service from the point of view of our determinations. That is incontestable, and from the practical point of view a system like that of Streintz is preferable. But Neumann's proposition renders tangible, so to speak, the statement that it is indeed absolute space which is at the basis of our formulae of motion. What tends to disguise this truth is that, because of inertia, we can assign only a relative value to uniform and rectilinear displacement. But it is clear, from the point of view of pure logic, that if we are to conceive of space as absolute in certain respects and relative in others, it is indeed the first of these conceptions which must prevail over the second. For it is impossible to construct the absolute by means of the relative; but the absolute may very well appear momentarily as a relative, because of the insufficiency of our knowledge. It is almost superfluous to show, moreover, that the notion of absolute space is in no way repugnant to our imagination. We have seen that it dominated science until the establishment of the principle of inertia, and we certainly find it very difficult to accustom ourselves to the idea that the state of rest of terrestrial bodies is only apparent.

It is not impossible, moreover, that it is all a question of a transitory stage of science. Electrical theories seem to show that we must take account not only of motions of ponderable bodies with respect to one another, but also of the motions of these bodies in respect to the universal medium, ether. The question is too complex, and the works of Lorentz and Michelson, to cite only these two celebrated names, are too well known by physicists to call here for even a summary exposition. It is sufficient to indicate that it is a question of determining by certain phenomena the absolute displacement of the earth relatively to the ether. As we have said before, one has succeeded so far in obtaining only contradictory results.(80) But the fact alone that this datum could be looked for proves, as Poincaré recognizes (although he holds strongly to the relativity of space), that this research was not absurd;(81) considerations based upon Newton's conceptions are, it seems, sufficient to show it. Besides, there is no proof that research of this kind must always remain sterile. Now what would happen if we really succeeded in determining our displacement with respect to the ether? Doubtless we might consider that this is only a relative datum, and that nothing prevents us from supposing that the ether itself is displaced in space. But this would be to sin against Occam's maxim. It is therefore infinitely more probable that eventually we should return to the logical conception of absolute space and absolute motion, considering the apparent relativity of rectilinear uniform motions as a simple consequence of the principle of inertia.

Yet we must recognize that, to consider only the most recent development of physics, this eventuality may appear infinitely far removed. For from the contradictory results just spoken of, as regards the measure of the absolute displacement of the earth in the ether, an entirely new theory has emerged, that of "local time," the work of Einstein and the lamented Minkowski. While referring the reader to Langevin's splendid article for an exposition of these conceptions—so strangely disturbing, so difficult to understand to anyone not acquainted with the experimental facts and mathematical considerations which gave them birth—we must, however, show in this place that the fundamental idea of this theory is that of relativity— absolute relativity in a way, if one may couple these terms seemingly so discordant. "If different groups of observers are in uniform translation with respect to one another (such as observers stationed on the earth in relation to the different *positions* of the latter in its orbit), all mechanical and physical phenomena will follow the same laws for all these groups of observers. Not one of them, by experiments which are internal to the material system to which he is bound, could obtain evidence of the uniform translation of the whole of this system."(82) This relativity therefore involves very curious and important consequences; it forces us to demolish entirely our concept of time, which too becomes relative. To what a point these conceptions deviate from all that we have been accustomed to consider as the natural perception of the phenomena of motion, may be seen by this example given by the same competent scientist: "A first group of observers sees a luminous wave propagated in a certain direction at a velocity of three hundred thousand kilometres a second, and sees another group of observers run after that wave at any velocity whatsoever; and yet this second group will see the luminous wave propagated at the same velocity as the first."(83) Thus relativity here ends in conceptions to which our intelligence submits with great difficulty. And it seems clearly to follow that this idea of relativity can under no circumstances be treated as axiomatic or serve as a basis for an *a priori* deduction.

Consequently the two *a priori* demonstrations of the principle of inertia are both equally inadmissible. As a more minute analysis of the principle itself will show us, far from being an instinctive notion of our mind, which subsequent reasoning has only to disengage (which is evidently the definition of the *a priori*), inertia, on the contrary, is a conception which offends our intelligence.

The principle of inertia stipulates the maintenance of rectilinear velocity. Velocity is the space covered in the unit of time, or, to express it more clearly, it is the quotient of the space covered by the elapsed time, both being measured by arbitrary units: $V = \dfrac{S}{T}$.

These definitions are exact on condition always that we remember that the terms *time* and *space* are here taken in a particular sense. *Space* means a path—that is, the length of a line limited by two points, and *time*, space of time—that is, duration equally included between two precise limits. That is the natural conception, alone conformable to our immediate experience. And we see to what a degree it is paradoxical to stipulate that velocity, a derived notion, abstract, deduced with the help of that of limit, shall persist beyond every limit. There is something there, doubtless, which shocks our understanding. Motion in its original sense means *displacement;* until Galileo and Descartes it had always been understood in this way. Aristotle assimilated it to *change.* In the most recent and most advanced theories of dynamic chemistry, those connected with the work of Gibbs, we may see that we are in the process of returning partially to these doctrines. But change operates between limits; also motion, when it takes place in a straight line, has always been conceived as directed toward a goal. "There is no change which is eternal," says Aristotle, speaking of motion, "because naturally every change goes from a certain state to a certain state; and by a necessary consequence, every change has for a limit the contraries between which it occurs."(84) "Impulsion is only motion proceeding from the impeller itself, or from another, and going toward another."(85)

This conception, assimilating displacement, change of position, to *change*, is quite in conformity with our natural feeling. Physicists combat it when it is a question of establishing the notion of inertia. "It must not be imagined," says Euler, "that the conservation of the state of a body includes fixity in the same place; this actually happens when the body is at rest, but when it moves with the same velocity and in the same direction, we say equally well that it remains in the same state, although it changes place at every moment."(86) But position and place certainly appear to us as things more real than velocity and even than direction. It is advisable, indeed, to note it: these two essential elements of the principle of inertia are equivalent; we have seen that in *a priori* demonstrations one is preoccupied with velocity, whereas the maintenance of direction is considered as requiring no proof. This feeling has sometimes been expressly stated by physicists. Laplace (87) and Poisson (88) thought that the principle of inertia should be considered *a priori* as regards direction and *a posteriori* as regards velocity. But it is quite impossible to maintain that the idea of rectilinear direction is really an integral part of our concept of motion. We know, on the contrary, that Aristotle and all physicists before and including Copernicus and Galileo tacitly accepted the idea that a body in motion which commenced to change direction must continue to change it, the radius of curvature remaining constant; for, translated into modern language, this is apparently the fundamental idea of the natural circular motion of celestial bodies. Let us remember, moreover, how much we were shocked to learn that a projectile, thrown by a sling, follows the tangent of the circle which it describes; this is doubtless because we had no previous feeling that the velocity of the projectile at each moment is rectilinear and directed along the tangent.(89) The modern astronomer *sees*, so to speak, the moon in the process of falling unceasingly toward the earth, and a body revolving with uniform speed in a circle appears to the physicist as undergoing an *acceleration*. But, as Duhamel remarks, this is to divert words from their natural meaning;(90) we should say that it does violence to our understanding. From the point of view of immediate experience, even that of a modern man, the idea of a body turning perpetually in a circle without a permanent cause is less shocking than that of a body which with uniform velocity goes off into space without a goal and without an end, passing the limits of the conceivable universe; and yet that is the formula of inertia. The modern physicist, for whom inertia constitutes the very foundation of his mechanical conception of the world, has, so to speak, lost the faculty of being astonished by this paradox, but it sometimes still attracts the attention of such philosophers as Duehring,(91) and even Lotze, who, however, as we have seen, attempted himself an *a priori* deduction of the principle. In the passage to which we allude this philosopher declares that it is strange to suppose that a body leaves its position without seeking another,(92) which is the very point of view of the pre-Galilean physics, conformable, moreover, to our immediate experience.

This analysis can be pushed still farther. Even the first part of the principle—that which deals with the body at rest, and whose *a priori* character has often been admitted by those, who, like Duehring,(93) would consider the remainder as empirical—is far from meriting this honour. We say: a body cannot set itself in motion, and this statement appears evident at first. But it is simply a truth of definition. In constituting the concept of matter we have separated it from motion; therefore it appears to us henceforth as immobile. This was explained by Berkeley with admirable clearness: "Let extension, solidity, figure be taken away from the idea of body, nothing will remain; but these qualities are indifferent to motion nor have they anything in them which can be styled the origin."(94) If, now, we wished to endow matter with motion, we should experience the same difficulty, whether this motion came from without or whether it had its principle in matter itself. We have seen that no way exists to render intelligible the impact of two bodies; and as to action at a distance, it is a mystery. If a body possesses this incomprehensible faculty of acting upon another across space, why could it not put itself in motion? "One of the most general characteristics of matter is the power, under propitious circumstances, of

putting itself in motion," said a physiologist known for his
attachment to materialistic doctrines.(95) But we can confirm
the result at which we have arrived by abstract considerations
through a closer analysis of certain conceptions of modern
physics.

There is nothing immobile in nature. Not only are all bodies
in motion, but even their parts are in a state of continual
agitation. Here is a mass of water in a vessel; it seems to be at
rest. But it suffices that an opening be made below the level
of the surface to put everything in motion. If we wish to understand anything about this phenomenon, we are obliged to
suppose that rest was only apparent, that in the interior of
the space filled by water motion already previously existed,
although it was invisible.

The agitation of the parts escapes us ordinarily; sometimes
it is only evident to us under the form of an energy, such as
heat; but Gouy has taught us to render it directly sensible to
the eye under the form of Brownian movement. Moreover,
every body is a source of continual motion for everything that
surrounds it, since it unceasingly radiates heat. If we do not
perceive it, it is because it receives as much motion as it gives
out. Thus immobility, even if relative, is only apparent, and
inert matter is but an unrealizable abstraction. It is therefore
not at all contradictory that, at a given moment, it should
exhibit motion somewhat like a billiard ball which is capable
of transforming its spin in translation; and it is in somewhat
the same manner that we are forced to imagine the action of
explosives. Thus our assent to the proposition which stipulates
inertia in a state of rest has its source in none of the motives
we are tempted to attribute to it, and from that fact there
can come no help for the *a priori* demonstration of the
principle.

It clearly follows from the examination just made that,
contrary to the opinion of d'Alembert and of Lotze, of Kant
and of Maxwell, the principle of inertia cannot be proved *a
priori*. Inertia is not "an integral part of the concept of motion"
(Lotze),(96) and in denying it one does not place himself
"in contradiction to the only system of consistent doctrine
about space and time which the human mind has been able
to form" (Maxwell).(97) On the contrary, as Mill clearly

perceived, it is a paradoxical proposition to which "humanity for a long time gave faith only with great difficulty."(98)

On the other hand, it seems scarcely contestable that this principle may be considered as an experimental truth. Assuredly *direct* experience is impossible. All bodies we know obey the law of gravitation, and we have no means of abstracting them from the action of that force. Rectilinear and uniform motion cannot therefore be realized. We may, it is true, resolve the motions of the celestial bodies; it has been sometimes said that they constitute the best demonstration of the principle of inertia, and that is true in a certain sense. But considered as an original fact, this resolution would lack demonstrative force; the other component, gravitation, remains enveloped in mystery. Hegel was doubtless wrong to protest, in a passage which has often served as a theme for those who scorn metaphysics, against the supposition that celestial bodies were pulled about in different directions, and to declare that they traversed space "like free gods."(99) But, after all, he only formulated the instinctive resistance which our reason opposes at the outset to a resolution of this kind.

It is better, then, to begin with terrestrial objects. We easily ascertain that bodies endowed with a rectilinear and uniform motion in relation to the earth (as are, for instance, those on board a vessel) act exactly as those which are at rest with respect to the earth. Moreover, this rest is only apparent. Consideration of the motions of celestial bodies forces us to suppose that the earth is displaced in space with considerable velocity, and all that is on our planet must, as a matter of fact, describe very complicated curves in space. Yet the radii of curvature of these lines are very great; for the motion of which the radius of curvature is the smallest, the rotation of the earth, we succeed in establishing perceptible effects; but in establishing them, we can eliminate them. We may, then, without risking an appreciable error, consider the paths described by terrestrial objects as straight lines, and to the uniform motion in a straight line belong consequently the properties which we attribute to rest. This is the principle of inertia in a nutshell, such as d'Alembert formulates it; for the composition of motions proceeds directly from it.

But if the principle of inertia is capable of being considered as an experimental truth, is it really as such that it appears to our reason, that it forces our assent? Is there not something really strange in the fact that men as eminent as those whose names we have cited were able to be deceived about it?

We can ascertain first of all that the demonstration here presented was not possible at the time when the principle was established, or at least it was then incomplete. One could not turn to account the motion of celestial bodies which for us contributes so much to confirm the apparently paradoxical idea, that motion is something perpetual, when we see every terrestrial motion rapidly disappear; one could not even rely upon the fact that terrestrial objects ought to be considered as in a state of uniform and rectilinear motion. Galileo was doubtless Copernican, and Descartes, too, although he sometimes used ambiguous expressions. But that theory certainly could not be treated as an indisputable truth, as it appears to us to-day, and if a logical bond was established between inertia (or the relativity of motion as in Cusa and Copernicus) and the motion of the earth, it was for the sake of basing the second of these conceptions on the first and not inversely. After the results of Galileo and until the discoveries of Newton there was even a source of contradiction therein, and if Galileo maintained, as did Copernicus, the conception of the natural circular motion of celestial bodies, it is certainly because he saw no other means of explaining their orbits. No one before Borelli attributed the motion of celestial bodies to the action of inertia.(100)

Consequently, one may ask how in spite of these difficulties, in spite of its profoundly paradoxical appearance, in spite of the fact that only a scarcely convincing demonstration was possible at that moment, the principle of inertia could have been so rapidly accepted as the foundation of all mechanics. Let us see in the first place in what way Galileo and Descartes presented it.

Galileo has sometimes been called a great experimenter; but that, says Tannery with much propriety, is to disregard completely historic truth.(101) Thus, in reference to inertia, he often speaks of stones falling from the top of a mast upon a moving ship,(102) and of animals walking on board a ship, (103) and he seems really to have made these experiments. But these are confirmations upon which he lays little stress.

Yet, in expounding the system, he seems to rely upon the observed facts; it is the experiment of the ball on a plane which Cusa and Benedetti both used. Galileo uses the following words in the exposition of it in the *Sixth Day* of *The Dialogues on the New Sciences:* "And it seems to me that there happens here what happens to a moving body that is heavy and perfectly round, which, if it is placed on a plane that is very polished and somewhat inclined, will descend of itself naturally while acquiring always greater velocity, but if, on the contrary, one wished to push it from the lower to the higher part we should have to confer upon it an impulse (*impeto*) which will always diminish and will finally be annihilated; but if the plane is not inclined but horizontal, such a solid sphere will do what we wish—that is, if we place it at rest, it will remain at rest, and if we give it an impulse in any direction, it will move in this latter, conserving always the same velocity which it will have received from our hand, not having the power (*azione*) to increase or diminish it, it being given that there exists on such a plane neither descent nor ascent." (104)

We can easily see that if this were an experimental proof, it would only apply to horizontal motion, and even within these limits it would be singularly weak. We shall admit that the moving body in remounting a plane, however little inclined it may be, will diminish in velocity. We shall admit equally that it will remain at rest on a horizontal plane. But it does not in the least follow that it must always descend a plane, however little inclined it may be, with a velocity constantly increasing. Let us suppose with Aristotle that motion by impulse continues only by the agitation of the medium, or with Benedetti that the impulse dies out little by little; in both cases we shall have what to-day would be called a "negative acceleration," and a certain positive acceleration would be necessary to re-establish the equilibrium—that is, the motion would become uniform at a certain inclination of the plane. This would be somewhat like the idea of Pappus, and, moreover, it is known that direct experience, given the unevenness of the plane and of the moving object and the resistance of the air, would tend to confirm a conception of this kind. But does not the very manner in which Galileo presents the facts show clearly that it is a question of experiments that are not real, but merely "imagined" ones, what the Germans call "thought-experiments" (*Gedanken-experimente*)? It was in his imagination that Galileo set up his infinitely smooth plane, and there he inclines it less and less, sometimes in one direction, sometimes in the other; this is why he does not deem it necessary to give a single precise datum, a single figure resulting from these experiments. Moreover, Galileo himself takes care to warn us of this. The passage from the *Sixth Day*, which we have just cited, is only the development of another passage, probably of older origin, which is in the *Fourth Day*. This begins with these words: "Any moving body projected upon a horizontal plane *I conceive of by Thought* (*mente concipio*) as isolated from every hindrance. . . ."(105)

What, then, is the real foundation of Galileo's demonstration? It is, so to speak, implied, and Galileo himself only feebly hints at it toward the end of the passage, but that is because he had already clearly indicated it in the pages which precede. It is, indeed, the *Third Day* that contains the real exposition of the principle, applied this time to motion in any direction and not only to horizontal motion. "But on the horizontal plane," says Galileo, after having spoken of the inclined plane, "motion is uniform, for there exists no cause of acceleration or of retardation. . . . It must, moreover, be remarked that every degree of velocity which is found in a moving object is, by its very nature, impressed upon it in an indelible fashion when one removes the external causes of acceleration or of retardation, as takes place in a horizontal plane alone. . . . It follows equally that motion on a horizontal plane is eternal."(106)

Descartes always presents inertia as a pure deduction; in this connection he scarcely mentions real circumstances, such as the resistance of the air, which would be of a nature to distort the observation. Descartes starts from a principle which he calls the "First Law of Nature," and which he thus formulates: "That everything remains in the condition it is in as long as nothing changes it." That is the title of the XXXVIIth Chapter of the Second Part of the *Principia*, and in the text this law is deduced from the fact that "God is not subject to change and He acts always in the same way." It follows, "when some part of this matter is square, it always remains square, if nothing happens which changes its figure; and that if it is at rest, it does not begin to move of itself. But when it has once begun to move, we have no reason to think that it must ever cease to move with the same force as long as it encounters nothing which retards or which stops this motion." After having thus established the perpetuity of motion, Descartes stipulates, in a special formula, that it must continue in a straight line. This is his second law, which he states as follows: "That every body which moves tends to continue its motion in a straight line," simply remarking in the text of the XXXIXth Chapter, of which this formula constitutes the title, "This rule, like the preceding one, depends on the fact that God is immovable."

This argument was sufficient to obtain the agreement of contemporaries: the principle of inertia, almost immediately dominated science, and this in spite of the fact that people had been accustomed for so many centuries to the antagonistic doctrines of Aristotle. Some have been astonished by this—wrongly, we think. Descartes, in rendering precise what was only obscurely hinted at by Galileo, clearly expounded what constitutes the true foundation of inertia, that by which this principle is impressed upon our minds.

We saw that originally the concept of velocity is only a relation between two limited terms, and that motion appears as a change, analogous to a change of colour. We no longer believe this. Motion appears to us as a state, analogous consequently not to a change of colour but to colour itself.

We see that this conception approaches that of Themistius and Cardanus, for whom impulse communicated to a body is something analogous to heat. It may be said that in this case it would have been sufficient to consider heat as a substance or as a substantial accident (which was quite conformable to the peripatetic doctrine) for the principle of inertia to have been conceived.

This conclusion may seem paradoxical. As a matter of fact we know of no principle of conservation of colour, and since the overthrow of Black's theory we no longer believe in the conservation of heat. But we have seen that there is a profound difference between the phenomena of motion and all others. The former appear to us as simple and primary, the latter as complicated and secondary, capable of being explained by the first, which must constitute the foundation of things. When the solution of permanganate of potassium, which used to be called a "mineral chameleon," successively changes colour, we are convinced that these modifications must have a cause, that they are the consequence of changes which are produced in the colouring substance; but these modifications in themselves, or, in any case, the bond which attaches them to changes of colour, may remain hidden provisionally. It is not so with a phenomenon of motion; there is nothing "behind" it. Consequently, if motion is a state, if it must maintain itself as every other state, we can express it under an absolute form, make of it a principle, without fear of the intervention of any mysterious agent.

It is thus that motion, having become a state, transforms itself into an entity, a substance—that is, in virtue of the principle of causality, our mind shows the invincible tendency to maintain its identity in time, to conserve it. The body which is displaced is in a "state of motion." What distinguishes this state from others, what constitutes, to follow our metaphor, its particular shade, is its velocity. When we have really grasped this idea, we immediately admit that velocity is not a quotient, that it has no need of limits, that it exists in each fraction of time, no matter how small, and that it is a derivative. And it is thus velocity whose conservation we are stating.

Here, it seems, is the true foundation of the principle. And although the possibility of an experimental proof exists, it is really this argument which produces our strong conviction, so different from that with which we receive purely empirical formulae. There is also that obscure feeling that there is, at the basis of the principle, something other than pure empiricism, which explains why *a priori* demonstrations have been so obstinately searched for. Consequently, Descartes has disclosed the essence of the principle in relating it to the "immutability of God," to the conviction that everything in nature persists. His, therefore, is the merit not only of having been the first loudly to proclaim the principle, but also to indicate its true foundation. And it is clear that Kant's formula, "Every change in nature has an external cause," is but a transformation of the *First Law* of Descartes, both being only forms of the principle of identity in time, as we have defined it. Schopenhauer simply summarized this teaching in declaring that the principle of inertia is *a priori*, because it is a consequence of the principle of causality;(107) and Spir follows the same tradition in deducing it directly from the principle of identity.(108)

We can now reply to the question we asked: Is the principle of inertia *a priori* or *a posteriori*? It is neither one nor the other, because it is both at the same time. Doubtless in the present state of our knowledge this principle admits of an empirical demonstration that is perfectly valid, although indirect; but, as a matter of fact, the principle was not thus established in the beginning, and even now this demonstration does not constitute the real foundation of our conviction. This latter rests upon the fact that the principle is capable of assuming a form which makes it appear as derived from the causal principle.

This latter principle certainly is *a priori*. But we have seen that this is not a statement from which we can directly deduce precise propositions; it is that which renders nugatory all *a priori* demonstrations from Descartes to d'Alembert and Spir. For, taken literally, the principle of identity in time would signify: *everything persists*, an affirmation immediately denied by experience; we can accept it only with the aid of this subsidiary proposition: *everything is motion*. Hence the statement becomes: *certain essential things persist*. But this is an indefinite formula, for it does not tell us what are the things which persist and which, consequently, we ought to consider as essential. It is experience alone which can teach us that. But in this matter experience plays a peculiar rôle, in the sense that it is not free, for it obeys the principle of causality, which we may call more precisely the *causal tendency*, because it manifests its action in commanding us to seek in the diversity of phenomena something which persists. The formula constitutes thus, according to Boutroux's admirable expression, not a law but a "mould" of laws.

From what we have just contended for the principle of inertia, we can draw this general conclusion: every proposition stipulating identity in time appears to us as invested *a priori* with a high degree of probability. It finds our minds prepared, it seduces them, and is immediately adopted, unless contradicted by very evident facts. Perhaps it would be wise to apply to statements of this category, intermediary between the *a priori* and the *a posteriori*, a special term. We should propose, for lack of a better one, the term *plausible*. Therefore every proposition stipulating identity in time, every law of conservation, is plausible.(109)

And in the light of the results to which we have come, one cannot indeed admire enough the force of this tendency. The principle of inertia demands that we conceive of velocity as a *substance*. Now this is a conception entirely paradoxical to the immediate understanding, according to which velocity is a simple relation, an idea which one must violate, so to speak, in order to show that it may be conceived as a quality. How does it happen, then, that our mind accepts so easily, without experiencing any shock, this strange notion? The reply does not seem doubtful to us; we accept it because it can serve to satisfy the causal tendency. It suffices that we be able to conceive of the conservation of velocity for the very nature of this notion to undergo immediately a prodigious transformation.

We must add also that at least for the modern mind the conception of motion as a state is fortified by the habits of thought which the infinitesimal calculus gives us. They certainly contribute in obliging us to accept the idea of velocity as a derivative. But we may ask whether without the principle of inertia these mathematical conceptions could ever have been applied to the science of motion, and though admitting that the fundamental ideas, upon which the methods of Newton and Leibniz rest, existed in embryo anterior to the work of these thinkers, yet one can hardly attribute to them an active rôle in the formation of the concept of "motion as a state." It is rather this last conception, born in the manner we have just shown, which seems to have helped in the growth of the notions which are the foundation of the infinitesimal calculus.

NOTES

1. Such seems to be the opinion of Paul Tannery, *Galilée et les principes de la dynamique. Revue générale des science*, Vol. XII, 1901, p. 333. Cf. also René Berthelot, *Bilbiothèque du Congrès de philosophie de 1900*, Vol. IV, p. 99.

2. Cf. MABILLEAU: *l.c.*, pp. 210–211. Mabilleau is certainly right in supposing that the passage from Aristotle translated by him (*Metaphys.*, XII,

6, 1071), and in which the natural motion of the atoms is in question, is a quotation from Democritus. The following, "there is properly neither cause nor reason for that which exists eternally," expresses an opinion of the atomist against which Aristotle constantly protested. Cf. also *De generatione animalium*, II, 6.

3. DIOGENES LAERTIUS (*The Lives, Opinions and Remarkable Sayings of the Most Famous Ancient Philosophers*, trans. London, 1688, Vol. II, p. 212), expressly affirms that Democritus declared that atoms are carried across space by a circular motion. For information about the motion of rotation in the ancients, cf., p. 115.

4. ARISTOTLE: *De Caelo*. J. L. Stocks. Oxford, 1922, Book I, Chap. II, § 5. "Supposing, then, that there is such a thing as simple movement, and that circular movement is an instance of it, and that both movement of a simple body is simple and simple movement is of a simple body—then there must necessarily be some simple body which revolves naturally and in virtue of its own nature with a circular movement." *Ib.*, Book II, Chap. I, § 2. "And this motion, being perfect, contains those imperfect motions which have a limit and a goal, having itself no beginning or end, but unceasing through the infinity of time." (*Metaphysics*. Smith and Ross. Oxford, 1918, Book XII, Chap. VI.) "And there is no continuous movement except movement in place, and of this only that which is circular is continuous."

5. Cf., p. 123.

6. PAPPUS: ed. Hultsch. Berlin, 1876, Book VIII, prop. 9 (Vol. III, p. 1055), Chap. X. A detailed exposition of the theory of Pappus will be found in Duhem, *Les origines de la statique*. Paris, 1905, p. 189 and ff.

7. PLUTARCH: *Moralia: Of the Face appearing within the Orb of the Moon*. Revised by Goodwin. Boston, 1871, p. 241.

8. Cf., p. 123.

9. Appendix II, p. 457.

10. Cf. WOHLWILL: *Die Entdeckung des Beharrungsgesetzes, Zeitschrift fuer Voelkerpsychologie*, XIV, p. 379.

11. *Quaestiones mechanicae*, ed. Van Cappelle. Amsterdam, 1812, Chap. IX, p. 433.

12. SEXTUS EMPIRICUS: *Adversus mathematicos*. II *adversus physicos*, Section II, *De motu*, § 55 and ff. *Opera*, ed. Fabricius. Leipzig, 1718, p. 643.

13. *Ib.*, § 57.

14. *Ib.*, ROSENBERGER (*Geschichte der Physik*. Braunschweig, 1884, Vol. I, p. 47) believes that the absence of conceptions which from our point of view result from the principle of inertia was one of the determining reasons for the triumph of geocentric theories in the astronomy of the ancients. Only philosophers were able to envisage the motion of the earth; the Alexandrians, accustomed to observe, were necessarily alienated from such a conception. It cannot be said that this opinion is contradicted by the exposition of Sextus Empiricus. It seems, indeed, that these theories only arose much later and that they were considered as a kind of paradox, capable of casting doubt on conceptions which common sense accepted as firmly established, but which could not serve as a basis for any precise statement. Yet one

should perhaps only make use of negative deductions of this kind with prudence. If to-morrow we were to find the writings of Aristarchus of Samos, who knows if we would not find arguments quite analogous to those employed by Copernicus?

15. W. WUNDT: *Die Prinzipien der mechanischen Naturlehre*, 2nd ed. Stuttgart, 1910, p. 36.

16. DUHEM: *Etudes sur Léonard de Vinci*. Paris, 1906–09, I, p. 111 and ff.; II, p. 194 and ff.

17. *Ib.*, II, pp. 247–249.

18. NIC. CUSANUS: *Opera*. Bâle, 1565, Chaps. X–XIII, p. 38 and ff.

19. Cf., pp. 121, 143.

20. We saw earlier that the theory of the *impetus* had, before Cusa, been expounded by Albert of Saxony. It is to be noticed that this latter had applied the concept also to rotating bodies, and especially to the motion of a mill, and the passage from the Parisian master cited by Duhem on this subject (*Etudes sur Léonard de Vinci*, 2nd series, Paris, 1909, pp. 198–199) seems evidently to be the source of Cusa's opinions on the same subject.

21. CUSANUS: *l.c.*, pp. 212–214.

22. NIC. COPERNICI: *De revolutionibus orbium coelestium*, Libri VI. Thorn, 1873, Book I, Chap. VIII, p. 23.

23. Bernardini Telesii Cosentini, *De rerum natura*, etc. Naples, 1570, Book II, Chap. L, p. 85.

24. Cf. Appendix III, p. 460 and ff.

25. CARPENTARIUS: *Philosophia libera*, 2nd ed., Oxford, 1622, p. 67. Concerning the use of proof through the absurd, cf., p. 123.

26. *Le livre de Hiérome Cardanus, médecin milanais, De la Subtilité*. Trans. Richard Le Blanc. Paris, 1556, f. 47. The term which Le Blanc translated by *impetuosité* is *impetus*. Cf. Hier. CARDANI. *De Subtilitate*. Nuremberg, 1550, p. 56.

27. According to Duhem's curious proof (*Etudes sur Léonard de Vinci*, I, pp. 111 and ff., 208 and ff.), it was Leonardo who, directly inspired by Albert of Saxony, introduced these conceptions into Italy. It would appear that he did not publish his studies on this question, and that his manuscripts were utilized by a certain number of people; Cardanus, and even Benedetti, in regard to the *vis impressa*, did scarcely more than pillage them.

28. Io. BAPTISTI BENEDICTI: *Diversorum speculationum liber*. Turin. 1585, p. 160 and ff.

29. Cf. DUHEM: *Les origines de la statique*. Paris, 1905, pp. 108, 109.

30. ROSENBERGER: *Geschichte der Physik*, Vol. I, p. 122. The current conception was less logical but for that very reason less contrary to evidence; the two straight lines were joined by the arc of a circle. The picture of the trajectory thus conceived will be found in CARDANUS, trans. Le Blanc, § 49. According to Duhem (*l.c.*, I, pp. 112–113) this opinion originated in Leonardo.

31. BENEDETTI: l.c., *Verum idem est impressum illum impetum paulatim decrescere*. . . .

32. GALILEO: *Sermones de motu gravium. Opere*. Florence, 1842–56, Vol. XI, p. 33.

33. Cf. E. WOHWILL: *Die Entdeckung des Beharrungsgesetzes. Zeitschrift fuer Voelkerspsychologie*, Vol. XV, 1884, p. 110.

34. *Ib.*, p. 124.

35. *Ib.*, p. 103 and ff.

36. Cf., p. 143

37. Cf. DUHEM: *Les origines de la statique*, p. 332.

38. Concerning the history of the principle of inertia useful indications will be found in Rosenberger (*Geschichte der Physik*. Brunswick, 1884), and in Lasswitz (*Geschichte der Atomistik*. Hamburg, 1890, Vol. II, p. 19 and ff.). In regard to Galileo and Descartes we have followed especially Wohlwill, *l.c.*, whose appreciation seems very just to us. Cf. also P. Tannery, *Galilée et les principes de la dynamique. Revue générale des sciences*, Vol. XIII, 1901, p. 333.

39. DESCARTES: *Principes. Œuvres*, Vol. IX. Paris, 1904, II, Chap. XLIII. "[A body] when it is at rest has the force to remain in this rest and to resist everything which could change it. In the same way, when it moves, it has the force to continue to move, with the same velocity and in the same direction."

40. D'ALEMBERT: *Dynamique*, 2nd ed. Paris, 1757, p. 3.

41. LOTZE: *System der Philosophie*. Leipzig, 1874–79, *Metaphysik*, p. 311. Lotze appears, however, to have changed somewhat his opinion on this point. Cf. id., *Grundzuege der Naturphilosophie*, 2nd ed. Leipzig, 1889, p. 11.

42. ARISTOTLE: *Physics*, Book IV, Chap. XI, § 8. "One may observe that projectiles continue to move when the object which threw them no longer continues to touch them, either because of the surrounding reaction, as is sometimes said, or because of the action of the air, which, having been stirred, stirs in its turn, producing a more rapid motion than is the natural tendency of the body toward the place proper to it. But in the void nothing like that can occur and no body can have motion unless this body is unceasingly sustained and carried like a load in a chariot." § 9. "It would be still impossible to say why in the void a body once put into motion could ever stop anywhere. Consequently, it will either necessarily remain at rest, or if it has motion, this motion will necessarily be infinite if some stronger obstacle does not happen to prevent it."

43. HERBERT SPENCER: *First Principles*. London, 1863, p. 246.

44. PAUL TANNERY: *Galilée, Revue générale des sciences*, XII, 1901, p. 334.

45. P. DUHEM: *La théorie physique*. Paris, 1906, p. 434.

46. Cf. TANNERY, *l.c.*, Colonel HARTMANN (*Bull. Soc. phil.*, 5th year, 1905, p. 103 and ff.) developed a very remarkable theory of mechanical motion, in entire abstraction from the principle of inertia as we formulate it to-day, and based, on the contrary, upon the fact that the body and the medium constitute an indivisible whole, the motion of the body being due to the existence, in the surrounding space, of material elements "which, from the moment that it is freed, at first cause and afterwards continue its displacement."

47. Cf. pp. 116, 117 f. It is well known that Descartes formulated it with great care. *Principes. Œuvres*, Vol. IX. Paris, 1904, 2nd Part, Chap. XXVIII,

title: "That motion in its real meaning has relation only to the bodies which touch that which is said to move."

48. KANT: *Metaphysische Anfangsgründe der Naturwissenshaft*, Trans. ANDLER et CHAVANNES. Paris, 1891, p. 21.

49. *Ib.*, p. 14. Cf. *ib.*, p. 87.

50. *Ib.*, p. 76.

51. MAXWELL: *Matter and Motion*. London, 1902, p. 36.

52. It goes without saying that the concept of the relativity of space, which we are here discussing and which is that bearing on the classical principle of inertia, is entirely different from those which Einstein employs in the two theories of special relativity and general relativity. Cf. for the first of these conceptions, p. 136. Cf. also what we say concerning the relations between the concept of relativity of space which the Copernicans used more or less implicitly with that of Einstein, *La Déduction Relativiste*, § 35.

53. DESCARTES: *Œuvres*, Vol. I. Paris, 1897, p. 216. *Lettre à Mersenne*, 1632.

54. Id., *Principes*. *Œuvres*, Vol. IX. Paris, 1904, 4th Part, Chap. XXI–XXII. Wundt (*Die physikalischen Axiome*, Erlangen, 1866, p. 37) has pointed out that in general Descartes' vortices constitute a manifest contradiction of the principle of inertia.

55. NEWTON: *Principia*. New York, 1848, pp. 80–81.

56. *Ib.*, p. 77.

57. Newton seems to have adopted in this question Henry More's ideas on the reality of empty space. Cf. on this subject Ludwig Lange. *Die geschichtliche Entwicklung des Bewegungsbegriffs*, etc. Leipzig, 1886, p. 44.

58. HENRI BERGSON: *Introduction à la metaphysique*. *Revue de métaphysique*, XI, 1903, p. 2.

59. BERKELEY: *De motu. Works*, ed. Fraser. London, 1871, Vol. III, § 59. *Concipiantur porro duo globi et praeterea nil corporeum existere. Concipiantur deinde vires quomodocunque applicari; quicquid tandem per applicationem virium intelligamus, motus circularis duorum globorum circa commune centrum nequit per imaginationem concipi. Supponamus deinde coelum fixarum creari: subito ex concepto appulsu globorum ad diversos caeli istius partes motus concipietur.* Cf. *ib.*, § 64.

60. E. MACH: *Die Mechanik*, trans. Emile Bertrand. Paris, 1904, p. 225. Mach, it is true, claims to be a partisan of the relativity of space, but in a very particular sense. The idea rejected by him comes back to that which we have qualified as absolute metaphysical space.

61. It goes without saying that instead of the totality of bodies one can also introduce the ether, which is only, it is true, a hypostasis of space (cf. p. 249 and ff.), but precisely of *physical space*. The essential point is that one does not attribute these properties to space properly so called, but to that with which it is filled. It is known that Mach's conception has since been used as a general basis by Einstein.

62. One may affirm, if necessary, that the complete establishment of the principle of inertia, in the sense which we give to it to-day, dates only from Newton's exposition, Descartes, we have already seen, having considered the rotation of the earth as a relative motion.

63. L. EULER: *Theoria motus*. Rostock, 1765, Chap. II, § 78 and ff.

64. POINSOT: *Théorie nouvelle de la rotation des corps.* Paris, 1852, p. 51.

65. CARL NEUMANN: *Ueber die Principien der Galilei-Newton'schen Theorie.* Leipzig, 1870.

66. Cf., for example, LODGE, in *Nature,* Vol. LVII, 1894; A. B. Basset, *ib.*; Andrade, *Les idées directrices de la mécanique. Revue philosophique,* Vol. XLVI, 1898, p. 400; and especially Painlevé, *Les axiomes de la mécanique et le principe de causalité. Bulletin de la Société française de philosophie,* 5th year, 1905, p. 27 and ff. Cf. also Henri Bergson, *Matière et Mémoire.* Paris, 1903, p. 214.

67. Doubtless, H. POINCARÉ formulated the general opinion of contemporary physicists in affirming that the fact that one can measure the velocity of absolute rotation "shocks the philosopher," but that the physicist is forced to accept it (*Des fondements de la géometrie. Revue de métaphysique,* Vol. VII, 1899, p. 269).

68. NEWTON: *l.c.,* p. 17.

69. NEUMANN: *l.c.,* p. 14.

70. It indeed seems that at a given moment science recognized, or at least understood, a principle which might be described as that of the relativity of motion. We have tried to appreciate its importance (cf. Appendix III), and it will be seen to be confused in no wise with our present principle of inertia. As to the principle of relativity conceived of in the sense of the contemporary electron theory, cf., p. 136.

71. STREINTZ: *Die physikalischen Grundlagen der Mechanik.* Leipzig, 1883, pp. 24–25.

72. Cf. p. 33.

73. EULER: *l.c.,* § 100.

74. In the *Revue générale des sciences,* 1904, p. 881, will be found the description of a new apparatus, but also based upon the principle of the gyroscope.

75. This conception presents also the difficulty of making the measure of time depend upon the principle of inertia (cf., p. 33 and ff.).

76. E. MACH: *Die Mechanik,* trans. Bertrand. Paris, 1904, p. 233; cf. also Kleinpeter, *Arch. fuer systematische Philosophie,* Vol. VI, 1900, p. 469.

77. NEUMANN: *l.c.*

78. EULER: *l.c.,* § 99.

79. NEWTON: *l.c.,* p. 79. "And therefore, as it is possible that in the remote regions of the fixed stars, or perhaps far beyond them, there may be some body absolutely at rest, but impossible to know, from the position of bodies relative to one another in our regions, whether any of these do keep the same position relative to that remote body; it follows that absolute rest cannot be determined from the position of bodies in our regions."

80. Cf. p. 65.

81. H. POINCARÉ: *La science et l'hypothèse,* p. 201. In a more recent work (*Science et méthode.* Paris, 1908, p. 233) Poincaré estimates also that to determine the absolute velocity of the earth (with respect to the ether) "would be perhaps less shocking than it seems at first."

82. P. LANGEVIN: *L'évolution de l'espace et du temps. Scientia,* July 1, 1911, p. 35.

83. Id., *L'évolution de l'espace et du temps. Revue de métaphysique,* July 1911, p. 458.

84. ARISTOTLE: *Physics*, I, VIII, Chap. II, § 2.

85. Id., *De Caelo*, trans. J. L. Stocks. Oxford, 1922, III, Chap. II, § 2.

86. L. EULER: *Lettres à une princesse d'Allemagne*. Paris, 1812, Vol. I, p. 332.

87. LAPLACE: *Mécanique celeste*. *Œuvres*. Paris, 1878, 1st Part, 1st § 4.

88. POISSON: *Traité de mécanique*, 2nd ed, Paris, 1833, p. 207.

89. It is known that astronomers for a long time searched for a force which makes the planets *move* (cf. Appendix III, p. 458 and ff.). Borelli in 1666 was the first to introduce the idea that they were displaced under the action of inertia, combined with a centripetal force, directed toward the sun. Cf. Rosenberger, *l.c.*, Vol. II, p. 166, and Duhem, *La théorie physique*, pp. 407–408.

90. DUHAMEL: *Cours de mécanique*, 3rd ed. Paris, 1862, p. 19.

91. DUEHRING: *Kritische Geschichte der allgemeinen Prinzipien der Mechanik*. Berlin, 1862, p. 32.

92. LOTZE: *Grundzuege der Naturphilosophie*, 2nd ed. Leipzig, 1889, pp. 13–14. Cf. *ib.*, p. 354: *es ist eine ortsbestimmende Kraft.*

93. DUEHRING: *l.c.*

94. BERKELEY: *Works*, ed. Fraser. London, 1871, Vol. III, *De motu*, § 29.

95. MOLESCHOTT: *La circulation de la vie*, trans. CAZELLES. Paris, 1866, p. 96. One may compare Moleschott's affirmation with this proposition of Maupertius, *Cosmologie*. *Œuvres*. Lyon, 1756, Vol. I, p. 33: "Although it was absurd to say that a part of matter which cannot move itself could move another."

96. Cf. earlier, p. 123.

97. MAXWELL: *Matter and Motion*. London, 1902, p. 36.

98. J. S. MILL: *A System of Logic*. London, 1884, p. 160.

99. HEGEL: *Naturphilosophie*, § 269, *Werke*. Berlin, 1842, Vol. VII. Cf. P. G. TAIT, *Les progrès récents de la physique*. Paris, 1886, p. 15.

100. Cf. p. 154, n. 89.

101. P. TANNERY: *Galilée*. Revue générale des sciences, Vol. XII, 1901, pp. 335–337.

102. GALILEO: *Dialogo interno ai due massimi sistemi*. *Opere*. Florence, 1842, Vol. I, p. 165 and ff. *Lettre à Ingoli*, *ib.*, Vol. II, p. 99 and ff.

103. Id., *Massimi sistemi*, p. 206.

104. Id., *Discorsi*. *Opere*, Vol. XIII, p. 323.

105. *Ib.*, p. 154.

106. *Ib.*, p. 200. *At in plano horizontali motus est acquabilis cum nulla ibi sit causa accelerationis aut retardationis. . . . Attendere insuper licet quod velocitatis gradus quicunque in mobili reperiatur, est in illo suapte natura indibiliter impressus dum externae causae accelerationis aut retardationis tollantur, quod in solo horizontali plano contingit. . . . Ex quo pariter sequitur motum in horizontali esse quoque aeternum.*

107. *Das a priori gesicherte, weil aus der Causalitaet folgende Gesetz der Traegheit.* SCHOPENHAUER. *Die Welt als Wille und Vorstellung*, ed. Frauenstaedt. Leipzig, 1877, Vol. I, p. 79.

108. SPIR: *Pensée et réalité*, pp. 411, 419; cf. Preface by Penjon, p. ix.

109. The fact that certain scientific statements constitute only a particular

expression of the metaphysical principle of substance, and that one must distinguish in this respect between the form and the content of statements was perceived by Kant (cf. later, p. 400). Following considerations of an entirely different order, Poinsot has formulated the very general proposition which we have placed at the head of this book (cf. concerning the context of this passage, p. 226). Whewell, in following the way traced by Kant, succeeds in rectifying a very important point in Kant's views (cf. p. 401). In one of his first philosophical works (*Die physikalischen Axiome und ihre Beziehung zum Causalprincip*. Erlangen, 1866, re-edited, with some changes, under the title, *Die Prinzipien der mechanischen Naturlehre*. Stuttgart, 1910) Wundt, while insisting on a very different aspect of these statements (in so far as they are due to "thought-experiments"), shows that they derive from a general formula which is that of the equivalence of cause and effect. Our reason tends to impose it upon Experience, which resists it. Reason is incapable of determining in advance the expression to which the formula must be applied; but every statement containing a causal relation, even though it be discovered by empirical means, may be reduced to a form which lends logical evidence to it (2nd ed., pp. 12, 86, 110, 115, 146, 147). A little later Spir (*Denken und Wirklichkeit*. Leipzig, 1873. French trans. of Penjon. Paris, 1895) discusses at great length the principle of identity. He determines its double content, analytical and synthetical (cf. earlier, p. 43), and shows the disagreement between this exigency of our thought and the external world (cf. 41) and recognizes the true nature of scientific explanation (*Pensée et réalite*, pp. 275, 493, 498). He also establishes the relation between his principle of identity on the one hand and atomism and the principles of conservation on the other (*ib.*, pp. 411, 419–424 and ff.). These deductions, so important but a little obscure, and at times, it seems, infected with some confusion (the principal source of which must be sought, doubtless, in the fact that Spir did not recognize with sufficient clearness the concept of lawfulness as distinct in itself, cf. later, p. 439), seem to have exercised but little influence afterwards. Kroman, probably, was unaware of them, when with more clearness but less energy than his predecessor he presented very analogous deductions (*Unsere Naturerkenntnis*. German trans. of Fischer Benzon. Copenhagen, 1833, especially p. 247 ff.). Kroman, moreover, tried to distinguish in a certain measure the two concepts which we have designated as those of lawfulness and of causality (cf. earlier, p. 18). With still greater precision, although in quite an incidental manner, Paul Tannery explains (in regard to the theories of certain pre-Socratic philosophers, especially of Melissus) that at the basis of the principles of conservation there is a more general formula, an exigency of our thought, which stipulates the permanency of something throughout the variability of phenomena, and that that is the true principle of causality or of scientific explanation (*Pour servir à l'histoire de la science hellène*. Paris, 1887, p. 264 and ff.). The same year Planck, in a book devoted to the principle of the conservation of energy (*Das Prinzip der Erhaltung der Energie*, Leipzig, 1887, 2nd ed. Leipzig, 1908), marvels at the very small number of experiments upon which Mayer, Colding, and Joule depended to establish the principle in question, and asks whether the rapid success of this conception was not due to the *a priori* elements which it contained (p. 150), these elements coming necessarily from the intimate relations of the principle with that of cause and effect (p. 30); and the analogy, which we are establishing with the principle of the conservation of matter (familiar for such a long time), helping to make acceptable the proposition relative to energy (pp. 41, 116). And yet Planck considers entirely negligible deductions such as those of Descartes and of Colding, and, in a note added to the second edition of his book, declares that the principle is "neither a tautology, nor a disguised definition, nor a postulate, nor an *a priori* judgment, but, in fact, an experimental statement" (pp. 151 and 116). Gaston Milhaud takes up the thought of Poinsot and of Paul Tannery. He affirms that the law of constancy and uniformity, which is the fundamental hypothesis of science, is not its consequence, but its very "directing principle" (*Essai sur les conditions et les limites de la certitude logique*. Paris, F. Alcan, 1898, p. 131), and states precisely the rôle of this *a priori* statement in the genesis of the principle of inertia (*La science rationnelle, Revue de métaphysique*, Vol. IV, 1896, pp. 290–291). Yet Milhaud follows at times a very different line of thought, assimilating the principles of conservation to definitions and conventions; moreover, constancy appears to him especially as a constancy of *relations*, and, as such, depending on the very fact that the world is governed by laws (*Essai sur les conditions* etc., p. 201, *Sur philosophie, science et hypothèse. Revue de métaphysique*, XI, 1903, p. 786; cf. later, p. 423. Cf. also concerning the impossibility of an experimental demonstration of inertia, *Essai*, etc., p. 91). Lalande points out that pre-existence is the real foundation of all explanation (*La Dissolution opposée à l'Evolution dans les sciences physiques et morales*. Paris, F. Alcan, 1899, pp. 36, 45) and connects with it the principles of conservation of matter and of energy (*ib.*, p. 414). Yet the explicable, the intelligible, is assimilated more often by this philosopher to that which is susceptible, in general, of being determined—that is, according to our terminology, to that which is simply conformable to law, and, just as in Milhaud, the necessity of the constancy of certain terms is directly deduced from the fact that nature is ordered (*ib.*, pp. 33, 35, 179). Kozlowski's views on this question approach those of Milhaud's and Lalande's. Wilbois has also insisted upon the close relation between the principles of conservation and the law of substance (*La méthode dans les sciences physiques. Revue de Métaphysique et de Morale*, Vol. VII, 1899, p. 598 and ff., Vol. VIII, 1900, p. 293). Perhaps, in spite of the limitations stated, the exposition which precedes will give to the reader the notion of a more continuous development than there has been in reality. Let us repeat, therefore, that the greater number of these thinkers (we believe that we have expressly mentioned contrary cases) seemed to have been entirely ignorant of their predecessors and to have arrived at their conclusions almost independently. The reader will find a more complete outline of these conceptions in *De l'explication dans les sciences*, Chap. XVII, pp. 314–342.

CHAPTER IV

THE CONSERVATION OF MATTER

WE find this principle stated in many different ways. In the first place, let us put aside the formula "Nothing is created, nothing is lost," which is still sometimes employed and which evidently is much too broad, for it would apply just as well to the conservation of velocity and to that of energy; this is not surprising, since the formula, we have seen, is only one of the expressions of the principle of causality. We must at least say: *Matter* is neither created nor lost. But even this formula lacks precision. Here is an ingot of silver: its colour, its lustre, its hardness, its malleability, its conductivity for electricity and heat, in a word, all the physical properties which I know it to have, are certainly an integral part of my conception of this matter. Does one mean to affirm that all of this is indestructible? Assuredly not, since it suffices to dissolve the metal in nitric acid for these properties to vanish. The term *matter* is therefore taken here in a narrower sense than the one commonly assigned to it, and the statement of the principle must be completed by a definition of this term. In order to follow the evolution of matter through modifications, analogous to that undergone by the ingot of silver, the chemist uses the balance. It was with the aid of the balance that Lavoisier accomplished his "chemical revolution," as Berthelot calls it. It seems, then, that the term *matter* must be defined as that which has weight. Let us remark, however, that this weight, the indestructibility of which we apparently affirmed, we see without surprise change with the place where the experiment is performed; it will not be strictly the same at the Pole and near the Equator, and we suppose that the same ingot of silver, weighed, of course, on a spring balance, would have an entirely different weight on the surface of the moon. These variations, due to the variations of the constant of gravitation in these different places, we shall eliminate in dividing the weight by this constant. We thus come to the concept of *mass*, related to that of weight by the equation $w = mg$, and our principle finally crystallizes into that of conservation of mass.

In this chapter this definition is to be our basis. We shall see later (p. 236 and following) that it does not really exhaust the contents of the principle, this latter including a statement much less easy to determine, but nevertheless very important.

The conservation of the weight of matter was formulated in antiquity. No one can doubt this while attentively reading the *De Rerum Natura*. Doubtless the *nil posse creari de nihilo* proves nothing; the context, even, clearly shows that Lucretius understood his formula in the most general sense—that is, that it was really the principle of causality itself.(1) But he applied this formula immediately to the atoms. They are eternal, uncreated, indestructible.(2) They are also heavy. All matter has weight; there exists no absolutely light body, having a tendency to rise,(3) and weight is the true measure of the quantity of matter.(4) It evidently follows that weight must remain constant, and although this rule is not explicitly stated anywhere in the *De Rerum Natura*, one cannot doubt that it was thus understood and taught in certain philosophical schools of antiquity. A curious passage of a treatise attributed to Lucian is evidence of it: "'If you burn a thousand pounds of wood, Demonax, how many pounds will there be of smoke?' 'Weigh the ashes,' says he, 'and all the rest will be smoke.'"(5) Demonax was a Cynic philosopher of the second century of our era. He appears to have been exclusively preoccupied with ethics, theology, and politics.(6) Nothing indicates that he professed atomistic opinions, nor that he had studied scientific questions. The quotation is all the more significant, because it proves that this reasoning, analogous to ours in principle, had become current in philosophic schools. It is certain, moreover, that Lucretius only repeated the teachings of his master Epicurus, and it is at least very probable that this part of the doctrine had already been formulated by Democritus and perhaps even by Leucippus.(7)

One can say that in a certain sense the ancient atomists must have conceived of the constancy of weight at the same time as that of mass—indeed, it seems that they completely confused these two concepts. It is not easy to imagine how Democritus and Epicurus represented to themselves the motion of atoms in space, since the principle of inertia and the whole order of ideas attached to it was entirely foreign to them. One can almost imagine, by the way in which Aristotle expounds his theory of motion in the *plenum*, that there must have been a gap in the conceptions of his adversaries—a gap over which the Stagirite exults with some complacency. However that may be, there is no doubt that in the poem of Lucretius, the atoms act in virtue of their weight; this last concept, already an inseparable attribute of matter, becomes therefore, at the same time, the direct measure of its principle of action, so that, instead of saying $w = mg$, we formulate $w = m$. It must be noticed also that this confusion is conformable to our immediate sensation; we are continually inclined to be guilty of it; from our first lessons in mechanics we have had to make an effort to separate the two notions.(8)

The conceptions of the atomists, however widespread we may suppose them, did not govern the minds of antiquity without rivals. Aristotle's doctrine, destined to such a brilliant fortune in the following centuries, consciously contradicted, on almost every point, the doctrine of Leucippus and Democritus. Aristotle, just as did the atomists, confuses mass and weight as principles of mechanical action. But, on the other hand, he completely dissociates the two concepts of matter and weight. Weight is an accidental quality of matter. It is the result of two opposed principles, heaviness and lightness. "There are things whose constant nature it is to move away from the centre, while others move constantly toward the centre. . . . By absolutely light, then, we mean that which moves upward or to the outer extremity, and by absolutely heavy, that which moves downward or to the centre."(9) This is the case of two out of the four elements which Aristotle's theory admits: "Fire is always light and moves upward, while earth and all earthy things move downward or toward the centre."(10) As to water and air, they have gravity as well as lightness, the former prevailing in water, the latter in air. We can see to what a degree what we call weight is in this theory a derived concept. It is also, evidently, an accidental property. Plato had already shown that elements unceasingly change into one another.(11) Moreover, it is a daily experience that air and fire intervene in the transformation of matter: water boils, wood burns. Aristotle and his followers therefore placed gravity on the same level with colour and heat.

It is well known to what extent these doctrines prevailed during the Middle Ages.(12) In the writings of alchemists there are doubtless to be found some considerations based upon weight. It may be that this was, in part, a heritage dating from the origins of that science—that is, from an epoch anterior to the domination of the philosophy of substantial forms. One may also suppose that atomic theories, whose reflection, we have seen, was found in certain widely dispersed writings, exercised some influence. But it must also be said that these arguments were not in direct contradiction with the reigning philosophy. It is doubtless very difficult to arrive at the numerical concept of *weight* by substantial forms; but supposing this concept taken for granted—common sense and daily experience sufficiently perform this task—there is nothing unnatural in attributing a certain importance to observations relative to weight, just as importance is accorded to observations concerning the colour or the heat of bodies. But what distinguishes these opinions from ours is that for us considerations based upon weight override all others without exception. This predilection was completely foreign to the science of the Middle Ages. It is not unusual to find, in the writings of that epoch, passages where the constancy of weight is more or less directly denied, the author being seemingly unconscious of having expressed a hazardous proposition. Thus alchemists, speaking of transmutation, sometimes mention the modification of the weight of the metal. "By our artifice," says Geber, "we easily form silver from lead; in the transformation this latter does not preserve its own weight, but is changed into a new weight." In the same way, pewter "acquires weight in magistery."(13) The moderns, in the presence of these affirmations, are always inclined to believe either that the author supposed only a modification of the specific weight, or else that he admitted the addition of a matter coming from air or fire; but, in truth, this addition appeared in no way indispensable; and as to the specific weight, it was most often confused with absolute weight. This confusion is still very frequent at a later date; not only Scaliger in the seventeenth century, but, on the very eve of the great revolution wrought by Lavoisier, Kunckel and Juncker make the same confusion.(14) This error, if the question is considered attentively, is quite natural. If weight is not an essential property, but an accidental quality of matter, is it not natural to suppose that at the instant when this quality is manifestly modified—that is, when the specific weight changes —the total weight must change also?(15) Francis Bacon, who professed on the qualities of matter opinions approaching those of the alchemists, affirmed the existence of absolutely light bodies (16) and change of weight through modification of their state,(17) although in another place he solemnly proclaimed the constancy of weight, probably borrowing this idea from the ancient atomists.(18)

Amongst the scientists of that time we sometimes find arguments implying the principle of conservation of weight. Such is the experiment of Cusa, who, to show that the plant draws its matter especially from water, weighed a quantity of earth in a pot, placed seeds in it which he watered, reweighed the earth after the grown plant had been taken out and stated that the weight remained almost the same.(19) But it is certain that only a very secondary importance was attributed to considerations of this kind. Wislicenus, summing up the beliefs of the alchemists, affirms that they were convinced that with the help of small quantities of magistery, pounds of lead or of mercury could be transformed into hundredweights of the purest gold.(20) It would probably be difficult to confirm directly this affirmation by means of a text drawn from an author of that epoch; but it is certain that a proposition of this kind would not have seemed to suggest anything miraculous, such as we see in it. If we rarely find among alchemists affirmations concerning the change of weight, it is not because they considered it as a rare phenomenon, but because they attached to it no importance; the least change of quality appeared to them much more remarkable. These affirmations are more frequent in later epochs where opinions on this question approach ours, precisely because of this last circumstance. Accounts like those of the experiments of Reussing, Dierbach, and Stahl in the eighteenth century, in which the weight of the mass originally employed is seen to increase and even almost to double,(21) would have astonished no one in the Middle Ages; the alchemist would have passed over this detail in silence, considering it too insignificant to strike the imagination of the reader.

If they did not believe in constancy of weight, did they believe in that of mass? They were certainly convinced that something essential in matter, its "substance," persisted throughout modifications. But since they had—rightly, moreover—disengaged the concept of matter from the phenomenon of gravity, it became infinitely more difficult to give a quantitative substratum to materiality. It would be more than useless to inquire whether in logically developing Aristotle's doctrine one might not have come upon a conception of mass permitting the determination of a numerical coefficient. The truth is that concern about relations of quantity was absolutely foreign to all who adhered to the philosophy of substantial forms. Everywhere in the Middle Ages, where one finds, as in Albert of Saxony, the germ of the idea of mass, this conception is developed in manifest opposition to Aristotelian ideas, and is related rather to the theory of *impetus*.(22) Toward the middle of the fifteenth century Gaetan de Tiene speaks in this connection of *accidental gravity*,(23) and this expression is also found in Leonardo.(24) Kepler, who grasped the essential contents of the concept of mass, compares it likewise to that of weight, without, of course, confusing it with the latter.(25) Still more distinctly does the idea of mass appear in Descartes. It is true that on every occasion (for instance, when he is explaining the laws of impact) Descartes is fond of speaking of the size of bodies;(26) and this expression appears troublesome when we recall his theory of matter. We know that Descartes, quite like the scholastics—the greatest revolutionists are always the most conservative on some point—was a partisan of the *plenum*. Extension was for him the only essential attribute of matter, gravitation being a secondary phenomenon which needed to be explained and which he explained indeed by the motions of one of its elementary substances. Weight, as for the scholastics, is an accident. The real quantity of matter is indicated by the volume: "When a vessel, for instance, is full of gold or lead it does not on that account contain more matter than when we think of it as empty."(27) Yet, in fact, Descartes distinguishes perfectly mass from volume, in supposing that, for mechanical motions, the quantity of its third element alone counted.(28) One might believe that he conceived the proportionality of mass (thus understood) and weight; but this idea was far from his thought, although in practice he often made use of weight in this sense. Indeed, weight being the consequence of a more or less complicated motion, strict proportionality would have been the effect of chance, and of chance difficult to explain. He, moreover, expounded his ideas on this subject in the Fourth Part of his *Principia*. The title of the XXVth Chapter is: "That their gravity does not always have the same relation to their matter." That is not, as one might suppose, a simple repetition of the sentence which we cited farther back; it must, in fact, be noticed that the matter spoken of in this chapter is *terrestrial* matter. This is confirmed by the text of the chapter in question; it is there stated that "gravity alone is not enough to make known how much terrestrial matter there is in each body." Thus "a mass of gold twenty times heavier than a quantity of water of the same size" might well contain not twenty times more matter, but only four or five times as much, "because as much must be subtracted from the water as from the gold on account of the air in which they are weighed; and then also for the reason that the terrestrial parts of the water, and in general of all liquids, as has been said of those of the air, have a certain motion which, in accord with those of subtle matter, prevents them from being as heavy as those of hard bodies."

It is indeed because one has to do with "terrestrial matter" and not with matter in general, that there could no longer be a question of identifying its quantity with the volume. It should be noticed that at the time when Descartes was writing, the gravity of air was already almost universally recognized. Gorlaeus,(29) Carpentarius (30) and Galileo,(31) had taken it for granted, and Descartes himself seems to be convinced of it. But we have just seen that this was not enough to make him conceive of the idea that gravity is an essential, immutable attribute of matter, for there still remains fire, and that element, Descartes, like the scholastics, believed to be without weight. "Let us take away the weight," he says, while trying to determine what "constitutes the nature of the body," "because we see that fire, even though it is very light, does not cease to be a body."(32)

Descartes' conception had a great theoretical advantage over that of the ancient atomists in completely dissociating the two concepts of mass and weight. But, of course, the constancy of weight became difficult to admit. Descartes would probably have admitted even variations of mass, since, on the whole, his different elements are composed of the same matter.

Before the publication of the *Principia*, but at a moment when Descartes' authority was already beginning to be recognized, the *Essays* of Jean Rey appeared. Was Rey influenced by the ancient atomists? It may be so, for Lucretius was read a great deal at that time, and, we have seen, a certain tradition of atomistic theories was perpetuated among physicians. This fact would in no way diminish Rey's merit, because what in Lucretius was only inferred and secondary appears here for the first time as the "immovable foundation," the great principle which regulates modifications in nature. Moreover, Rey does not relate this statement to any particular theory of matter. He is attempting a kind of *a priori* demonstration of the principle. It is contained in a few lines: "Let there be taken a piece of earth, which has in it the least weight possible and beyond which nothing smaller can exist; let that earth be converted into water by means known and practised by nature. It is evident that this water will have weight, since all water must have it; then it will be either larger than that which was in the earth, or smaller, or equal. They will not say that it is greater (for they profess the contrary), nor do I wish to; smaller it cannot be, because I took the smallest that could be; it therefore remains that it is equal to it, which I undertook to prove."(33) Evidently the deduction is singularly weak; it rests especially upon the fact that it considers in great part as self-evident what is to be proved.(34) One is led to imagine that Rey himself did not attach too much importance to this proof. On the other hand, he makes a great effort to establish that air has weight and that it may be thickened by different operations. It is this thickened air which, mixing with lime of pewter (Rey seems to have conceived of the addition of the air and the formation of lime as of two distinct operations),(35) increases its weight, assuming that every other cause must be excluded, as Rey proves with much exactness, relying on the experiments of others and also upon his own.(36) Finally, from the point of view of the principle of conservation of weight, Rey establishes that, in two particular cases where it might be believed to fail, the anomaly might be explained by supposing the intervention of the air; and, as the remainder of the title indicates, it is the explanation of this particular phenomenon rather than the principle itself which forms the true object of this little work, so justly celebrated in the opinion of posterity, but which remained completely unknown to his contemporaries.

It is not very difficult, it seems, to understand why the clear exposition of the physician of Bazas had so little success. Doubtless Rey was an unknown man, lost in a little country place; in that century when communication by letter was particularly lively amongst scientists, he does not seem to have been in correspondence with anyone except Mersenne. Father Mersenne certainly knew everyone. Yet the causes must be looked for in the doctrine itself. Chemistry was only just coming out of the semi-mystic fog of alchemic formulae; it was entirely dominated by the conception of the element of quality; we shall recognize later the vitality of that theory and what a defence it was still able to furnish against the vigorous attacks of Lavoisier and of his disciples a century and a half later, when the domain of known facts had been immensely extended. It is easy to understand that, under these conditions, Rey's theory, in which no account was taken of quality, should be immediately set aside by chemists. As to the physicists, they must have found themselves repelled by the fact that Rey, although formulating no theory of matter, placed himself in flagrant opposition to the two theories which divided the prevailing opinion at that time concerning a question on which these theories remained in accord: Aristotle as well as Descartes considered weight as an accidental quality of matter, whereas Rey returned to the ideas of the ancient atomists. Aristotle and Descartes were right from a logical point of view, and in a certain sense Rey's conceptions were a real regression.

Descartes' ideas triumphed finally in science as well as in philosophy. "All other accidents besides magnitude or extension (of bodies) may be generated and destroyed," declares Hobbes (37), and we see that in this theory there is no place for the conservation of weight. Leibniz sometimes reasons in an analogous manner. Water contains in equal volume as much matter as mercury, only to the particular matter of water is added, "a foreign matter, without weight, which passes through its pores," for, he concludes, "it is a strange fiction to make all matter heavy."(38) Yet Leibniz saw with much clearness what we now designate by the term *mass*;(39) it would perhaps be exaggerated to affirm that he had "invented"(40) it; but it is certain that he disengaged it from the fogs in which it was still partly enveloped in Descartes.

Huygens affirms clearly that it is weight which measures the quantity of matter.(41) Newton, by precise experiments,(42) ascertains that weight is proportional to mass, as had already been deduced from Galileo's experiments.(43) Newton did not admit imponderable matter, but soon after him this concept was firmly established in science—a circumstance which did not favour the success of the principle of conservation of weight. It is, in general, rather difficult to discover the true opinion of the physicists of the seventeenth and eighteenth centuries about what we call chemical phenomena. It was a domain but little known, we might almost say of ill-repute, made up of a formidable array of half mysterious facts. Physicists ventured into it unwillingly, or, if they spoke of it, they treated it in an entirely general manner without pre-occupying themselves either with the statements of chemists or with their theories.(44) The methods of both were also totally different. Physicists followed the mathematical method, whereas chemists were interested in quality only. Robert Boyle is the only man of that time forming an exception. Eminent at once as a physicist and a chemist, he tried to unite the advantages of the two methods. It is very remarkable that Boyle, though he nowhere formulates the principle, reasons constantly as if he admitted the conservation of weight.(45) But Boyle founded no school; after him, the separation between physicists and chemists continued as before. This fact makes it difficult to say whether physicists of that time did or did not admit the possibility of a change of weight during the course of a chemical operation. In considering everything we arrive at the conclusion that at least those who assumed the existence of imponderable forms of matter saw nothing shocking in the hypothesis of their intervention in chemical reactions and of consequent modifications of weights.

Such was, indeed, the general opinion of chemists. The imponderable, of which they most often made use, was none other than "elementary fire," Aristotle's fourth element; the "sulphur" of Paracelsus was derived directly from it, and also, later on, the phlogiston of Becher and of Stahl. Through all these modifications it had the privilege, so to speak, of escaping considerations of weight. Even on the eve of Lavoisier's chemical revolution, the idea that phlogiston was an absolutely light substance, endowed with negative weight, did not appear shocking. This is clearly seen in the manner with which this supposition is treated in the notes accompanying the translation of Kirwan's *Essay on Phlogiston*—a collective work of the new and triumphant school of which it forms a kind of breviary.(46)

Yet in the seventeenth century the gravity of fire had already been affirmed at about the same time as that of air. Carpentarius (47) and Galileo (48) took it for granted as Robert Boyle did later.(49) If, contrary to what happened with regard to air, this conception was not so generally accepted, it is due doubtless to the fact that the hypothetical matter described under the name "elementary fire" appeared to be of a particular nature. Yet little by little this conception spread. In the eighteenth century, Duclos and Homberg (50) were partisans of it; and it is a remarkable fact that those who profess this opinion reason instinctively (as did Boyle) as if they presupposed the principle of conservation of matter. "In the analysis of inflammable bodies," says Berkeley, after having commented on Homberg's experiments, "the fire or sulphur is lost and the diminution of weight showeth the loss. But the fire or *vinculum* disappears, . . . but is not destroyed."(51) Nothing is more correct from this point of view than the reasoning of Musschenbroek.(52) He, like Jean Rey, is looking for the cause of the increase of weight that certain metals undergo when they are heated. He rejects the hypothesis according to which this augmentation might come from the "saline acid or oily parts of the fire." Indeed, the augmentation was ascertained for antimony heated with the aid of a concave mirror, the rays of the sun forming the purest fire. Therefore it is the elementary fire itself which must be heavy. It is true, it might be objected, that the increase of weight is too considerable, but "we do not know the weight of a sun-ray." These opinions were rather widely circulated in the second half of the eighteenth century. Thus Diderot says that "the fire of our furnaces considerably increases the weight of certain forms of matter, such as calcined lead."(53) However, care must be taken not to exaggerate the importance of these arguments; those who use them do not consider them nearly as conclusive as they appear to us, and it is certain that considerations based upon quality seem to predominate greatly over considerations of quantity. Kopp notes that the greater number of the chemists of the eighteenth century do not even take the trouble to explain the change of weight, so devoid of interest does this pheno- menon appear to them.(54) Stahl is satisfied to state that the weight of metals which are calcined increases, "although" (*quamvis*) the phlogiston disappears.(55) Moreover, Stahl adopts Lémery's opinion, according to which the metal calcined and reduced afterwards weighs less than originally.(56) Macquer, in 1778, considers this fact as beyond doubt, without supposing in the least, any more than did his predecessors, that this statement allows the inference of a loss of matter of the metal.(57) He apparently considers weight as a purely accidental property, capable of being modified. Nothing is more characteristic from the point of view of this state of mind than the declaration of Macquer, considered at that time as the most authoritative of the French chemists, at the news that Lavoisier was going to attack the theory of phlogiston. Macquer admitted that he had been worried for a moment, but that he was quite untroubled about the fate of that theory, having learned that Lavoisier had drawn his objections solely from considerations of quantity.(58)

As is well known, certain of Lavoisier's adversaries, and amongst them his most illustrious contemporaries, Priestley and Cavendish, remained obdurate to the very end. Cavendish —and this is quite remarkable—who in his experiments used the balance with great care, manifestly did not believe in the conservation of matter.(59) But the difference between these conceptions and ours, the little importance attributed to considerations of weight, the facility with which the interven- tion of "imponderable" substances are accepted, are nowhere perhaps so clearly evident as in the work of the man who, although a mediocre theorist, was probably the most prodigious "discoverer of facts" of that marvellous time. Scheele believes that heat is a composite of phlogiston and air of fire (oxygen). He believes both components to have weight; but he none the less takes for granted that they can give rise to an imponderable substance. Heat "united to a very little phlogiston" is transformed into light; but surcharged with a greater quantity of the same phlogiston, it becomes inflammable air—that is, hydrogen.(60) One can still perceive, in Lavoisier himself, traces of analogous conceptions. Thus he regards gas, and especially oxygen, as resulting from a combination of a ponderable matter with an imponderable fluid, caloric. And this is not simply an image. Berthelot properly observed that Lavoisier really considered heat as a material element, constitutive of gases, and that the conception he had of these latter was confused in his mind, by a series of hypothetical intermediaries, with that of imponderable fluids.(61) Thus in the enumeration of simple substances light and caloric are cited side by side with oxygen and nitrogen,(62) so that combustion appears as a real substitution of caloric.(63)

The definite re-establishment of the principle of conservation of matter may be dated from Lavoisier's memoir on *Changement de l'eau en terre*, which appeared in the *Mémoirs de l'Académie* of 1770, really published only in 1773.(64) To be sure, the principle is nowhere stated. But Lavoisier applies it implicitly, searching in the first place for the relation of weights, using as unanswerable arguments the considerations which he draws from them. Lavoisier proposes to verify the affirmation of several chemists of the eighteenth century, according to which water in boiling changes to earth; they gave as a proof that water boiled for a long time in a glass vessel left in evaporation a residuum of earth. For one hundred days Lavoisier had water boiled in an apparatus called a *pelican*, where the product of distillation returned into the vessel. He procured an extremely precise balance, the limit of whose errors he had carefully noted; he surrounded his experiment with various precautions of a nature to guarantee the exclusion of all foreign matter. He weighed the empty vessel, and reweighed it filled with water; he also reweighed the whole after the experiment, and he stated that the weight was almost exactly the same; from which there was a first conclusion—to wit, that in this case there was no question of the fire passing through the glass and combining with the water.(65) He emptied the apparatus and noted the diminution of weight. He collected the residuum, which the water had deposited during the operation, and joined to it what he obtained by the evaporation of the water: the two together were just about equal to the loss of weight of the pelican. But the divergence this time was much greater than the limit of the errors of his balance. Indeed, the pelican had only lost 17·4 grains, whereas the two residua together weighed 20·4. Lavoisier, very justly, attributed the error to the fact that the water had attacked not only the matter of the pelican, but also that of the other receptacles with which it was in contact, and he concluded that the earthy deposits came really from these vessels. Because of the slender quantity of the deposit he could not submit it to many experiments. Yet he performed one which did not fail to trouble him. The earth obtained was not fusible, as was the glass at that temperature. "I admit that this last circumstance would form a rather strong objection to what I have reported in this memoir, if it were possible to argue against facts."

Grimaux notes as a curious coincidence that Scheele, preoccupied with the same problem, arrived at the same result by an entirely different way: analysing the earthy residuum, he found in it silica, potassium, and lime—substances which enter into the composition of glass—and from this he concluded that these substances came from the vessel.(66) There is no doubt that to their contemporaries Scheele's demonstration was much more convincing than that of Lavoisier. Scheele used methods really belonging to chemistry, whereas those of Lavoisier seemed borrowed from a foreign domain.

In the *Opuscules physiques et chimiques*, which appeared in 1774,(67) Lavoisier, still employing the balance, decided between the two rival theories of Black and Meyer. According to the former, limestone, in being transformed into lime, lost a component (which to-day we call carbonic acid) ; according to the latter, on the contrary, it acquired an element designated as *acidum pingue*, which came from the fire. Lavoisier showed that calcareous earth loses in calcination a part of its weight, which it recovers if it is again transformed into ordinary lime.(68)

The same work contains the beginning of his immortal studies on combustion. Lavoisier, who at that time did not know of the existence of oxygen, discovered later by Priestley, remarked that in calcining pewter and lead in a closed vessel by means of a lens these metals increased in weight; that was an ancient experiment, as we know. But Lavoisier discovered that it was the same thing for sulphur and phosphorus, and, what is more important, he proved that the volume of air underwent a diminution of about a fifth, and that the weight of the vanished air was about identical to the increase of that of the burned substance. Moreover, since he weighed the vessel before and after the operation, and found the weight almost identical (except for a very slight increase which he justly attributed to the deposit which the fire had left on the outside), the hypothesis of the intervention of elementary fire was eliminated and the increase of the weight could have only come from the air.

His contemporaries felt, indeed, that there was something new in these considerations of quantity. The commissioners from the Academy (Trudaine, Macquer, Leroy, and Cadet) said in their report: "We see that M. Lavoisier has submitted all the results to measurement, to calculation, and to the balance, a rigorous method which happily for the advancement of chemistry is becoming indispensable in the practice of that science."(69)

The new conceptions triumphed but slowly. Resistance did not cease even after the composition of water had become known and Lavoisier had been able to establish a theory embracing all the phenomena which we now include under the name of "phenomena of oxidation." Neither Scheele, nor Priestley, nor Cavendish ever adhered to the new ideas. In studying these polemics one finds that there is, so to speak, no question of the principle of conservation of matter. But it is certain that this principle was at stake. Some emphasized the arguments of quantity, implicitly affirming that all other considerations should give way before them; others put in the first rank arguments based upon quality, which was to deny to the principle its dominant position, and, consequently, to deny its very essence. The final triumph of Lavoisier's theory was, at the same time, the victory of the principle of conservation of matter.

Is this principle of empirical origin? This has often been affirmed, and J. S. Mill especially formulated this thesis with much clearness. According to him, the conservation of matter is suggested to us from the very beginning, so to speak, of our observations by a great number of concordant phenomena, whereas others, on the contrary, seem to contradict it. The hypothesis was formulated that this principle was, not partially, but entirely, true, and as such it was verified afterwards. The verification having succeeded, the principle was established, exactly as any other experimental law.(70)

Littré has expressed himself in an analogous manner. "The essential axiom of materialism is the eternity of matter—to wit, that it has had no origin and that it will have no end. We know that this has not always been the opinion of philosophers, and that formerly the creation and destruction of substances was believed in. And, indeed, how did we come to this axiom which now has an irresistible authority over our minds? By experience, *a posteriori.*"(71)

The history of the principle, as we have just sketched it, suffices, it seems, to establish that this theory is far removed from reality. What are the experiments upon which the ancient atomists relied in stating the principle? It would be most embarrassing to say. They were satisfied to affirm that all matter was necessarily heavy, but that was a thesis which of itself needed experimental proof. That proof was impossible to furnish at that time, and nothing certainly indicated at the moment when the *De Rerum Natura* was written that the Aristotelian theory of the absolute lightness of certain bodies was inexact. Can Jean Rey's two very imperfect experiments be taken as proofs? It is sufficient to peruse the *Essays* to convince oneself that nothing was farther from the author's thought than to present them as such. The principle seemed to him established prior to any experiment, and he used it afterwards to explain particular phenomena; at no moment did he indicate that the success of this operation could be considered as a confirmation of the principle, which evidently, in his opinion, had no need of it. Lavoisier, we have seen, at first applied the principle without formulating it. In his later writings we find it sometimes stated with much clearness—indeed, as is everything which comes from that admirable mind, perfect in lucidity and precision. Thus, in the *Traité élémentaire de chimie*, he remarks in passing that "no substance in an experiment can furnish anything beyond the totality of its weight," and that "the determination of the weight of substances and products before or after experiments" is "the basis of all that is most useful and exact in chemistry." Sometimes he puts it more emphatically by declaring that "nothing is created in the operations of art or in those of nature," and that "one can lay down as a principle that in every operation there is an equal quantity of matter before and after the operation."(72) But at no moment does he indicate that that statement need be proved. Does this mean that at that epoch the demonstration had become useless, since it resulted implicitly from a quantity of known facts? Such was assuredly not the opinion of contemporaries, even the most illustrious, as exemplified in the case of Scheele. One might still suppose that Lavoisier made use of the principle as a sort of provisional hypothesis, "a working hypothesis," waiting to confirm or to refute that supposition in the course of his experiments. But it is enough to peruse his works to be convinced that this is not so; that, like the ancients and like Jean Rey, he applied it in all certainty, not doubting for a single moment that experience would confirm it; that every anomaly must only be apparent and must find its explanation. Sometimes he happens, in the course of a series of experiments, to weigh directly a substance whose weight he had already determined by an indirect method. He counts this verification useful, for "it is never permissible in physics to assume what can be determined by direct experiments." But he indicates at the same time that the conclusion, according to which the weight of the body in question must be equal to the sum of the weights of its components, appears to him as "evident and was easy to foresee *a priori*."(73) One cannot even affirm that the definite triumph of the principle was due to very searching experiments. Let us take a later work of Lavoisier, one of the most justly celebrated, which bears the title *Expériences sur la respiration des animaux*, etc.(74) During twelve days he heated 4 ounces of mercury in a vessel containing 50 cubic inches of ordinary air. At the end of the time he noticed that about a sixth of the air had disappeared, whereas there had formed 45 grains of mercury precipitate *per se*, or calx of mercury. Having carefully collected them, he put them into a little glass retort of which the curved neck penetrated into a receiver filled with water, and proceeded to the reduction. He stated that he found in this operation "about the same quantity of air which had been absorbed during the calcination—that is, about 8 to 9 cubic inches"—and that in adding this air (which was what he later called oxygen —he qualified it as "eminently respirable" air) to that which had been "vitiated by the calcination of the mercury," he re-established the latter "almost exactly in the state where it was before the calcination—that is, in the state of ordinary air." He concluded that this is "the most complete kind of proof at which one can arrive in chemistry, the decomposition of air and its recomposition." It is evident, however, by his very expressions (*nearly, almost exactly*), that he only sought, from a quantitative point of view, for an entirely approximative agreement. There is no doubt that had he noticed a slight departure from the principle of the conservation of weights, he would not have hesitated to formulate auxiliary hypotheses, like those of the action on accessory vessels or of the deposit formed by the carbon fire of his previous studies. The basis of his thought is, like that of Jean Rey's, that if we admit the principle the experiments in question do not expressly contradict it.

What is the situation to-day in regard to this question? Since the time of Lavoisier the balance has become the chosen instrument of the chemist; it may be said—this, for example, is Ostwald's opinion (75)—that in a certain sense every quantitative analysis accomplished by a chemist constitutes a verification of the conservation of matter. Yet we must not try to prove too much. Generally these analyses agree but *grosso modo;* it is rare in a somewhat complicated series of operations not to observe deviations too great to be attributed to measuring instruments, as Ostwald is obliged to admit.(76) The causes of error are numerous and difficult to avoid. One notices it if one examines the studies of the highest scientific order, which have helped to determine the atomic weights of the elements. We know what a truly stupendous amount of effort Stas spent to obtain knowledge of the equivalent of silver, the basis of all later determinations; but it has since been recognized that the results of Stas were marred by error, and it would be temerity to affirm that that rectification must be the last. For other elements, even the widest and best known, the determinations are still often quite uncertain, as one can easily be convinced by the studies of the commissions recently formed for the precise purpose of mastering these data and of reaching an agreement.(77) Nor must it be forgotten that quantitative analysis rests in the last instance on these constants insufficiently known as yet. The chemist only very rarely isolates the constituents of a combination; he directs them into other combinations and determines their weight indirectly by calculations of which atomic weights are the basis. The precision of his results in the most favourable case cannot surpass that of these fundamental data.

Where an effort has been made to verify directly and with precision the conservation of weight in chemical phenomena, it has not always been successful in obtaining results absolutely confirming this principle. It is well known that anomalies have been noticed quite recently by Landolt.(78) The results of the German chemist, although sometimes questioned,(79) seem to have been received in general with but little scepticism by the scientific world.(80)

It follows from the data which we have just briefly summarized that even at the present moment the certainty with which the principle of the conservation of matter appears invested exceeds the certainty permitted by the experiments which are supposed to serve as its basis. Thus the theory of John Stuart Mill and of Littré is adaptable neither to the genesis of the principle in history nor to its real place in contemporary science. The principle of the conservation of matter, as Maxwell saw, must "rest on some deeper foundation than the experiments which suggested it to our minds."(81)

Is this principle then *a priori*? This seems to be the most widely diffused opinion in our time among scientists and philosophers, an opinion sometimes clearly stated, sometimes implicitly affirmed. Moreover, contrary to what happened in the case of inertia, we shall not have to search long for the basis of this opinion; all those who have endeavoured to demonstrate by an *a priori* method the conservation of matter have brought directly into play the principle of causality to such a point that, as we have seen at the beginning of the

chapter, the very expressions of the two principles are sometimes confused. Yet this difference in the way of treating
inertia and constancy of matter is comprehensible. Velocity is
a derived and very abstract concept, whereas matter is a
common-sense notion which is found at the basis of all
experience.

Kant concerned himself with this question repeatedly. It is
even incidently mentioned in *The Critique of Pure Reason*. In
elucidating the concept of substance, Kant, in a rather curious
fashion, cites almost textually (but without indicating its source)
the passage from the Demonax of Lucian, thus summarily
attaching weight to substance.(82) He explained himself more
in detail in the *Metaphysische Anfangsgründe der Naturwissenschaft*.
There he formulates "his first theorem of mechanics" in these
terms: "Through all the modifications of material nature the
quantity of matter remains in total the same, without increase
and without diminution." In the "demonstration" of this
theorem, Kant makes use of the principle which he borrows
from "general metaphysics," which states that in all the modifications of nature substance is neither created nor lost. He
establishes, then, that, for matter, substance is the quantity,
matter being also defined as "that which is mobile in space"
(*das Bewegliche im Raume*).(83) In the treatise *Vom Uebergange
von den metaphysischen Anfangsgründen der Naturwissenschaft zur
Physik* we see how Kant means to pass from that notion
to that of weight. The transition is made with the help of
the intermediary concept of "matter, in so far as it is endowed
with motive power";(84) this is the physicists' concept of
mass at least under its active aspect. Kant immediately joins
to it that of weight and affirms that an "absolutely imponderable matter would be an immaterial matter—that is, a self-
contradictory concept."(85) This sudden transition is explained
by the fact that, for Kant, attraction in the inverse proportion
to the square of the distance, and consequently gravitation in
its most general conception, is an integral part of the concept
of matter.(86) On the whole, we see that it is a completely
a priori demonstration. It is just to observe that Kant seems to
have felt some scruples in that which concerns the transition
between mass and weight. In the *Metaphysische Anfangsgründe*
he only deduces the law of attraction with certain reservations,

as "a construction perhaps possible."(87) But the passages of his later work which we have just cited prove that his convictions had grown stronger at a later time.(88)

Schopenhauer, often cited on this question,(89) merely follows Kant; he too deduces the conservation of matter from the persistence of substance, but with less clearness than his predecessor, being content to affirm that substance is only a synonym for matter.(90) He recognizes, however, that gravity is an "occult quality," but, according to him, such also are all the fundamental forces which constitute matter and the persistency of which is guaranteed by causality.(91) Whewell also believes that he can directly deduce the conservation of weight from the principle of causality—indeed, he confuses mass and weight, and this last concept for him is an integral part of that of substance.(92)

Herbert Spencer has expressed himself with much force in the same sense: "Our inability to conceive Matter becoming non-existent is immediately consequent on the very nature of thought. . . . The annihilation of Matter is unthinkable for the same reason that the creation of Matter is unthinkable, and its indestructibility thus becomes an *a priori* cognition of the highest order, not one that results from a long-continued registry of experiences gradually organized into an irreversible mode of thought, but one that is given in the form of all experiences whatever." Evidently Spencer, in writing these lines, was thinking not of mass and weight but of causality and substance; yet the context clearly indicates that he intended to establish thus the principle of conservation of matter in the sense attributed to it by modern science. He was thus behind Kant, who had indicated the necessity of a double transition between substance, mass, and weight. On the other hand, it is curious to notice that Spencer, who wrote at a time much farther removed from that at which the principle was definitely established (Kant's *Metaphysische Anfangsgründe* appeared at a moment when the polemics about the theories of Lavoisier were not yet completely stilled), saw more clearly the difficulty which that assumption involved from the historical point of view. "Doubtless it will be considered strange that a truth only in modern times accepted as unquestionable, and then only by men of science, should be classed as an *a priori* truth, not only of equal certainty with those commonly so classed, but of even higher certainty. To set down as a proposition which cannot be thought, one which mankind once universally professed to think, and which the great majority profess to think even now, seems absurd. The explanation is, that in this, as in countless other cases, men have supposed themselves to think what they did not think."(93)

We have already indicated in regard to inertia the objections which every assumption of this kind encounters. Indeed, the conservation of matter has never been called absurd, as the persistence of rectilinear motion was by Aristotle. But generations of scientists and philosophers have advanced opinions clearly implying the negation of the principle. Can one say that the idea had never been suggested to them? It is in itself of great simplicity and is so directly deducible from the principle of causality that it occurs, so to speak, immediately to our minds. We have seen, moreover, that at least at two different times it appeared in the history of science to disappear afterwards. The *De Rerum Natura* was much read after the Renaissance, and it would be strange if no one had noticed in it the conception of the conservation of matter; and it is just as strange that Jean Rey's book had made so little impression if we assume that the idea which constitutes its basis was really *a priori*.

The enigma disappears if we consider what really is the *a priori* demonstration of the principle. It is entirely based on causality. Now what we call causality is only a tendency, the tendency to maintain the identity of certain things in time. At most one may say that the causal tendency generates in us the hope that these things are such that we can without too great violence consider them essential. But, as we have seen, this inclination is sufficiently strong to conquer if need be all the resistance which our mind could offer in this regard, to the point of transforming into something immutable, into substance, a derived and abstract concept.

At the basis of the principle of conservation of matter there are three distinct notions: matter, weight, mass. Matter is a common-sense notion, a complex one, which synthetizes an infinite number of properties. It is manifestly contrary even to the most superficial experience to suppose the conservation of *all* these properties. Therefore, in affirming the conservation of matter, one only postulates the persistence of *certain* properties; hence this affirmation cannot interest science as long as one does not state at the same time precisely what must be conserved. In our history of the principle we thought it necessary to pass over in silence statements of this kind, such as that of Locke.(94)

Yet we saw that, among phenomena of matter, those of a certain class appeared to us, because of the causal tendency, to enjoy a sort of privilege: these are the phenomena of displacement which we conceive of as being simple and fundamental. Of all the properties of matter the most important will therefore be the property of being the cause of displacement of some other matter: this will be the true criterion of materiality. Thus, Lucretius, in order to show that air is real matter, celebrates in verses of imperishable beauty the destructive action of the tempest.(95) This action which substances exert upon one another is capable of being measured; we call mass the coefficient resulting from these measurements, which we can reduce to an arbitrary unit. These coefficients, moreover, can be added to one another; mass is, as one says, an additive property; it seems quite natural to us that mass exercises an action which is the sum of those which would have been exercised by its parts, and experience confirms this manner of thinking. Mass appears to us then as measuring the quantity of matter; it is under this name that Descartes introduced it in the first place, and since then this notion has been currently used. We find it in Newton, in Laplace, in Poisson. To be sure, as A. Gautier (96) has set forth, matter can be measured according to still other properties, for example, by its thermal or electric capacity, and the measures resulting from them would be very different. But if Mach, relying on analogous motives, means to reject the term quantity of matter as a synonym of mass,(97) it is because in virtue of his theory he disregards the theoretical superiority of mechanical considerations. It seems clear, on the contrary, that mass, which is the mechanical expression of matter, appears to be not only its measure, but one of its fundamental properties, perhaps its true substratum.

Thus this tendency of which we have spoken, and which makes us wish that persistent things were essential, here finds full satisfaction, and, doubtless, persistence on its side makes the notion of mass appear to our eyes as still more essential.

Let us observe, however, that this concept of mass, which now seems so important to us, was not grasped instinctively and immediately by our mind; it appeared to us rather as surrounded by a certain obscurity. We need only recall our memories of school to be convinced that it is so; in the manuals of elementary physics one generally takes account of this state of things, taking great care to let the distinction between mass and weight penetrate into the mind of the reader. An attentive and competent observer has remarked that the mind of his students was refractory, so to speak, to the notion of mass, to such a degree that he believed that he must choose a method of exposition in which this concept would not be treated as fundamental.(98) This explains why this concept was disengaged only very late and why the confusion between mass and weight, which was the very basis of the theory of the ancient atomists, could still be reproduced in the nineteenth century, not only in a metaphysician like Schopenhauer, but even in a thinker as informed about scientific things as Whewell. A curious proof of the facility with which these two notions are confused is furnished by the fact that legislation in different countries, intending evidently to define mass (since the constant of gravitation did not present any interest from this point of view), has most often defined weight.(99)

We can, we think, perceive the profound source of this difficulty. The action by which one kind of matter displaces another and which appears to us as fundamental remains at the same time irremediably obscure. We have seen that we cannot really comprehend the "why" either of action at a distance or of impact. In books on mechanics, mass is generally defined by making action at a distance intervene in a more or less direct manner.(100) It is certainly preferable to define it by impact, as Andrade (101) and Wulf (102) have done. Yet this definition has something difficult about it; we cannot predict exactly what will happen afterwards, because that will depend upon the elasticity of the bodies. Doubtless, it is better to leave indeterminate the nature of the action which the masses exercise upon one another and to be content to stipulate, as Mach has done, that if there is action, if bodies inter-communicate velocities or accelerations, this communication occurs in conformity with immutable coefficients called masses:(103) the indetermination here is neither accidental nor provisional; it is the manifestation of something profound and essential.

Contrary to what we have just stated for mass, weight is an immediate notion of common sense; but it is a purely empirical notion. All matter, of course, must act; but can it be affirmed that all matter must gravitate toward all other matter? In this respect it is enough to remember with what astonishment humanity learned through Newton's discoveries that a force analogous or identical to that which we call gravity on the earth acts among the celestial bodies. Even at the present hour gravitation seems to us an enigma for which we are seeking an explanation. Now, in view of this explanation, the equation $w = m\,g$, far from being necessary, assumes, on the contrary, all the appearances of a paradox. The proportionality of mass and weight constitutes, as de Freycinet says, "a surprise."(104) The weight really ought to depend upon the position of the bodies with respect to one another.(105) It is surprising that ten cubes, which balance a given weight, when laid on the pan of a balance, exert the same effect when we pile them on top of each other, and they form a screen for each other with respect to the earth, and it is very difficult to understand that the entire mass of the earth is absolutely permeable to the attraction of the sun, as the theory of tides demands. Gravitation seems, so to speak, to ignore the intermediary space and the obstacles which are there accumulated: here again we meet this antispatial aspect of the concept which has already struck us (p. 82).

The association of weight and mass appears to physicists as purely fortuitous and accidental.(106) So much so that Boussinesq (107), by a curious theory, which counts Ostwald amongst its partisans,(108) has tried to explain this association by a sort of evolution of our universe, an evolution which would have had as a consequence to remove all matter where that association was not present.

In imagining ether, physicists have been obliged to endow it with mass; it was indeed created to act, and ma s is the principle of mechanical action; but ether has no weight, it is imponderable by definition: moreover, we have seen that in the past also there had been recourse to fluids, imponderable yet acting—that is, endowed with mass. In speculating on the constitution of matter, physicists have often taken care not to separate ether and ponderable matter by an insuperable abyss. That, we shall see later, is a tendency inherent in the human mind, a tendency whose manifestations may be easily followed from the time of Descartes, whose different elements have the same origin, until Tait and Thomson, who constitute their atoms with the aid of ether rings. It cannot, therefore, be said that the idea according to which ponderable matter could resolve itself into something imponderable has ever really appeared inadmissible, and, from this point of view, the new theories, which are connected with the discovery of radioactive substances, have found the ground already prepared for them.

It is doubtless because they confused mass and weight that the ancient atomists had succeeded in conceiving of the conservation of weight of matter; and inversely, we have seen, the dissociation of the two concepts, wrought by Descartes, has certainly contributed in a great measure to prevent the contemporaries of Jean Rey from adhering to his doctrine. At the present moment, mass and weight are again associated; but this linkage is not logical, and any attempt to deduce *a priori* the principle of the conservation of weight would certainly be sterile.(109) The contrary illusion can only have its source in the causal tendency; and it is this same tendency, which in ancient atomists, in Jean Rey, probably in Lavoisier himself, and surely in his contemporaries, has contributed to the growth of the principle, permitting its formulation, without proof, as a self-evident truth, and assuring its domination.

Like everything else we desire mass to be constant; but we desire it more strongly because it is capable of appearing as the essence of matter. This explains why, in the electric theory of matter, where the concept of mass no longer occupies the same dominant position, its conservation has been disregarded. Indeed, according to Lorentz, mechanical masses are not constant but vary according to the same laws as the electro-dynamic masses, and these variations become perceptible if the bodies are endowed with velocities comparable to that of light.(110) The fact alone that a theory of this kind could arise and triumph would suffice, it seems, to show, in the absence of other proofs, that the conservation of mass cannot be considered as an *a priori* verity; and the aggregate of the considerations which we have brought out tends, we believe, to establish clearly that we have here to do with a plausible proposition, just like the principle of inertia.

NOTES

1. LUCRETIUS: *De rerum natura*, Book I, line 150 and ff.

2. *Ib.*, Book I, lines 486–487, 500.

3. *Ib.*, Book II, lines 185–186.

4. *Ib.*, Book I, lines 361–363.

5. LUCIANUS SAMOSATENSIS: *The Works of Lucian*, trans. Thomas Francklin. London, 1781, Vol. II, p. 70.

6. Cf. J. BERNAYS: *Lucian und die Kyniker*. Berlin, 1876, pp. 27, 43, 57, 95. Bernays doubts whether the treatise on Demonax is Lucian's, but attributes it to a contemporary of Demonax.

7. Cf. for example ARISTOTLE: *De Caelo*, Book I, Chap. VII, where it seems to be pointed out that the atomists clearly affirmed the universal weight of bodies. In what concerns atoms direct evidence from antiquity is somewhat contradictory. Yet after having discussed them, Mabilleau (*l.c.*, p. 211) comes to the conclusion that Democritus really attributes weight to them.

8. Cf., p. 179.

9. ARISTOTLE: *De Caelo*, trans. J. L. Stock. Oxford, 1922, Book IV, Chap. I.

10. *Ib.*, Book IV, Chap. II, § 7.

11. PLATO: *Timaeus*. *The Dialogues of Plato*, trans. Jowett. New York, 1892, § 33. ARISTOTLE: *De Caelo*, Book III, Chap. III, § 1. Cf. the exposition of the peripatetic doctrine in Galileo. *Massimi sistemi, giorn.* I.

12. According to certain more recent works, the domination of peripatetic philosophy in the Middle Ages was much less absolute than has been supposed until now. Picavet, especially, has attempted to prove in his *Esquisse d'une histoire générale et comparée des philosophies médiévales* (2nd ed., Paris, F. Alcan, 1907) that the real master of the philosophy of the Middle Ages was not Aristotle but Plotinus. This thesis, based upon a profound study of the texts has, however, had numerous critics (*ib.*, p. 110 and ff., note). Its adoption would not materially modify our exposition. Picavet points out all that Plotinus owes to Aristotle; Porphyry had already stated that, "the Metaphysics of Aristotle were entirely contained" in the work of the Neoplatonist (*ib.*, 49); in a word, it was Aristotle who gave him his logic and his science of the perceptible world (*ib.*, pp. 88, 113). Therefore, although Aristotle was more cited than read or studied during a great part of the Middle Ages (*ib.*, p. 143), it was from him, directly or indirectly, that the philosophy of that period was derived, at least in what concerns the study of the perceptible world (*ib.*, pp. 89–91, 177). But he is only imperfectly known especially through neoplatonic commentators; not

always being understood, he is often interpreted and enlarged upon too freely (*ib.*, p. 93). We shall find, in the course of our study, certain facts which lend their support to this view (cf. especially p. 325 and ff.).

13. KOPP: *Geschichte der Chemie*. Brunswick, 1845, Vol. III, p. 119. Kopp thinks it is a question of the augmentation of weight which lead and pewter undergo during oxidation. It would then be the same phenomenon which finally contributed so much to establish the conservation of weight, which would have served originally to demonstrate the contrary, because of the preconceived opinion that by oxidation the body lost something.

14. Id., *l.c.*, pp. 120, 126, 128. It is curious that Kopp himself has yielded to temptation and has explained in the modern sense (adding to the word *weight* the adjective *specific*) a passage from Albertus (*Die Alchemie in aelterer und neuerer Zeit*. Heidelberg, 1886, I, p. 17). It is enough to examine without prejudice the passage cited by him to be convinced that Albertus really meant to affirm an augmentation of weight.

15. JEAN REY, wishing to establish the principle of the conservation of weight, declares that he is going "from now on to give the lie to the erroneous maxim, which has existed since the birth of Philosophy, that elements changing mutually from one to the other lose or gain weight, in so far as in this change they become rarefied or condensed." (*Essays*, New Impression. Paris, 1896, p. 48.)

16. BACON: *Works*. London, 1837, Vol. I, p. 173 (*Sylva sylvarum*, § 789).

17. *Ib.*, Vol. II, p. 361 (*De augmentis scientiarum*, Book V, Chap. III).

18. Id., *Novum organon*, trans. Buchon. Paris, 1838, Book II, § 40; cf. *Historia densi et rari*. *Works*, Vol. II, p. 538.

19. Cf. ROSENBERGER: *Geschichte der Physik*, Vol. I, p. 107. This is evidently the experiment which is generally credited to the honour of Van Helmont and by which the latter meant to prove the transformation of water into earth.

20. WISLICENUS: *Die Chemie und das Problem der Materie*, Rectoratswechsel. Leipzig, October 31, 1893, p. 24.

21. Cf. concerning these transmutations, KOPP, *Geschichte*, Vol. II, pp. 176–177. Stahl is not the celebrated chemist but a homonym.

22. Cf. DUHEM: *Léonard*, I, p. 8; II, p. 203.

23. *Ib.*, II, p. 204.

24. *Ib.*, p. 233.

25. Cf. on this subject Appendix III.

26. DESCARTES: *Principia*, 2nd Part, Chap. XLVI and ff.

27. Id., *Le Monde*. *Œuvres*, Paris, 1909, Vol. XI, p. 21.

28. Id., *Principia*, 3rd Part, Chap. CXXI.

29. GORLAEUS: *Exercitationes philosophicae*, etc. Leyden, 1620, pp. 154, 332.

30. CARPENTARIUS: *Philosophia libera*. Oxford, 1622, p. 66.

31. GALILEO: *Alcuni scritti ineditti*, etc., ed. Favaro, *Bulletino di bibliografia*, etc., Vol. XVI. Rome, 1885, pp. 28, 53, 95.

32. DESCARTES: *Principia*, 2nd Part, Chap. XI.

33. JEAN REY: *Essays sur la recherche de la cause pour laquelle l'estain et le plomb augmentent de poids quand on les calcine*. Bazas. 1630; New Impression, Paris, 1896, p. 49.

34. It is to be noted that Rey understood well enough that not only the

dimunition but also the increase of the weight following a chemical operation was generally admitted (cf. earlier, p. 184, note 15).

35. Cf. our article on *Jean Rey*. *Revue Scientifique*, VII, 1884, p. 302.

36. *Essays*, pp. 100–129.

37. HOBBES: *Elements of Philosophy*, ed. Molesworth. London, 1835, p. 116.

38. LEIBNIZ: *Opera*, ed. Erdmann, p. 767.

39. Cf. Appendix I, pp. 449 and ff., and III, p. 465.

40. Cf. L. COUTURAT: *Sur le système de Leibniz d'après M. Cassirer*. *Revue de métaphysique*, Vol. XI, 1903, p. 89.

41. HUYGENS: *Discours de la cause de la pesanteur*, Leyden, 1690, p. 140: "I shall prove . . . that . . . the weight of bodies follows precisely the proportion of matter, which composes them."

42. NEWTON: *Principia*, trans. Motte, New York, 1848, Book III, Prop. VI, p. 394.

43. Cf. BRILLOUIN: *Recherches récentes sur diverses questions d'hydrodynamique*. Paris, 1891, p. 37.

44. Cf. KOPP: *Geschichte*, Vol. I, p. 281.

45. BOYLE: *Works*. London, 1744, Vol. III, *New Experiments to make Fire and Flame Ponderable*, etc., pp. 318, 342–352.

46. *Essai sur le phlogistique et sur la constitution des acides, traduit de l'anglais de M. Kirwan; avec des notes de* MM. DE MORVEAU, LAVOISIER, DE LA PLACE, MONGE, BERTHOLLET ET DE FOURCROY. Paris, 1788, p. 3.

47. CARPENTARIUS: *l.c.*, p. 73–74.

48. GALILEO: *l.c.* The writing published by Favaro belongs to Galileo's youth and seems to reflect opinions which at that moment were current in certain schools of Italy. One may see from the *De Motu* of Galileo (*Opere*, ed. Favaro, Florence, 1890, and ff, Vol. I, p. 252), which is also a scholastic treatise, that this affirmation of the universal weight of bodies is directly connected with the reaction against peripateticism.

49. BOYLE: *l.c.*, Vol. III, p. 717.

50. There will be found a good summary of the question as it appeared in the middle of the eighteenth century, in Musschenbroek, *Cours de Physique expérimentale*, trans. Sigaux de la Fond. Paris, 1769, Vol. II, p. 371.

51. BERKELEY: *Works*, ed. Fraser. Oxford, 1901, Vol. III. Siris, § 192; Siris appeared in 1744.

52. MUSSCHENBROEK: *l.c.*

53. DIDEROT: *Pensées sur l'interpretation de la nature*. *Œuvres*. Paris, 1875, Vol. II, p. 28.

54. KOPP: *l.c.*, Vol. III, p. 124.

55. *Ib.*, p. 127.

56. *Ib.*, p. 141.

57. *Ib.*, p. 141.

58. *Ib.*, Vol. I, p. 223.

59. Cf. BERTHELOT: *Lavoisier*, 2nd ed., Paris, 1902, pp. 41 and 122.

60. Id., *l.c.*, pp. 88 and 96.

61. *Ib.*, pp. 43, 97.

62. *Dictionnaire de chimie de l'encyclopédie méthodique* (by GUYTON DE MOR-VEAU), Vol. I, p. 638. Also in LAVOISIER's tables in the *Traité élémentaire de*

chimie (*Œuvres*, Vol. I, pp. 149, 152, 155, 157, etc.), heat appears amongst the elements, followed by oxygen, hydrogen, etc. Light is not cited, but in the text of the same treatise (p .141) the question is raised of its "great affinity with oxygen" and "of the fact that it combines with certain parts of plants and that to this combination is due the green colour and the diversity of the colours of flowers."

63. LAVOISIER: *l.c.*, p. 52. "This experiment proves, in an evident manner, that at a certain degree of temperature, oxygen has a greater affinity for phosphorus than for heat; that consequently phosphorus decomposes oxygen gas, that it takes possession of its basis and then heat becomes free." Cf. *ib.*, pp. 65, 78, 141.

64. Id., *Premier mémoire sur la nature de l'eau*, etc. Mem. Acad., 1770, p. 73, *Œuvres*, Vol. II, p. 1.

65. We have seen (p. 167) that such was at that time the most general explanation which chemists gave of the augmentation of the weight of calcinated metals. Lavoisier himself seems to adopt it in the memoir in question. "Physicists know, indeed, that the matter of the fire augments the weight of the bodies in which it is combined" (*l.c.*, p. 16). But it may be that the results of his experiments on water inspired him with doubts as to the value of this theory, and that is why this work belongs to the series of his great studies on oxidation.

66. GRIMAUX: *Lavoisier*. Paris, F. Alcan, 1899, p. 99.

67. LAVOISIER: *Œuvres*, Vol. I, p. 439.

68. It is to be noted that the loss of weight by calcination of lime, established by Black, did not prevent the development of Meyer's theory. Cf. later, p. 332.

69. LAVOISIER: *l.c.*, p. 663.

70. J. S. MILL: *A System of Logic*, etc., London, 1884, p. 163.

71. LITTRÉ: *La science au point de vue philosophique*, 3rd ed. Paris, 1873, p. 322.

72. LAVOISIER: *l.c.*, Vol. I, pp. 76, 101, 251.

73. Id., *l.c.*, pp. 52–53.

74. *Ib.*, Vol. II, p. 175 and ff.

75. OSTWALD: *Lehrbuch der allgemeinen Chemie*, 2nd ed., Leipzig, 1891–93, p. 2.

76. *Ib.*

77. Cf. in F. W. CLARKE: *Chemical News*, 86, 1902, the comparative table of atomic weights adopted by the German commission and the international commission. The variations of atomic weights stated by chemists have been more recently explained by the theory of *isotopes*. But there results from the existence of these latter that one cannot, as a matter of fact, make use of the ordinary reactions of the laboratory as a confirmation of the principle of the conservation of matter.

78. Cf. HEYDWEILLER: *Wiedemann's Annalen*, V, 1901, p. 394 and ff. LANDOLT has more recently published a series of very minute observations which seem to confirm his previous results (*Sitzungsberichte der Kgl. preuss. Akademie der Wissenschaften*, 1906, VIII). The discussion of the results of other observers will be found here (p. 3 and ff.).

79. Cf. Lo Surdo: *Il Nuovo Cimiento*, July 1904, p. 45.

80. Cf. Ostwald: *Vorlesungen ueber Naturphilosophie*. Leipzig, 1902, p. 283.

81. Maxwell: *Whewell's Writing and Correspondence. Scientific Papers*, Cambridge, 1890, Vol. II, p. 153.

82. Kant: *Kritik der reinen Vernunft*, ed. Rosenkranz und Schubert, Leipzig, 1838, pp. 156–159.

83. Id., *Metaphysische Anfangsgründe der Naturwissenschaft*, Leipzig, 1838, p. 404. Cf. *Premiers principes*, trans. Andler and Chavannes, p. 74.

84. Id., *Vom Uebergange von den metaphysischen Anfangsgründen der Naturwissenschaft zur Physik*, ed. A. Krause. Frankfort, 1888, p. 9.

85. *Ib.*, p. 6; cf. *ib.*, p. 159.

86. Kant: *Premiers principes*, etc., p. 153. "That which is mobile in space is given *a priori* as attraction and repulsion, for otherwise no space could be filled." From this Kant deduces that ponderability "belongs just as much to the metaphysics of nature as to physics, and consequently to the transition from the first to the second." Cf. *ib.*, p. 15, where this attraction is defined as being exerted in the inverse proportion of the square of the distance.

87. *Ib.*, p. 52. He affirms, however, the principle of attraction as *a priori* (pp. 41, 50).

88. Kant, in general, is less of a "dynamist" in the *Uebergang* than in the *Metaphysische Anfangsgründe;* thus he no longer attributes cohesion to the action of a force of attraction, but to that of the medium. Yet we feel that Rosenberger (*Geschichte*, Vol. III, pp. 41–42) is wrong in believing that he had succeeded in deducing the action of gravitation in the same way. On the contrary, from this point of view, his conviction seems to have become rather more absolute.

89. Cf., for example, Ostwald: *Vorlesungen ueber Naturphilosophie*. Leipzig, 1902, p. 283.

90. Schopenhauer: *Ueber die vierfache Wurzel des Satzes vom zureichenden Grunde. Werke*, ed. Frauenstaedt. Leipzig, 1877, Vol. I, pp. 43–44.

91. *Ib.*, Vol. II, p. 95.

92. Whewell: *The Philosophy of the Inductive Sciences*. London, 1840, p. 30. Cf. Maxwell, *Scientific Papers*, Vol. II, p. 531.

93. Spencer: *First Principles*, London, 1863, p. 241.

94. Cf. Reid: *On the Human Mind. Works*, ed. Hamilton. Edinburgh, 1846, p. 136.

95. Lucretius: *De rerum natura*, Book I, lines 278–298.

96. A. Gautier: *Les manifestations de la vie. Revue générale des sciences*, Vol. VIII, 1897, p. 291.

97. E. Mach: *Die Principien der Waermelehre*. Leipzig, 1896, p. 425.

98. Clementitch de Engelmayer: *Sur l'origine sensorielle des notions mécaniques. Revue philosophique*, 39, 1895, p. 517.

99. Cf. L. Poincaré: *La physique moderne*. Paris, s.d., pp. 33–34. Lord Kelvin: *Sur le Mouvement*, etc. *Congrès international de physique de 1900*, Vol. II, p. 21.

100. It is known that Newton defined mass by density. This definition is

certainly inadmissible, as Thomson and Tait have shown. Cf. H. Poincaré : *La science et l'hypothèse*, p. 120. Cf. also later, p. 388.

101. ANDRADE : *Les idées directrices de la mécanique.* *Revue philosophique*, Vol. XLVI, 1898, p. 402.

102. WULF : *Zur Mach'schen Massendefinition.* Wiedem, Annalen, Spl., 1899.

103. This also seems to be H. Poincaré's opinion. (*La science et l'hypothèse*, p. 127.) Duhem's definition (*L'évolution de la mécanique*, p. 227), which makes use of the notion of work, without stating clearly how it is to be applied to body, belongs, from this point of view, to the same order of ideas.

104. DE FREYCINET : *Sur les principes de la mécanique rationnelle.* Paris, 1902, p. 26.

105. Cf. MAXWELL : *Whewell's Writings and Correspondence.* *Scientific Papers*, Vol. II, p. 532.

106. According to the electric theory of matter, a variation of weight, following a chemical reaction, would not be in the least surprising. Cf. Rutherford, *l.c.*, p. 474. It is to be noticed that Sir J. Thomson believed that it was necessary to establish by experiment the proportionality of weight and mass for certain radio-active bodies.

107. C. E. GUILLAUME : *Revue générale des sciences*, Vol. VIII, 1897, p. 56.

108. OSTWALD : *Vorlesungen ueber Naturphilosophie.* Leipzig, 1902, pp. 180, 192.

109. Weight and mass are again associated in Einstein's theory of general relativity. But in examining this conception one may be convinced how considerable has been the effort necessary to effect this association and how little these arguments resemble those by the aid of which, to this day, one has attempted to deduce *a priori* the conservation of weight.

110. Cf. H. POINCARÉ : *L'état actuel et l'avenir de la physique mathématique.* *Revue des idées*, I, 1904, pp. 811–812 ; id., *La valeur de la science*, p. 196.

CHAPTER V

THE CONSERVATION OF ENERGY

THE most general formula for this principle can be stated in these terms: in every modification of an isolated system the total energy of the system conserves an invariable value.(1) If no account is taken of the condition of isolation, whose importance we shall see later, this formula resembles that of the conservation of matter. There is this difference that the concept of matter, which originates from common sense, is vast and without precision whereas that of energy, created *ad hoc* by science, seems to present all the desired precision. We shall see, however, in a later chapter that this is not absolutely so.

Energy is ordinarily defined as the capacity of producing an effect or of accomplishing work, to use Duhem's terms, from whom we have borrowed the formula of the principle. We shall stop provisionally at this definition, which is really applicable only to a particular form of energy (pp. 209, 218), but has certain advantages, amongst others the advantage of having great historical value, since it is in conformity with the conception of Leibniz, whose influence on the development of this chapter of physics was decisive. "Absolute force"(we know that this term for a long time designated what we call energy), says Leibniz in his *Essay de Dynamique*, "must be estimated according to the violent effect which it can produce."(2) A projectile moving with a certain velocity can, if it strikes an obstacle, produce a determined effect: we say that it possesses a certain energy. But this same cannon-ball, placed at a certain height above the earth, will be able, in falling, to act in an analogous way. We have the right therefore, from the point of view of consequences, to assimilate these two very different concepts, motion and position, and to form the concept of energy of position, as we have just formed the concept of energy of motion or kinetic energy. The energy of position is more commonly qualified as *potential:* we shall have occasion to return to the signification of this term. The sum of the two energies, composing the total energy of the system, must remain constant by virtue of the principle just formulated

The conservation of energy is the most recent of the three great principles mentioned by us, it was only definitely established about the middle of the nineteenth century. Yet its origin is more ancient. There can be no question of it in antiquity, since inertia itself, as we have seen, was then unknown. Only a few more or less obscure indications, relative to the movement of the arms of a lever and the effect of falling bodies, which we encounter in Aristotle,(3) can be reported here. But in Leonardo we already find important beginnings. He recognizes that in all machines the work of resistance equals that of power, and that what one gains in power one loses in time. The force exerted in bending the bow is as much as the *accidental weight* communicated to the arrow.(4) These views are more completely developed by Galileo; he seems to be more or less indirectly influenced by the notes of Leonardo which have remained in manuscript form. The great physicist clearly explains that one cannot, with the aid of machines, create work. On the other hand, according to Poincaré,(5) he does not say that work cannot be destroyed; it cannot therefore be pretended that he affirmed the conservation of energy for the machines in question. Yet in a particular case—to wit, in that which concerns the falling of heavy bodies, Galileo gave a formula which leads directly to this principle.

Descartes was the first to announce that something definite, a determined quantity, must be conserved throughout the modifications which the motion of bodies undergoes. This is the principle of the conservation of motion. It is well known that Descartes was completely deceived as to the expression of the quantity itself which remains constant; he supposed that it was equal to the product of mass by velocity, instead of the square of velocity as we now hold. This is what Leibniz called, rightly moreover, his "memorable error."(6) The merit of Descartes in this matter is none the less very great. It was in following ideas indicated by him that Huygens and Leibniz succeeded in establishing the principle of the conservation of *vis viva*.

This discovery is generally attributed to the latter of these great thinkers. But it seems that Huygens had stated it before him. Only he formulated it as if it were a proposition of pure geometry, and without recognizing its great importance. It was Leibniz who proclaimed it as a fundamental principle of mechanics. At least it is thus that Jean Bernoulli related the story, and he was almost a contemporary and in a favourable position to judge things.(7)

It should be noticed that Descartes as well as Leibniz held that the principles formulated by them applied to the totality of the phenomena of the universe. "God," said Descartes, "never changes his fashion of acting, and conserves the world in the same action with which he has created it. . . . And in order that he may still maintain them with the same action and the same laws which he made them observe in their creation, he must conserve now in them all the motion which he had given them from the beginning, with the property which he had given to this motion of not always remaining attached to the same parts of matter and of passing from one to the other, according to their different encounters."(8) Leibniz expressed himself with great clearness in the same sense. Let us add the following passage to those cited above, when speaking of the principle of causality (p. 29) : "I had maintained that *vires vivae* are conserved in the world. It is objected that two soft or non-elastic bodies colliding with each other lose their force. I reply that it is not so. It is true that the 'wholes' lose it in relation to their total motion, but the parts receive it, being agitated internally by the force of the collision. Thus this loss is only apparent. The forces are not destroyed but dissipated amongst the small parts. This is not losing them, but it is doing what those do who change large pieces of money into smaller ones."(9) Jean Bernoulli expounded the same ideas. Having formulated the law of the "conservation of the quantity of *vires vivae*," he adds : "To try to demonstrate this law would be to obscure it. Indeed, everyone regards this as an incontestable axiom, that an efficient cause cannot perish, either as a whole or in part, without producing an effect equal to its loss. The idea that we have of the *vis viva*, in so far as it exists in a moving body, is of something absolute, independent, and so positive that it would remain in the body even though the rest of the universe should have been annihilated. It is clear, therefore, that the *vis viva* of a body diminishing or increasing on encountering another body, the *vis viva* of that other body must in exchange be augmented or diminished by the same quantity ; the augmentation of the one being the immediate effect of the diminution of the other; and this necessarily implies the conservation of the whole quantity of *vires vivae*; therefore this quantity is absolutely unalterable by the impact of bodies."(10) Just like Leibniz, moreover, Jean Bernoulli affirmed that the loss of *vis viva* by the impact of imperfectly elastic bodies could only be apparent.(11)

These declarations were clearly understood in their general sense, as can be ascertained by the manner of thinking in the eighteenth century on the part of men who were not physicists by profession, such as de Haller (12) or Voltaire.(13)

It seems paradoxical at first, that these statements in which only mechanical expressions are involved and from which, furthermore, the concept of potential energy is absent can be as general in appearance as our formula for the conservation of energy. But, for Descartes, there existed in the world no other phenomena than mechanical phenomena; and Leibniz was well known to be a pure Cartesian on this point. Moreover, for Descartes as for Leibniz everything was mass and motion, there existed no action at a distance and consequently no potential energy; therefore the conservation of the energy of motion alone sufficed. And although he naturally supposed that heat was motion, Leibniz, in speaking of the dissipation of forces, certainly did not think of the transformation of mechanical energy into heat, but of purely mechanical, although indiscernible, motions of particles.

During the eighteenth century the concept of "heat-matter" prevailed little by little over that of "heat-motion." This was the result of Newtonian physics: the concept of heat-motion, as Duhem remarks,(14) was a survival of Cartesian physics. Especially after the work of Deluc, of Black, and of Wilke,(15) the triumph of the first of these theories seemed complete. Thereafter heat is treated as a real substance passing from one body to another without its quantity (which they had learned to measure) undergoing any modification, which if it ceases to manifest itself to our sensation, and if the thermometer does not disclose it, continues none the less to exist in a particular state. Black had called it the "latent" state, and this concept of latent heat—that is, heat not manifesting itself, but capable of manifesting itself under certain conditions— belongs evidently to the same family as that of potential energy employed by modern physics. Indeed, energy which has been motion and which is capable of becoming motion again no longer manifests itself as motion so long as it remains *potential;* just as in the case of latent heat we are obliged to attribute to it a particular state. We shall see later on that Lazare Carnot designated as *force vive latente* what we call potential energy.(16)

The invention and rapid popularity of the steam engine in no way changed this situation: neither Watt nor his successors considered these phenomena from the point of view of the transformation of heat into mechanical motion.

Yet the ideas of Leibniz continued to bear fruit, and by a sort of slow and powerful undercurrent all the conceptions constituting our principle of conservation of energy were gradually developed.

Toward the end of the eighteenth century Lavoisier and Laplace,(17) completing the work of Leibniz, related the production of heat by friction to the conception of heat-motion, and defined heat as the sum of the products of the mass of each molecule by the square of its velocity—that is, the "force which results from insensible motions of the molecules of a body."

In the beginning of the nineteenth century Rumford, and a little later, Humphry Davy,(18) with the aid of direct experiments which received great publicity, demonstrated the transformation of motion into heat. Fresnel, in a popular work, clearly affirms that "the quantity of *vires vivae* which disappears as light is reproduced in heat."(19)

On the other hand, Lazare Carnot formulates the concept of latent *vis viva*, which Poncelet renders precise by calling it *available work*,(21) a concept identical with that which we designate at present as *potential energy*.

And now the birth of the principle is entirely prepared for. In 1839 an engineer, Séguin, in a work on the construction of railroads, formulates, one might almost say in passing, ideas which are very near to it.(22)

Before Séguin the powerful mind of Sadi Carnot had clearly conceived the principle in all its extent; he calculated a number for the mechanical equivalent of heat. But these discoveries, because of the premature death of the great theorist, remained buried in his manuscript notes, which were only published in 1871.(23)

In spite of everything, the theory of heat-matter remained dominant. Sadi Carnot, in his celebrated work which appeared in 1824, had based his researches on that conception. "The production of motive power in steam machines is due, not to a real consumption of caloric, but to its transfer from a hot body to a cold body."(24)

The study of J. R. Mayer,(25) published in 1842, is the first publication on the principle of the conservation of energy in its present sense. The studies of Colding are almost contemporary with those of Mayer, but they were published a little later.(26) The attention of the scientific world was attracted only by the experimental researches of Joule, whose first publication dates from 1843.(27) The work of Helmholtz,(28) published in 1847, which gave a complete mechanical interpretation of the principle, contributed toward assuring its triumph.

Is the conservation of energy an empirical law? Physicists have sometimes found it convenient to treat it as such; but H. Poincaré, while doing this, took care to warn the reader that this conception is not in conformity with historic truth.(29) In fact, it is then necessary, neglecting completely the development which we have just attempted to trace, to take Joule's experiments as a point of departure, considering them not as a verification of the principle (which, in fact, they were), but as an experimental demonstration. But Joule's (30) results lend themselves far less to a process of this kind than do those of Lavoisier for the conservation of matter. The numbers of the English physicist vary within extraordinarily large limits; the average at which he arrives is 838 foot-pounds (for the quantity of heat capable of increasing the temperature of a pound of water by 1° F, which is about equivalent to 460 kilogrammeters to 1° C.); but the different experiments from which this average is drawn furnish results varying from 742 to 1,040 foot-pounds (or from 407 to 561 kilogrammeters)—that is, by more than a third of the lowest value—and he even notes an experiment which gives 587 lb. (322 kilogrammeters) without seeing in it any source of particularly grave experimental errors. It is only in the postscript of this work that Joule tells of a series of experiments yielding as a result 770 foot-pounds (423 kilogrammeters), which approximates our present estimations. Moreover, if one considers that at this same moment Sadi Carnot (31) and J. R. Mayer (32) had already, each one for himself, calculated the equivalent of heat and had arrived at the figures of 370 and of 365 kilogrammeters (which is more than an eighth lower than Joule's value), it becomes really difficult to suppose that a conscientious scientist, relying solely on experimental data, could have been able to arrive at the conclusion that the equivalent must constitute, under all conditions, an invariable datum.

Since the time of Mayer and Joule a considerable number of careful researches have been made on this important question. The results have not always been in agreement, as Lippmann remarks.(33) To be sure, physicists are able to calculate an average value, and the deviations are sufficiently reduced so that they can be charged to experimental errors. It is nevertheless true that this explanation is necessary; which means that the immediate results of research do not lead directly to the establishment of the invariability of the equivalent.

It should be noted that all the data just mentioned are derived from researches especially undertaken for the sake of determining the relation in question and carried out under certain very special conditions, considered most favourable from the point of view of the technique of these experiments, such as, for example, average temperatures, etc. We cannot invoke the results of daily experiences, as we did for the conservation of matter. Hirn tried to deduce the equivalent with the aid of a great number of observations on steam machines; he succeeded in obtaining figures varying between 300 and 400,(34) and these results have been generally considered remarkable, in view of the difficulties of the problem.

These difficulties arise from a fundamental physical fact; energy much more than matter tends to dissipate itself, and it is extremely difficult to prevent this dispersion. Matter, since we have learned to confine gases, is always and everywhere easily retained. It is not the same with heat. We know of no substance which is completely impermeable to its action, and even empty space is but an imperfect isolator. This explains why in the formula of the principle of the conservation of energy we are obliged to specify the isolation of the system. We tacitly make the same reservation for the conservation of matter; we do not state it very often, because it is readily understood.(35) We know, however, since the work of Bunsen and Berthelot, that solids are not entirely impermeable to gases;(36) and we have learned from Warburg and Guillaume (37) that under certain conditions glass can be traversed by sodium or lithium. We have only to imagine this permeability considerably increased to be obliged to formulate analogous reservations.(38)

What really would be a valid experimental demonstration of the conservation of energy? We should need a considerable series of experiments showing that through all kinds of change, under the most varied conditions, different forms of energy transform themselves into one another according to equivalents remaining constant within the limits of error of measuring instruments. It seems to be a demonstration of this kind that Helmholtz was thinking of in 1847 when, after having furnished the double deduction, which we shall mention later on, he ended by declaring that "the complete confirmation of the law must be considered as one of the principal tasks which physics will have to accomplish in the years to come."(39)

Even to-day the task thus understood cannot be accomplished. It is not even very certain that if we were able to measure very exactly all the energy known to us, as present in any phenomenon, we should find it really constant, and this for the quite simple reason that we are in no way sure of knowing all the forms of energy. To affirm the contrary it would be necessary to establish between the known forms a relation which would make it evident that they were the only forms. But we do not know of any relation of this kind, or rather those which we do know seem to indicate that there must be great gaps in our knowledge. Here is a pencil of solar rays—that is, of all kinds of energy which come to us from the sun through space or the semi-material medium whose existence we are forced to suppose. We make these rays pass through a prism; they are dispersed and form the visible spectrum. But this pencil, we know, also contains vibrations of greater and less frequency than that of the luminous rays. On this side of the red rays there are heat rays; and on the other side of the violet rays, the ultra-violet, whose presence is indicated by chemical action, phosphorescent substances, etc. Can we affirm that there are no vibrations in the solar rays beyond those which we have just indicated? This is hardly even probable. In studying the explored parts of the spectrum, as arranged, for instance, by W. E. Guillaume,(40) one finds that these parts are arbitrarily distributed. One arrives at an analogous conclusion in studying the relations between electricity and the rays of the spectrum. Between the most rapid electric oscillations and the longest waves of the spectrum, there remains an interval equal to that which separates the most distant ultra-violet and infra-red rays.(41).

Even supposing these intervals entirely filled, who would dare to affirm that there can be no manifestations of energy beyond these limits? We are entirely ignorant of the nature of the fundamental phenomenon which at present we suppose to be electric, and which we assimilate to an undulation. One cannot, therefore, maintain a priori that ether is incapable of developing energy under an entirely different form.

As a matter of fact, our knowledge of forms of energy is due to purely accidental causes, to the circumstance that we possess organs of sense for the perception of certain amongst them, and that for others we have discovered, more or less fortuitously, phenomena which make them apparent, such as the action of the ultra-violet rays upon certain chemical substances. Thus, as Le Bon has stated, for twenty-five years one used Crookes's tubes and was in ignorance of the Röntgen rays. We should still be ignorant of them were it not for photographic plates and phosphorescence.(42) It must be recalled how very recent is the discovery of electricity. It certainly appears to us to-day as one of the fundamental forms of energy, even the fundamental form. But it dates from the works of Gilbert, scarcely three centuries ago. The only electric experiment known to antiquity and the Middle Ages, rubbing amber, seemed to be a mere amusement; to connect it with the spectacular phenomenon of lightning would have seemed the strangest of paradoxes. Would it not be temerity to affirm that the future reserves no surprises of this kind for us? The latest discoveries in this domain, the Hertzian waves, the Röntgen rays, and the most celebrated of all, the discovery of the radio-active substances, date only from yesterday. We can thus legitimately ask whether in many transformations there do not arise forms of energy which have remained unsuspected to this day; it is certain that even in supposing the constancy of E, experimental results obtained thus far, which, we have seen, vary between relatively extensive limits, do not permit the affirmation that some of the transformations which we believe that we thoroughly know will not give us material for discoveries of this nature in the future.

Thus, just as in the case of the principle of the conservation of matter, so here, but in a far superior degree, our conviction grows that the certainty with which the principle of the conservation of energy appears invested far exceeds what the experimental data would seem to admit. This "privileged position" of the principle has very justly impressed H. Poincaré.(43) Another master of contemporary physics, Lippmann, summarizing the researches upon the mechanical equivalent of heat, expresses himself in these ᐧterms: "The deviations between the different values obtained for E are always small enough to be laid to the account of experimental errors. An important consequence flows, nevertheless, from the totality of determinations made of E—that is, its invariability; some uncertainty may remain in the mind about the true value of this number, but no doubt is possible about the absolute exactitude of the principle of equivalence."(44) It is evident that if experiments cannot satisfy us about the true value of the number, they can still less prove to us that it is really invariable. Therefore the conviction of the absolute exactitude of the principle must come from another source; we saw that its history concurs in this demonstration.

Just as in the case of the conservation of matter, the *a priori* character of the conservation of energy was proclaimed by philosophers almost the day after the discovery of this principle. Herbert Spencer, under the rather hazy form of "the persistence of force," combined with "continuity of motion," assigns to it an axiomatic character, just as in the case of inertia and conservation of matter.(45) Stallo states also that conservation of energy, "though but recently formulated as a distinct scientific principle, is now universally regarded as of equal evidence and axiomatic dignity" to that of the indestructibility of matter. Stallo seems to attach this opinion to mechanical theories; but since he does not refute it later, contrary to what he does for these theories in general, one is led to conclude that he approves of it.(46) Lasswitz believes that he is able to deduce *a priori*, by a rather indirect method, either conservation of energy itself,(47) or at least that of some function of motion.(48) Spir attempts to deduce directly conservation of energy from the necessity of a transmission of motion.(49)

Of course, it is causal identity which we shall find at the bottom of all these deductions. If Spencer declares it inconceivable that motion and force can be created or destroyed, it is because, in his imagination, he has transformed them into entities, or substances. It is for the same reason, doubtless, that Stallo believes that the constancy of mass and that of energy will be able to preserve their "axiomatic dignity," whereas mechanism, upon which these principles seem to rest, will be invalidated. Lasswitz's demonstration is also tantamount to affirming *a priori* that *something* must persist in the transformation of motion, which is, we have seen, the most exact form of the causal principle.

If from this point of view we examine more closely the principal writings already enumerated in connection with the history of the principle, we shall be assured in the same way that everywhere causality constitutes the real motive power. Descartes, we saw, deduced his principle of conservation of motion directly from "the immutability of God"—that is, from the identity of the universe in time; and it is in regard to the conservation of *vires vivae* that Leibniz gives precisely to the principle of causality the rigorous formula which we made use of in our first chapter. Indeed, one could not find a clearer or more striking example of the use of the notion of identity in time. With his marvellous vigour of intellect and penetration, Leibniz clearly saw what he was doing and went straight to the goal. Cause and effect must be identical, interchangeable. But that is only possible if the product of the mass by the square of the velocity remains constant. Therefore it is this very expression which is maintained throughout the changing phenomena and which is the true measure of the force.

J. R. Mayer expresses himself thus at the very beginning of

his celebrated work of 1842: "Forces are causes, and consequently it is reasonable to apply to them in full the principle: *causa aequat effectum.*"(50) He deduces from this that forces are "indestructible objects, changing (*wandelbar*), imponderable,"(51) and he again repeats: "We end our theses which are necessarily deduced from the principle *causa aequat effectum.*"(52) After which, with the aid of a single calculation, he tries to determine the equivalent; that is a proof that he was sincere in his deduction, for this calculation would have had no sense if Mayer had not reached, by another method, the conviction that E must be a true constant. We see that this argument applies also to Sadi Carnot, who appears equally to have sought to determine E with the aid of a single calculation, probably the same as that of Mayer.

Colding reasons as does Bernoulli: "Since forces are spiritual and immaterial beings, since they are entities which are only known to us by their empire over nature, these entities must be doubtless very superior to any other existing material thing; and since it is evident that it is by forces only that that wisdom expresses itself which we perceive and which we admire in nature, these powers must be in relation with that very spiritual, immaterial, and intellectual power which guides the progress of nature; but, if this be so, it is absolutely impossible to conceive that these forces should be anything mortal or perishable. Without any doubt, consequently, they must be regarded as imperishable."(53) Thus Colding estimates that it is enough to establish the great importance of the notion of force, to exalt, so to speak, the rank of this notion in order to deduce from it that force must be a *substance*, that it must be conserved. The somewhat theological form of the reasoning recalls that of Descartes' analogous deduction concerning inertia (p. 144).

At first sight Joule seems to proceed by induction. "Having proved that *heat* is *generated* by the magneto-electric machine . . . it becomes an object of great interest to inquire whether a constant ratio exists between this heat and the mechanical power gained or lost."(54) Nothing, it seems, is more correct from the point of view of the principles of *a posteriori* reasoning than to state the problem in this manner. Only, when once these experiments were instituted—since their results were, we saw, very divergent—Joule, instead of concluding that this relation was not constant but variable, made an average from all, and proclaimed it the real value of the aforesaid relation, thus proving that he was convinced in advance of its constancy.

Moreover, Joule took great care to indicate the sources of this conviction. In an article published a little later he says: "We might reason *a priori* that such absolute destruction of living force $\left(\dfrac{mv^2}{2}\right)$ cannot possibly take place, because it is manifestly absurd to suppose that the powers with which God has endowed matter can be destroyed any more than that they can be created by man's agency; but we are not left with this argument alone, decisive as it must be to every unprejudiced mind."[55] Mach remarks amusingly concerning this passage that Joule would doubtless not have consented to submit his affirmation concerning God to a religious synod.[56] But this is evidently only a sally (as Mach himself suggests); the God of whom Joule is speaking has nothing in common with theology: He is, like the God of Descartes and of Leibniz in many analogous passages, like the God of Colding in the extract just cited, a symbol of the general order of nature, and, in this particular case, of the essential immutability of things—that is, of the causal principle.

Helmholtz, in his study of 1847, invokes, as did his predecessors, the causal principle;[57] and ten years later, Faraday, in expounding his ideas on the conservation of energy, does not think for a single moment of treating it as an experimental law, but bases his conviction upon the equality of cause and effect.[58]

Besides these purely causal deductions which incontestably predominate, others are found where causality seems less directly called into play. They belong to two principal types: demonstration by central forces and demonstration drawn from the impossibility of perpetual motion. Both are found formulated in the work of Helmholtz in 1847. The first consists in supposing that all phenomena of motion are exclusively regulated by forces radiating from centres, whose action is produced along straight lines which join these centres two by two according to a law which only depends on the distance; conservation of energy can then be deduced by mathematical methods. We have discussed earlier (p. 75 f.) the legitimacy of this hypothesis; we saw that it did not agree with the reality of things. But for the moment let us set aside these objections. What is the assumption of bodies or of discrete particles exerting immutable forces in time? It is, we saw, a form of the mechanical hypothesis—that is, a purely causal conception, an image of the world created by our intellect, solely with the view of satisfying our tendency to conserve identity in time. At the basis of this demonstration there is therefore nothing more than identity between the antecedent and consequent, the cause and the effect, just as in Leibniz and Mayer.

The impossibility of perpetual motion was affirmed very early. Leonardo da Vinci makes use of this principle,(59) and so does Cardanus.(60) Galileo asserts that one cannot create such a motion with the aid of simple machines (p. 190). Yet he does not believe it to be an independent principle; he deduces it from the conditions of the functioning of these machines. A little later Stevinus, on the contrary, uses this impossibility, which he considers self-evident, to deduce rules for machines. Stevinus supposes an endless chain placed upon a triangle of unequal sides whose base is horizontal. The two parts of the chain, placed upon the inclined sides, must necessarily balance, for the part which hangs downward, being symmetrical, cannot exert any influence; and if one of the parts of the chain had the power of drawing the system to its side, since, after this motion the same situation would be reproduced, "this motion would have no end, which is absurd."(61) Leibniz employs the impossibility of perpetual motion to demonstrate the conservation of *vis viva*,(62) and Huygens, too, uses it.(63) Sadi Carnot also places it at the basis of the demonstration of his principle.(64) In 1839 Séguin, while formulating his anticipation of the principle of the conservation of energy, took the same impossibility as his point of departure.(65) Finally the complete demonstration was furnished by Helmholtz in 1847.

In order that the demonstration be valid, it is important, of course, to know exactly what attitude to take toward the statement which forms the basis of it. Is it an *a priori* truth or an empirical rule? For Leibniz it is a simple corollary from the causal principle: if perpetual motion were possible, the effect would be greater than the cause.(66) Huygens expresses himself with great caution; the impossibility for purely mechancial systems seems to him to be established, but he admits that for others "*physico-mechanice*, as in the employment of the magnet, there may be some hope."(67) Carnot also considers that perpetual motion is "proved impossible by mechanical actions alone." But, he adds, "can one conceive of the phenomena of heat and of electricity as due to anything but certain motions of bodies, and, as such, must they not be subject to the general laws of mechanics?"(68) For Helmholtz it is an experimental truth; the impossibility has been shown by the absolute fruitlessness of innumerable researches, and solemnly proclaimed at a certain time by the Academy of Science at Paris.(69) Helmholtz's opinion is evidently paradoxical. It is doubtless not entirely inconceivable that by experiment alone we may arrive at a proposition purely negative and very general. Such, more or less, is the case with Carnot's principle, to which we are certainly inclined to attribute a negative formula. But this principle, without need of interpretation, flows immediately from experiments which we are constantly making. There is nothing like this for perpetual motion; daily observation in no way gives us the conviction of its impossibility, as witness the very multitude of seekers.(70) One might suppose, also, that a very vast experiment, undertaken according to a rigorous plan, in order to include phenomena within very vast limits, would lead us to a proposition of this kind. But can one really compare such an experiment with the often very extravagant researches of these inventors? No one has ever given himself the trouble to classify methodically their work—the task would be as arduous as sterile. But no series of experiments, undertaken without success, could suffice to prove the insolubility of a problem, otherwise many of the great discoveries, on the eve of their realization, might have been proved impossible. Humanity has probably been looking for artificial flight during a longer time than it has looked for perpetual motion, as witness many of the legends which are in the folk-lore of a great number of nations. These researches have been fruitless up to the present,(71) and yet no one thinks of setting up this sterility as a principle. It is true that a certain discredit is to-day attached to the search for perpetual motion; but everything is wanting in order that a *consensus omnium* (a true Catholic sentiment) be established on this subject. Perpetual motion still continues to be invented, even by purely mechanical means, and these attempts sometimes have as their authors ingenious minds, not entirely devoid of technical culture, as, for instance, the invention which *The Times* recently reported.(72) Let us observe that the contributor to this English journal, in order to emphasize the sterility of this attempt, did not lay stress upon negative results in the past, but upon the conservation of energy. This incontestably is the general feeling; the impossibility of perpetual motion is based upon this latter principle and not inversely. Moreover, this feeling is in conformity with the opinion of the great minds whose names we have cited before. There can be no doubt about it in the case of Leibniz; but Huygens and Carnot, in affirming the impossibility for purely mechanical actions, were doubtless thinking of the principle of *vis viva;* perhaps Carnot was thinking besides of a deduction of the conservation of energy on the hypothesis of central forces, and most certainly the impossibility of perpetual motion did not appear to them as an experimental fact. The famous decision of the Academy of Science invoked by Helmholtz could not serve his thesis—quite the contrary. It was taken in 1775. The Academy proclaimed that in the future it would no longer examine "any solution of the problems of the duplication of the cube, of the trisection of the angle, or the quadrature of the circle, nor any machine announced as perpetual motion." In these terms the *l'Histoire de l'Académie* renders account of the motives of this last decision: "The construction of a perpetual motion is absolutely impossible. Even if friction, the resistance of the medium, would not in the long run destroy the resistance of the moving force, this force can only produce an effect equal to its cause. If, then, one wishes that the effect of a finite force last for ever, this effect must be infinitely small in a finite time. Setting aside friction and resistance, a body to which one has once given a motion would conserve it always; but it is by not acting upon other bodies, and the only perpetual motion possible on this hypothesis (which, however, cannot occur in nature) would be absolutely useless for the object proposed by the constructors of perpetual motion."(73)

This, we see, is again the demonstration by conservation of *vis viva*, based, as in Leibniz, upon the equality of effect and cause. Doubtless, according to its authors, this resolution only applied directly to pure mechanics; some of them were probably of the opinion, as was Huygens, that, except in the case of the latter, the impossibility had not been proved. At any rate, it was thus that this resolution was understood by the scientific world. Perpetual motion continued to be sought for, and the seekers, as Duhem has justly remarked,(74) were not all fools. In the same way Volta's ideas on contact electricity were accepted with great docility, although they involved the possibility of finding a system capable of furnishing indefinitely electric energy without being used up and without being directed, a possibility which the great Italian physicist expressly affirmed.(75) Again, in 1833 a notable physicist, Muncke, maintained, entirely in the sense of Huygens, that physical perpetual motion was possible, citing in support of this view the planetary system, the rotation of the earth, rivers, the barometer, and the magnetic needle.(76) And if at present the contrary conviction has become general, this, without doubt, is due to the fact that everyone believes in the conservation of energy.(77)

However, there still remains Stevinus's demonstration. Duhem (78) thinks that Stevinus placed faith in Cardanus—that is, in the considerations on the power necessary to maintain a machine in motion. That may be so, but it does not follow from his deduction, which is direct and incontestably of a great demonstrative force, although some contemporaries, amongst others Mersenne, have expressed doubts on this subject.(79)

There are certainly motions which we instinctively feel impossible, and whenever one can, in a demonstration, simplify the phenomena enough to reduce the demonstration, for example, to the type of "the stone which goes up by its own weight," our conviction will be established. But this clarity, seemingly perfect as long as it is a question of simple phenomena, becomes attenuated in the face of more complicated ones. This is so because we are here not dealing with rational truth. The law of gravity itself is purely empirical. Since we continually see bodies tend toward the earth, we conceive the idea that this is a general rule, a law. But this does not lead us to understand what gravity is; we do not succeed in according it a logical necessity, and our reason refuses to commit itself as soon as we hear of circumstances fundamentally different from those we know. At bottom, the fact that a little weight may raise a big one is entirely contrary to our immediate sensation, and we have all been astounded to learn that this result might be obtained with the help of an appropriate lever. This explains why there are so many people always searching for perpetual motion, even by purely mechanical means.(80)

Thus the conservation of energy, like inertia, like the conservation of matter, is neither empirical nor *a priori*; it is plausible.

This truth can be established, if not more completely, at least more directly, for energy than for velocity or mass.

In the first place, from the historical point of view, we have seen that conservation is postulated even before the concept is precisely stated. We *want* something to be conserved. Descartes and his contemporaries affirm it, though completely deceived as to the nature of what is conserved. It may be that the error is of experimental origin,(81) but it is certain that Mersenne's experiment, which furnished the point of departure, supposing even that it was exact, was far from countenancing such a vast generalization. It is certainly remarkable that during all the discussions which took place in the seventeenth and eighteenth centuries on the question of the measure of force, measure and conservation should have been absolutely confused. If a force (we say, an energy) is able to bring about a certain effect, the force which can exercise an identical effect must be counted equal to the first; but it does not follow that the force must equal its effect. Now, it is this second formula, as we can easily perceive, which is at the bottom of the discussions under consideration. Finally, it is clear that the discovery of Mayer and of Joule only substituted one concept of constancy for others, already pre-existing, which it destroyed by that very fact. Leibniz supposed mechanical energy to be indestructible and, on the other hand, Deluc, Black, and Wilke admitted the indestructibility of heat-matter. What we call the principle of the conservation of energy consists in the opposite proof, namely, that heat as well as mechanical energy, taken separately, can be created and destroyed, the disappearance of mechanical energy being accompanied by the appearance of a certain quantity of heat energy and vice versa.

We come to analogous conclusions through a close examination of the concept of energy, such as we find it in science of to-day. The concept of mass is only the expression of the relation following which bodies act upon each other. This action, really, is strictly determined: it is mechanical action; the relation would be entirely different were we to take for a basis electric or thermal action. Yet, because of the preference which we accord to phenomena of displacement over all others, the concept of mass certainly appears to us as invested with particular importance (p. 179 f.). Moreover, in virtue of the principle of inertia, stipulating that the state of motion of the body is indifferent, provided only the motion be rectilinear and uniform, we have the possibility of determining the relation in question by starting from an initial state which appears to us as identical: relative rest. Finally, continual experiments disclose to us the relations between the bodies surrounding us and a unique body, always the same— that is, the earth. This is why mass no longer appears to us as a relation between two bodies, but as a coefficient becoming attached to each particular body, as a property of the body, which causality is then charged with transforming into a substance. But it is not the same with energy; it remains a relation, and if one wishes to conceive of it as a property, it will be the property of a system and not that of a body. To be sure, we sometimes find, especially in popular books, expressions which would make us suppose the contrary. It is said, for instance, that such a body constitutes a "reservoir of energy"; but this is because one takes for granted a host of conditions. Thus a mass of coal in burning is capable of liberating a known number of calories. But if our atmosphere were composed of gaseous chlorine this relation would be quite different. Two celestial bodies, falling one upon the other, would liberate a quantity of heat energy which we can calculate; but if afterwards chemical reactions were produced between the components of these masses, this heat would be increased by an unknown amount. But even remaining in the purely mechanical domain we do not succeed in attaching energy, as a property, to bodies. To be convinced of this it is sufficient to consider the mathematical formula of kinetic energy. It contains the square of velocity; but we only know relative velocities. All terrestrial masses which surround us, seen from the sun, are displaced with considerable velocity, drawn along by the motion of the earth; they therefore possess an enormous kinetic energy. But we take no account of this; we treat it as if it did not exist—rightly, moreover, since, unless we encounter an aerolite, it can in no way interfere with what passes on the earth. With still greater reason the conception of potential energy is inseparable from the consideration of a system. This mass which I am holding in my hand may fall upon the floor of my room, into the street, or into a well which I can imagine as deep as I wish. I can also imagine that it falls upon the sun, which, incontestably, attracts it, and the sum of energy which each one of these phenomena liberates will be very different. It is impossible to gauge in advance, considering only a body and not a system, the sum of energy susceptible of being disengaged; this latter is strictly infinite even in the interior of each body, for we have only to suppose the substances composed of centres of forces in order to obtain infinite work by causing two of these centres to coincide.(82) Lord Kelvin introduced the term *total intrinsic energy*, and many physicists have used it since. But it must be remembered that this quantity is defined in relation to a standard state; it is therefore capable of having a negative value.(83) Hertz pointed out that this assumption would be absurd for a real substance, which, of course, is incapable of being conceived except as a positive quantity, and that under these conditions potential energy resists any definition attributing to it the properties of a substance.(84) For our imagination, matter is something real and energy is only an integral.

There are other difficulties quite as serious. Until now we have supposed that energy was composed of two quantities, namely, energy of motion or kinetic, T, and energy of position or potential energy, U. We therefore have $T + U = $ constant. But as a matter of fact this decomposition only applies to purely mechanical phenomena. If, on the contrary, we have to take into account, at the same time, thermal, chemical, or electric energy, we must introduce a third term Q, to represent this internal energy, and the equation will have to be written:

$T + U + Q =$ constant. To make the equation clear the three terms must be absolutely distinct—that is, T will have to depend solely on the square of the velocity, whereas U will only depend on positions and will be independent of these velocities and of the state of the bodies, and finally Q will be independent of the velocities and the positions of the bodies and will depend exclusively on their *internal* state. But these are assumptions which experience does not confirm. Electrostatic energy, due to the mutual action of electrified bodies, does not depend only on their charge—that is, on their state; it depends also on their position and their velocities. Under these conditions we can no longer make the selection of the terms T, U, and Q—that is, separate the three forms of energy. Now if $T + U + Q$ remains constant it will be the same with any function $\phi \ (T + U + Q)$. If the terms T, U, and Q were entirely distinct one from the other there would be amongst all of these functions one alone having a particular form, and that one we should call energy. But if these terms depend on the conditions just indicated, this particular form does not exist. Therefore, says Poincaré, from whom we have borrowed almost textually the preceding development, "we no longer have anything which can guide us in our choice. Nothing more remains but a statement for the principle of the conservation of energy : there is something which remains constant."(85)

This is evidently the most general formula—the typical formula—for the principle of conservation; it clearly shows that it is a question of a tendency prior to experience : this something we do not know, we cannot indicate its nature in advance, but we hope that it will remain constant in time; we demand it. The fact that a mind as eminent as Poincaré's, without theoretical preconception, and animated by a simple desire to render precise the tenor of the principle, should have arrived at a formula of this kind, singularly fortifies the conclusions to which our analysis has brought us.

NOTES

1. DUHEM : *L'évolution de la mécanique*. Paris, 1903, p. 227.
2. LEIBNIZ : *Mathematische Schriften*, ed. Gerhardt, Vol. VI, p. 218.
3. Cf. ROSENBERGER : *Geschichte der Physik*, Vol. I, p. 19.

4. DUHEM: *Léonard*, I, p. 246; II, p. 233 and ff. What Leonardo here qualifies as *accidental weight* is the same concept which in other places he calls sometimes *forza* and sometimes *impeto*.

5. H. POINCARÉ: *Thermodynamique*. Paris, 1892, p. 2 and ff.

6. LEIBNIZ: *Opera*, ed. Erdmann, p. 117. *Brevis demonstratio erroris memorabilis Cartesii.* . . .

7. J. BERNOULLI: *Discours sur les lois de la communication des mouvements. Œuvres.* Lausanne, 1772, Vol. III, p. 58. LEIBNIZ sometimes seems to affirm that he is the sole author of the discovery and that Huygens knew of it through him. Cf. *Lettres à l'Hôpital. Mathematische Schriften*, Vol. I, p. 320.

8. DESCARTES: *Principia*, 2nd Part, Chap. XLII.

9. LEIBNIZ: *Opera*, ed. Erdmann, p. 775.

10. J. BERNOULLI: *l.c.*, p. 56. The *Discours* was printed in Paris in 1727.

11. Id., *De vera ratione virium vivarum*, etc., § IX; *ib.*, p. 243.

12. A. DE HALLER: *Elementa Physiologiae corporis humani*. Lausanne, 1762, Vol. IV, p. 557: "*Cartesius et Leibnitius et plerique mathematici negant aut oriri in rerum natura motum novum aut disperire: per circulum autem corpora impelli et se impellere, ut tantum de motu in aliqua parte universi dematur, quantum in alia videtur accedere.*"

13. VOLTAIRE: *Œuvres*, ed. Beuchot. Paris. 1830, Vol. XXXVIII, p. 500.

14. DUHEM: *Le Mixte*. Paris, 1902, p. 61.

15. Cf. ROSENBERGER: *Geschichte der Physik*, Vol. II, pp. 345–348.

16. "*Potentielle Energie ist also ein dem aprioristisch feststehenden ersten Hauptsatz zu Liebe ersonnener Ausfuellbegriff.*" Driesch. *Naturbegriffe und Natururtheile.* Leipzig, 1904, p. 58. It is known, moreover, that at the moment when the word was introduced into science by Rankine, about 1857, Faraday protested, claiming that for it should be substituted a physical substratum—that is, a modification of the medium. Cf. Planck, *Das Prinzip der Erhaltung der Energie*, 2nd ed. Leipzig, 1908, p. 98.

17. LAVOISIER and LAPLACE: *Mémoires sur la chaleur*. LAVOISIER, *Œuvres*. Paris, 1862, Vol. II, pp. 285–286. Yet the authors formulate these suppositions only with a certain reserve, presenting them, at most, as equivalents of the theory of heat-fluid. It is known, moreover, that Lavoisier clearly leaned toward this last hypothesis. (Cf. earlier, p. 173.)

18. RUMFORD: *An Inquiry concerning the Source of the Heat which is excited by Friction.* Transactions of the Roy. Soc., London, 1798 (January 25). H. Davy, *An Essay on Heat*, etc. (1799), *Works*. Vol. II. London, 1836, p. 11. According to H. Poincaré (*Thermodynamique*, p. 28), Rumford's experiment was not absolutely conclusive. One can see, moreover, in Biot (*Précis élémentaire de physique expérimentale*, 2nd ed. Paris, 1820–21, Vol. II, p. 683) how contemporary science adjusted itself to this experiment.

19. We quote from BOHN: *Notice sur la théorie mécanique de la chaleur. Annales de Chimie et de Physique*, 4th series, Vol. IV, 1865, p. 280. We have not succeeded in finding Fresnel's treatise, *Sur la chaleur*, which has not been included in the edition of his works (Paris, 1866–70).

20. LAZARE CARNOT: *Principes fondamentaux de l'équilibre et du mouvement.* Paris, an XI, 1803, p. 37.

21. PONCELET: *Introduction à la mécanique industrielle physique ou expéri-mentale*, 2nd ed. Metz, 1841, § 138: "Water enclosed in the reservoir of a mill represents a certain force ready for action, which is changed into kinetic energy when the sluice-gate is opened; in its turn the kinetic energy acquired by this water, in virtue of its fall from the reservoir, is changed into a certain quantity of work as it acts upon the mill-wheel, and this latter transmits its work to the mill-stones, . . . which finish the task."

22. SÉGUIN L'AÎNÉ: *De l'influence des chemins de fer et de l'art de les tracer et de les construire*: Paris, 1839, p. 382. "Since the theory actually adopted would nevertheless lead to this result (i.e. to perpetual motion), it seems more natural to me to suppose that a certain quantity of calories disappear in the very act of the production of the force or mechanical power, and conversely; and that the two phenomena are bound together by conditions which assign to them invariable relations."

23. Cf. POINCARÉ: *l.c.*, p. 51. These notes have been reproduced in the 2nd ed. of *Réflexions*. Paris, 1878.

24. SADI CARNOT: *Réflexions sur la puissance motrice du feu*. New Impression. Paris, 1903, p. 10. In the last pages of this work Carnot expresses doubts on the legitimacy of this conception (cf., p. 203). These reservations have not been noticed.

25. J. R. MAYER: *Bemerkungen ueber die Kraefte der unbelebten Natur*. *Liebig's Annalen*, Vol. XLII, 1842.

26. Cf. later, p. 212, note 53.

27. J. P. JOULE: *On the Calorific Effect of Magneto-Electricity and on the Mechanical Value of Heat*. *Philosophical Magazine*, Vol. XXIII. London, 1843.

28. HELMHOLTZ: *Ueber die Erhaltung der Kraft*, 1847; reproduced in *Wissenschaftliche Abhandlungen*, Vol. I, p. 12 and ff.

29. H. POINCARÉ: *l.c.*, p. 65.

30. JOULE: *l.c.*, pp. 437–439.

31. Cf. H. POINCARÉ: *l.c.*, p. 51.

32. J. R. MAYER: *l.c.*, p. 240.

33. LIPPMANN: *Cours de thermodynamique*. Paris, 1889, p. 11 and ff. There will be found in the report presented to the Congress of Physics of 1900 by Ames on *L'équivalent mécanique de la chaleur* (Vol. I) a thorough discussion of the most remarkable investigations on this matter. Of the twenty-one physicists recently engaged upon this, Ames rejects the results of fifteen as marred by too great errors, and calculates his averages from the results of the other six. The maximum and minimum limits which he determines still present a difference of more than ½ per cent.

34. LIPPMANN: *l.c.*, p. 35.

35. M. J. PERRIN: *Traité de chimie physique* (Paris, 1903, p. 16) expressly formulates, nevertheless, this condition.

36. R. W. BUNSEN: *Ueber die Verdichtung der Kohlensaeure an blanken Glasflaechen*. *Poggendorf's Annalen*, Vol. XX, 1883, p. 558. M. BERTHELOT, *Comptes rendus de l'Académie des sciences*, Vol. CXL, 1905, p. 817, 1253.

37. Cf. W. SPRING: *Propriétés des solides*, etc. *Congrès de physique de 1900*, Vol. I, p. 421, and DASTRE, *La vie et la mort*, p. 264.

38. Let us remark, in order to avoid all misunderstanding, that the conservation of energy and that of mass would not become on this account strictly analogous, energy not being able to be conceived of as a property of a body (cf., p. 207). Our observation has only to do with the condition of isolation.

39. HELMHOLTZ: *Wissenschaftliche Abhandlungen*. Leipzig, 1882, I, p. 67.

40. CH.-E. GUILLAUME: *L'échelle du spectre*. *Revue générale des sciences*, X, 1899, p. 7 and ff.

41. This gap is almost filled at the present moment, but the rest of the argument remains true.

42. G. LE BON: *L'évolution de la matière*. Paris, 1905, p. 120.

43. H. POINCARÉ: *l.c.*, p. vii. One can place in the same category the following declaration of Helm's, *Die Lehre von der Energie, historisch-kritisch entwickelt*, Leipzig, 1887, p. 2: "*Mancher hat daher wohl das Gefuehl, als sei die Unterlage eine unsichere, auf der das moderne Energiegesetz ruht und als habe seine Entwicklung leichtfertige Schritte gemacht.*" The admission is all the more significant because it emanates from a man whose doctrine exalts the importance of the principle.

44. LIPPMANN: *l.c.*, p. 13.

45. SPENCER: *l.c.*, p. 251 and ff.

46. STALLO: *La matière*, p. 27 and ff.

47. LASSWITZ: *Geschichte der Atomistik*. Hamburg, 1890, Vol. II, p. 377.

48. Id., *Zur Rechtfertigung der kinetischen Atomistik. Vierteljahrsschrift fuer wissenschaftliche Philosophie*, IX, 1885, p. 154.

49. SPIR: *Pensée et réalité*, p. 424.

50. J. R. MAYER: *l.c.*, p. 233.

51. *Ib.*, p. 234.

52. *Ib.*, p. 239.

53. A. COLDING: *Lettre aux rédacteurs du Philosophical Magazine sur l'histoire du principe de la conservation de l'énergie*. Trans. Verdet. *Annales de Chimie et de Physique*, 4th series, Vol. I, 1864, p. 467. The original article of Colding, inserted in the minutes of the Academy of Copenhagen, 1843, does not appear ever to have been translated into a more accessible language.

54. JOULE: *l.c.*, p. 435.

55. Id., *Scientific Papers*. London, 1884–87, p. 268.

56. MACH: *Die Principien der Waermelehre*. Leipzig, 1896, p. 261.

57. HELMHOLTZ: *Wissenschaftliche Abhandlangen*, p. 13: "*Wir werden genoethigt und berechtigt . . . durch den Grundsatz, dass jede Veraenderung in der Natur eine zureichende Ursache haben muesse.*" Later Helmholtz, adding notes to his study, declared that he had been too much influenced by Kant and that the principle of causality was only the hypothesis of the reign of law in all phenomena (cf. earlier, p. 18). It is the confusion which we know well, and it is quite easy to discover that the principle, of which Helmholtz made use in affirming that phenomena must be reduced to immutable forces in time, is really that of causality. It is also seen from the sequel to the passage (*ib.*, p. 68) that what had caused him to go astray was the confusion between the laws and the properties of bodies: *Das Gesetz als objektive Macht anerkannt, nennen wir Kraft.* (Cf. earlier, p. 39 and ff.)

58. FARADAY: *On the Conservation of Force. Phil. Mag.*, (4), XIII, 1827, p. 239; cf. id., *Experimental Researches on Electricty.* London, 1839–55, Vol. II, §§ 2069, 2073. It is curious to notice that Tait's violent attacks upon J. R. Mayer and Séguin, accusing them of being "speculating philosophers" and "metaphysicians" (cf., for example, Tait, *Conferences.* Paris, 1856, pp. 18, 73, 77), rebounded against Faraday, and even, we have seen, against Joule.

59. Cf. DUHEM: *Les origines de la statique*, p. 21.

60. *Ib.*, p. 58.

61. STEVINUS: *Œuvres mathématiques*, trans. GERARD. Leyden, 1634, p. 448. Cf. DUHEM, *l.c.*, p. 266 and ff.

62. Cf. especially LEIBNIZ: *De legibus naturae et vera aestimatione virium motricium. Mathem. Schriften*, Vol. VI, p. 204 and ff.

63. Cf. *Lettre de Huygens*, ib., Vol. I, p. 140.

64. SADI CARNOT: *Réflexions sur la puissance motrice du feu.* New Impression. Paris, 1903, p. 21.

65. Cf. earlier, p. 211, note 22.

66. LEIBNIZ: *l.c.*, p. 204: "*Docui ex contraria essentia sequi inaequalitatem causae et effectus, imo motum perpetuum, quae absurda videantur.*" Ib.; "*nascitur motus perpetuus seu effectus potior causa.*" P. 206: "*Saltem negabunt quidem motum perpetuum seu effectum causa potiorem esse possibilem.*" Cf. COUTURAT, *Revue de métaphysique*, XI, 1903, p. 89.

67. LEIBNIZ: *Mathem. Schriften*, Vol. I, p. 149.

68. S. CARNOT: *l.c.*, p. 21, note.

69. HELMHOLTZ: *Wissenschaftliche Abhandlungen*, p. 73. "*Uebrigens ist dieses Gesetz, wie alle Kenntniss von Vorgaengen der wirklichen Welt, auf inductivem Wege gewonnen worden. Dass man kein Perpetuum mobile bauen, das heisst Triebkraft ohne Ende nicht ohne entsprechenden Verbrauch gewinnen koenne, war eine durch viele vergebliche Versuche, es zu leisten, allmaehlig gewonnene Induction.*

Schon laengst hatte die franzoesische Akademie das Perpetuum mobile in dieselbe Kategorie wie die Quadratur des Zirkels gestellt und beschlossen, keine angeblichen Loesungen dieses Problems mehr anzunehmen. Das muss doch als der Ausdruck einer unter den Sachwerstaendigen weit verbreiteten Ueberzuegung angesehen werden."

70. "That the doctrine of the conservation of energy is not self-evident is shown by the repeated attempts to discover a perpetual motive power." Maxwell, *Theory of Heat*, Chap. VIII, p. 144.

71. These lines were written in 1907.

72. *The Times. Engineering Supplement*, April 19, 1905, p. 64.

73. *Histoire de l'Académie Royale des sciences, année 1775.* Paris, 1777, pp. 61, 65.

74. DUHEM: *Les origines de la Statique*, p. 279.

75. Cf. M. LE BLANC: *Les idées nouvelles sur la théorie des piles. Revue générale des science*, X, 1899, p. 725.

76. MUNCKE: *Perpetuum mobile* in GEHLER'S *Physikalisches Woerterbuch.* Leipzig, 1833, Vol. VII, p. 408.

77. J. PERRIN: *Traité de chimie physique* (Paris, 1903, p. 77) deduces the impossibility of perpetual motion from the principle of the conservation of energy.

78. DUHEM: *l.c.*, p. 279.

79. *Ib.*, p. 298.

80. HELM, although he clearly perceives that the affirmation of the impossibility of perpetual motion is not a purely empirical statement (*Die Lehre von der Energie*. Leipzig, 1887, p. 92), believes that he is able none the less to use it as a basis for an inductive demonstration of the principle of the conservation of energy (*ib.*, p. 41). In our opinion the *a priori* conceptions (*aprioristische Vorstellungen*), of which Helm admits the intervention apropos of perpetual motion, have to do with the conservation of energy; the first of these principles is based upon the second and not inversely.

81. Cf. ROSENBERGER: *Geschichte*, Vol. II, p. 95.

82. It is known, moreover, as a result of recent discoveries, and especially that of radio-active bodies, that the consideration of intra-atomic energy has left the purely speculative domain and has entered that of experimental physics. The figures at which one arrives are really enormous, compared to those furnished us by the usual sources of energy (cf. later, p. 273 f.), without being able, of course, to affirm that they really exhaust all the latent energy which the body contains.

83. Cf. on this subject Helm, *l.c.*, p. 35.

84. HERTZ: *Gesammelte Werke*. Leipzig, 1895, Vol. III, pp. 25–27. HELM, *l.c.*, p. 16, expresses an analogous opinion.

85. H. POINCARÉ: *Thermodynamique*, p. 9. Id., *La science et l'hypothèse* pp. 152–153, 158, 195.

CHAPTER VI

THE ELIMINATION OF TIME

WE have seen, in what precedes, the postulate of the identity of things in time intervening powerfully in science. It is that which constitutes completely, so to speak, atomic theories, and, again, it is this postulate which impels us to hope that determinate objects of thought, capable of being considered as substances, are conserved amongst phenomena eternally changing; it is this *causal tendency* which prepares the way for the principles of conservation, suggests them, and once stated, lends to them an authority which "brings them close to those truths of which the contrary is inconceivable," and which makes them "offer almost a character of universality and metaphysical necessity."(1) It is powerful enough to create in us illusions that are contrary to evidence; it makes us accept as substance what in the beginning is but a relation between two limited terms, such as velocity, or a concept impossible to define clearly in its entirety, such as energy.(2) It is this strange prestige of the principles of conservation which explains why we are inclined to exaggerate immoderately their importance to the extent of making their formulation coincide with the causal postulate itself: Nothing is created, nothing is lost. And to this same reason is also due the obstinacy with which we try to maintain these rules, and to ignore or to explain somehow the facts which afterwards are revealed and which seem to contradict them. Poincaré has observed this tendency of which the theories devised to explain the action of radio-active bodies furnish an excellent example, since it is especially a question of the constancy of energy, a conception whose experimental basis, we have seen, is not very firmly established.(3)

But the action of the postulate is not confined to mechanism and principles of conservation; it is easy to perceive that its intervention in science is not only powerful but incessant; that it manifests itself everywhere; that science is, so to speak, impregnated with it. We shall see this clearly in examining the most rational of the physical sciences, "rational mechanics." It well merits its name, for it is the science which is the most adequate to our reason, and, we shall see, the farthest removed from reality.

The perfect identity between cause and effect, as the causal tendency postulates it, would imply from all evidence their equivalence—that is, the possibility of reversing the phenomenon, of arriving at the antecedent by starting from the consequent. On the other hand, this "reversibility," as we say in physics, does not imply identity. I can exchange a ten-franc gold piece for two five-franc silver pieces, or vice versa, from which it follows that these things have the same value, are equivalent, but not identical.

The postulate of reversibility was clearly formulated by Leibniz. Let us recall here the most trenchant of the sentences quoted before upon the relations between causes and effects: "The integral effect may reproduce the entire cause or its equal."

Is this really so? We have only to consult our inner consciousness to reply to this question. We notice that we have the absolute feeling that nature follows an immutable course in time. We know that to-day is not like yesterday, that between the two something irreparable has happened: *fugit irreparabile tempus*. We feel ourselves growing old. We cannot invert the course of time. An able novelist has recently tried to render tangible the contrary supposition; his stories are instructive precisely because of the strange effect which emanates from them. And yet Wells, in supplying his hero with a machine which permits him to displace himself in time as we displace ourselves in space, takes the precaution to have him travel chiefly in the future,(4) which appears to us necessarily as undetermined because of our ignorance. But let us suppose a displacement in the past. Wells's hero, on the eve of the Battle of Hastings, will warn Harold of the subterfuge meditated by William, and the Normans will be beaten. Thus the entire course of history will be modified; but it will be altered, in fact, without these bold suppositions, for any individual who is added necessarily modifies the state of the universe at a given moment, and from that very fact it becomes impossible that the result should be what it has been. To re-ascend to the past is to modify the past, and that seems contradictory to us.

We feel, moreover, that not only the entire universe, but

also each particular phenomenon which we observe, follows a determined course in time, has a beginning and an end, and that it is impossible for us to represent it in reverse order. We have only to think of events in organic nature: the birth of beings, their maturation, their decline and death. Who can imagine fruits preceding flowers, the fowl being transformed into an egg? But it is the same also in phenomena where the fact of evolution seems less marked to us; everything unfolds in a certain direction, and if, by chance, we saw something produced in the opposite direction we should be immediately struck by it as by something contrary to the course of nature. We need not, as a matter of fact, have here recourse to imaginations such as those of Wells; we can *see* this reversed world. To do this we have only to provide ourselves with a cinematograph, to insert within it a reel of pictures representing moving phenomena—such as the jumping or the falling of a horse, a drop of water dripping into a pond, the descent of a mass of stones or of sand—and to turn the crank in the opposite direction. It is impossible to describe the strangeness of the impression which comes from the aspect of these pictures. It is not sorcery; but is something more or less like it: it is a world manifestly absurd, which presents no analogy with the one we know.

Doubtless if we look in this way at a machine the impression will not be the same: a locomotive will simply have the air of "going backward," and the phenomenon thus reversed in no way shocks our sensation of reality. But if we observe the fireplace we shall see that the smoke, instead of leaving it and of being dissipated, is formed in the distance, approaches, thickens, and finally rushes into the fireplace, a phenomenon which certainly will appear impossible to us. We can, moreover, explain that even the resemblance between one part of the reversed phenomenon and the going backward is only apparent and is due mainly to the imperfection of our senses. The different parts of the machine, however well oiled they may be, rub against each other just as the wheels rub against the rails, all of which become heated, and the heat is dissipated in the air. Everyone knows, moreover, that the friction of the moving wheels on the rail constitutes one of the essential conditions of the phenomenon, the locomotive *skids* when this friction is insufficient. But could we *see* these waves as we see the smoke, the reversed picture of the moving locomotive would shock us as much as what occurs in the fireplace.

It is clear that the observation just formulated is quite general. The stellar movements seem to be an exception; we are, indeed, forced to suppose that the medium in which they act offers no resistance; therefore it seems that all could turn backward and that, endowed with equal velocity and an opposite direction, the planets would pass again in the reverse direction through the same series of perihelions and eclipses. But this is probably only an appearance; where we can study the phenomenon more closely the illusion of reversibility is dissipated. Thus, in respect to the earth, the flow of the tides plays, as we know, the rôle of a brake; it tends to oppose itself to its rotation and converts a part of the kinetic energy of this motion into heat which is dissipated afterwards. On the earth, at any rate, there can be no mechanism absolutely deprived of friction, and therefore there exists none that is really reversible.(5)

It is quite different in rational mechanics: there all motions are reversible. At the outset, with the help of a postulate tacitly assumed, the very essence of the concept of time is completely altered. Mechanical time no longer always flows uniformly in the same direction; on the contrary, one can move in it freely in the desired direction, as we do in space. It is doubtless this which Lagrange felt in affirming that time could be considered as a fourth dimension of space. This is a strikingly strange statement; we have, indeed, the immediate sensation that it is not so, and this sensation, we have seen, is justified, because there is no real parallelism between our concepts of time and space. But in rational mechanics time is indeed something analogous to space. There the effect may really "reproduce the cause or its like," according to the postulate of Leibniz.

H. Poincaré puts forth the ingenious supposition that the form of our mechanics is due to the influence of celestial mechanics, a science which was completed before it, and which impressed minds by its beautiful orderliness. The motions of celestial bodies appearing to us, we have just seen, as reversible, one might explain why rational mechanics was based on the same hypothesis. Without denying this influence (for it has certainly strengthened conviction and has favoured the ignoring of real conditions), we believe, however, that the cause has been more profound. We see in it an evident manifestation of the principle of causality, of the general tendency which is in us and which leads us to postulate the equality between antecedent and consequent.

Having at the outset transformed the intimate nature of time with the help of an audacious postulate, rational mechanics next uses all of its efforts to eliminate it altogether from its statements. At the beginning of the development one is often obliged to regard modifications as functions of the time, but the permanent, although often unconscious, concern of the scientist is to eliminate that variable later, to reduce what is variable in time to what is constant. We have seen, from the passage which we quoted in the first chapter (p. 37), that Cournot perfectly understood that science imposes this reduction. Hertz was of the same opinion. "We consider," he said, "the task of mechanics to be to deduce, starting out with properties of material systems independent of the time, phenomena produced by these latter and taking place *in* time, as well as the properties of these systems dependent on the time."(6) Where the great physicist was mistaken is when he believed that the simple search for empirical rules, for laws, was enough to impel us to these deductions. This conviction of his was the logical consequence of his system. Hertz, we know, wished to put aside completely the notion of force, by reducing mechanics to mass and motion. The masses are joined to each other and particularly to hidden masses by rigid connections (*starre Verbindungen*). Hertz conceived the existence of these connections as a law, and laws not varying in time, the connections must also be independent of it.(7) But these same connections appeared to him also as properties, from which he concludes, as we have just seen, that the search for the law leads to that of properties independent of the time. This is evidently a simple consequence of the error whose origins we have explained in the first chapter (p. 39). Ostwald, who starts from principles entirely opposed to those of Hertz, denying the possibility of any reduction of natural phenomena to mechanism, yet affirms that the search for laws is reduced to that for an "invariant—that is, to a quantity which remains invariable when all others vary between possible limits," and one sees from the context, where Ostwald cites as examples of these invariants mass and weight, that he is thinking of conceptual elements remaining immutable in time and capable of appearing to us as beings, as substances.(8) But this demands a more profound analysis.

We have seen (Chapter I, p. 35) that science concerned purely with laws does not treat things and laws in the same way in relation to time. Laws are supposed to be immutable; things may vary. This same science having prevision as its end, variation of the object in time is what it must study in the first place, and the most natural form of the law is that which indicates the evolution of the phenomenon as a function of the time as independent variable. In the first chapter we have cited examples of laws of this kind. Let us take up again that of radio-active bodies. This is particularly instructive because the phenomenon appears fundamental and because its variation in time seems entirely independent of every other circumstance. Thus, in formulating the statement that in 3·70 days the radio-activity of the emanation of radium is reduced by one-half, we stipulate a change in time and as a function of the time. We affirm that if we happen to observe somewhere that body called the emanation of radium, it cannot remain the same during two consecutive moments, but must be modified from one to the other in a determined manner. Throughout this change of the body, does something remain constant? Assuredly. What remains constant is the law according to which this change is produced, or, if you prefer, the relation between this change and time. There is no contradiction between this constancy and the continual change which we have stipulated for the body, or rather the very constancy of the relation includes the change, on the assumption that the second term of the relation is time, and that time in its essence flows always and uniformly in the same direction.

Let us pass now to a phenomenon of apparent motion, as the fall of a body in the void. We can begin by measuring the spaces traversed by a body starting from rest, and we shall be able to formulate the rule that these spaces are in proportion to the squares of the times which have elapsed since the beginning of the motion.(9) Under this form the law is strictly analogous to that which has been stated for the emanation of radium; it stipulates the maintenance of a relation whose second term is time, which consequently includes the concept of change.

But we can present this law under still another form. Instead of searching for the spaces traversed, we shall have recourse to a concept a little more abstract, and we shall determine the velocity which the body will have acquired at the precise moment of its fall. Again, we shall be able to state that a relation remains constant (since it is the very essence of the law), and in retaining time as the second term of the relation we shall say that the velocity increases in proportion to the time elapsed.

Let us observe, moreover, that time being the independent variable, its increase is constant. We express this fact in popular language by saying that to know the velocity in question we measure the time—that is, we divide it into equal intervals, into seconds for instance. Therefore, in virtue of the formula we have just stated, the velocity of the body will increase in the same manner—that is, if we create a special term for the increase of velocity, calling it *acceleration*, we shall be able to state the formula by saying that the acceleration is a constant.

In making these transformations, purely verbal in part, we seem only to have served the interest of rendering the formula briefer and easier to retain. Let us notice, however, what this term acceleration becomes. It is evidently a simple relation, and a very abstract relation, since it is the difference of two velocities; it is something comparable to the relation between the quotient of the space and that of the squares of the time in our first formula. Moreover, from the very fact that the concept of acceleration (as its etymology indicates) is derived from that of velocity, like this latter, it is based on the concept of time, and consequently it contains virtually that of change in time, being a function of the time. And yet, since we can stipulate the constancy of this term in time itself, we transform it into an attribute which we call *force* and which is no longer a simple relation, but a thing, a reality—a reality, let us carefully remark, which we know only by this one manifestation, since force, by definition, is only the cause of acceleration.

Let us observe also that this new thing created by us is distinguished from all the things of common sense in that it does not evolve in time, that it is constant. Therefore, what really guided us in the transformations which we have made is not solely the desire for simplification; it is also the tendency to transform a relation into a thing in order to see conserved, not only the law, but also the object, and this, we know, is the true sense of the causal tendency. It is because we obey this tendency that we prefer to give to our laws such a form that the change does not appear to depend directly on the flow of time—in other words, that we seek to eliminate time from our formulæ.

This is why the form of the law as a function of the time, although the most natural with a view to prediction, is rarely found in science, all the more rarely as the science is more "rational"; in observing, in experimenting, and, especially in reasoning about our observations and experiences, we are dominated by the constant and powerful concern for the *cause*—that is, for the conservation of objects in time.

Nowhere, perhaps, does this tendency manifest itself so clearly as in the development of chemistry. Here is a substance which was called in the eighteenth century *calx of mercury*, or *mercury precipitate per se*. We heat it and we perceive that drops of a liquid and metallic substance are formed in the neck of the vessel. Chemists tell us that the phlogiston uniting with the calx has formed a matter which we call metallic mercury and which is the calx of mercury phlogisticated. The fact that the reaction is found to be accompanied by the appearance of a gas does not essentially modify the explanation; the "phlogisticians," and amongst them the discoverers of the gas, Priestley and Scheele, considered this phenomenon as secondary, and formulated on this subject auxiliary hypotheses.

In what did the "explanation" in question consist? You wished to know, we were told, why this red and powdery substance becomes metallic. It is because the phlogiston which has been added to it has the power of giving to the substance these very metallic qualities. Doubtless the phlogiston does not always manifest these qualities; that is because it is sometimes in a peculiar condition, but as soon as it is united to certain substances these qualities appear. The phlogiston which pre-existed has simply changed place in going from the fire to the calx of mercury. We can sum up this explanation by presenting it in the form of an equation :—

Calx of mercury + phlogiston = metallic mercury.

To be sure, the phlogistician did not state this equation, the use of chemical equations coming a little later. But it none the less translates their thought, and modern chemists have often had recourse to this translation in trying to understand and to state precisely the conceptions of their predecessors. The general sense of the explanation was thus really the following: by the reaction nothing was created, nothing was lost; the red mercury and the phlogiston which existed before subsist in the metallic mercury, and this profound change was really only a displacement.

To overthrow these conceptions Lavoisier remarks that weight is a permanent property of the substance, a property which is never obliterated; we shall, therefore, be able to recognize by an infallible sign whether something has really been added to it. Lavoisier states, making use of the balance, that the calx of mercury weighed more than the metallic mercury obtained after the operation, and that the difference is just about equal to the weight of the gas produced. Hence the logical conclusion that we must reverse the terms of the relation established by the theory of phlogiston, that it is the metallic mercury which is the simple substance, the element, and that the calx of mercury is a compound of metallic mercury and of the gas which Lavoisier called oxygen. This interpretation is thus written in the equation :—

$$HgO = Hg + O$$

which has in comparison with the preceding one the inestimable advantage of taking into account weights, of being quantitative, as we say. Indeed, following a formal convention the symbols which we have just used indicate not only the substances, but also the definite weights of these substances, and the equation signifies that 216 grammes of oxide of mercury yield 200 grammes of metallic mercury and 16 grammes of oxygen. Thus the identity between the antecedent and the consequent is still more precise; not only the metallic mercury and the oxygen pre-existed in the oxide, since they are the "components" of it, but they even existed in determined quantities, equal to those we have just obtained after the separation.

Later it was perceived that the decomposition of oxide of mercury is accompanied by another phenomenon—to wit, the absorption of a certain quantity of heat. It was observed that it was an almost general phenomenon, that, save for certain quite explainable exceptions, the substances in combining liberated heat and that, on the contrary, in dissociating they absorbed it. This quantity of heat (expressed, as we know, in calories) was successfully measured and it was seen that it really constituted a characteristic of the reaction.(10) We can, therefore, thus complete the above equation:—

$$HgO + X \text{ cal.} = Hg + O.$$

We have written out three different equations, yet they represent one and the same phenomenon. Doubtless we might completely set aside the first, declaring it to be false, since we no longer believe in the existence of phlogiston. But this would be wrong, for the theory in question furnished, we have seen, a very acceptable interpretation of the phenomenon as it was observed at the time. It has even been noticed, and rightly, that there is a certain analogy between the most recent conceptions and those of the chemists of phlogiston. These latter had a feeling that a "principle" must be added to the calx of mercury to produce metallic mercury, and that this was a general condition; the fact that, in replacing the term phlogiston by that of energy, we obtain, in many cases, statements which are nearly true, is not a pure coincidence.(11)

These three equations close up on the phenomenon more and more. But all three are *equations*—that is, they tend to establish a relation of equality between terms representing prior and subsequent states of the phenomenon. As the explanation advances, the identification becomes more and more perfect. In the beginning it treats only of the qualitative side of the fact, and is lacking in numerical precision; then come the considerations of quantity, and finally the thermal energy changes are "explained" in their turn—that is, they enter into the equation between the antecedent and the consequent.

Can it be affirmed that here the equality is directly suggested by the experiment? Is it not, on the contrary, paradoxical to

state that a metallic liquid and a colourless gas are together
the same thing as a red powder? This is, indeed, Ostwald's
opinion. He affirms that it is not a question of a true equality,
but only of bodies, which in certain operations can be mutually
substituted, the one for the other, without the result being
thereby modified.(12) It would perhaps be rather embarrassing
to indicate the operation where mercury and oxygen on one
side and oxide of mercury on the other might replace each
other under the same conditions, unless one wishes previously
to resort to the operation which is precisely the object of the
equation. But is it exact to say that in formulating this equation
the substitution in question was thought of? Let us go back
to the time when this mode of expression originated and
developed, and let us completely disregard the more recent
theories on chemical equilibrium and that which could contain
in germ the conceptions of Berthollet, which, we know, have
from this point of view remained almost without influence on
the progress of science. Let us write:—

$$BaCl_2 + Na_2SO_4 = BaSO_4 + 2NaCl.$$

It is incontestable that a reaction of this kind, a reaction
which seems to take place rapidly and completely as soon as the
substance whose symbols are written to the left of the sign of
equality are in the presence of one another under the right conditions, represented, so to speak, the typical reaction; there was
no question that the sulphate of barium and chloride of sodium
might give in their turn sulphate of sodium and chloride of
barium; this supposition, on the contrary, would have seemed
paradoxical to every chemist. Everywhere and always it was
understood that the left side indicated the point of departure
and the right side the point of arrival. The equation, then,
really expresses the dynamic progress of a phenomenon, and
not, contrary to appearances, a relation of equivalence between
two static states. This is so true that in his studies on the state
of equilibrium van't Hoff replaced the sign $=$ by that of
$\rightleftarrows$ in order to indicate clearly that the reaction might
operate in the two directions, the sign of equality in chemical
equations having irremediably acquired the sense of an action
in a determined direction, from left to right.(13)

This being understood how does it happen that people believed that they could use the sign in question? Evidently one arrow → would have much better expressed the sense of the relation. And how explain that we are not shocked by this term *equation*, so unsuitable for the occasion? It is because beyond and beneath the produced phenomenon, the apparent phenomenon, we believe that we see something else; we believe, we at least wish to believe, that the totality of the antecedents, if we were able to embrace them at a glance and recognize their intimate nature, would be recognized as equal to the totality of the consequents and identical with it. Moreover, in support of this opinion we may cite the authority of the man from whom is derived this whole manner of thinking in modern chemistry. Lavoisier, in his *Traité élementaire de chimie*, wrote what may be called the first true chemical equation, and with his usual clearness explained the sense which he attributed to this formula.

After having affirmed that "nothing is created, either in the operations of art, or in those of nature," and that "it may be stated as a principle that in every operation there is an equal quantity of matter before and after the operation," he adds: "It is upon this principle that is based the entire art of making experiments in chemistry. We are obliged to assume in all experiments a true equality or equation between the principles of the substance which we are examining and those which we take from it by analysis. Thus, since grape-must yields carbonic acid gas and alcohol, I can say that grape-must = carbonic acid + alcohol."(14)

Therefore, to Lavoisier the equation is really the expression of complete equality, of identity between the antecedent and the consequent in a chemical reaction.

Poinsot says: "In perfect knowledge we know but one law— that of constancy and uniformity. To this simple idea we try to reduce all others, and it is only in this reduction that we believe science to consist."(15) No truer or more penetrating word; the purely empirical law seems external at once to things and to our mind, impenetrable, opaque. Only the laws which affirm identity, which flow from it or lead to it, appear to us as adequate either to the essence of things and to our understanding; these, alone, we know "in perfect knowledge." And we see also that science thus defined by the great mathematician is quite other than a group of empirical rules. It is the effort of the mind toward comprehension, of the intellect toward the rationalization of things, an effort which is the normal function of the intellect and which cannot be accomplished except with the aid of the principle of identity in time.

Thus these chemical equations are the expression of the tendency to identify things in time; one can also say "to eliminate" time. Let us suppose that the process of identification continues and that we really succeed in expressing the entire phenomenon in an equation, in identifying completely the antecedent and the consequent; everything has been preserved, everything has remained as it was—that is, time has exercised no influence. To be sure, we know in advance that that complete identification is impossible. But, in part, we can verify with the aid of our equations that it is really so. Elementary matter which existed before the phenomenon has subsisted afterwards; from that point of view there has been no change. Weight has also remained the same; there, too, nothing has been modified. Finally, energy also has been conserved. On the whole, as far as our explanation reaches, *nothing has happened*. And since phenomenon is only change, it is clear that according as we have explained it we have made it disappear. Every explained part of a phenomenon is a part denied; to explain is to explain away.

It is true that there remain the phenomena of displacement. They are, we have seen, privileged by their very nature in that we can, according as it suits us, consider them sometimes as implying a change and sometimes as conserving identity. It is upon this particularity that all possibility of causal identification rests, and in our equations we likewise have done nothing else than use this means, in assuming that elementary masses and energy displace themselves even while remaining self-identical. Moreover, the nature of this displacement has remained undetermined; an indetermination which evidently is quite provisional, for if we wished to penetrate more deeply into the explanation of the phenomenon, to scrutinize its mechanism, we should be obliged to determine exactly the molecular motions—that is, to commit ourselves upon the mode of displacement. We have avoided it by the simple fact that the explanation of chemical phenomena is still too little extended; chemistry is not yet advanced enough to admit of true mechanical explanations. But we cannot doubt that universal mechanism demands explanations of this kind. Yet this provisional indetermination has served us in our demonstration, in this sense that it has permitted us to set forth better the identity between antecedent and consequent.

It seems, indeed, more difficult if we turn to the science of motion itself, mechanics. Here we have the fundamental phenomenon, that to which explicative science tends to reduce all others. Shall we say that science tends to disavow it?

And yet if the analysis we have just made is correct, if explanation by mechanism is not an end, but a means, and if the explicative value of mechanical theories rests upon the fact that they satisfy our causal tendency, it is evident that our manner of treating bodies in motion must feel the effects of it. And we can foresee from the double aspect of motion, which is at once conservation and change, that rational science will apply itself to emphasizing the first.

Let us come back to the three principles of conservation. That of mass has nothing to do, strictly speaking, with mechanics, since it is understood by definition that the phenomena with which that science is concerned exclude any transformation whatever of matter. But the principle of conservation of energy is, in part, mechanical, and that of inertia is entirely so. These two propositions completely dominate that part of science, and it is especially under this aspect that we are prone to deal with these phenomena. A stone was attached to something. It has become detached and is in the act of falling—that is, because its energy, which was originally potential, has become kinetic; but the energy was there, and still is there. I threw a stone into the air; it moved at first with a certain velocity, constantly diminishing until it stopped completely. The stone began to come down again, falling faster and faster; but, I am told that during all of the time when this remarkably changing phenomenon was taking place, something supposed to represent its most essential aspect, energy, has, on the contrary, remained immutable, for at every moment the sum of the kinetic and potential energies has remained the same. A cannon-ball passes, hurled with great velocity. Here, it seems, is continual change, clearly characterized; doubtless so, science assures me, if we consider this motion as change of position with respect to surrounding bodies. But if I imagine a being placed upon this cannon-ball, he will believe himself to be at rest just as we have the same sensation on the earth; for him this motion, provided it be uniform and rectilinear, will not exist. It is generally said that the principle of inertia makes the notion of rest disappear, and we ourselves have considered it especially from this point of view; but the truth is that between motion and rest there is a reciprocal assimilation, and we can affirm with as much reason that the motion is suppressed, since immediately, and one might say almost instinctively, we henceforth apply to rectilinear motion all the norms our mind establishes for rest. "Inertia," says Hermann Cohen justly, "does not include motion; it is rather even supposed to exclude it in a certain sense."(16)

That motion, considered in itself, should, like every other change, in reality be inconceivable, is clearly shown by the reasonings or, if you will, the paradoxes of the Eleatics, and more particularly the paradoxes designated under the name of Achilles and the Arrow. It is incomprehensible that Achilles should ever overtake the tortoise, and likewise that the arrow occupying at a given moment a determined spot should leave it. It is generally affirmed that the origin of these paradoxes lies in the fact that we cannot conceive of the actual infinite, and consequently of the continuous, that our reason can only grasp the discrete. Without wishing to probe this question, which is a digression from our subject, let us observe that our understanding does not seem to revolt against the concept of the continuous, so long as the consideration of motion is not in question. In synthetic geometry the body appears to us as really continuous, and also the surface in so far as it is the limit of the body, the line in so far as it is the limit of the surface. The difficulties of the continuous appear only with motion. It may, however, be that these difficulties are not so great for us as they were for the Greeks; thus we need to make a certain effort to grasp the sense of the argument about the arrow which seems, at the very moment when it is at a certain spot, to have nevertheless conserved *velocity*. Our habit of mind has been created in us by the concept of inertia

(Cf. p. 148) and is doubtless strengthened by the infinitesimal calculus. It has been said that the infinitesimal calculus is an effort to grasp the concept of continuity with the help of the discrete. This observation is quite correct, but it must be added that in this calculus continuity always appears in the act of being generated by motion. It is this motion that we try to grasp by making it discontinuous, by decomposing it into small indivisible phases which are so many small rests. There is, therefore, an analogy between the methods of the mathematician and those of the physicist, in the sense that both reduce motion to immobility.(17)

In a word, science in its effort to become "rational" tends more and more to suppress variation in time. And it is clearly seen that empiricism has nothing to do with it. Indeed, the instinct of preservation demands prevision; it is, therefore, evolution in time which especially interests us, and it seems that the essential form of the law, of the empirical rule, must be that expressing a modification as a function of the time. But it is in no wise so. If many statements expressing functions of the time are found in the sciences of organic nature it is because they are still in the beginning of their evolution. But these statements are the more rare as the science becomes more rational.

Let us suppose for a moment that science can really make the causal postulate prevail; antecedent and consequent, cause and effect, are confused and become indiscernible, simultaneous. And time itself, whose course no longer implies change, is indiscernible, unimaginable, non-existent. It is the confusion of past, present, and future—a universe eternally immutable. The progress of the world is stopped. And, of course, simultaneously, or rather previously, the cause has vanished. For as soon as cause is confused with effect, when there is identity between antecedent and consequent, when nothing happens, there is no more cause. The principle of causality, as Renouvier (18) has justly remarked, is the elimination of the cause.

In appearance it is a paradoxical result. At a glance, however, we can take in the ground covered, and verify the fact that we have not lost ourselves on the way, that the terminus had really been demanded by the starting-point. We have searched for the causes of phenomena and we have searched for them with the help of a principle which, we know, is only the principle of identity applied to the existence of objects in time. The ultimate source of all causes can thus only be identical to itself. It is the universe immutable in space and time, the sphere of Parmenides, imperishable and without change.

In contemplating in thought this sublime image of the great Eleatic we cannot but observe its strange resemblance to a quite modern conception, that of the nebula, which, according to Laplace, is the origin of our solar system. On that account is it proper to see in Parmenides a precursor of the French astronomer? Not at all. The sphere was a purely metaphysical conception, an eternal symbol of the universe; the nebula is a scientific hypothesis, based upon particular facts, designed to indicate the physical state of a limited part of the universe at a determined moment. And yet it is more than a simple coincidence. Both sphere and nebula are, indeed, causal conceptions. Only the sphere, being the entire universe, cannot change in its relation to space; it must, therefore, remain immutable, whereas the nebula, being only the solar system, can revolve in absolute space. This movement, playing the rôle of the diversifying principle, which the Eleatics designated under the name of *war* or *discord*, allows the nebula to be differentiated subsequently in order to procreate, by mere evolution, by the development of what must have been therein potentially contained, the entire series of worlds. As Wilbois says: "The theory of the nebula ends by affirming that evolution is only an appearance which covers a true fixity."(19)

The nebula, the last link in a causal chain, which through a singular privilege we can represent to ourselves as almost isolated from the rest of the universe, is, like the sphere of Parmenides, a translation into the concrete of the principle of the immutability of being.

However, in closely scrutinizing Parmenides' conception we perceive that all the characteristic features of this symbol cannot be deduced solely from the application of the principle of identity in time. An essential feature remains unexplained. This we shall examine in the next chapter.

NOTES

1. H. FOUILLÉE: *L'avenir de la métaphysique*. Paris, F. Alcan, 1889, p. 18. Hertz (*l.c.*, p. 11) has expressed analogous ideas. Moreover, both Fouillée and Hertz saw that the increase of prestige of the principles of conservation must come from the fact that *a priori* elements were implicitly contained therein.

2. We shall see in a later chapter (p. 280) that this impossibility has extended still farther than we have been able to show (p. 209), and that even where the modern concept of energy seems most familiar, in thermal phenomena, for which it had been created, it no longer admits of a true *verbal* definition other than that resulting from the very fact of conservation, conforming to Poincaré's formula.

3. ARRHENIUS (*L'Evolution des mondes*, trans. Seyrig. Paris, 1910, pp. 75–76), happening to speak of the theory according to which heat radiating from the sun had its origin in radio-active bodies, esteems this idea "singular" assuming "that one must admit that heat is created from nothing." He adds: "Before we can lend ourselves to the scientific discussion of such an explanation, we must be told what is the origin of this radiation and where its reserve, its provision of energy, is found." Evidently, energy is here a real substance; its conservation is considered as an irrefutable truth, superior to direct experience, such as that of the radiation of radio-active bodies.

4. H. G. WELLS: *The Time Machine*. Leipzig, 1898.

5. HERTZ (*l.c.*, Vol. III, p. 284), distinguishing between "conservative" and "dissipative" systems, is very careful to make known that the first constitute an exception. But one sees from his very exposition that the number of hidden masses and their degrees of freedom being infinite with respect to the visible masses and their co-ordinates, these exceptions must be infinitely rare—that is, cannot be encountered in reality.

6. Id., *l.c.*, p. 162.

7. *Ib.*, pp. 90, 161, 199, 202.

8. OSTWALD: *La déroute de l'atomisme contemporain*. *Revue générale des sciences*, Vol. VI, p. 954.

9. One can see, moreover, in the work of Wohlwill (*l.c.*, XIV, p. 402), that it is indeed under this form of a simple variation in time that Galileo first conceived the law of falling bodies.

10. The reader's indulgence is asked for what is schematic and, therefore, inexact in this exposition. Lavoisier began his calorimetric studies upon chemical reactions at the same time that he was engaged in his other works. Yet it is really only much later that general ideas were formulated on the rôle played by heat in chemical combinations. It goes without saying that one must, in order to separate mercury from oxygen, add the heat of vaporization of this gas.

11. Cf. G. HELM: *Die Lehre von der Energie*. Leipzig, 1887, p. 7.

12. W. OSTWALD: *Vorlesungen ueber Naturphilosophie*, 2nd ed. Leipzig, 1902, pp. 114, 225–226.

13. JEAN PERRIN shows, justly, that irreversibility seemed to be an integral part of the concept of chemical phenomena, and that as soon as there was reversibility the phenomenon was considered to be physical (*Traité de chimie physique*. Paris, 1903, p. 10 and ff.).

14. LAVOISIER: *Œuvres*, Vol. I, p. 101.

15. L. POINSOT: *Eléments de statique suivis de quatre mémoires*, etc., 10th ed. Paris, 1861, p. 239. The sequel weakens the significance of this passage. In it Poinsot limits research to that of the constancy of the *relation*. The tenor of the sentences quoted in the text seems to show however that from the very first he saw the real importance of his statement, but that in trying to render it more precise his thought deviated from it, probably because of a confusion analogous to that which we pointed out in Helmholtz and in Hertz (cf. pp. 41, 302).

16. HERMANN COHEN: *Logik der reinen Erkenntnis*. Berlin, 1902, p. 206.

17. Cf. p. 94, where we examined this question from a slightly different point of view.

18. RENOUVIER: *La méthode phénoméniste*. *Année philosophique*, 1890, p. 26. Cf. *ib.*, p. 89.

19. WILBOIS: *L'esprit positif. Revue de métaphysique*, Vol. X, 1902, p. 334.

CHAPTER VII

THE UNITY OF MATTER

PARMENIDES imagined the universe as a material sphere, apparently composed throughout of a single and identical matter. In other words, he affirmed at once the immutable essence and the unity of material being.(1)

This conception is to be found again in most of the atomistic systems. Kanada, it seems, had conceived of his atoms as diverse, but, according to the Jainas, they are constituted of a single and identical matter.(2) Leucippus and Democritus have expressed themselves with great clearness on this subject. "They are distinguished, we are told, from one another by their figures," says Aristotle, speaking of atoms as they were conceived by these two philosophers, "but their nature is one, like many pieces of gold separated from one another."(3) The Greek atomists of the subsequent period constantly maintained the teaching of the masters. We know from a passage of Galenus, himself an adversary of atomistic theories, that the unity of matter was considered in his time as an integral part of these doctrines.(4) In the Middle Ages, when Aristotelianism reigned supreme, belief in the unity of matter was almost general; it was the basis of the alchemists' theories and of their attempts at transmutation.(5) It is possible that we have here, as has been said, an influence exercised by a sort of undercurrent of atomistic doctrines,(6) which really existed, drawing its source from certain medical writings; but we shall see later that there is no need to have recourse to this hypothesis and that Aristotle's theories themselves are sufficient to explain this tendency. Since the renascence of mechanical theories the unity of matter is affirmed and encounters, so to speak, no opposition. For Descartes it is a fundamental and self-evident truth: "There is but one and the same matter in the whole universe."(7) After him, everyone seems agreed upon this point. In the ardent polemics raised by the question of Newtonian attraction there will not be found the slightest mention of this objection which appears so readily to the modern mind; how attribute one and the same property to material fundamentally diverse? Without doubt partisans and

adversaries of action at a distance were to an equal degree
convinced of the unity of matter. Chemists were of the same
opinion, and Boyle, a firm adherent of the corpuscular theories,
openly affirms the unity of matter, which seems to him to be
inseparable from these theories.(8) In the eighteenth century
a crisis begins, a crisis which becomes more and more accentuated, almost until our time; and this is all the more interesting
to observe as it is to a certain extent latent and unacknowledged.
It is, indeed, very remarkable, from an historical point of
view, that the evolution of which we are speaking takes place
without attracting the attention of anyone. Nothing, it seems,
is more essential in chemistry than the concept of the element,
and it is precisely this concept which is in the act of being
completely transformed. And yet the historians of chemistry
have never taken this transformation as the point of departure
of a new epoch. This is because it is so slow, imperceptible, and,
as it were, spontaneous; there is found there a kind of extremely
powerful undercurrent of which even the protagonists of
chemistry are not conscious, which carries them along, so to
speak, in spite of themselves.(9) At the beginning of the chemistry
of phlogiston, Becher was firmly convinced of the possibility
of transmutation (10), and even believed that he had found
a process of bringing it about within certain limits.(11) Therefore not only these metals, but also the metallic calces (which
we call oxides) did not appear to him as the true elements.
Indeed, he believed that these latter were only three in number
—at bottom they were the same as those of Paracelsus, although
Becher invests them with different names.(12) Even Stahl,
who was the first to use the term *phlogiston*, did not doubt in
the least, at any rate during the first part of his career, the
existence of a substance called *Elixir* or *Tincture*,(13) whose
principal property consisted in transmuting metals; he expressly
affirmed the possibility of a transmutation of lead.(14) Later
he changed his opinion and became the adversary of the alchemists;(15) however, we do not find that he has ever declared
that he considered metallic calces veritable elements.(16) Yet
little by little this last opinion (prepared in the seventeenth
century by the writings of Boyle,(17) who, however, we have
already said, believed, himself, in the unity of matter) tends
to prevail amongst his successors. It is certainly found already

solidly established on the eve of Lavoisier's (18) discoveries, and from this point of view, at least, the "chemical revolution," of which he was the author, found the way prepared. Without doubt the remembrance of Aristotle's elements and those of Becher had not entirely vanished, and especially in manuals it was sometimes still referred to. Lavoisier, in the preface to the *Traité élémentaire de chimie*, shows, with his habitual clearness, the inconsistencies of these ancient conceptions. "This tendency to desire that all the bodies of nature be composed of only three or four elements comes from a prejudice which arose originally in the Greek philosophers." On the contrary, the chemical element is a notion resulting from experience. "The last term at which analysis arrives, all the substances which we have been unable as yet to decompose by any means, are elements as far as we are concerned." (19) But we feel from the brevity of his declarations that he has no controversy to fear in this matter. Indeed, his most competent contemporaries were in agreement with him.(20) Kopp remarks that Lavoisier never took the trouble of proclaiming the inanity of transmutations.

Since the definite triumph of Lavoisier's theory nothing seems more assured from the empirical point of view than the existence of "elements"—that is, of substances differing from one another as regards their fundamental qualities, substances which appear to us as indestructible, capable of uniting amongst themselves to form combinations, but incapable of transformation within themselves. Helmholtz designates the chemical principle of which we are speaking as that of the "unalterability of substances" (*Unveraenderlichkeit der Stoffe*) or of the "constancy of elements," and considers it to be fundamental.(21) Armand Gautier also remarks that it is one of the bases of our chemistry and very justly attributes to it the first place in the enumeration of these fundamental notions.(22) Etard is of the same opinion.(23) It is, moreover, easy to understand why this notion is in a way an integral part of the principle of the conservation of matter. It is precisely this undetermined but extremely important part of the principle of which we have already spoken (p. 158).

I burn a piece of sulphur with the aid of oxygen and I collect the sulphurous anhydride thus produced. On the other hand, I make water by combining oxygen with hydrogen and by dissolving potassium in this water, a solution of potash; finally, I make this solution absorb the sulphurous acid. In this way I obtain bisulphite of potash. Evidently in this whole series of operations the same weight has been preserved—that is, if I add, on the one hand, the weights of the constituents, which I put into these several combinations—sulphur, oxygen, hydrogen, and potassium—and, on the other hand, the weights of the products, sulphite of potash and the accessory products, such as hydrogen, which was regenerated by the dissolution of the potassium, etc., the two sums will be exactly the same. This is the principle of the conservation of matter; but is this the whole principle? Can nothing more be said about this conservation? On the contrary, I can affirm that not only the weights, but the constituents themselves will be preserved, that the sulphur will remain sulphur, the oxygen oxygen, and so on. The proof of this is that I do not hesitate to designate my final product by the symbol $KHSO_3$. Doubtless, if necessary, it may be affirmed that this formula signifies, not that the elementary substances are actually found contained in the bisulphite, but only that they can be released under certain conditions. This is Henri Sainte-Claire Deville's (24) opinion, and Ostwald (25) seems to agree to it. On this hypothesis the elements would disappear in the combinations. This in itself is not paradoxical. Problems of this kind have often been stated in chemistry without always receiving identical solutions. Thus it may be asked whether the water, which we see is easily added under certain conditions to the molecules of the substances, remains there afterwards as such. Chemists generally believe this to be so as regards water of crystallization. But in regard to the water of the acids hypotheses have varied. Formerly it was supposed that sulphuric acid, for instance, was a compound of what we now call anhydride (which at that time was considered as the true acid) and water; this latter was, therefore, preserved as such in the compound molecule. In our present formulae, on the contrary, the molecule of water which is added to the anhydride is divided, the hydroxyl and the hydrogen settling in two different parts of the atomic chain.

Having thus stated the conditions of the problem it is

sufficient to examine the theories of chemistry to see that the
doctrine generally accepted is the opposite of Sainte-Claire
Deville's. Let us re-read the passage from Lavoisier, quoted
in the preceding chapter, weighing carefully these words:
"We are obliged to suppose in all these [experiments] a true
equality or equation between the principles of the substance
which we are examining and those which we take from it by
analysis."

If we had any doubts about the import of this passage we
should only have to refer to what precedes; in a sentence
which we omitted from our citation, Lavoisier declares that
before or after the operation "the quality and the quantity of
the principles are the same, and there are only changes and
modifications." So what Lavoisier is affirming is that the
"principles" (it is a question of the kind of substances which he
knew to be compounds, but this applies evidently *a fortiori*
to the elements) pre-exist as such previously to their isolation.

We may, moreover, easily convince ourselves that chemistry,
on this point, has remained faithful to the idea of the most
illustrious of its votaries. It is affirmed that the substances not
only have been composed, but that they *are* really composed
of their elements, that these latter are really therein contained,
that they persist in their combinations. We are even searching
for the way in which their ultimate parts may have been
grouped. All theories from Berzelius to van't Hoff about these
formulae, now called structural formulae, in which the progress
of chemistry is summed up, would lose their meaning if we
doubted for a single moment this persistency.

To be sure, no one affirms that the elements in entering these
combinations preserve all their properties; it seems at first
sight that there could be no relation in this respect between
the potassium metal, the hydrogen gas, etc., on the one hand,
and the bisulphite, on the other. It is well known, however,
that such relations have been discovered. The most important
of these, formerly called the law of equivalents, was established
by Gay-Lussac and transformed by Avogadro, who added to
it some considerations on the molecular weights of the gases.
Since then chemists have found others; patiently they continue
to search, convinced in advance that these relations exist,
that it is only a question of disengaging them; what we call

physical or general chemistry is indeed only the study of the influence exercised on the properties of substances by their chemical composition, i.e. by the totality of the properties of their elements and their manner of grouping.

It is difficult, it seems, to doubt under these circumstances that the heterogeneity of the fundamental elements really constitutes the basis of chemistry. If, however, we ask for the opinion of chemists themselves on this question, and especially of the theorists of chemistry, we encounter manifest doubts and even sometimes the clear affirmation of the unity of matter. This is of long standing. Lavoisier already hesitated to place in the same rank all the elements whose existence he had established. Oxygen, nitrogen, hydrogen, seemed to him more simple than the other substances, which, consequently, would only have been compounds.(26) In 1815 Prout formulated his well-known theory according to which hydrogen was a fundamental element of which all the others were compounds; this conception had an extraordinary vogue and counted amongst its adherents many well-known chemists, among others J. B. Dumas, who, it is true, modified it slightly in starting from a submultiple of the atomic weight of hydro-gen.(27) Later research has not confirmed this conception, but it flourished for a long time and is far from having definitely disappeared.(28) Still more considerable was the success of the conceptions based upon the periodicity of atomic weights, conceptions initiated by Chancourtois,(29) but to which Mendeleef gave their final form. The theories of this Russian chemist have been the starting-point for a great number of scientific investigations, and although the polemics aroused by them are far from being extinct, it is certainly not going too far to affirm that at present they are an integral part of theoretical chemistry.(30)

Assuming that the surrender of the immutability of elements would profoundly derange, as we have seen, the entire edifice of chemistry, one would be inclined to believe that every assumption with that tendency would be received with extreme distrust and that extremely convincing experimental proofs would be necessary to enlist science in that task. Now, neither in Prout's time nor in that of Mendeleef was there evidence of the shadow of a fact which could inspire doubt as to the fixity

of chemical elements. And what is more, the experimental
bases of the two theories were always extremely slight and at
the moment of their appearance an extreme good will was
necessary to admit of such lofty constructions erected upon
foundations of so little solidity.(31)

These considerations clearly show, it seems, that chemists,
in spite of the experimental results and the exigencies of the
theory which they ostensibly profess, have only accepted against
their will the fact of the existence of some sixty elements.
Berthelot assures us that chemists have always cherished the
hope of going beyond what they considered as a provisional
limit.(32) It is significant also that Gibbs, whose celebrated
theoretical works seem to necessitate the orientation of all
science in a new and fruitful direction, has not hesitated to
base one of the fundamental postulates of his doctrine on the
possibility of transmutation;(33) and that Friedel, after having
declared that "the notion of a single elementary matter is a
philosophical conception rather than anything else," has
asked, three pages farther on, for "a mechanical explanation of
the general fact to which the name of atomicity or valence of
atoms has been given."(34) Atomicity or valence is an expression of affinity, the most intimate property of chemical atoms,
that by which, finally, the others must be able to be explained.
If it, in its turn, demands an explanation, it is because it is
acknowledged to be an occult quality—that is, that everything
is supposed to be reducible to a single matter stripped of
qualities.

We can also cite the testimony of philosophers such as
Spencer, Lotze, Wundt, and Hannequin. For Herbert Spencer
the properties of different chemical elements "result from
differences of arrangement arising by the compounding and
recompounding of ultimate homogeneous units."(35) Wundt,
after having stated that "chemistry still attributes the diverse
qualities of matter to an original qualitative difference between
atoms," immediately adds, "but the general tendency of
atomism in physics is to derive all the qualitative properties of
matter from the forms of atomic motion. Thus atoms themselves
remain as elements entirely devoid of qualities."(36) In the
same way Hannequin declares that the unity of matter is
"the secret postulate of all atomism."(37) But it is perhaps

still more significant that this tendency should be emphasized by Lotze,(38) for this metaphysician is the adversary of the concept of the unity of matter, and these tendencies of chemists and physicists surprise him.

Evidently, a tendency so general and powerful must have a profound cause. But we cannot directly invoke causality as we have defined it according to Leibniz—that is, as the identity between cause and effect, antecedent and consequent. This principle postulates conditions for the existence of things in time; but, from this point of view, in supposing that sulphur remains sulphur and oxygen oxygen, it is indifferent whether the sulphur be, as has been supposed, a simple polymer of oxygen(39) or else a radically distinct kind of matter. Rather, from the point of view of the import and the facility of the deductions, it is preferable, on the contrary, to start with as large a number as possible of elements having very different properties. Indeed, for the moment we are far from knowing how to explain completely the properties of the compounds by those of the elements; but conceivably that would be easier, there would be less ground to cover, in order to arrive at qualitatively different kinds of matter, than if all had to be reduced to a single matter: the properties of sulphites could certainly be explained with less difficulty by those of sulphur, etc., than if, for instance, all had to be reduced to hydrogen. Thus, far from being able in this way to deduce the unity of matter from the causal principle, we observe that this latter impels us in the opposite direction.

Yet if, abandoning the position of chemistry and the problem of the explanation of the properties of material substances, we consider the phenomenon as a "becoming," the deduction for which we are searching may seem to be possible. Indeed, we can give the following form to the reasoning by which we have tried to establish the fundamental principles of mechanism. The phenomenon is change—that is, modification in time; but there is only one modification which is intelligible: it is displacement.(40) What is displaced we call matter, and nothing but matter exists in the physical world. Therefore matter cannot be displaced (the modern physicist will formulate it rather: cannot modify its inertial motion—but this variation leaves the basis of the reasoning intact, since inertial motion is assimilated to rest, and it is, moreover, manifestly insufficient as a means of explanation) except under the action of other matter. It is this action (collision, attraction) which constitutes the fundamental phenomenon, the only phenomenon of all reality, and, consequently, matter has need only of this single property and hence is one, everywhere the same.

But it suffices to press the argument farther to perceive that its rigour is only apparent. Doubtless, the phenomenon is modification in time, but it is modification of an *existing* diversity; at no moment do we find reality anything but diverse—infinitely diverse. This diversity is manifestly qualitative, since it is the diversity of our sensation. It becomes modified, and it is this modification which we must explain: the substance was cold; it has become warm. Let us admit that there was displacement of something, that that which was displaced consisted of discrete particles, very small because invisible, and that they began to move by the action of other particles. Why are not these displaced particles simply warm? Whence comes to me the strange idea that heat does not exist outside of my sensation—that it is only a sort of motion?

It is true that this conception seems to correspond to a distinction which, since the time of Locke, has become quite commonplace—that is, the distinction between the primary and secondary qualities of matter; we count amongst the former, considered as inseparable from the concept of matter itself, impenetrability, which we have seen is only action transformed into a property (p. 72). But whence comes this distinction? Is it true that, mentally, we can strip the concept of matter of certain properties and not of others? Matter, the object of our sensations, has diverse qualities; it is hot, coloured, electrified, magnetic, etc. Can we eliminate the first of these qualities and suppose a matter which would have no temperature? That is literally inconceivable, our imagination balks at a substance which to the touch would not give either the sensation of cold or that of heat—that is, of which the temperature would approach that of our blood; indeed, this same substance would give us a heat sensation under other circumstances, if, for instance, we had previously dipped our hand in cold water. The same is true for colour, which alone permits us to *see* matter. "All vision is colour vision," said

Maxwell,(41) after Berkeley had already said it.(42) Doubtless for electric and magnetic conditions we cannot follow the same analysis, since an organ for the immediate sensation corresponding to it is lacking; but it is clear that the situation is the same and that matter devoid of these properties could not exist. As object of our sensations, as a common-sense notion, matter is consequently a complex concept which must be defined by the totality of the properties enumerated above; we are obliged to consider them all as primary qualities. It is also known that ideas on this subject have varied; the peripatetics considered as primary qualities, cold and heat, dryness and humidity. If, on the contrary, we were to look for properties conceivable *a priori*, impenetrability would certainly not be of the number; we have seen that no one has succeeded in placing it in the atom, in respect to which it indeed appears as a true occult quality. Therefore, from this point of view, impenetrability enjoys no privilege compared with other properties of matter.

In view, therefore, of the causal explanation we ought to endow the particle, the atom, with a principle in virtue of which it will be able to act upon others. But since it must, in the last analysis, act upon us in order to give rise to sensations, it would be manifestly convenient to locate in it the principles creative of these sensations also. In other words, we should arrive not at a purely mechanical atomism, such as that of Democritus, but at a qualitative atomism, even at a theory like that of Anaxagoras, who, we know, supposed the existence of an infinite number of elements or of principles differing from one another in quality. Indeed, we have clearly seen, precisely from the example of chemical substances, that explanation is the less difficult as the elements to be transformed are more diverse, and consequently the infinite diversity of the fundamental elements appears as a direct consequence of the infinite diversity of the phenomena. But we shall perhaps render the argument clearer by limiting its range. All matter, of course, must react mechanically upon other matter. But must this action always be the same—could there not be diverse types of matter, endowed with different mechanical properties? Why, for example—and nothing, in this line of thought, is so good as a precise example drawn from genuine science and from its real history—did not Democritus assume a series of kinds of matter of different hardness? Instead of all atoms being like pieces of gold, why did he not admit of an entire scale going from iron to wax? Why did Friedel ask for the explanation of chemical valence? Why should not such or such an atom possess the power of attracting, of grouping, which would be lacking in some other atom, and for what reason does it seem immediately indispensable to us to *explain* this diversity, which evidently can only be done by the diversified grouping in the element itself of one and the same matter? Is it not manifest that in both cases we deprive ourselves of important means of explanation, that we complicate, so to speak, wantonly a task which is already sufficiently arduous? We end, therefore, after all with this conclusion: in holding rigorously to the principle of identity in time, we cannot succeed in explaining this important feature of mechanical theories, namely, the unity of matter. Must we, therefore, have recourse to obscure and general principles, such as a tendency toward unity or simplicity? Must we infer with Lotze that our motives are of an æsthetic order? (43) Is it really possible to attribute to a cause of this kind a tendency which, in spite of immense obstacles which it seems to ignore at will, manifests itself with such singular vigour, a tendency which a very cautious and well-informed metaphysician has recently qualified as "irresistible"? (44) Seemingly, there must be a more profound cause.

Let us start from the image of the universe as it is presented to us by current atomic theory; that corpuscular masses have, besides the faculty of displacing themselves, the power to cause mutually their displacement, but are destitute of every other quality. In order to fix our ideas, let us try to confer upon them that one quality, which is called in chemistry atomicity or valence—that is, let us try to give to a certain number amongst these atoms the power of attaching to themselves in some way a determined number of other atoms. If we try to represent to ourselves, to realize, this new image, our understanding, or, if you prefer, our "imagination," will resist. How shall we relate this quality to the image of the atom which we have already formed? Where shall we place it? This seems mysterious to us; atomicity, as the adversaries of this concept have many times shown, appears inexplicablé. "Every genuine force of nature is essentially *qualitas occulta*," says Schopenhauer.(45)

Let us pause at this last term. Until now we have only spoken of explanation as regards the relations of phenomena in time. But, manifestly, there is no question of this relation here; these atoms, as well as the quality with which we claim to endow them, must be eternal, immutable, independent of time. This reality does not become; it is. It is, therefore, no longer an explanation of becoming for which we are asking, but an explanation of being.

The question has been treated by Aristotle in the VIIIth book of his *Physics*. He was there concerned precisely, as in the case which has just occupied us, with a quality of the atoms. Democritus, in order to explain their agitation, affirmed, we know, that it had existed through all time. Aristotle finds this explanation insufficient. He says: "To admit in general that it is a principle and a sufficient cause of a fact to say that this fact is always of such or such a manner does not at all satisfy reason." And he adds: "Yet it is to that that Democritus reduces all the causes in nature by pretending that things are actually of such a kind, and that they were so previously. But as to the cause of this eternal state, he does not believe that he must look for it."(46)

Aristotle, we see, employs the term "cause," although it is a question of an "eternal state"; we must have here a relation quite cognate to that of causality proper.

Let us go back to the statement of the principle of determining reason given by Leibniz: "Nothing ever happens without there being a cause or, at least, a determining reason—that is, something which can explain *a priori* why this is existing thus rather than in any other way."(47) The first part of the formula, "Nothing ever happens," appears to have bearing on *becoming* alone, but in the second part, Leibniz, by a kind of mental leap, evidently goes farther, since he demands a reason for that which "is existing."

Another passage which we borrow from a work recently brought out by Couturat is, perhaps, still more clear. "This is why," says Leibniz, "we must explain even eternal things; if we suppose that the world has existed since eternity and that there are in it nothing but globules, we must explain why they are globules rather than cubes."(48)

There is no doubt that he intended by the extension of the principle to protest against the indiscriminate attribution of certain qualities to substances. He says: "Thus in the order of nature (miracles set aside) it is not optional with God to give indifferently such or such qualities to substances; and he will never give to them any but those which will be natural— that is, which can be derived from their nature as explicable modifications."(49) Wolf has, therefore, really summed up the teachings of his master when he formulates: *Nihil est sine ratione cur potius sit quam non sit*, and this formula, which, we have seen, has been adopted literally by Schopenhauer,(50) clearly indicates that it is here a question of the reason for being and not only for that of becoming.

Earlier we asked: Why have things changed? And causality replied: They have not changed; they have remained the same. Now we ask: Why, supposing they are such from all eternity, are they thus and not otherwise? Evidently the two questions correspond to one and the same current of thought. The external world is for us a verity of fact, a fortuitous verity; we would like to explain it, to conceive of it as a verity of reason, a necessary verity. How shall we go about it?

Let us come back to our concept of the mechanical atom. Is it really devoid of quality? No, for it possesses at least one faculty, that of being the cause of motion for other atoms. But in discussing this faculty we have shown, it seems, that it could not be attributed to the atom, that it is incompatible with our image of it; it is, therefore, still an "occult quality." To understand how we succeeded in recognizing it as such we have only to consider what this image of the atom is with which the faculty in question cannot agree. What remains of the corpuscular atom if we take from it action at a distance and impenetrability? There evidently remains but a bit of space. Lasswitz says, in the passage which we have already used in establishing the fundamental concept of the corpuscular atom: "I conceive as atom a mobile portion of space whose geometrical parts are at rest in relation to each other."(51) Therefore we really tried to conciliate impenetrability with the properties of space, and we have at last established that it cannot be deduced from these properties; thus it is that we have been able to treat it as an "occult quality." This term, indeed, should be defined thus: that which is not a part of the concept (Leibniz, in the passage just cited, said, "which can be derived from their nature"). Whether such or such a quality is or is not "occult" will, therefore, depend on the manner in which we form the concept of matter—that is to say, on its definition. Here we have confused matter with space, and, of course, the latter being absolutely inert, its concept excluding both activity and passivity, therefore impenetrability and with still greater reason action at a distance have become "occult qualities."

To be convinced of this it is enough to consider the statements of Descartes and of Locke on the subject of primary qualities. Descartes affirms that "the nature of matter or of body, taken in general, does not consist in the fact that it is something hard or heavy or coloured or which touches our senses in some other fashion, but only in the fact that it is a substance extended in length, in width, and in depth." (52) Locke declares as follows: "These I call original or primary qualities of the body which, I think, we may observe to produce simple ideas in us, viz. solidity, extension, figure, motion or rest, and number."(53) With the exception of the first, these are purely spatial qualities. Locke, besides, does not try any more than Leibniz, in his discussions with the Cartesians, to establish that solidity (Leibniz employs *impenetrability* or *antitypy* and *power*) can really be lodged in the spatial image. He assumes it by postulate, declaring that body can only act by impulsion.(54)

Therefore, from a logical point of view, Descartes is right and Locke is wrong. It has frequently been said that Descartes annihilates space in favour of matter, and it is true, for with him there is no space outside of that which matter fills. But it is really a bilateral assimilation, for if matter absorbs space, matter, in turn, is nothing by hypostatized space, since, we have just seen, it has no other property than spatial magnitude. With the prodigious vigour of his intellect, Descartes, in this question as in many others, has gone at one bound to the limits of human thought; there is no other "explanation" of matter and of being in general (intellectual and moral reality, of course, put aside) than by space, and it is really in view of this ulterior explanation, as tending toward it, just as we saw in the case of time, that we are trying to eliminate from matter every "occult quality"—that is, every specific property in general.(55)

Moreover, on this point Descartes simply makes more precise the ideas of the ancient atomists. Leucippus and Democritus, Aristotle tells us, knew only three differences, causes of all phenomena: figure, order, position.(56) There is no doubt that the term *figure* is employed here in its spatial sense; hence these are purely spatial relations.

If our supposition is correct there must be manifested in modern science, parallel to the tendency to unify matter, another tendency toward the reduction of matter to space. And this, indeed, is what has happened.

Let us note, in the first place, to strengthen our affirmation, certain explicit statements of careful observers. H. Poincaré protests against the unreasonableness of certain partisans of extreme mechanical theories, who wish to reduce everything to a matter, "having nothing but purely geometrical qualities."(57) But this matter apparently is in reality nothing but space. Duhem states, concerning very different theories, that they tend equally to reduce matter to space.(58) The fact that these two competent authorities consider these tendencies as reprehensible adds still more, if possible, to the weight of their evidence.(59)

But there is still more to be said; it seems possible to show that it is in no wise a question of some monstrous excrescence of science, but of its natural products. Everyone, indeed, will agree in noting in science a current manifestly directed toward the explanation of matter by a universal medium filling space. "For a long time the more or less avowed ambition of the greater part of physicists has been to construct all the possible forms of corporeal existence out of particles of ether," says Lucien Poincaré.(60) This began immediately after Descartes, who, we have seen, had explicitly assimilated matter to space; as soon as they are differentiated, by necessity the tendency to identify them becomes manifest. Leibniz, in his *Theoria motus concreti*,(61) states that space is filled everywhere by a homogeneous matter, fluid and incompressible; this matter is capable of whirling motions, and it is to these latter alone that are due all the phenomena of the sensible world. Malebranche expounds views that are entirely analogous.(62) It is almost useless to insist on the analogy between these theories and those of certain modern physicists, notably Thomson and Tait and Helmholtz, about vortex atoms. But it is not a lack of respect for these great scientific names to state that the experimental basis of these conceptions was entirely out of proportion to the edifice they pretended to erect upon it, and that the number of facts or of relations which they were capable of explaining was quite insignificant; it is surprising that these theories have had such considerable success, and, still more astonishing, that their authors have been able to be deceived about their value; this fact alone would make us suspect the presence of some secret propensity of the human mind. At a more recent period the current seemed to have gained still greater force. That ether should, as Hertz said, explain in the last analysis everything, even "the essence of the old matter itself and its most intimate qualities of gravitation and inertia," and that this explanation should be the "ultimate end of physics,"(63) seemed to the scholars of the nineteenth century the least contested of principles. In the electrical theories of matter, in so far as they conserve the notion of ether, the new atom, the electron, appears only as a "singular point in the ether."(64)

Now what really is ether? We have seen that physicists have formulated about its properties the most diverse and often the most contradictory and least acceptable of assumptions. But there is one characteristic which dominates all these hypotheses; it is that ether fills space; that is its essential function, that for which it was created. This genesis was very clearly explained by H. Poincaré.(65) The light which comes to us from distant stars takes, we know, considerable time to reach us. Where is it during this lapse of time? We cannot suppose that it does not exist, for then the light reaching the earth would no longer be the consequence of an immediately preceding fact, but would be directly and without continuity the consequence of a fact separated by an interval of time, and this is inadmissible. Therefore, it must be somewhere, and it can only be in the intermediary space, a space which in other respects appears to us as empty. The properties which we attribute to ether are, therefore, in reality those of vacuum, as Maxwell(66) said, and ether itself, as Helmholtz declared, is nothing but space hypostatized. Kant, moreover, had already applied precisely the same term to the "caloric fluid" (*Waermestoff*), which played, in the physics of his time, a rôle analogous to that of our ether.(67)

Thus, reduction to ether is really only an attempt at reduction to space; and this reduction really constitutes the process by which we try to explain material existence, to determine its sufficient reason.

Let us state at the same time that if the leading thought from which this tendency emanates is analogous to that which engenders the principle of causality proper, the process, too, is strictly similar. When we wanted to know the "why" of becoming—that is, the reason for the modifications which are produced in time—science replied that they were only apparent modifications, that under this appearance was hidden a real identity. We want to know now the "why" of being —that is, the reason for diversity in space. Just as we asked a little while ago: Why does that which appears to me at this moment differ from that which appeared to me at the preceding moment? We now ask: Why does that which appears to me in such a place differ from that which appears to me in such another place? Consequently the only "rational" reply is: This difference does not exist; it is only apparent, superimposed on a real identity. Everywhere where space appears empty, or where it seems to be, on the contrary, filled with bodies, there is but one and the same being, ether,(68) "a continuous fluid, incompressible, not viscous, of uniform and constant temperature";(69) thus the physicists imagine it in order to deduce their theories from it; the ideal is to define it by purely negative attributes, as E. Du Bois-Reymond explicitly claimed to do (70) in conformity with the hypostatization of space. It goes without saying that being conceived in this fashion it is not capable of any real change. In a medium endowed with purely negative qualities the parts cannot be different. How, then, could motion be possible in it—how conceive of the rings of Thomson and of Helmholtz or the singular points of Larmor? How can the ether in either of these cases be distinguished from the surrounding ether? Leibniz said that: "If one grants the *plenum* and the unity of matter, adding to it only motion, equivalent things constantly being substituted for each other, the state of one moment cannot be distinguished from the state of another, not even by an angel, and consequently there can exist no variety in phenomena";(71) and this is also the same idea that Russell expresses when he declares that, "For so long as we leave matter out of account, one position is perfectly indistinguishable from another and a science of relations is impossible. In order that spatial relations may appear, the homogeneity of empty space must be destroyed, and it is matter which must destroy it."(72) These conceptions are so contradictory that they could only have arisen, just like those of the corpuscular atom, at the command of an *a priori* tendency. This is so because, as we saw previously in the case of motion, we *wish* differentiation and identity to be present at the same time, and that wish is the creator of illusions. That is why ether, so to speak, is double-faced. On the one hand, we expect it to explain phenomena, and, consequently, we attribute to it the properties susceptible of engendering the diversity which we are forced to suppose in empty space because of the propagation of light and electricity, etc., and, on the other hand, we remove from it every quality in order to assimilate it to space. And that is one of those deceits (as the unity of the atom or the state of "power") which we are in the habit of committing unconsciously when it is a question of satisfying our causal tendency.

The profound analogy between the two tendencies, or rather the absolute continuity of the main idea from which they both spring, will be still better revealed if we follow the evolution which the concepts of time and space undergo because of the successive explanations of "becoming" and "being." We began by considering both time and space as homogeneous with respect to laws; we have stated at the same time the identity of bodies during their motion through space. These three conditions characterize the empirical part of science, the science of laws. Then, postulating the identity of bodies during their motion through time, we arrived at the notion of cause, and we saw arise the rational part of science, the science of hypotheses. But having succeeded in this, the analogy between time and space, which we had thought established by this operation, shows itself, on the contrary, as again inadequate.

Substances identical through time are also immobile in time, whereas though identical throughout space they could still move within it. Because of the fact that time has but one single dimension along which everything moves with a uniform motion in the same direction, the postulate of identity of bodies throughout time, which constitutes causality, empties thereby with one sweep, so to speak, time of its content. Successive instants have become identical; but in space the parts are still distinguishable by the bodies which fill them. In this case identification is, therefore, more complete for time than for space. And so the "explanation" continues its work and definitely reduces space to the condition of time in identifying all its parts.(73)

It is to this last identification that mechanical hypotheses owe the unity of matter which characterizes them, this unity being, moreover, but a step toward the reduction of matter to space. And the two tendencies have again this feature in common that, the end envisaged by our understanding appearing exceedingly distant, our understanding is quite ready to be contented with partial satisfactions, however small and even imaginary they may be. All progress, even purely apparent, in one or the other of these directions, appears to us always as an explanation, and we readily see why Aristotle at a given moment could confuse them and designate by the term "cause" that which manifestly had no relation to identity in time.

Obeying these two tendencies, from theory to theory and from identification to identification, we have made the real world completely disappear. We have explained, or rather denied change, identifying antecedent and consequent, and the process of the world was stopped. There then remained a space filled with bodies. We have formed bodies of space, reduced bodies to space, and bodies vanished in their turn. It is emptiness, "nothing at all," as Maxwell says, non-existence. For time and space have been dissolved. Time whose course no longer implies change is indiscernible, non-existing; and space emptied of bodies, being no longer determined by anything, also disappears.

It could not be otherwise. We have searched for the "why" of the real world, and we did it with the help of the principle of identity. The ultimate source of all reality can, therefore, only be eternally identical to itself and with indiscernible parts; this is, indeed, the sphere of Parmenides. But, on the other hand, how would this thing in itself, having no diversity, enter into relation with this diverse world? As Renouvier wisely says: "It is too clear that uniform matter, homogeneous and immobile, is neither the cause nor the reason for anything in the world."(74) Not being the cause of anything, not acting, it is as if it were not, and consequently it vanishes.

In still another way we can render evident the logic of this result. Causal reasoning because of its very essence tends to go back to an ultimate cause, since each cause discovered becomes immediately, by that very fact, a consequence whose cause in turn must be sought for. Now what can be this ultimate cause? To speak with Spinoza (who, moreover, only reproduced an expression of Saint Anselm), it can only be something which is the cause of itself, *causa sui*—that is, that of which the essence involves its existence.(75) Therefore, to arrive at non-existence is simply to state that it is impossible to find this *cause of itself*.

Is this, then, the ultimate result of science, and is there left to us, as to the hierophant of Saïs, only regret that with daring hands we have torn from truth its veil? In order that this should be so, this statement would have really to be at the very end of science. Now this is not so. Mechanism is not the fruit of science, for mechanism and science were both born at the same time. From the beginning of science, we find it established, fixed, and including this latter term, the unity of matter. Men have pretended to brush aside the analogy between the atoms of the ancients and ours, by affirming that the first were chimerical, whereas the existence of the second could be shown experimentally; we know that, from this point of view, there exists only a difference of degree between them. The origin of mechanism is not experience; its roots are deeply immersed in what is the basis of science itself, in those initial metaphysical notions which condition our entire knowledge. Spinoza clearly perceived it, when, in opposition to Boyle, he affirmed that mechanism is proved by "reason and calculation," and not by chemical experiments;(76) Leibniz, on this point as well as many others, is in entire accord with him, and for once has clearly and explicitly recognized it: "Spinoza (whom I do not hesitate to cite when he says something good), in one of his letters to the late Oldenburg, Secretary of the Royal Society of England, printed amongst the posthumous works of that subtle Jew, makes a similar reflection on a work of Boyle,(77) who insists a little too much, to tell the truth, on drawing from many beautiful experiments only the conclusion which he could take as a principle—to wit, that all is done mechanically in nature—a principle which may be rendered certain by reason alone and never by experiments, no matter how great their number."(78)

Mechanism and its ultimate end, the reduction of reality to nonentity, are an integral part of science, because the latter cannot escape from the dominion of the principle of identity, which is the essential form of our thought. But far from passively yielding to its dictation, science resists it vigorously, as we shall soon see.

NOTES

1. Cf. ZELLER: *A History of Greek Philosophy*, trans. S. F. Alleyne. London, 1881, p. 000.

2. Cf., however, on this subject, p. 108, note 91.

3. ARISTOTLE: *De Caelo*, trans. J. L. Stocks. Oxford, 1922, Book I, Chap. VII, § 18; cf. *ib*. Book IV, Chap. II, § 14. For the filiation by which the doctrine of the Greek atomists is allied to that of Parmenides, cf. earlier, p. 95 and ff.

4. GALENUS: *Opera*, ed. Kuehn. Leipzig, 1821; *De elementis*, I, pp. 416–417, cf. Lasswitz, *Geschichte der Atomistik*, Vol. I, p. 231 and ff.

5. Cf. BERTHELOT: *Les origines de l'alchimie*. Paris, 1885, p. 282 and ff.

6. Cf. MABILLEAU: *l.c.*, p. 389 and ff.

7. DESCARTES: *Principes*, Book II, Chap. XXIII.

8. BOYLE: *Works*, London, 1772, Vol. III, p. 15: "I agree with the generality of philosophers so far as to allow that there is one catholick or universal matter common to all bodies."

9. One can see in KOPP, *Geschichte der Chemie*, Vol. IV, *passim*, with what slowness the concept of the specificity of the greater number of chemical substances was elaborated, especially of metals. Cf. also *ib*., Vol. I, pp. 121–214, 219, 258.

10. There is found in KOPP, *Die Alchemie in aelterer und neuerer Zeit*. Heidelberg, 1886, Vol. I, p. 67, the titles of two writings of Becher, where he defends alchemy against its adversaries. *Ib*., p. 241, a passage from Becher in which he affirms that the "spagyrists" may easily make gold with the help of different ingredients (such as silver, mercury, sulphur, etc.), since nature itself proceeds in this way. Cf. *ib*., p. 104, and id., *Geschichte*, Vol. I, p. 178.

11. Cf. in KOPP: *Alchemie*, Vol. I, pp. 144, 147, details on the proceedings and negotiations with the States of Holland.

12. *Ib.*, pp. 67, 71: cf. *Geschichte*, Vol. I, p. 133; Vol. II, p. 277.

13. KOPP: *Alchemie*, I, p. 69.

14. *Ib.*, I, p. 71.

15. *Ib.*, I, p. 72.

16. One may see in KOPP, *Geschichte*, Vol. II, p. 278, what a curious mixture his opinions presented in this matter.

17. Cf. DUHEM: *Le mixte*. Paris, pp. 16, 17, 48, and Kopp, *Geschichte*, Vol. II, p. 275.

18. Id., *Alchemie*, Vol., II, p. 164; *Geschichte*, Vol. II, pp. 279–280.

19. LAVOISIER: *Œuvres*. Paris, 1864, Vol. I, pp. 5–7.

20. DUHEM, however, justly points out that the creation of a new nomenclature contributed largely in stabilizing the notion of a chemically simple body. *Le mixte*, p. 47.

21. HELMHOLTZ: *Populaere wissenschaftliche Vortraege*, p. 192.

22. A. GAUTIER: *Les problèmes de la chimie moderne. Revue générale des sciences*, 1890, p. 225.

23. ETARD: *Revue générale des sciences*, Vol. XIV, p. 540, while enumerating laws special to chemistry, gives the first place to the statement: "There exist specific indestructible elements."

24. Cf. DUHEM: *Le mixte*, p. 164.

25. OSTWALD: *Vorlesungen ueber Naturphilosophie*. Leipzig, 1902, p. 287.

26. Cf. BOUASSE: *Introduction à l'étude des théories de la mécanique*. Paris, 1895, p. 166.

27. *Ib.*, p. 169.

28. Cf. E. BOOTH: *Prout's Hypotheses*, etc. *Wiedemann's Annalen*, 1902, Spl.—R. J. Strutt, *Ueber die Tendenz*, etc.; *ib.* C. Halluis, *Atomgewichtsgrundzahlen, ib.*, 1903; Hinrichs, *The Elements of Atom Mechanics*, Vol. I (quoted in the *Revue générale des sciences*, Vol. VI, 1895, p. 756).—Since the really surprising change in the evolution of chemical conceptions, Prout's hypothesis which for a long time seemed so adventuresome, is, at the present moment, almost universally accepted by chemists. (Cf. on this subject, *La Déduction Relativiste*, § 202.)

29. A. E. BEGUYER DE CHANCOURTOIS: *Vis tellurique*. Paris, 1863.

30. Cf. on this subject, SCHUTZENBERGER: *Traité de chimie générale*, Paris, 1880, Vol. I, p. VIII, where it is clearly seen that what especially attracts the chemists in these conceptions is that they appear as an approach to the unity of matter. This supposition has been plainly confirmed by the recent developments of chemical theories. Cf. *La Déduction Relativiste*, § 202 and ff.

31. In A. ETARD, *Les nouvelles théories chimiques*, 3rd ed., Paris, s.d., p. 51, and *Revue générale des sciences*, Vol. VI, 1895, p. 782, will be found certain indications concerning the objections which Mendeleef's theory encounters. The fundamental contradiction between the generally adopted concept of the chemical element and the postulate of the unity of matter has been clearly brought out by Kozlowski (*Sur la notion*, etc. *Congrès de philosophie de 1900*, Vol. III, p. 536 and ff.; *Zasady przyrodoznawstwa*. Warsaw, 1903, p. 272 and ff.). Let us note, however, that according to Kozlowski, the

postulate in question has its source in the unity of tactile sensation (*Zasady*, p. 264).

32. M. BERTHELOT: *Les origines de l'alchimie.* Paris, 1883, p. 289.

33. Cf. LE CHATELIER: *La loi des phases. Revue générale des sciences,* 10, 1899, p. 760.

34. CH. FRIEDEL (Preface to J. B. Stallo): *La matière et la physique moderne,* 3rd ed. Paris, 1899, pp. 9 and 12.

35. H. SPENCER: *Mr. Martineau on Evolution. Contemporary Review,* June 1872, Vol. XX, p. 143.

36. WUNDT: *Die Theorie der Materie. Deutsche Rundschau,* December 1875, p. 387.

37. HANNEQUIN: *l.c.,* p. 166.

38. LOTZE: *System der Philosophie.* Leipzig, 1879, Vol. II, p. 376.

39. M. BERTHELOT: *Les origines de l'alchimie.* Paris, 1885, p. 297.

40. Cf. p. 292, Descartes' deduction.

41. MAXWELL: *Scientific Papers.* Cambridge, 1890, Vol. II, p. 267.

42. BERKELEY: *Works,* ed. Fraser, Vol. I, *An Essay towards a New Theory of Vision,* § 130, 158.

43. LOTZE: *l.c.,* p. 382.

44. A. BALFOUR: *Réflexions sur la théorie nouvelle de la matière. Revue scientifique,* July 1, 1905, p. 11.

45. SCHOPENHAUER: *Ueber die vierfache Wurzel,* etc. Leipzig, 1877, p. 46.

46. ARISTOTLE: *Physics,* Book VIII, cap. 1, § 27. One can compare with this passage his definition of science in *Posterior Analytics,* Book I, Chap. II, § 7, trans. Ross, *Aristotle Selections,* New York, 1927. "We suppose ourselves to possess unqualified scientific knowledge of a thing, as opposed to knowing it in the accidental way in which the sophist knows, when we think that we know the cause on which the fact depends, as the cause of that fact and of no other, and, further, that the fact could not be other than it is."

47. Cf. earlier, p. 28. One might also quote on this subject certain passages from Descartes, where he seems to ask equally for the explanation of being, as, for instance: "As to physics, I should think I knew nothing about it, if I only could say how things may be, without showing that they cannot be otherwise, for having reduced it to the laws of mathematics this is a possible thing." (*Lettre à Mersenne. Œuvres,* Vol. III. Paris, 1899, p. 39.) One will see, moreover, later on, to what a degree this way of stating a problem was conformable to the fundamental principle of Descartes.

48. COUTURAT: *Sur la métaphysique de Leibniz. Revue de métaphysique,* Vol. X, 1902, p. 3.

49. LEIBNIZ: *Opera,* ed. Erdmann. *Nouveaux Essais,* p. 203.

50. Cf. earlier, p. 29.

51. Cf. earlier, p. 71.

52. DESCARTES: *Principes,* 2nd Part, Chap. IV.

53. LOCKE: *An Essay concerning Human Understanding.* London, Book II, Chap. VIII, § 9.

54. *Ib.,* Chap. VIII, § 11.

55. One can see in Cassirer (*Erkenntnisproblem,* Vol. I, p. 390 and ff.) that this conception dominates not only Descartes' physics, but also his

mathematics. Everything being reducible to spatial modifications, it is the study of these latter related to a system of co-ordinates which becomes the central problem of science. Hence the importance of analytical geometry in Descartes.

56. ARISTOTLE: *Metaphysics*, Book I, Chap. IV, § 13.

57. H. POINCARÉ: *Electricité et optique*. Paris, 1901, p. 3.

58. DUHEM: *L'évolution de la mécanique*. Paris, 1902, pp. 177–178.

59. Relativistic conceptions culminate clearly in the dissolving of matter into space, or, which amounts to the same thing, in its transformation into a purely spatial construction. Cf. *La Déduction Relativiste*, Chap. XI.

60. LUCIEN POINCARÉ: *La physique moderne*, p. 278.

61. LEIBNIZ: *Theoria motus concreti seu hypothesis nova*. Mayence, 1671. *Mathematische Schriften*, ed. Gerhardt, Vol. VI, p. 17 and ff. Leibniz, however conceived the necessity of a principle of differentiation (p. 250).

62. MALEBRANCHE: *Réflexions sur la lumière et les couleurs. Histoire de l'Académie Royale des sciences, année 1699. Mémoires*, p. 22.

63. HERTZ: *Ueber die Beziehungen zwischen Licht und Elektricitaet. Gesammelte Werke*. Leipzig, 1895, Vol. I, p. 352.

64. H. POINCARÉ: *l.c.*, pp. 298, 301. LARMOR: *Aether and Matter*. Cambridge, 1900, p. 171.

65. H. POINCARÉ: *La science et l'hypothèse*, p. 199.

66. MAXWELL: *Scientific Papers*, p. 323. "These are some of the already discovered properties of that which has often been called vacuum or nothing at all."

67. KANT: *Vom Uebergange*, etc. Frankfort, 1888, pp. 111, 119, 121. In LALANDE's *Lectures sur la philosophie des sciences*, pp. 249, 250, will be found a passage from the *Physique* of Abbé Nollet, who expounds the current opinions of the middle of the eighteenth century concerning caloric fluid. Cf. also, Rosenberger, *Geschichte*, Vol. III, p. 38.

68. HENRI BERGSON (*Matière et Mémoire*, 3rd ed., p. 223) has admirably understood that the essential character of the explanations of matter by ether will put to flight "the discontinuity which our perception has established on the surface."

69. DUHEM: *L'évolution de la mécanique*. Paris, 1903, p. 171.

70. E. DU BOIS-REYMOND: *Reden*. Leipzig, 1886–87, p. 109.

71. LEIBNIZ: *Philosophische Schriften*, ed. Gerhardt, Vol. II, p. 295; *Lettre à Des Bosses*, February 2, 1706.

72. RUSSELL: *An Essay on the Foundation of Geometry*. Cambridge, 1897, p. 77. This passage may be compared with that of Berkeley, cited p. 131; assuming that unified matter merges with space, the arguments against absolute space, emptied of all material content, are applicable here.

73. The obscure but powerful tendency which incites rational science to establish, with the aid of successive assimilations, an identity between the concepts of time and of space, is manifested also in recent theories of "local" time. Minkowski's formula (cf. p. 59, note 54) is very remarkable in this respect, and one may see in Langevin's admirable exposition that the creators of these theories considered it a great advantage to have made the asymmetry between the two concepts disappear, in the sense that the

interval in time, as distance in space, varies with the system of reference, and with the motion of the observer. (*L'évolution de l'espace et du temps. Revue de métaphysique,* July 1911, p. 461.)

74. RENOUVIER: *Critique philosophique,* Vol. XI, I, p. 188.

75. SPINOZA: *Opera.* The Hague, 1887. *Ethica,* I, 39. The fact that Spinoza's system culminates in *acosmism* was very clearly seen by Hegel. Cf. on this subject, Cassirer: *Erkenntnisproblem.* Berlin, 1906–7, Vol. II, p. 42.

76. SPINOZA: *Opera,* Vol. II, Ep. VI (to Oldenburg).

77. It is probably a question of the treatise entitled *The Origin of Forms and Qualities according to Corpuscular Philosophy,* which appeared in 1666.

78. LEIBNIZ: *Œuvres philosophiques,* ed. Raspe. Amsterdam, 1765. *Nouveaux Essais,* Book IV, § 13.

CHAPTER VIII

CARNOT'S PRINCIPLE

THE principle bearing the name of Sadi Carnot dates from the publication of the invaluable monograph which appeared in 1824 and was entitled *Réflexions sur la puissance motrice du feu*, a publication constituting the only scientific title of that man of genius, so prematurely cut off, whose work, according to Lord Kelvin and Lippmann,(1) was unsurpassed by any other during the nineteenth century. Carnot states his principle without any pretension, almost in passing; he seems to value it only because it permits him to formulate rules for the functioning of heat engines, the establishment of which is ostensibly the only end of his effort; in scrutinizing it more closely, we perceive, however, that he had conceived the principle in all its generality, and that from this point of view posterity has been able to add but little to it.

It is possible that, in spite of the marvellous clearness and simplicity of the monograph, the manner in which Carnot expounded his ideas was responsible for the scanty comprehension of which his contemporaries gave evidence and for the strange oblivion to which these ideas were doomed for nearly thirty years. The way in which Clapeyron stated the teachings of his master was doubtless an additional cause, as has been already remarked. Finally, from the time of the researches of Mayer and of Joule, the fact that Carnot believed that he ought to limit himself to the conservation of heat (although at that time he had already conceived of heat as motion)(2) contributed equally to this neglect. But we shall see later that this lack of recognition can also be explained, perhaps, by the action of a more profound cause.

Clausius, who at the beginning of his work was unacquainted with that of his illustrious predecessor, discovered the principle anew; he had, besides, the great merit of proving that it could be brought into agreement with that of the conservation of energy;(3) finally, he stated it more precisely, as especially applicable to the phenomena of thermodynamics, in order to guard it against certain objections. Clausius, moreover, was himself led later on to modify his first statement, and other modifications have been proposed since. It was with the work of Clausius that the principle definitely entered the domaiŋ of science, where its enormous importance and its great fertility were soon recognized. That is why it is sometimes designated by the name of the principle of Clausius or yet again by that of the principle of Carnot-Clausius, although Clausius himself, recognizing the incontestable rights of his predecessor, assigned to it only the name of Carnot.

The principle is formulated by Duhem in these words: "The transformation value of a modification is equal to the diminution that a certain magnitude, connected with all the properties which fix the state of the system, but independent of its motion, undergoes through this modification."(4) This magnitude is what is called the entropy of the system, and its conception for heat phenomena is closely related to that of temperature, and this results in investing this property with a very particular and essential rôle. Poincaré formulates several statements of the principle of which this is the briefest. "It is impossible to make a heat engine function with only one source of heat."(5) The term "source" here generally indicates a body or a group of bodies capable of yielding heat, or of causing other bodies to yield it, and in order that a heat engine may function, it must have two sources, one hot and the other cold. From this statement it is seen even more directly perhaps than from that of Duhem that this principle rests upon what Poincaré calls "the axiom of Clausius": "Heat cannot be made to pass from a cold body to a hot one." Under this form Clausius has stated in the first place what we designate as Carnot's principle. We might also call it Carnot's axiom, for if Carnot did not formulate it in these terms, it was doubtless because he considered it as sufficiently self-evident, but it cannot be contested that this is the true foundation of his work, as is apparent notably in the comparison which he establishes between the height of a water-fall and the difference of temperature between two bodies.(6)

This comparison will enable us to recognize the nature of the "axiom." Is it what Leibniz called a truth "of reason" (*de raison*)?

We saw that the gravitation of bodies, their tendency to approach the earth, is in no way deducible from considerations of mass and motion; this is true also of our proposition. Physicists, conscious of the important rôle which kinetic theories have played in the domain of thermodynamics, have often, very justly moreover, emphasized the fact that Carnot's principle is completely independent of these theories and that assumptions about the mechanical nature of heat have in no way contributed to its discovery.(7) We shall even see later on that, as in the case of gravitation, considerable difficulties are encountered if one tries to make this principle agree with mechanism.

Can it be said that the axiom is implicitly contained in our concept of heat itself? Doubtless, for this concept, like that of matter, is complex and embraces a collection of properties of which the most essential is evidently a tendency to be communicated. But originally heat is a sensation which we transform into a quality. It may be objected that we feel heat only because the hot body tends to communicate it to us; but the fact that when I touch a hot object its temperature diminishes and that of my skin increases is an observation, and as such has nothing to do with my immediate sensation, according to which heat is something like redness or roundness: I say a hot body, a cold body, in the same way that I say a red body or a round body. When I imagine a hot body touching a cold body there is no more "reason" for the heat passing from one to the other than there is for the redness of a body passing to one that is green or the roundness to that which is rectangular. The fact that heat has an invincible tendency to "fade," as we should say if it were a question of the colour of an object, is pure observation, exactly similar to the fact that bodies tend to fall. To push the analogy farther, one may convince oneself that the concept of a heavy body in no way includes, contrary to what is sometimes affirmed, that of motion. In forming this concept we think of our effort which is, to be sure, an immediate sensation: but this sensation is totally different from that of motion; it is independent of it and cannot be deduced from it.

Moreover, for gravity, as for heat, the evidence is only established as long as it is a question of *simple* phenomena; our conviction is shaken as soon as they become complicated. That a body must tend to fall constantly and cannot rise by its own weight seems incontestable to us; yet our understanding does not succeed, without the help of the principle of causality, in conceiving perpetual motion as impossible *a priori*, even purely mechanical motion, provided it be realized by complicated means (p. 205). In the same way we are quite sure that heat could not pass directly from a cold body to a hot one. But Clausius himself saw very well that this conviction only holds in "ordinary circumstances." Even now in radiation, he says, it may well be asked whether, by an artificial concentration of heat rays with the aid of mirrors or of lenses, it would not be possible to engender a temperature higher than that of the body which emits these rays, thus making heat pass into a warmer body.(8) It is known also that there has been much subsequent discussion on the question whether Carnot's principle held good under all circumstances; and we shall see later on that an eminent scientist, one of the founders of our modern thermodynamics, has formulated propositions which imply the direct negation of Clausius's axiom. If we reflect upon it we shall find that to our immediate sensation the fact that a body can receive considerable quantities of heat without its temperature being modified by it, as, for instance, in melting snow, is just as surprising as would be the passage of heat from a cold body to a warm one.

The axiom, therefore, reveals to us a factual truth, a mode of existence peculiar to hot bodies. This truth seems to us entirely general, and essential in the sense that it conditions all the phenomena of heat. In manuals it is now habitual to treat phenomena of this order only after fairly complicated considerations on thermodynamics; but in fact, as Aries (9) and Mouret (10) have well shown, this method of exposition, justified from an historical point of view, is not justified from the logical standpoint. Moreover, it is easy to understand why our axiom is explicitly postulated at the very beginning of the physics of heat. How can temperature be defined? "By definition," says Poincaré, "two bodies are at equal temperatures or in temperature equilibrium when, placed adjacent, they undergo no variation of volume."(11) This evidently supposes that bodies, placed adjacent, always tend to establish between themselves an equal temperature or an equilibrium of temperature; this, indeed, is "the axiom of Clausius."

This behaviour of hot bodies appears to us at the same time as very peculiar. If we consider a round or a red body, its quality no doubt gives us the effect of something which can change, without the substance of the body being modified; according to scholastic terminology, these are accidents. But these accidents in themselves have no tendency to change. It is not so with heat; when two bodies of different temperature are placed adjacent, instead of each one conserving its own quality, they react immediately one upon the other, each tending to modify its own quality and that of the other. There is, therefore, a tendency toward modification of that which exists, in the sense of a future state not realized, and which we designate by the term equilibrium. That Carnot recognized (better perhaps than Clausius and many of his successors) the generality and the precise nature of the principle from this point of view was clearly established by Mouret.(12) More recently Helm has formulated a principle apparently more general than that of Carnot;(13) scientists such as Ostwald (14) and philosophers such as Lasswitz (15) seemed to attribute great importance to it. Without wishing to deny to it a tentative interest from the point of view of the precision and the parallelism of certain nomenclature, the principle, nevertheless, does not seem to add much to the establishment or the re-establishment of equilibrium in Carnot's sense.

On the other hand, generalizations of this kind are not exempt from danger. This is because heat holds a very special position, not only in so far as quality is concerned, but also considered as a form of energy. Temperature is compared to a level; the comparison is fair in a certain sense, and we have already seen (p. 260) that Carnot himself made use of it. But it must not be forgotten that the analogy is only partial, and that if pushed too far it ends in errors. Water tends to descend from an elevated level and, in two communicating vessels, to establish a state of equilibrium, which is indicated by the equality of the levels. At first sight heat may seem to act in an entirely identical manner. But water, in descending, will have acquired *vis viva* or kinetic energy, which (disregarding the resistance of course) will be the exact equivalent of the potential energy it will have lost (it was to mark this equivalence that the two terms kinetic energy and potential energy were created).

It will manifest this capacity externally by rising again under the proper conditions to the level which it has left. Similarly a pendulum displaced from a vertical position will have a tendency to return to it, but it will immediately go beyond it, ascending on the other side to the height it has just left. Thus equilibrium is not directly established; what we first observe in the case of the pendulum are the oscillations. Moreover, it is easy so to arrange the experiment of the falling of water that the oscillations will be made equally visible in this case. Newton had already studied the oscillation of a column of water in a curved tube according to the laws of the pendulum.(16)

Nothing like this happens in the case of heat. Adopting for the moment (as Carnot did) the point of view of the hypothesis of heat-fluid, we may say that it is a substance which manifests no inertia, unlike all the material substances; by the fact of its displacement it acquires no *vis viva* tending to make it go beyond the position of equilibrium. This is established not by oscillations, but as the result of an asymptotic approach, indefinitely, but directly increasing.

It is evident, moreover, that if equilibrium is attained finally in the case of the pendulum, it is due only in the end to friction; if this did not intervene the oscillations would last indefinitely. The case is the same for the column of water oscillating in Newton's tube, and also for water falling into a basin and of which the *vis viva*, on account of friction, has been transformed into heat, which is later dissipated. Thus there intervenes the propensity possessed by the other forms of energy to *degrade* themselves into heat, correlative to the tendency of heat to become dissipated; and equilibrium is finally established in virtue of Carnot's very principle and its direct consequences; but not by the action required of a principle, which would be analogous and applicable to the phenomenon of gravitation. The purely mechanical phenomena are those of rational mechanics; we have seen that they all appear to us as entirely reversible.(17)

Because of its external form Carnot's principle is clearly distinguishable from the usual statements of science. Principles or laws are generally formulated as equalities; now it is impossible to reduce Carnot's principle to this form. Physicists who have noted it have sometimes shown a certain embarrassment and have tried to attenuate what appeared almost as a shocking anomaly, by calling attention to the fact that the precision of laws is always limited by errors of observation. But Poincaré understood perfectly that there was a more profound reason for this anomaly, inherent in the very nature of the principle.(18) We believe that this reason readily follows from what precedes. We saw that not only the principles of conservation, but also scientific statements in general, are conceived with the constant, though perhaps latent, prepossession of causality and of identity in time. Hence the tendency to give to the rule which determines the modalities of change a form which emphasizes that which endures throughout the change, a tendency which manifests itself externally by the equation, in which this change is, so to speak, suppressed and conjured away. On the contrary, Carnot's principle is clearly a statement, not of conservation, but of change. It affirms not even an apparent identity, but a diversity. Given a state, this principle establishes that it *ought* to modify itself, and in what direction. It is a principle of becoming, *des Geschehens*, as Ostwald has remarked concerning Helm's principle. In this lies its originality and this is what explains its great fruitfulness for science.

In opposition to the illusions of identity to which mechanical theories, the principles of conservation, and even the form of laws in general give rise, Carnot's principle stipulates that the whole universe is modifying itself in time in a constant direction. Clausius formulated this with great clearness: "We frequently hear that everything in the world has a circular course. Whereas some transformations take place in one direction, in a determined place and at a certain time, other transformations are accomplished in an inverse direction, in another place and at another time, so that the same conditions are generally reproduced and the state of the world remains invariable, when we consider things broadly and in a general manner. The world, therefore, may continue to exist eternally in the same fashion. When the first fundamental principle of the mechanical theory of heat was announced, it might perhaps have been considered as a striking confirmation of the aforesaid opinion. . . . The second fundamental principle of the mechanical theory of heat contradicts this opinion in the most explicit manner. From this it results that the state of the

universe must change more and more in a determined direction."(19) The world (unless we interject the notion of its
infinity) seems to us to be moving toward an end, although
this end may seem to us infinitely far off.

We have seen that the principles of conservation share the
characteristic of being anticipated to some extent by our
understanding and always easily accepted by it. We shall not
be surprised to note that Carnot's principle, running counter
to the principles of conservation, in no way participates in this
"plausibility." Science has certainly accepted it with much
difficulty. It is really strange to notice how tardily this principle
appeared. Doubtless the conservation of matter is in itself a
very simple statement. But it affirms something which at first
sight seems contrary to a great number of phenomena which
we observe unceasingly, such as boiling or combustion. Inertia
is a paradoxical conception in no way confirmed by direct
experience. But if we bear in mind that these two principles
were formulated before that of Carnot, it is, at first, very
difficult to understand the priority of the principle of the
conservation of energy, a complicated proposition, really
admitting of no verbal formula as soon as we go beyond
purely mechanical phenomena.(20) The basis of Carnot's
principle, Clausius's axiom, "Heat passes of itself from a
warm body to a cold one and not in an inverse dirction,"
constitutes, on the contrary, a simple statement which sums up
an immense number of observations we make at every moment.
Its real place, we have seen, is at the very beginning of the
physics of heat. Yet the conservation of energy, anticipated to
a certain extent by Descartes, was announced, although under
a very hypothetical form, at the end of the seventeenth century
by Huygens and Leibniz. It was more than a century later that
Sadi Carnot formulated his principle, and thirty years more
were necessary before its importance began to be recognized.

Nowhere before Carnot do we find a true anticipation of
his principle; at most, far removed analogies might be cited.
The passages where Heraclitus proclaims the πάντα ῥεῖ, the
eternal flux of things, are the best known and the most important
in this line of thought. "Heraclitus says that everything passes
and that nothing endures, and, comparing things to the
flowing of a river, he maintains that one cannot enter twice

into the same river." "All that exists is in motion and nothing remains." Yet Heraclitus was convinced that this flux was circular, that the current came back to its original point. This is perhaps the part of his doctrine we know best and which is preserved in the least obscure fragments. He had given to this doctrine of eternal recurrence a striking expression by imagining "the great year," at the end of which all events must begin again.(21) There is thus a fundamental difference between his ideas and those which are the result of Carnot's principle, the latter making us envisage a continual change from which all supposition of return is excluded. We can also cite Aristotle on this subject, when he speaks of being "tending to its own end," so that "from a man one does not become a child," (22) which seems to imply that Aristotle had a clear feeling that the course of phenomena has a determined direction, involving something irreversible. In the same line of thought also are the conceptions of Leonardo da Vinci and of Cardanus, cited by Duhem, about the force which desires repose, conceptions which come, moreover, from scholastic physics through the same Aristotelian channel.(23) In rather a different order of ideas, and as if related to the mechanical representation of Carnot's principle rather than to the principle itself, one can cite the hypothesis of Anaxagoras on uniformity by the mixture of heterogeneous elements,(24) and a passage from Descartes, where he asserts that motion must pass more often from larger bodies to smaller ones rather than inversely.(25) However curious certain of these statements may be, it is evident that they are only very indirectly connected with what we call Carnot's principle.

Equally remarkable is the long oblivion into which Carnot's ideas fell until the time when they were exhumed by Clausius. Carnot, unlike J. Rey or J. R. Mayer, was not a man criticized as not belonging to "the profession"; on the contrary, no one contested his competency. His monograph did not pass unnoticed, and the practical applications which he made of his principle were retained by science.(26) Clapeyron, of course, misrepresented the teachings of his master; but there can be no doubt that he and his contemporaries showed a strange lack of understanding in regard to them.

The impression obtained from this bit of history is confirmed if we look at contemporary science. Earlier we spoke of the place which the principle occupies in textbooks. Evidently from the beginning the irreversibility of the transfer of heat is implicitly affirmed. But it might be said that this truth was purposely left in the shade as long as possible. We saw, in examining the principles of conservation, with what specious demonstrations people are accustomed to be satisfied concerning them, and how they never hesitate to have recourse to the vastest extrapolations. With these hasty generalizations let us compare the manner with which we believe we should proceed in respect to Carnot's principle. The demonstration, admirable in its strictness and prudence, given by Poincaré in his *Thermodynamique*, is a true model of the kind. The contrast is, perhaps, still more marked if, abandoning science proper, we turn to popular summaries. As long as it is a question of the principles of conservation, no generalization seems too vast, no metaphor too bold. Let energy (the word *force* is also used, since this term seems to cover more), let matter (as vague a term as one could hope for) persist, this really seems a guarantee that what has been, is, and will continue to be, that "nothing is born nor perishes," that there is "nothing new under the sun." As to Carnot's principle and to the demonstration of the irreversibility which is its basis, these are generally either passed over in silence or "explained" in a manner to re-establish identity. We shall readily understand why, under these conditions, philosophers are excusable for having too often followed these examples, and have been content to accept results such as science appeared to show, quite happy in their apparent "philosophical" generality.

In the same line of thought we notice that as soon as Carnot's principle was solidly established in science by Clausius, attempts were made to escape from the consequences which it entails. Not that one could deny the fundamental phenomenon, nor even the propositions that are deduced from it with absolute rigour. But a sort of secret repugnance was felt to the idea of a continual change of the universe in the same direction. Helm very clearly observed this mental attitude of the contemporaries of Clausius and saw that it had its source in the concepts of conservation.(27) But we can follow the manifestations of the same current of thought at a much later date and even in our times. A very characteristic example is found in Haeckel: "If this theory of entropy were true, we should have a 'beginning 'corresponding to this assumed 'end' of the world. Both ideas are quite untenable in the light of our monistic and consistent theory of the eternal cosmogenetic process; both contradict the law of substance. . . . The second thesis of the mechanical theory of heat contradicts the first and so must be rejected." Carnot's principle can only be applied "to distinct processes," but "in the world at large quite other conditions obtain."(28) Declarations of the same kind are found in Arrhenius. This scientist considers that it is indispensable to *free* ourselves from the difficulties of the theory of Clausius. "If the ideas of Clausius were true, this thermal death ought to have been realized in the infinite time of the existence of the world." Moreover, we cannot suppose that there was a beginning, since energy cannot be created. Consequently, "this is totally incomprehensible to us."(29) It is clearly seen that it is a question both with Haeckel and Arrhenius of an *a priori* tendency, anterior and superior to all experience. What shocks them is that on Carnot's principle we must suppose ourselves to be at a precise moment of a continuous development. Lack of identity between the antecedent and the consequent necessitates the admission of a datum which must necessarily appear to us as inexplicable, like the diversity which matter engenders in space and from which we are trying to free ourselves by assimilating matter to ether and to space itself.

It is evidently this profound tendency which has given rise to all sorts of hypotheses about the transformation and the reconcentration of heat lost by radiation from the sun.(30) Let us summarize the theory formulated by Macquorn Rankine, all the more remarkable because it comes from a most eminent physicist, one of the creators of thermodynamics.(31) The object sought for by Rankine is clearly indicated in the title of his work, *On the Reconcentration of the Mechanical Energy of the Universe*.(32) After having stated that "in the present state of the known world" the tendency to the conversion of all forms of energy into heat and to the diffusion of this same heat dominates nature, the author asks whether one cannot imagine that this energy could be again concentrated. The interstellar space must be filled with a perfectly transparent and diathermal medium that is incapable of transforming light or radiant heat into anything else. Let us suppose, now, that this medium possesses, in every direction about the visible world, fixed limits beyond which there would be nothing but empty space. Consequently, in reaching these limits, the radiant heat emanating from the visible world would be reflected, and in that case concentrated in foci. In each one of these the heat would be such that if a celestial body, which in this period of its evolution no longer consisted of anything but a completely extinguished mass, were to attain it, it would immediately become volatilized and dissolve into its elements, thus producing an accumulation of chemical energy. Rankine ends by asking whether some of the luminous points which we perceive in far-off space might not be, not real stars, but precisely foci of this kind in the interstellar ether.

It is hardly necessary to note that this curious hypothesis gives rise to a host of objections. To indicate only the most apparent: we are obliged to endow the ether with an enormous force of elasticity. Then how admit that it abruptly ends somewhere? A diamond wall would be necessary. But what is most curious is that Rankine, in unconscious fashion, sins manifestly against the very foundations of Carnot's principle, since he assumes that heat is capable of passing by radiation directly from colder bodies (the bodies of the visible world) to warmer bodies (the foci of interstellar space). It was Clausius who drew attention to this anomaly.(33) It may be that Rankine himself had a vague suspicion of it, for in one part of the work in question he seems prudently to propose to accept the dissipation of energy for the present period and to reserve its "reconcentration" for a period "infinitely removed."

In this way one escapes the pressure of the law of change by admitting that change will operate in an inverse direction at a future time, apparently only to react again in the same direction once this new time is at an end. In other words, strict identity is not maintained, but we return to it indirectly by the notion of periodicity. This is the same conception which Herbert Spencer amply developed in his well-known theory of "half periods of organization and of disorganization." Spencer, perhaps (and certainly Rankine), was not conscious of employing a very old subterfuge. But the questions to which we are now alluding are related to the eternal foundations of the human mind; here especially "nothing new under the sun" has a chance of being at least partially applicable; one must not be surprised, therefore, to see the periods somewhat confused. To be sure, the ancients had never heard of Carnot's principle. But if this statement has the immense advantage of giving a scientific form to the fact of the irreversibility of phenomena, it is incontestable that humanity has been at all times, more or less obscurely, conscious of this fact. That phenomena take place in a determined direction, that they have a beginning and an end, that to-day is not absolutely like yesterday, that time progresses—of this we all have an immediate sensation. Yet in the eternal flux of things certain of them, if they do not remain absolutely identical, appear to undergo cyclic changes which bring them back to their point of departure. Day and night, the moons, the seasons follow each other in a determined order, and the evolution of the organized being, if it cannot be reversed at will, is renewed, however, automatically reproducing at certain intervals identical or very similar situations. And thus, quite naturally, arises the supposition that the universe, if it is not immutable, as strict causality would demand, might, however, only move along a closed curve, returning after a determined lapse of time to a former condition. This is the serpent (ouroboros) which bites its tail. Hypotheses of this kind are found in Hindoo beliefs. With the Greeks they are expressed in the conception of Heraclitus's "great year," which became later the cycles of Empedocles and was afterward developed by the Stoics with scientific exactness.(34) It is to this same conception that the verses of Virgil refer when he foresees that past events will be reproduced and that "the great Achilles will again be sent to Troy."(35) These conceptions are very near kin to that of Rankine and Spencer. The only difference is that in our science, having a much greater compass than that of the Hindoos and Greeks, since geology seems to indicate a continuous development during thousands of centuries (figures which astronomical hypotheses compel us to multiply still more), we need millions or billions of years where antiquity was satisfied with thousands. Indeed, Herbert Spencer supposes that even in returning after two half periods to the primitive nebulous state, the system in its second evolution would not pass through the same phases which it traversed the first time. But, as Renouvier (36) has very justly remarked, that is a self-contradiction, and the Stoics were more logical in supposing that the world, in virtue of its immanent law of spontaneous origin and development, would reproduce exactly the same nature, with the same beings and the same accidents, the same empires and the same republics, the same men and their same acts, as many times as the ether accomplished its destiny and travelled through its career of universal becoming.(37)

This hypothesis of "eternal return" under its strictest form has also had its representatives in modern philosophy. The most celebrated, doubtless, is Nietzsche, who has greatly insisted on this conception and has made of it one of the bases of his system.(38)

But if these conceptions resemble each other, we have no longer the same attitude toward them as the contemporaries of Virgil. Carnot's principle has given us an infinitely clearer consciousness of the irreversibility of phenomena. Though an experimental truth, the degradation of energy appears to us, nevertheless, as the most general of laws, as that which governs all that happens, all that becomes. Can we admit that it can be violated, as it would necessarily be during Rankine's periods of "reconcentration"? Can we admit, to be more precise, that heat instead of passing from a warm body to a cold one may take the opposite path? Hindoos and Greeks might believe that the universe, in continuing its evolution in time, would reproduce the same phenomena; we are forced to suppose, on the contrary, that it would reverse its course. This will, then, truly be the inverted world of the cinematograph moved in the opposite direction, the world in which heat vibrations will be concentrated on the wheels and axles of the locomotive, in which the smoke, formed in the distance, will re-enter the chimney with the gas of combustion to be remade into coal, or the living being will be born old to grow younger with time and to enter into the egg, or to walk backward and digest before he has eaten. How imagine the end of a period of "dissipation" and the beginning of a period of "reconcentration"? A ball thrown at right angles against a wall bounces back in the opposite direction; but that is because it has encountered an obstacle. Where would be the wall against which the history of the universe, or even that of a planetary system, would rebound? We feel that the universe is indefinitely approaching a future state, the state of equilibrium; but this state, supposing that it can be attained, appears to us to be infinitely and indefinitely stable. Wherever energy is on the same level throughout, our imagination refuses to believe that new "descents" can be created, or, what comes to the same thing, this creation seems infinitely improbable to it.

And so the most recent development of physics tends rather, for the phenomena supposedly possessing great stability in time (such as solar radiation), to give predominance to explanations very different from those of which we have just spoken. Since we know that there is no equivalence between the phenomena of dissipation and those of concentration, and since the reversal of the present advance of the world, even in distant space or time, appears to be inadmissible, we are seeking for the energy which dissipates, a source, if not infinite (this is impossible), at least so abundant that it may be adequate, without appreciable diminution of nature's enormous prodigality. This source is believed to have been found in intra-atomic energy. It is supposedly of a magnitude far superior to all those we are accustomed to see manifested. About a half century ago, Weber and Kohlrausch were surprised at the quantity of energy liberated by chemical reactions. "If all the particles of hydrogen in one milligram of water contained in a column of the length of one millimetre were attached to a string, the particles of oxygen being attached to another string, each string would have to be under a tension, in a direction opposite to that of the other, of 2,956 cwt. (147,830 kilograms) in order to effect a decomposition of the water with a velocity of one milligram per second."(39) But what is this energy, the greatest that we are able to produce, compared to that harboured by atoms? The emanation of radium, which we must consider as a very unstable gas, emits, in transforming itself into a non-volatile matter, three million times more energy than the explosion of the same volume of hydrogen and oxygen.(40)

Evidently a source of such power can maintain almost

without effort the radiation of the earth and even that of the sun into space.(41) Consequently the world's process may be conceived of as being irreversibly fed by reserves whose abundance surpasses the limits of observation.

In the same category of explanation by the concept of the *immense* may be placed certain curious speculations by means of which Boltzmann has tried to reconcile identity in time with Carnot's principle. Boltzmann conceives a world in which the eras we are accustomed to qualify as eternal (*Æonen*) have a comparatively insignificant duration. Thermal equilibrium prevails throughout, except in relatively insignificant domains of the dimension of our stellar world. "For the whole universe the two directions of time are, therefore, indistinguishable, just as in space, there is neither upper nor lower." But a human being living in a determined phase of time in such an individual world will designate one state as beginning and the other as ending. For the same domain one would necessarily have "at the beginning of time an improbable state." There can exist, therefore, "in the totality of all the individual worlds, phenomena succeeding each other in the inverse order." The beings who observe them perhaps count time in a manner opposite to ours, but "they are separated from us in time by eternal eras, and in space by $10^{10^{10}}$ times the distance of Sirius, and, above all, their language has no relation to ours."(42)

At first sight we might be tempted to connect Boltzmann's conception with that of Rankine and of Spencer, but it differs in that it does not result in the "eternal return." When, in one of Boltzmann's individual worlds, equilibrium is re-established, it is the death of the world, a definite death, since an awakening is only produced at infinite distances in time and space. This awakening, moreover, is purely accidental, and becomes possible precisely because it is a relatively small accident. It is, therefore, as we have said, an explanation by the notion of the *immense*. It shows us clearly how rigorously this conception of advance without return is imposed by Carnot's principle, and, moreover, how much, on the other hand, it is repugnant to our understanding which seeks by every means to re-establish identity.

But is it impossible to bring about an indirect agreement between the principle of causality and Carnot's principle by mechanical theories? We saw that this is the real object of these conceptions which, profiting by the ambiguous character of displacement, succeed in confusing, so to speak, change and identity. Given the strength with which the causal tendency shows itself in us, we notice without surprise the numerous attempts in this direction. Poincaré classes them in two groups. First, the theories which are related to an hypothesis due to Helmholtz. It is supposed that the motions of visible masses are connected with the motions of hidden masses. It results from this that the first, which alone are known to us, become irreversible. But this theory, Poincaré remarks, cannot completely explain the constant increase of entropy. It adapts itself, in general, rather badly to reality; accordingly it entails this consequence, that if two bodies of equal temperature are put in contact with each other, there would be a passage of heat from one to the other, which evidently is contrary to the basis of Carnot's principle. The evasion of this difficulty by an auxiliary hypothesis has not proved very satisfactory.(43)

The conceptions of the other group were developed by Maxwell, and after him by Gibbs and Boltzmann; they start from the principle that, the number of elementary particles being necessarily very large, it is possible to produce apparent changes by modifying the order in which they are arranged. Thus let us suppose two containers filled with the same gas at different temperatures; according to the kinetic theory, the average of the velocities of the particles in each container will be different. Put them into communication; the particles will tend to mix, and at the end of a certain time we shall have everywhere the same average velocity which necessarily will be comprised within the limits of the average velocities of the original gaseous masses: the temperature is equalized and is found to be an average between the respective temperatures of the two containers. It is, we see, a model causal explanation, since under the appearance of change, and by the single artifice of displacement, we are made to see a real identity. Irreversibility in this hypothesis would cease to be a general rule if our means of action were less insufficient—that is, if we were able to act directly on the elementary particles. Let us suppose a being sufficiently endowed to do this (Maxwell's famous "demon"); after the temperature had become equal in the two containers, by limiting communication between them at the orifice which he would open and close at will, he might allow the particles having a greater velocity to pass from the first to the second container, and in the opposite direction those having a lesser velocity. At the end of a certain time he will have thus re-established the two original gaseous masses at different temperatures. Moreover, the equality of temperature which is finally established between the masses which intercommunicate, being, as we say, only a "statistical" fact, it is not impossible, absolutely speaking, that differences are produced by the hazards of distribution; this is only infinitely little likely and this probability is the less as the number of particles is greater. It is the same if we consider the final state of the entire universe; this is no longer death, it is a kind of sleep, but it is infinitely unlikely that there can ever be an awakening.

Is Maxwell's hypothesis, which constitutes, according to Poincaré's judgment, "the most serious attempt at conciliation between mechanism and experience" (44) really sufficient? Poincaré seems definitely to have come to the opposite conviction,(45) and Duhem,(46) Lippmann,(47) and Mach (48) are of the same opinion; but perhaps the last word has not been said about this theory. At any rate, it must be noted that the conception which forms the basis of Maxwell's theory and which consists in supposing that Carnot's principle only rules the phenomena of perceptible bodies, but is not applicable to their elementary particles, has received a curious and unexpected confirmation from a recent discovery. We are referring, of course, to Gouy's phenomenon or the Brownian movement. Brown was the first to observe, about 1825, that sufficiently small particles of matter, seen through a microscope, show a continual agitation. This fact, confirmed daily by numerous scientists using this instrument, had attracted but little attention until Gouy decided to study it more closely. He proved by elimination that not one of the causes to which it might be attributed could be invoked for this particular case; it could not be a question either of imperceptible movements of the earth, or of differences of temperature, or of the action of light. He recognized, moreover, in studying bubbles of liquid contained in the cavities of crystal quartz, that the phenomenon must be considered as permanent, for apparently it has existed since the far-off geological epochs when those crystals were formed. It is, therefore, a movement which does not cease or which is continually re-born without borrowing energy from the outside, and this is manifestly contrary to Carnot's principle. Gouy did not hesitate under these conditions to relate this phenomenon to the kinetic theory of matter.(49) The particles of a liquid must be in constant agitation; their number is very great, their velocity doubtless considerable, but their masses are very small. If the solid substance immersed in the liquid is not itself of a size comparable to the size of the particular elements, the impacts which it receives from all sides bring about an equilibrium of sufficient exactitude to prevent any movement. Below a certain limit this equilibrium is no longer produced, and the immersed body consequently begins to move; it ought to move more rapidly as it is smaller—experience confirms this. But we have no hope of indefinitely increasing the penetrating power of our microscopes—the nature of light is against it—and the smallest bodies that we are capable of observing are still very large in comparison with the elementary particles of the liquid; that is why the movements of the former are very slow compared to the movements which we must suppose the latter to possess.

Gouy's theory has been almost universally accepted, and it seems to follow, as Poincaré has said, that "in order to see the world turn backward we no longer need the infinitely subtle eye of Maxwell's demon, the microscope being quite sufficient."(50)

It may be predicted that even if Maxwell's theory, or one analogous to it, could adapt itself exactly to the facts, it would not entirely satisfy the mind; concerning explanations of this kind we would always feel a certain discomfort. Poincaré has well expressed it by stating that he mistrusts reasoning "where reversibility is found in the premises and irreversibility in the conclusions."(51) This is the crux of the question. The phenomena of nature seem to us to have a determined direction in time, to be irreversible; to explain them, to determine their causes, is to establish identity in time and consequently reversibility. As Boltzmann has said, it is then absolutely necessary "to use as the symbol of the universe a system whose variations in time are given by equations in which the positive and the negative direction of duration play the same rôle, and which, nevertheless, permit the explanation by a special hypothesis of the appearance of irreversibility observed during long intervals of time."(52) This is why, as we have seen in a preceding chapter, rational mechanics is founded entirely on the postulate of reversibility. In stating how profound is the divergence between this mode of representation and reality, we had anticipated Carnot's principle. The reason for the existence of this principle is to give precision to irreversibility, to make it tangible; it is, therefore, natural that we should experience great difficulties in finding for it a mechanical explanation—that is, in reducing it, in its turn, to identity. And in supposing this reduction possible, it would always be, in a certain measure, repugnant to our ideas, for the two antagonistic concepts of identity in time and of irreversibility are here found face to face with each other in a manner far too precise to be easily reconciled to our understanding.

But whatever we may think and whether it appears adequate or not to our minds, Carnot's principle is a fact, and by far the most important fact, of all science. Indeed, it is enough to regard reality without prejudice to be convinced that that which is permanent is but little compared with what is changing. It is solely the causal illusion which impels us to exaggerate the importance of the first at the expense of the second; what has remained is the essential, the "substance," whereas what is modified is only the "accident." Now inertia, we have seen, is a purely ideal conception; no one has ever seen a uniform motion in a straight line, and still less could ever have verified that it was indefinitely maintained. Again, is velocity really something more essential than place, and direction than velocity in a curved line? When I see a red and pulverized body give rise to a liquid metal and a colourless gas, can I affirm, because I noticed that the weight has remained the same, that what has changed is of little importance compared with what has remained? Yet doubtless it is our conception of the phenomena of energy which, owing to Carnot's principle, has been the most profoundly modified. This modification, indeed, affects the very concept of energy.

We have seen that Leibniz defined this concept as the capacity of producing "a violent effect" and that this definition has been perpetuated by tradition to this day. Now it is easy to understand that it is in contradiction with the immediate consequences of Carnot's principle. Leibniz was convinced that the conservation of "absolute force" guaranteed the indestructibility of motion: "Those who imagine that active forces diminish of themselves in the world do not understand rightly the principal laws of nature and the beauty of God's works."(53) The universe which Leibniz thus conceived was, like that of our rational mechanics, composed of entirely reversible phenomena. All bodies having to be absolutely elastic, and, of course, every idea of a transformation of motion into heat being absent, there must, indeed, be produced a kind of endless rebound which necessitates that any fall can only be apparent, and is compensated for by an elevation somewhere else. To a modern physicist, on the contrary, the passage in Leibniz is quite equivocal. The proposition remains correct if by the term motion we understand also the interior agitation of the parts—that is, if we include in it all the forms of energy. But if we wish to speak of motion, properly so called, as the displacement of bodies in relation to one another, the proposition becomes certainly erroneous. This motion, as Carnot's principle demonstrates, tends continually to transform itself into heat, and afterward to become dispersed—that is, to be extinguished. In order to be convinced that there is a real contradiction between the two conceptions, it suffices to think of the final state toward which, according to Clausius's conception, the universe is irresistibly and indefinitely approaching. Let us suppose this state reached. It is clear that there will nowhere be any fall of temperature nor lack of equilibrium of any sort; therefore, all capacity of producing an effect, of operating a transformation, will have disappeared.

Must one, therefore, infer that there is incompatibility between the principle of the conservation of energy in its modern sense and that of Carnot? Evidently not, since, as we have just seen, the modern physicist can maintain Leibniz's thesis by modifying its sense. For him the universe, in arriving at the final state of which we were speaking, will have "conserved" its energy.

The conclusion is obvious: the definition of energy is not such as we had formulated it; what the modern physicist understands by this term is no longer the capacity of producing an effect. This definition can only be applied to a world of purely mechanical phenomena. As soon as we introduce the consideration of thermal phenomena (or, if you wish, considerations of *statistics*), it falls to pieces. One can, therefore, say that the transformation began with the establishment of the principle of conservation of energy—that is, with J. R. Mayer (although he was evidently unconscious of it, since he stated the *causa aequat effectum* without any restriction). It was completed the day when Clausius showed how this principle could agree with Carnot's, an agreement which is only possible by modifying the meaning of the word energy.

We may ask how it happens that the old definition of energy, so obviously untenable, should, nevertheless, have remained in use. One reason is very evident—to wit, that it is impossible to find a verbal definition really in conformity with the concept which the modern physicist employs. It is quite easy to see that this is not a temporary difficulty. Energy really is only an integral (p. 208); now, what we want to have is a *substantial* definition, like that of Leibniz, and this demand is justifiable to a certain degree, since our very conviction of the conservation of energy rests in great part on this foundation. But when this conviction is once acquired, the physicist has no longer need of the verbal definition. Indeed, what he needs for the study of thermal phenomena is the mathematical definition, the knowledge of the expression which, because of the principle, must remain constant. That definition he possesses, and knowing also its mechanical equivalent, he can follow the phenomena of the two orders in their mutual relations. And so the manuals on physics contain really two discordant definitions of energy, the first which is verbal, intelligible, capable of establishing our conviction, but false; and the second which is mathematical, exact, but lacking verbal expression. To begin with, the professor gives the first definition, foreseeing with unconscious but accurate psychology that the student in his work will really only make use of the second. This situation in general causes no inconvenience to the scientist as long as he remains in the field of the calculus; but when he lends himself to theoretical generalizations, the memory of the verbal definition of energy may intervene to trouble him (as has been the case, we believe, in certain "energetic" speculations). And very certainly to the popularizer, inclined, as is natural, to make use of the verbal definition, this divergence is in some ways a permanent source of error—as was certainly the case in the affirmation of the incompatibility between the conservation of energy and Carnot's principle which we have noted in Haeckel.

The reader will pardon the digression: these lines really should have been placed in the chapter on the conservation of energy; we could not insert them there because these considerations demand developments based upon Carnot's principle. But in this way we shall at least have had the advantage of showing by a typical example to what point this principle is an integral part of our conception of reality. It is also obvious, moreover, that understood in its true form, which is the mathematical one, the principle of the conservation of energy may guarantee the identity of the universe in time still less, possibly, than the other two. I have used the water from a high reservoir to turn a mill, much of the energy was dissipated on the way by friction, etc., what was left was used to transform the wheat into flour; and yet the energy was "conserved," it remained "constant." Thus, when it is said that the principles of conservation regulate the world, more precision is necessary. They do regulate it in the sense that they limit the change, that they teach us that certain relations cannot be modified whatever happens. But these principles do not show us *what* is the change which is to take place, nor even *whether* a change will take place. "In every case where the principle of the conservation of energy has contributed toward the extension of our knowledge about elementary processes still other laws have entered into play—laws which imply the concept of 'tendency,'" Helm has very justly remarked,(54) and he cites as examples of these concepts of tendency, force, pressure, temperature.

As far as heat itself is concerned, the consideration of entropy, of heat convertible or not into motion, is evidently from every point of view much more important for a system than that of its energy. Everywhere, always, contrary to what the causal illusion would have us believe, the flux of things is more essential in itself and more important for us to know than their conservation.

Now we can understand better than we did in one of the preceding chapters how illusory is the sign of equality applied to the representation of phenomena. If we pass from that representation to reality the illusion of identity immediately disappears. I break a plate, I put together its pieces, none is lacking, so I shall not hesitate to express this fact by an equation: calling the plate A and the pieces B, C, and D, I shall write, $A = B + C + D$. This equation seems to affirm that there is equality between the two conditions of the plate; yet I know very well that if I were to try to use it now I would have a mishap. Four and three are surely equal to seven; but if the first number represents a beam of 4 metres and the second one of 3 metres an architect will doubtless not be able to use them when he needs a beam of 7 metres. These things do not shock us; we have not for a moment forgotten that at bottom it is here a question of a diversity, and not of an equality. Science, however, often goes far in this line of thought. Thus an expression such as "quantity of motion" is rather badly chosen in that it may produce the illusion, if only superficially, that motion is a real quantity susceptible of addition or subtraction. Now even if I have two moving objects impelled by the same velocity in the same direction, by no artifice can I transform them into one object endowed with a double velocity; both conditions being, moreover, as we know, very different from the point of view of energy. What one means in this case by quantity is not motion itself, but its projection upon an axis, which evidently has only distant relations with reality.

Can one pretend that the equation, if it does not affirm equality between two terms, affirms their equivalence? We have already seen that that is not the real object of chemical equations; the real object is to express not static relations but a becoming. Moreover, in expressing it, they deny it, since they re-unite the antecedent and the consequent by the sign of equality. The equation $Hg + O = HgO$, taken literally, seems to signify that nothing at all has happened, since all that was in the antecedent is found in the consequent. What really happened in the course of this phenomenon was described by Lavoisier, who, we saw, made use of this reaction in order to establish his theory: "I enclosed in a suitable vessel, of which it will be difficult to give an idea without recourse to drawings, 50 cubic inches of ordinary air. I then put into this apparatus 4 ounces of very pure mercury, which I proceeded to calcinate by keeping it for twelve days at a degree of heat almost equal to that which is necessary to make it boil."(55) At the end of this difficult operation he saw one part of the metal transformed into oxide. But of all this, which constitutes the phenomenon, the equation says nothing at all, or, what is worse, it juggles it away by affirming that things have remained after the operation what they were before. A chemist in his laboratory trying to perform over again a slightly complicated operation in organic chemistry knows what irony is often hidden in this sign of equality.

But is it not really obvious that *phenomenon* and *change* are one? How, then, could there be identity between the antecedent and the consequent? I let a ray of light enter through a hole made in the shutter and this ray has formed a white spot on the opposite wall. I interpose a prism and I see a spectrum. You prove to me very learnedly that the white light refracted by the prism has produced the many-coloured spectrum. I am willing to believe you on condition that you do not try to persuade me that there is identity, and that the white light plus the interposed prism is equal to the spectrum. That I shall never believe; nor will I believe that nothing happened at the moment of the oxidation of mercury. I know very well that there is not identity, that something has happened; had something not happened you would not have gone to the trouble of an explanation. As Boutroux said: "How conceive that the immediate cause or condition really contains all that is necessary to explain the effect? It will never contain that which distinguishes the effect from it, that appearance of a new element, which is the indispensable condition of an effect of causality. If the effect is in every point identical with the cause, they are but one and there is no true effect."(56)

Even admitting for a moment that it is a question, not of the representation of a phenomenon, but of a static relation between two terms, we can now prove that there cannot be equivalence. This expression is borrowed from the language of economics. When I affirm that such a thing is worth such a price, this means that I can buy it or sell it at that price, convert it into a sum of money or convert a sum of money into this thing. If, for example, French stocks are at par I shall be able to buy a 3-franc bond for 100 francs and resell for the same amount. Phenomena seem to act in a like manner. We are told that the pendulum will have acquired, at the lowest point of its path, a velocity sufficient to rise to the height from which it started; and if we have formed oxide of mercury by the union of mercury and oxygen, we can find these substances by decomposing it. But we now know that this is only an appearance. As a matter of fact, no phenomenon is possible without a flux of energy, and this flux always takes place in the same direction. And the energy which we find again at the end is always degraded; it never is worth what it was worth in the beginning—never can the consequent be the equivalent of the antecedent. If we still want to use the imagery of buying or selling, we must think not of negotiations on the Exchange, not of what has a current price, but of what we buy in a store; if, our purchase being made, we should wish to convert it back again into money, we would inevitably lose by it.

Identity is the eternal framework of our mind. We can only find it again, therefore, in all that it creates, and we have, in fact, noted that science is penetrated by it. But this does not make up the totality of science. On the contrary, Carnot's principle is an integral part of science. It is not quite fair to state, as Hannequin does, that "science penetrates no part of the real Becoming,"(57) or else we must give to the verb *penetrate* the meaning of *render intelligible, rational.* Indeed, this proposition is only correct for explicative science. On the contrary, the task of empirical science is to penetrate the becoming; change in time is its proper domain. And that is why science—which includes both one and the other—is more and more dominated by Carnot's principle.

Science itself, therefore, reinstates reality in its rights. It proves that, contrary to what causality postulated, it is not possible to eliminate time, since this elimination would have reversibility as its preliminary condition, and reversibility does not exist in nature. The reversible phenomenon is purely ideal.

It is only a limiting case of real phenomena, all irreversible at bottom. Antecedent and consequent are not "interchangeable," as we say in speaking of the pieces of a machine; they cannot be equivalents. The effect is not equal to the cause, contrary to what the scholastics affirm, because it cannot "reproduce the entire cause or its like," as Leibniz postulated.

We said a little while ago that Carnot's principle must be placed at the beginning of the physics of heat. But, if we grasp it in all its generality, it is clear that it constantly is taken for granted in all physics. Indeed, what it formulates is a tendency of things to be modified in time. It is this tendency and its uniformity which, we have already seen (p. 33), serve as a basis for the measure of time; and it is in consequence of the existence of this uniformity that we can conceive of the uniformity of the flow of time, whereas, on the other hand, the uniform advance of phenomena is directly stipulated by the principle of law itself—that is, it is an integral part of all science and of all prevision. In a word, Carnot's principle is at one with the concept of time and gives precision to this concept; this precision consists amongst other things in assuring us of the impossibility of a long-dated cyclic return which our immediate feeling does not exclude. That is why if we look for a quite general expression for this principle, covering the totality of phenomena, we shall find statements like those of Perrin: "An isolated system never passes twice through the same state," and "The universe never assumes the same aspect twice."(58) These statements approach in meaning proverbs existing in every tongue, such as *fugit irreparabile tempus, tempi passati*, etc.—proverbs formulated or adopted by the wisdom of nations and simply expressing the conviction of the irrevocableness of the past, an integral part of our concept of time. And this idea that as time advances the world does not remain identical to itself, but is unceasingly modified—in other words, that *something is happening*—is the foundation of our concept of time. If we suppose that nothing happens, this concept thereupon vanishes away.

Thus we see the real reason why Carl Neumann's notion of the measure of time is inferior to that of d'Alembert and of Poisson (p. 33 f.). Our consciousness of the flow of time rests upon the difference between antecedent and consequent—that is, upon the irreversibility of phenomena—and from this point of view the phenomena of motion not only enjoy no privilege but their consideration introduces, as it were, a disturbing element into these notions.

We, indeed, here postulate change. But the aspect of motion seen from this angle is twofold; motion is and is not a change. The principle of inertia, from the very fact that it is a principle of conservation, depends upon the second of these two aspects in assimilating rectilinear and uniform motion to rest (p. 228). The principle of inertia and the reduction of phenomena to motion, to displacement, belong as it were to a different line of thought, to a different conception of the world—the causal conception, which is derived from the postulate of the persistence of objects, and tends consequently in the last analysis to the elimination of time. On the other hand, the definition of the measure of time according to d'Alembert is really allied to the very essence of the concept.

According to Bergson's profound formula great discoveries have frequently been made by "soundings cast into pure duration."(59) The master sounding—the final discovery—is Carnot's principle, because it renders precise what is the very foundation of our concept of the sensible world which we, however, only feel obscurely: notions of time, of change, and of irreversibility.(60)

We now clearly see how wrong we would have been to attribute to science the progressive elimination of reality, which is the consequence of successive identifications. We carry this idealistic theory with us before we constitute science, since it is with its aid that we have constituted science. "Human intelligence," says Bacon, "is given to abstraction by its very nature; and it pretends to find constant those things which are in flux."(61) It is we who try to establish identity in nature, who bestow it upon her, who "suppose" it hers, if we may give to this word the meaning it has in the expression "supposititious" child. And that is what we call understanding and explaining nature. It yields itself to a certain extent, but it also resists. Reality rebels and does not allow us to deny it. Carnot's principle is the expression of the resistance which nature opposes to the constraint which our understanding, through the principle of causality, attempts to exercise over it.

NOTES

1. LIPPMANN: *Cours de Thermodynamique*. Paris, 1886, p. 3.

2. Cf. earlier, p. 203.

3. The works of Clausius were published in the *Poggendorf's Annalen* from 1848 to 1862. The principal article, *Ueber die bewegende Kraft der Waerme*, etc., was in 1850. In the beginning Clausius, just like Carnot, considered heat as an indestructible substance (*ib.*, Vol. LXXXVI, 1849, p. 46). It was only after the following year that he rectified his opinions on this point.

4. DUHEM: *L'évolution de la mécanique*, p. 111. MOURET (notes to the translation of Maxwell, *The Theory of Heat*, trans. *La Chaleur*. Paris, 1891, p. 199) remarks that Carnot's principle "has received many statements, a proof that the fact which it expresses is better felt than understood." DASTRE (*La vie et la mort*. Paris, s.d., p. 87) says: "It is very remarkable that no one can give a very general statement of this principle the authority of which has changed physics."

5. H. POINCARÉ: *Thermodynamique*, p. 120. This statement has the advantage of being very like Carnot's own ideas. Carnot does not use the word *source*, but the definition which he gives of the words *hearth* and *refrigerator*, which he uses, is entirely conformable to the concept of source in modern physicists (cf. *Réflexions*. Paris, 1903, p. 17).

6. S. CARNOT: *l.c.*, p. 28. Cf., concerning the reservations necessary to formulate in regard to this assimilation, earlier, p. 264.

7. DUHEM: *l.c.*, p. 362.—HANNEQUIN (*l.c.*, pp. 140, 141) was, on the contrary, of the opinion that Carnot's principle should have been foreseen by the mechanical theory, since space offers the possibility of escape to atoms. Doubtless, progress by deduction is possible—in mathematics, for example; but in physical sciences, where it is a question of not very complicated deductions, it is well, as a general rule, to be suspicious of those conclusions to which Herbert Spencer was devoted and which impute more or less a lack of intelligence to those who reasoned in the past. If the thing was not foreseen, it is safe to wager that it was impossible to foresee it—that is, that it is not a pure deduction, but that empirical elements enter into it. As a matter of fact, the atomists, if they supposed space to be infinite, posited at the same time, at least implicitly, an actual infinity of atoms, so that those which escaped were replaced by others coming from the infinity of space. Cf. Lucretius, Book I, *l.* 1050: *Infinita opus est vis undique materiai*, which serves precisely as the conclusion of a demonstration in which the necessity of an infinite number of atoms is deduced from the persistence of laws and of things in time.

8. CLAUSIUS: *Théorie mécanique de la chaleur*. Paris, 1868, p. 315.

9. ARIES: *Chaleur et énergie*. Paris, s.d., p. 12 and ff.

10. G. MOURET: *L'entropie*. Paris, 1896, p. 4.

11. H. POINCARÉ: *l.c.*, p. 16.

12. G. MOURET: *Sadi Carnot et la science de l'énergie*. *Revue générale des sciences*, Vol. III, 1892, p. 467 and ff.

13. GEORG HELM: *Die Lehre von der Energie.* Leipzig, 1887, p. 61 and ff.

14. OSTWALD: *Vorlesungen ueber Naturphilosophie.* Leipzig, 1902, pp. 246–265.

15. LASSWITZ: *Wirklichkeiten,* 2nd ed. Leipzig, 1903, p. 105 and ff.

16. NEWTON: *Principia,* Book I, Sect. VII.

17. We shall see later that mechanical interpretations of Carnot's principle have been sought for; but to do this recourse was necessary to conceptions of a particular order involving the intervention either of hidden masses or of statistical considerations (cf. p. 274).

18. H. POINCARÉ: *La science et l'hypothèse,* p. 162.

19. R. CLAUSIUS: *Le second principe fondamental de la théorie mécanique de la chaleur. Revue des cours scientifiques,* 1868, p. 158.

20. Cf. p. 232, note 2, and p. 278 and ff.

21. Cf. p. 272 and Appendix IV.

22. ARISTOTLE: *Metaphysics,* Book II, Chap. II, § 8.

23. DUHEM: *Origines de la statique,* pp. 53, 58–60.

24. Cf. P. TANNERY: *Pour l'histoire de la science hellène.* Paris, 1887, pp. 206, 207. It must be noted, however, that for Anaxagoras, the direction of evolution was exactly the opposite of that which we are obliged to suppose according to Carnot's principle; he affirmed that all was intermingled in the beginning and that things became differentiated afterwards under the influence of intelligence (*ib.,* p. 298, fragment 8).

25. DESCARTES: *Principes,* 3rd Part, Chap. LXXXVIII.

26. Carnot is, amongst others, quoted as an authority by Helmholtz in his celebrated study of 1847 on the conservation of energy (*Wissenschaftliche Abhandlungen,* p. 17).

27. G. HELM: *Die Lehre von der Energie.* Leipzig, 1887, p. 53.

28. HAECKEL: *The Riddle of the Universe,* trans. Joseph McCabe. New York, 1900, p. 247.

29. ARRHENIUS: *L'évolution des mondes,* trans. Seyrig. Paris, 1910, p. 4, 204.

30. One will find the exposition of an hypothesis analogous to that of Rankine in Siemens, *Scientific Works.* London, 1899, p. 433. Suppositions of the same sort were formulated, amongst others, by Lyell, *Principles of Geology,* 10th ed., London, 1868, p. 242, and also, more recently, by Zehnder, *Die Mechanik des Weltalls,* Freiburg, 1897, p. 166, and by Arrhenius, *l.c.;* cf., concerning the objections to the hypothesis of Arrhenius, H. Poincaré, *Leçons sur les hypothèses cosmogoniques,* Paris, 1911. Poincaré concludes that according to this system the death of the universe would only be retarded (p. 256), and that in any case we ought to give up the dream of "an eternal return" and of the perpetual re-birth of the world (p. 23). It is therefore, in a word, an explanation by *immensity* like that which calls into play radio-active bodies or like Boltzmann's hypothesis (cf., pp. 273–275).

31. This is Maxwell's opinion. *Scientific Papers,* Vol. II, p. 62.

32. M. RANKINE: *On the Reconcentration of the Mechanical Energy of the Universe. Phil. Mag.,* IV, 4, 1852, p. 358 and ff.

33. Cf. VERDET: *Théorie mécanique de la chaleur.* Paris, 1868–72, p. 167.

34. Cf. RENOUVIER: *Esquisse d'une classification systèmatique des doctrines philosophiques.* Paris, 1885, p. 129.

35. VIRGIL: *Bucolics*, Eclogue IV, 34–36.
"*Alter erit tum Tiphys et altera quae vehat Argo*
Delectos heroas; erunt etiam altera bella;
Atque iterum ad Troiam magnus mittetur Achilles."

36. RENOUVIER: *l.c.*

37. One will find also a curious example of the perennial character of these conceptions, flowing directly from our causal tendency in *L'Evolution des mondes* by Arrhenius (pp. 231, 245). This scientist, whose theory, as is known, envisages the possibility of cyclic return in the history of planetary systems, joins to this conception that of *panspermia*, and thus arrives at the supposition that beings, in the entire universe, resulting from the development of the same germs, have a certain relation. "The dream which makes us see worlds inhabited by living beings, in whose constitution carbon would be replaced, for example, by silicium or by titanium, falls into the domain of improbabilities." It is clear that nothing hinders us from supposing space filled equally with germs of silicium or of titanium which, of course, will be able to develop only if they reach the surface of a celestial body offering favourable conditions. But the propensity which Arrhenius obeys is evidently that which inspired the conceptions of those ancient scientists of whom we have spoken, and this is why his theory tends to approach that of the "same beings and the same accidents" of the Stoics.

38. Cf. OSCAR EWALD: *Nietzsche's Lehre in ihren Grundbegriffen, die ewige Wiederkunft des Gleichen und der Sinn des Uebermenschen.* Berlin, 1903, *passim*; and G. BATAULT, *L'hypothèse de l'éternel retour. Revue philosophique*, Vol. LVII, p. 158 and ff.

39. W. WEBER and R. KOHLRAUSCH: *Ueber die Elecktricitaetsmenge*, etc. *Poggendorf's Annalen*, XCIX, 1856, p. 24.

40. RUTHERFORD: *Radio-Activity.* Cambridge, 1906, p. 327.

41. *Ib.*, pp. 492–496.

42. BOLTZMANN: *Vorlesungen ueber Gastheorie*, trans. *Leçons sur la théorie des gaz*, GALOTTI et BÉNARD. Paris, 1905, p. 252 and ff.

43. H. POINCARÉ: *Thermodynamique.* Paris, 1892, pp. 440–422.

44. Id., *Le mécanisme et l'expérience. Revue de métaphysique*, I, 1893, p. 535.

45. *Ib.*, p. 537.

46. DUHEM: *L'évolution de la mécanique.* Paris, 1903, p. 153.

47. LIPPMANN: *La théorie cinétique des gaz et le principe de Carnot. Congrès international de physique de 1900*, Vol. I, p. 549.

48. MACH: *Die Principien der Waermelehre.* Leipzig, 1896, p. 364.

49. G. GOUY: *Le mouvement brownien et les mouvements moléculaires. Revue générale des sciences*, 1895, p. 5 and ff.

50. H. POINCARÉ: *La valeur de la science*, p. 184. Cf. id., *La science et l'hypothèse*, p. 209.

51. Id., *Le mécanisme et l'expérience. Revue de métaphysique*, Vol. I, 1893, p. 537.

52. L. BOLTZMANN: *Leçons sur la théorie des gaz*, 2nd Part. Paris, 1905, p. 252.

53. LEIBNIZ: *Recueil des lettres*, etc., 4th Writing, § 38, ed. Erdmann, p. 757.

54. HELM: *Die Lehre von der Energie.* Leipzig, 1887, p. 58.

55. LAVOISIER: *Œuvres.* Paris, 1862, Vol. III, p. 175.

56. BOUTROUX: *De la contingence des lois de la nature.* Paris, F. Alcan, 1874, p. 29.

57. HANNEQUIN: *l.c.*, p. 285.

58. J. PERRIN: *Traité de chimie physique.* Paris, 1903, pp. 142, 178.

59. BERGSON: *Introduction à la métaphysique. Revue de métaphysique*, 1903, p. 30.

60. PLANCK, whose eminent authority in these questions need not be emphasized, after having stated that the limits established between the traditional chapters of physics (such as mechanics, acoustics, heat, electricity, etc.) tend more and more to be obliterated, comes to the conclusion that the physics of the future will know but one important division, that of reversible and irreversible processes, members of the first having a greater resemblance to one another than any of them can have to a process of the other class (*Die Einheit des physikalischen Weltbildes.* Leipzig, 1909, p. 18).

61. BACON: *Novum Organon*, Book I, Aph. 51.

CHAPTER IX

THE IRRATIONAL

MECHANICAL theories reduce the universe to a vortex of corpuscles colliding with each other according to immutable laws. It has been humorously said, and not altogether unjustly, that these theories consist in supposing that a supreme intelligence—God—in contemplating the world, would have approximately the same sensation as we experience in the presence of a game of billiards.(1)

Our sensations are very different. Our universe is not mute, cold, colourless; it is sound, heat, colour. But mechanism tells us that these qualities cannot belong to the object itself; the latter conserves those qualities only which have to do with space and the occupancy of space. At one fell swoop all our senses become dispossessed (we shall see presently that, contrary to a rather general opinion, the sense of touch is dispossessed like the others)—irretrievably dispossessed; for, having at the outset destroyed the quality of sensations—their *quid proprium* —mechanism is unable to reconstitute it. On this point the insufficiency of kinetic theories is absolute and irremediable.

Philosophers, more or less influenced by materialism, have sometimes pretended to question this; and D. F. Strauss declared that the future alone would decide it.(2) But scientists are more cautious. "Physiologists," said Alexander Herzen, "might indeed have studied objectively for centuries the nerves and the brain, they would not have succeeded in having the faintest idea of what a sensation is, if they themselves did not experience subjectively these states of consciousness."(3) It is not, perhaps, superfluous to emphasize the fact that this is not an opinion peculiar to contemporary scientists. The passage just cited is only a paraphrase of what Leibniz, with just as much precision and more picturesqueness, said in the *Monadology:* "We must, moreover, confess that perception and that which depends upon it is inexplicable by mechanical causes—that is, by figures and motions. Let us pretend that there is a machine the structure of which engenders thinking, feeling, perceiving; we might conceive of it as enlarged, but keeping the same proportions, so that we might enter therein as into a mill. This done, we shall only find in visiting its interior, parts pushing against each other, and never that which will explain a perception."(4) All of this, moreover, was virtually contained in the passage of Democritus which has been preserved by Sextus Empiricus: "For it is by opinion and convention that things are sweet or bitter, by opinion that they are hot or cold, by opinion that they have colour; but in reality there are atoms and the void."(5) As Bergson says: "It is of the very essence of materialism to affirm the complete relativity of sensible qualities."(6)

But if modern science has made no innovations in this point of view, its discoveries incontestably have confirmed the theories in question in rather a striking manner. That heat and light can only be a movement of particles follows doubtless from the *a priori* conceptions which constitute the foundation of mechanism, and Descartes, in boldly proclaiming it, only based his opinions on these conceptions: "Add fire to it, add heat to it, and let it burn as much as you please, if you do not suppose in addition that its particles move, or are detached from those contiguous to them, I cannot imagine that it receives any alteration or change."(7) Spinoza and Leibniz have likewise (p. 253) affirmed that the axiom, "everything is motion," can only be proved by *a priori* reasonings and not by experience. It is, none the less, true that the phenomena of interference and polarization which we observe directly and which are not explainable, at least not easily, by any other supposition, lend peculiar weight to the thesis, as also does the Brownian movement, as it was observed by Gouy, since by its effects it renders directly visible the agitation of particles.

But its most striking confirmation has come from physiology, from what is called the theory of the "specific energy of sense organs." This, too, is a theoretical conception, but one that is based upon directly observable physical and physiological facts. It was formulated about 1830 by the physiologist Johannes Müller and consists in affirming that the specific nature of the sensation depends not on that of the external cause which produces it, but solely on the organ which transmits it. Thus, if the optic nerve be affected by some sort of excitation, whether it be what we properly call light, or a mechanical action, an electric excitation, or even a pathological process, what we feel will always be a sensation of light. Müller's original theory has since undergone certain modifications, but in spite of numerous attacks its essential parts seem to have held their own.(8) Physiological facts tend to confirm it. Helmholtz, who was its decided supporter, made the observation, amongst others, that our sense organs seem so constituted as to be accessible to excitations of a certain nature and protected against all others. Thus the retina is protected against pressure and electric excitation, whereas light can easily penetrate to it.(9) He also showed that the purest colours that the eye is capable of perceiving are merely subjective.(10) But very substantial physical facts also come to its help. Thus, since the work of Ampère (11) and of Melloni,(12) there can be no doubt about the identity of the vibrations that give rise in us to sensations of heat and of light. One and the same movement of ether which strikes our skin and our eye can be felt by us under these two very divergent forms. It is to be noted that facts of this kind had not been foreseen by deductive reasonings; certain phenomena known for a long time, such as the appearance of sensations of light caused by pressure exerted upon the eye, were, as Helmholtz pointed out, explained in quite a different fashion: former opticians supposed that in this case there was really created objective light, and Johannes Müller had to prove the contrary by experiment;(13) science, though confirming *a priori* conceptions, went beyond them.

To experimental demonstrations it is proper to add slightly more indirect arguments, which also seem to prove that the form of sensations, their quality, must belong to us. Thus the physicists agree in supposing that sound, light, and heat can only be vibrations outside of us. They are multiplicities, but they do not appear to us as such; a beautiful solid colour gives us certainly the impression of unity. The intensity of our sensation, as Tyndall (14) noted, varies quite differently from the energy of the movement of vibration which is its cause. Moreover, there is no analogy in the way in which our different organs perceive what we are nevertheless obliged to conceive of as being analogous outside of these organs. The ear perceives ten octaves, whereas the eye must be content with scarcely a sixth. Within these limits the different sensations appear to the ear as clearly graduated; between three notes it will designate without hesitation that which must be situated between the other two, whereas for the eye the sensations are equivalent. If we have not learned by heart the scale of the colours of the spectrum we see no more reason for placing the yellow between the red and blue than for putting the red between the yellow and the blue. And yet, even for the ear, sensation has nothing quantitative in it; that of a g, as Cournot (15) justly remarked, is not equal to one and a half the sensation of its c. The ear perceives each elementary sensation separately and two simultaneous sensations always give it the impression of something compound; whereas, to the eye, a mixture of colours creates the impression of a simple thing: a mixture of red and blue gives the sensation of violet, and a mixture of blue and yellow that of green—both appearing comparable to the colours of the spectrum. A mixture of very similar tones affects the eye agreeably and the ear very disagreeably.(16)

It is just as certain that, in addition to the vibrations by which our organs are directly affected, others exist entirely analogous but which we do not perceive directly. The real spectrum, we know, extends enormously on two sides beyond the red and the violet. These vibrations make no impression upon our retina, and yet in every other respect they act exactly like the light which we know, for they can be refracted, reflected, polarized, and can undergo interference. In the same way we do not perceive directly the Hertzian waves, the X-rays, or the cathode rays; we do not even perceive electricity, which is one of the most important forms of energy—perhaps its fundamental form. It is clear that if, after the manner of Condillac,(17) we suppose a being whose sense organs are different from ours, whose eye, for example, would perceive as does the ear, or would perceive, in a distinct manner, polarized light, or would have organs for directly perceiving one or the other of the movements of the ether of which we have just spoken, the external world would appear to it very differently from what it does to us. It is even possible that this supposition really takes place in nature, for it is not certain that the organs of animals are absolutely like ours; on the contrary, it is quite possible that they are still affected when ours cease to function—indeed, animals may possess organs which we entirely lack.(18)

Yet in spite of the imposing array of concordant facts which tend to confirm in this matter atomistic conceptions, objections have been raised by philosophers. Czolbe has gone the farthest in this direction. He supposes that sound and light waves are themselves endowed with these qualities, and that they are propagated in the brain only by a purely mechanical process; all the opposing proofs of science seem to him to be merely apparent and destined to disappear with the future progress of physics.(19) Lotze expressed himself with more reserve; he believes that the proofs given are insufficient. Nothing prevents us from supposing that things in themselves are red in colour or sweet to the taste; they act upon us only by movements which are not, as such, either red or sweet, but it might be that these movements recreate in us the original qualities of the objects, on the analogy of the telephone of which the receiver gives back to the electric energy its original form. (20). Boutroux attacks still more closely the problem of the specific energy of the nerves. "If it happens that the same agent impresses differently the different senses, it is perhaps because, appearing as something simple, it is really complex, comprising as many distinct agents as it causes diverse sensations. Heat, light, and electricity, for instance, may accompany each other in a more or less constant manner, without being on that account confused in one and the same agent."(21) The greater part of the phenomena cited on this subject are based upon electric excitations; it is, therefore, especially important to expatiate on the nature of these latter, as Bergson has done. "One may ask," he says, "whether the electric excitation does not include diverse components corresponding objectively to sensations of different kinds, and whether the rôle of each sense is not simply to extract from it the component pertinent to it." The physicist has been able to identify light and electro-magnetic disturbance. Inversely, it may be said that what he calls here electro-magnetic disturbance is light.(22)

In spite of the great and legitimate authority attached to the names of Lotze, Boutroux, and Bergson, we do not observe that science has as yet taken these doctrines into consideration.

This is easily explained. Bergson, who formulates the problem with superlative precision, alters ingeniously the electromagnetic theory of light, but this inversion profoundly modifies its essence. The physicist, who considers electric phenomena to be simple and light to be a form of these phenomena, will certainly refuse to follow what he will regard as an absolutely opposite theory. At the most he will be able to concede that electric vibrations, because of an unknown process which they undergo at the extremity of the nerves, become complicated in such a manner as to be transformed into waves which we call luminous. But this hypothesis will be of no help to Bergson, since it will always remain a fact that vibrations, outside the body, are purely electric, participate in no way in the nature of light, and are capable of creating in us sensations other than luminous.

It is curious that these conceptions have come forward only since the nineteenth century—that is, since the theory of the specific energy of the nerves was formulated; whereas, for many years, it had been admitted that sound was due to material vibrations—in other words, that the same vibrations could be felt directly as such by the organs of touch and as sound by the ear.

But this theory only states precisely what in fact constitutes the fundamental postulate of mechanism. At the outset, and *a priori*, mechanism must recognize that from its point of view sensation is unexplainable. It can but make the most of a bad bargain, extolling as a result obtained the simple recognition of an unsurmountable barrier. To declare that the quality of the sensation, its *quid proprium*, is engendered by the organ, and does not exist external to it, is apparently to define more clearly the limits of the problem—to withdraw it from physics and to lodge it in physiology, putting off its solution until this latter science will in its turn have achieved a progress analogous to that of the former; but this is only a deception. In supposing that physiology will some day become nothing more than a chapter of physics and that we shall succeed in understanding exactly what takes place in a nerve, we know in advance, according to Leibniz and Herzen, that in penetrating the nerve we shall only find mechanical movement and nothing resembling a sensation. There is nothing left us, therefore, if we wish to continue the pretence of explaining the universe, but to deny sensation, or, if you prefer, to treat it as a negligible quantity, as an opinion or a convention, as did Democritus; or, as we should call it, an epiphenomenon. That, evidently, is strange. Phenomenon is only sensation; to explain the phenomenon, therefore, is to explain the sensation. How can one pretend to accept as an explanation what is a pure and simple negation?

We are not surprised at this situation. We know the true rôle of mechanism and we remark only that, as the faithful servant of causality, it begins at the very start, in denying a part of reality, the work of the destruction of the external world, a work which the principles of conservation and of unity are designed to bring to final consummation. Surely, the objections of philosophers are from this point of view entirely justified. But it is clear, in so far as science is concerned, that they are condemned to remain without effect. If our efforts have not been entirely in vain, the reader has realized how profoundly mechanical conceptions penetrate science, to what a degree they are a part of it. But sensation remains and will inevitably remain always a stranger to mechanism. Yet let us understand each other; we spoke of sensation and not of sensibility. We can easily imagine a theory explaining mechanically how an organism reacts in a predetermined fashion under the influence of a ray of light. Light, being a movement, we understand that it can engender movement. But if I suppose that the organism in question has a sensation of light, this sensation remains inaccessible to mechanical explanation, as does my own sensation. To say that it is a movement has no meaning; for my sensation of light, I am immediately certain, has nothing in common with that of movement.

We here find, therefore, a real limit to causal explanation, in so far at least as the latter takes place under the form of mechanism; and it is clear that this limit is insuperable. It may be said that here there is something unknowable, transcendent, but these terms perhaps give rise to equivocation. It must be remembered that what we affirm we do not know here is solely the *manner* by which mechanical movement is transformed into sensation. As to the two terms of the transformation, we believe, on the contrary, that we know them perfectly. That light is a movement, we have seen, is as certain as a theoretical conception in science can be; and as to sensation, it is the primordial fact from which all others are deduced. We conceive both of them perfectly; we are obliged also to suppose that they must be bound to each other. Indeed, this movement gives rise to that sensation; but it is a relation which we do not succeed in rendering logical, it remains in its turn a pure and simple fact. It is, therefore, preferable, in order to prevent all misunderstanding, and to mark more clearly the peculiar nature of the unknowable, of the transcendent, which we here assume, to designate it by a different term.(23) We shall make use of the term *irrational*. The very definite meaning assigned to it in mathematics need not embarrass us, and, on the other hand, the signification which we here attribute to it is like that which it has, for instance, in the expression—*rational* mechanics. It has the advantage of clearly indicating that it is a question of a *fact*, which we believe to be certain, but which remains and always will remain incomprehensible, inaccessible to our reason, irreducible to purely rational elements.

It must be understood, on the other hand, that in admitting the existence of this limit we affirm not only that we shall never succeed in understanding this "irrational," but that we shall never approach this understanding—that we shall approach only the limit. It is this which distinguishes our concept from that which Leibniz at times formulates. Leibniz seems to admit that nature could not bring into being anything which was contradictory or unintelligible. What appears to us as such is really infinitely complicated: to be understood it would demand an interminable analysis;(24) for want of which we make use of experiment. Leibniz sums up this doctrine in one of those striking figures of which he had the secret by saying that all things are created by intelligible causes—that is, by causes which could be seized by us "if an angel wished to reveal them to us."(25) We shall say, with Schopenhauer (26), that the revelation of the angel would be of no service to us, the organ for understanding it being absent. We believe, therefore, as Spir does,(27) that on this point there is irremediable contradiction between our intellect and nature, or (what amounts to the same thing) sensation, the intellect postulating identity and sensation demanding diversity.

This irrational, lying as it were beyond mechanical theories, is not the only one whose existence we are obliged to assume, in accepting the image of reality, as these theories present it to us; an analogous element exists in the very heart of these doctrines. We have already encountered it in treating of impact and of action at a distance. Indeed, the manner in which bodies act upon each other is as little conceivable as their action upon our senses. It will, perhaps, be useful to examine from a slightly different point of view the obstacle here presented.

There can be no doubt, in the first place, that this mutual action of bodies is an essential element, one of the bases of mechanical theories. We have seen that, as a matter of fact, all presuppose it; but it is easy to be convinced that this supposition is necessary. Their fundamental postulate, indeed, is the existence of matter. Now Schopenhauer has told us that for matter to be is to act. "We cannot even conceive of a manner of being other than that."(28) The molecules, which a little while ago formed liquid water, when transformed into vapour are removed from my perception—that is because they are simply dispersed in the air—but they continue to exist, each one of them occupies a determined part of space, which becomes from that very fact impenetrable to every other molecule. If this *action* of the atom were to cease, the atom itself would cease to exist. One might object that, according to the kinetic theory of gases, the atom which is supposed to exert no action at a distance, while it is freely traversing space (that is, between two impacts), does not, strictly speaking, act. Doubtless; but precisely in order to conceive that it exists in the interval, we are obliged to suppose that it is unceasingly prepared for action—that action exists in it in the state of a faculty or "power," without which it would be inconceivable that it could be exerted at the next impact. Rosenberger,(29) the very competent historian of physics, was astonished that the laws of percussion, which constitutes the fundamental phenomenon of physics—that to which we seek to reduce all others—were studied so very late and incompletely in a century, nevertheless, devoted to experiments; indeed, the first work of this kind was that by Mariotte in his *Treatise on Percussion* (1677). But this is no just indication of the rôle which this phenomenon was destined to play in mechanical theories. That it should explain other phenomena, rendering them intelligible, was to suppose it itself intelligible. Doubtless this was an illusion; but we have seen (p. 97) that this illusion was determined by the very nature of mechanical explanation. It is, therefore, quite natural that people pretended to deduce the rules of impact *a priori*; to search for them *a posteriori* would have been contradictory. The most one could do was to verify them.

Following the same line of thought, we can easily understand why, as Cournot (30) and Stallo (31) very carefully proved, impenetrability is not an empirical notion and does not even seem to be suggested by experience. It is quite sufficient to refer to the opinion of Leibniz already cited.(32) What Leibniz means to prove is that unless a notion of this kind is accepted, all reciprocal mechanical action between bodies—that is, all phenomena—becomes impossible. It is, therefore, as he himself says, a metaphysical principle, and Schopenhauer has admirably singled out the essence of this concept by declaring that impenetrability is none other than the principle of activity (*Wirksamkeit*) of bodies.(33)

And now, knowing the true nature of scientific explanation, we can directly ascertain that this phenomenon eludes it. To do this we have only to resume the investigation which we undertook in the second chapter, and to try to determine to what point the hypotheses formulated as regards the mode of action of atoms can yield to the exigencies of the principle of identity. The radical inability of the dynamic conception strikes us at once. Indeed, in this case the movement must be born of something which is fundamentally heterogeneous to it (p. 77): that which emanates from the *centre*, traverses space—travels—is certainly not a movement; the dynamic hypothesis expressly prevents us from conceiving it as such. There is here, therefore, an incomprehensible transformation, a lack of identity—that is, there is no longer any explanation.

The concept of action by contact appears in the first place more satisfying. The body causing motion was itself in motion, it only *communicated* this motion to another body. Identity, therefore, seems to have been maintained. Something—

motion—was simply displaced, passing from the first body to
the second; this, in a word, is motion considered as substance,
which is the conception from which emanates the principle
of inertia. But as we make a closer study of this concept,
we see it escaping our imagination. There can be no motion
without material substratum, without something which moves.
Motion has nothing in common with a substance, and the
most we can do is to consider it as a *state*. Supposing we were
to accept this last concept, considering that this state must last
indefinitely, as the principle of inertia demands, how could
it be detached from one body to be attached to another?
This would necessitate, as Lotze has very justly remarked,(34)
that between the two this state had existed for a moment—
infinitely short, if one will—in itself, as a true substance, which
is absurd. But it is not possible to suppose that this transmission
would require only an infinitely short space of time. Everything
in nature takes place in time, and to admit that something
can be produced outside it is to concede that the course of the
entire universe is no longer conditioned by time.(35) As a
matter of fact, it is absolutely impossible to imagine the transmission of motion from atom to atom without introducing
a special faculty, a mysterious agent (p. 72). The deduction
of phenomena by mechanism succeeds in appearance only
because we retain, more or less explicitly, for the atom a
principle of transitive activity, which we call impenetrability
(solidity, antitypy), and because this occult quality is allied
by a singularly powerful association of images to matter.

Let us notice, however, that if this mechanical action seems
unintelligible to us it is not because of its unfamiliarity. Action
by contact appears to us in every respect as the most natural
thing in the world. We have the immediate consciousness of
it by the sense of touch and the muscular sense; we come under
its influence and we exercise it ourselves continually, and it is
the principal source from which our concept of matter is
derived. As to the notion of force which characterizes the
dynamic hypotheses, it is certain that at every moment I
submit to the action of gravitation—that I have only to hold
an object in my hand to feel it bear down toward the earth,
and that every part of my body bears downward equally;
and I feel this very distinctly and at every moment, since I am

obliged to calculate my movements in consequence of it. The notion of force is derived, moreover, from a sensation which we designate sometimes by the same term, but which we distinguish better by calling it effort. But this action which I exert or of which I am the object, certain as it is as a fact, remains inaccessible to my understanding. No one has grasped this better nor expressed it more vigorously than Hume. "The first time," says this philosopher, "a man saw the communication of motion by impulse, as by the shock of two billiard balls, he could not pronounce that the one event was *connected*; but only that it was *conjoined* with the other. After he had observed several instances of this nature, he then pronounces them to be *connected*. What alteration has happened to give rise to this new idea of *connection?* Nothing but that he now *feels* these events to be *connected* in his imagination, and can readily foretell the existence of one from the appearance of the other."(36) In other words, mechanical action is a law, but is not and never can become a deduction.

Let us notice in passing that Hume was by no means the first to utter opinions of this kind. The transcendent nature of the obstacle which our comprehension encounters had been recognized for a long time. The problem, indeed, is none other than that which is known under the name of "communication of substances." The scholastics treated of it, and Holkot notably developed ideas regarding it, the likeness of which to those of Hume's is surprising.(37) Locke also stated that the communication of motion is incomprehensible.(38) Leibniz makes this incomprehensibility an integral part of his conception of "pre-established harmony," everything taking place, apparently, as if mechanism alone determined the course of the world, but really each monad manœuvring alone, with no possible communication with others, and offering only, in virtue of an order established from the beginnings of things, an image, a mirror of the world. The occasionalism of Cordemoy, developed by Malebranche, states precisely that each encounter of matter necessitates the intervention of a mysterious agent—the will of God. "Bodies have no action," says Malebranche," and when a ball which is moving encounters and moves another, it communicates to it nothing which it has; for the ball itself has not the force which it communicates to it.

A natural cause is, therefore, not a real and a true cause, but only an occasional cause, which determines the Author of nature to act in such and such a manner, in such and such an encounter."(39) Let us note that what Malebranche here calls "a real and true cause" does not enter into the concept of what we have designated under the term of scientific causality. We shall consider later the notion of which he makes use. Having said this, let us return to Hume's very precise analysis.

His statement, as we reflect upon it, provokes amazement. It is true that we proved in Chapter II that the atom could not act, even by contact; but that is because, as we have stated in Chapter VII, the atom is no longer matter; it was stripped of all the properties which constitute matter, and is, strictly speaking, only a bit of space. But we are here reasoning, it seems, about true matter, such as common sense knows it, and Hume, in speaking of his billiard balls, represented them certainly as real, visible, and tangible. Can it be that even this concept does not include transitive action?

We have just used the term *tangible*. This was because the sense of touch seems to some to be the supreme judge of reality. This is the theory of the primacy of touch, which especially since Berkeley has become generally current, and which Buffon, Condillac, Maine de Biran, John Stuart Mill, Spencer, and Bain(40) have adopted. In what concerns more particularly the sense of sight, it admits, as Berkeley has stated, in his admirable *Essay Towards a New Theory of Vision*,(41) that our visual impressions are only signs which we translate, in consequence of instantaneous associations of ideas, into tactile images, our notion of space being solely due to the sense of touch.

Let us say at once that this theory hardly seems acceptable. If really one of our senses had the power of imposing its law upon the others, it would seem that a fact of such importance ought to be revealed by signs impossible to mistake, by a profound and universal sentiment which would allow no doubt to exist.(42) Now it is quite easy to determine that this is not the case. Modern psychology offers us valuable testimony on this point. We refer to observations upon the comparison of spatial sensation in those born blind and in those who can see. Already, in the seventeenth century, Molyneux and Locke had noticed that there was a problem there to solve.(43)

Since then Hamilton has drawn attention to Platner's observation.(44) Finally, Charles Dunan has given exactitude to these conceptions by observing that if we are obliged to suppose that the sensation of space is different in those born blind and in those who see (about which everyone is agreed), we must recognize also that with the latter the sensation of space results from the sense of vision alone, and that far from transforming visual images into tactile images, as Berkeley stated, we translate the latter into the former.(45) Quite recently, Lalande has made observations which tend also to demonstrate that in certain cases visual perceptions give us a more powerful feeling of objective reality than any other sensation.(46) These opinions have been profoundly discussed by the French Philosophical Society.(47) What we especially wish to retain from this interesting debate is that apparently no precise argument was furnished in favour of the primacy of touch, which, let us repeat, would be surprising if touch were the true sense of externality. On the contrary, it is possible to show that it enjoys as such no privilege, and to recognize at the same time whence comes our illusion in this respect.

Let us state in the first place that the term, like many others based on everyday life, is not precise. Our language is full of figures of speech. Thus touch appears to us, on the one hand, as a peculiar sense with which we are endowed; but on the other, having conceived the existence of the external world, we apply immediately the same term to the exterior phenomenon which seems to condition this sensation. Just as we call *light* our sensation and the vibration of the ether which takes place outside us, we also say: these two bodies touch each other, although of course we do not at all mean to attribute to them the sense of touch. But if we put aside what has to do with this transposition, we very quickly see that it is a question for touch of specific sensory impressions, just like those of hearing and sight.

One can be directly assured of this by observing that the tactile sensations, like the visual or auditory sensations, are purely qualitative and in no degree contain that element of continuous quantity which seems to us to be an integral part of our concept of space. When we state that one ball is twice as large as another, will the second give to our touch a sensation double that of the first? Not at all. We shall have simply two analogous but different sensations, something like two shades of the same colour or two tones differing by an octave. We shall come back to this question and we shall see how the element of quantity is superposed upon this qualitative sensation (p. 34).

If we start from the mechanical conception of the external world, the tactual sensation, like every other sensation, is inexplicable. This seems to be less evident than for sight and hearing, because for touch the confusion between our sensation and the external phenomenon is more complete; but it is enough to analyse the concept in order to recognize that the notion of matter, acting mechanically, displacing other matter, contains nothing of the *quid proprium* of our sensation of touch. The "mill" of Leibniz will produce no more of that sensation than of any other. Doubtless if, as Lotze supposes, the real world contains, beside mechanical actions, other elements, these latter could not penetrate into this mill, whereas the first would enter therein freely. But this, too, is an illusion based upon the fact that in trying to *understand* the functioning of our brain, we are constrained to imagine it as some kind of mechanism. Really we have no immediate knowledge of the manner in which it functions. The very fact that the brain is the seat of sensations and ideas is a recent discovery. The ancients sought for this seat, at least partially, in the heart, and modern languages still keep certain traces of this opinion as in "to learn by heart," "the heart's desires." We know, having learned it by external observation, that the brain has pretty nearly the form of a large sponge; but were it to have the form of an artichoke or an orange, we should not be any more surprised, for we are ignorant of the relation that exists between that form and its activity; and even if we were to know it, it would never appear to us—as Leibniz so well explained—as logical or necessary.

Motion being considered the fundamental phenomenon, it is quite natural that the faculty possessed by one piece of matter of moving another appears to us as an essential property; hence the concept of impenetrability, which is the basis of the definition of matter and the concept of mass, which is the numerical expression of that faculty, and which in mechanical theory is entirely substituted for the concept of matter. It is, therefore, this faculty which for us becomes the true criterion of materiality. But, as we have just stated, there is constant confusion between the touch sensation and the external touch phenomenon. This latter, in consequence of the considerations already mentioned (p. 82), appearing to us indispensable for material action, the touch sensation benefits by it and immediately appears to us as if clothed with a particular dignity, as the revealer of materiality, and consequently of space. Lucretius proclaims: "For, if it be not body, nothing can touch and be touched."(48) Here, at first sight, is a statement which clearly stipulates the primacy of touch. But it must be noticed that Lucretius supposes that the *thing* can touch, which evidently has no relation to the touch sensation. Moreover, in the lines which immediately precede, Lucretius has superbly celebrated the destructive effects of the tempest, and ends with this declaration: "Wherefore again and again there are unseen bodies of wind, inasmuch as in their deed and ways they are found to rival mighty streams, whose body all may see."(49) And so what seems to him to be the distinctive sign of materiality—in our case materiality of the air—is, indeed, the power of producing some effect, as we should say *mass*.

But, important as is this rationally deduced concept of matter, it is less immediate. In the beginning, we doubt not, the image of the external world is only made up of hypostatized sensations. Can we resolutely abandon this procedure? The effort which we would thus impose upon our imagination would seem to be very great. Indeed, the external world being only sensation, how suppose the reality of something which would have been completely stripped of it, and which consequently could no longer become sensation? For this bit of matter, of course, could move another bit, but neither it nor any of the others upon which it would act could become a cause of sensation to us; it would, therefore, be without any relation to our sensation, and consequently would fade away. That is why in thinking of matter we retain by a powerful and unconscious effort this element of sensation. If we try to dissociate it entirely, the imagination rebels. In other words, and in spite of the definition which we give, matter continues to be for us especially a hypostatized tactual and visual sensation. Bergson has aptly remarked that atoms supposedly stripped of physical qualities are really only determined "in relation to a possible vision and a possible contact."(50) Let us here observe, that from this point of view again touch enjoys no special privilege. It is sometimes said that the world of atoms is a world of blind people: this is very inexact, for if it is certain that we shall never see the particles, the movement of which constitutes what we call *light*, it also seems just as evident that corporeal particles will never be able to give us the touch sensation, this latter being very probably, just as is the sensation of light, a consequence of the agitation of the terminations of our nerves by the *movements* of these corpuscles. The world of atoms is, therefore, also a world of anæsthetized people— that is, as we said at the beginning of the chapter, without any possible relation to our sensation.

We see this still more clearly in the electric theory of matter. There, indeed, the bold leap has been made, all relations between the sensation and the supposed substratum of reality, the electron, have been cut. Obviously, "this singular point in the ether" is not at all tangible. Nor do we pretend any more that it is material. It must explain matter, but it is not matter. Moreover, the fact that this theory was able to arise and to acquire so rapidly a preponderant place in science constitutes one more proof against the primacy of touch. If this sense were really the supreme revealer of external reality, a theory of reality so completely in abstraction from its impressions would be inconceivable.

But when we think of *tangible* matter, it is the touch sensation which is at the bottom of this concept, and Hume's billiard balls are made of the same matter. It is not astonishing, then, that transitive action is not amongst their properties. It is the simple statement that two sensations which differ from each other are also independent of each other, whence it follows that hypostatized into qualities they also remain so. "Solidity, extension, motion—these qualities are all complete in themselves, and never point out any other event which may result from them," says Hume.(51)

The transitive action of matter, the power of displacing an other matter, is, therefore, something irrational, in the sense which we have previously given to this term—that is, it remains and will remain irreducible to purely rational elements.(52) Consequently, the explanation of the phenomenon as mechanism presents it to us seems to us to be encompassed or limited by two irrationals: one turned toward the object—we cannot understand how bodies can act upon each other; the other turned toward the subject—we cannot understand how movement in us can be transformed into sensations.

It is also clear that in both cases the irrational is of the same order, and we can even believe that it is identical. It becomes so if, abandoning resolutely all hypostasis of tactile sensations, we form our concept of matter only with the aid of the notion of transitive action, as we do in the electric theory of matter; indeed, and as a consequence, the sensations of touch becoming analogous to those of hearing and sight, the enigma for all of them is the same.

But we can come to the same result in another way—by assimilating what takes place outside us with that which takes place within us. When movements of matter strike certain of our organs and are transformed, they become sensations; on the other hand, there are formed in the depths of our being what we call volitions, which, passing through other organs, become movements. We can suppose that the second are the consequence of the first. And so, sensation being only the interior aspect of the action of bodies upon us, and volition being the interior aspect of our action upon bodies, we may rightfully suppose that it is through sensations and volitions that matter reacts. As Schopenhauer said, in exercising an act of volition we are "behind the scenes" of nature.(53) To be sure, our will seems to us to be free; but the stone thrown in the air, were it endowed with consciousness, would also, doubtless, imagine that it went up and down by an act of free will.(54) It is evident, moreover, that this simile explains nothing, for we do not understand how a volition in us is transformed into movement. But we do understand at least that the irrational may well be unique.

If we refer to the analysis we made of the significance of the term *cause*, it is evident that we have merely assimilated an act of brute nature to a phenomenon depending not on scientific but on theological causality. Have we, then, gone too far in affirming that the latter is entirely excluded from science? Yes and no. Let us note in the first place that this concept by entering into science is transformed. The act of volition is free in essence; but as science can embrace only the phenomena subject to the domination of law, we are necessarily led to eliminate this liberty, to treat it as an epiphenomenon—to conceive, as it were, of a volition stripped of the feeling of liberty, which is, of course, contradictory but for the moment indispensable. This is clearly seen in the passage of Malebranche (p. 303), who, bringing divinity into the question, is obliged to suppose that its acts are strictly determined—that is, to strip divinity in these circumstances of its free will. It is, therefore, no longer only a theological causality; it is a concept akin to and intermediary in some degree between this latter and scientific causality. It is like the first in supposing a fundamental dissimilarity, an absolute heterogeneity, between cause and effect; and like the second in that it excludes liberty. This concept may be designated as that of *efficient causality*.

Moreover, this notion appears only at the extreme limit of the domain of explanation. Science, with a powerful and untiring effort, is looking for identity in phenomena, and, on occasion, even imposing it upon them. Where this effort remains sterile, where irrationality shows itself, the mental association between the two concepts of causality—one issuing from reason and the other emanating from the immediate sensation of the will—insinuates, surreptitiously, so to speak, the second, or at least its reflex, into the place of the first. This is what Malebranche did when he attributed the action of bodies to the will of a divinity. With the one difference, that we substitute for this pseudo-theological conception a pseudo-metaphysical conception; we act in the same way when endowing atoms with a mysterious power which we call *impenetrability* or *force*, but which, of course, under this aspect remains just as irrational as the act of Malebranche's divinity; for the effect which we mean to produce is movement, and what we place in the body can only be a faculty. It is enough, moreover, in scrutinizing these concepts to recognize that they are derived from sensations indissolubly linked to acts of will. Leibniz, in introducing his notion of the principle of action or of passion, declares that it is "very intelligible even though it be in the province of metaphysics"; but this term "intelligible" has not the same force with him as it has with us. What he means to affirm is that the concept sought for corresponds to something which we feel distinctly and directly, and the accumulation of the terms *power, action, resistance,* and *effort,* leaves no doubt that the sensation which is evoked by that association of ideas was really that one which accompanies in us the accomplishment of an act.(55) Of course, just like Malebranche's divinity, this metaphysical entity, although derived from volition, cannot be free. Impenetrability or force surrounding the atom, both appear to us as constant. Doubtless, if necessary, they could vary in time according to a definite rule—that would be to suppose a law without any possible reason—but they cannot vary freely without invalidating the very foundations of science.

The four concepts of which we have recognized the existence, and which constitute four different ways of understanding the relation between antecedent and consequent, have different domains. *Law,* without exception, governs all phenomena, which are the objects of science, and each phenomenon in particular under all its aspects, in so far at least as we conceive of it as coming within the purview of science. We try to apply *scientific causality* equally to all phenomena of science, and we always find, by more or less violating nature, one side of the phenomena to which it can adapt itself; but, just as Boutroux states in the passage which we quoted (p. 283), that adaptation is never complete, so that there can never be entire persistence, coincidence, complete identity, between antecedent and consequent. The typical phenomenon—that to which we reduce the others—motion, is not itself explicable unless we assimilate it to rest. As soon as we conceive it as change, difficulties become apparent which we succeed in overcoming only with the help of such artifices as the infinitesimal calculus. The domain of this concept is, therefore, more restricted than that of the preceding one. *Theological causality* rules phenomena, in so far as we conceive them as evading science, prevision; and finally, *efficient causality,* which is a kind of hybrid concept, intermediary between the last two, and is applied, more or less happily, to that part of the phenomena of science which

evades scientific causality—that is, their irrational side. Theological causality, in its very essence, is entirely foreign to
science; efficient causality enters into it, optionally, as a
make-shift. Only the concepts of law and scientific causality
are applicable constantly to it—science is their work, and is
in truth governed by them.

Here we must mention still another concept, that of *purpose*.
In a quite recent past, teleology was held in great esteem by
science. Without speaking of the more or less surreptitious use
made of it by the physical sciences properly so called (a use
which we shall see has not completely ceased) it alone appeared
capable of furnishing truly synthetic points of view in the
biological sciences. To be sure, Descartes had stated that the
organism was only a machine, and in the eighteenth century
the materialists had magnificently developed this thesis. But
it was not apparent that this view was capable of contributing
ideas upon the genesis of the organism or of its parts. That
there was in each organic being a whole marvellously adapted
to its environment and to its mode of existence was what
even a superficial observation made clear and what a profound
study confirmed. Upon this agreement was based the teleological
proof of the existence of God, which we know dominated for
many centuries a large portion of human thought. Almost on
the eve of Lamarck's work, in an atmosphere very favourable
to materialism, the Abbé Galiani stated this idea with great
force and eloquence.(56) Kant also was of the opinion that
one could never dispense with considerations of teleology in
the explanation of organic beings: "It is absolutely certain
that we cannot learn to know in a sufficient manner and with
still more reason explain organic beings and their internal
possibility by purely mechanical principles of nature, and
it can be boldly affirmed with equal certitude that it is absurd
for men to attempt such a thing and to hope that some new
Newton will some day come to explain the production of a
blade of grass by natural laws over which no purpose has
presided: this view must be absolutely denied to men."(57)

The situation is completely modified with the emergence
of the theory or principle of evolution. Yet on this point we
must be more specific. Indeed, if we try to fix precisely the
scope of this principle, we notice that it does not seem to

be interpreted in the same way by everyone. Thus certain philosophers accuse biologists of perverting its meaning; declaring that in order to find its real signification we must "rid it of its materialistic flavour."(58) This situation cannot fail to astonish, if we recall that the concept of evolution arose in relation to biological facts and theories, and that even to-day it is especially in this science that it finds its application. One immediately suspects that between the two adversaries there must be a misunderstanding. We believe that it is possible to show that this is really so, that the principle of evolution is double, or, if you prefer it, that it presents two aspects, the ambiguity coming from the fact that the biological sciences, in comparison with the physical sciences, are in an infinitely less advanced stage of development, and that consequently the differentiation achieved in the former is not simultaneously imposed in the latter.

Let us go back to the time of the great discussion between Cuvier and Geoffroy Saint Hilaire. What did the prevailing theory affirm? It maintained that species must be considered as fixed, invariable, each one having arisen with determined characteristics and having kept them, if it still exists, or if it has disappeared, until its disappearance. The innovators, on the contrary, maintained that the species, by the very fact of its existence, modified itself. Everyone was, and still is, seemingly, more or less in agreement upon the sense in which this modification of the species, or its evolution, as this concept was called later, is produced. The species adapts itself more and more to its environment; it manages better to avoid or to overcome the dangers which threaten it, and to hold in the world the most favoured position.

If we stop at this conception, we see that evolution postulates a becoming, the changing of the present state in view of a future state. It is, therefore, a concept analogous to Carnot's principle: just as the substance of which the temperature is higher than that of the substances surrounding it tries to put itself in equilibrium with them, so the animal species, carried into an environment which does not suit it, tries to modify itself in such a way as to bring about a condition which can also be called a state of equilibrium. Consequently we understand why Jean Perrin, while trying to designate Carnot's principle by a general term, hit upon the name, "principle of *evolution*," analogous to the German *des Geschehens*, which we have already mentioned.(59) It is in this sense that the philosophers of whom we have already spoken have understood the principle.

But we saw that Carnot's principle in itself was not rational.(60) It is rational that things remain, not that they change. The biological principle of evolution, taken in this sense, is, therefore, not rational either. *Why* does the animal species try to adapt itself? And what is the mysterious force which impels it? These are questions which our intellect will never cease to ask and to which explanatory science must always reply. That is why all the efforts of philosophers, tending to limit its bent, to maintain for the principle of evolution its sense of principle of change, are, and always will remain, useless. Just as with Carnot's principle, our intellect will not be satisfied unless it can adapt it to mechanism. This necessity is even more urgent in biology than in physics. Indeed, Carnot's principle is an empirical law, directly observable; it is the most general and the most common of rules—it governs the totality of phenomena. This is far from being so for the variability of animals and vegetables; even admitting that this is an absolutely demonstrated fact, it is far from impressing itself upon our attention as much as the fact of the establishment of the equilibrium of temperature. That is why it could not really become a part of science until an explanation of it had been found, or at least until a way had been indicated by which it seems possible to find an explanation. This was done, or at least attempted, by the initiators of the concept of evolution in biology—Lamarck, Darwin, Wallace. Did they succeed? Opinions differ on this subject, even amongst biologists.

Yet a certain number of points seem established. At any rate, biologists, who are partisans of evolution, seem convinced that either one of the causes already indicated at present— such as heredity of acquired characteristics, selection by sexual attraction, selection by the struggle for existence, etc.—or the entirety of these causes, or even the intervention of causes not yet imagined are sufficient to explain what appears to us as a tendency toward a future state. The principle of evolution thus *explained* resembles Carnot's principle interpreted by Maxwell's theory. It becomes a causal conception, a principle of *conservation*; it tends, indeed, to make us see that all forms of organic life known to us emanate from a single and simple form, through many gradual transformations and under the action of explainable, that is, mechanical causes. It is a development quite analogous to that of the primitive nebula supposed to have engendered in its bosom, in virtue of forces which from all eternity were inherent in it, all the diversity of our planetary system.

Evolution thus becomes, as Wilbois has remarked, a pure appearance covering a true fixity(61)—in other words, an epigenesis has been substituted for the genesis.

If this aspect of the principle is adopted, and this is, naturally enough, the way it appears to most biologists,(62) the arguments of Abbé Galiani and of Kant seem no longer to be valid, and there seems to be no necessity to have recourse to teleology in order to explain the organic world. Causality appears capable of undertaking this task, which amounts to saying, as we have seen, that we may entertain the hope of reducing organic being to pure mechanism. We have pointed out (p. 63) how enormously far off this result must now appear to us; but, at any rate, we have not the feeling of being separated from it by an insuperable barrier. We see here nothing unknowable, nothing transcendent,(63) with the exception, of course, of sensation and volition. These are and will remain, like the transitive action in inorganic nature, eternally irrational. If we suppose that the explanation of an organic being can be complete, sensation and volition will appear as epiphenomena, since they are only the internal form of a phenomenon of which the external aspect alone is accessible to rational science.

Moreover, in supposing this reduction to mechanism carried to its very limit, it is evident that the primitive being, the source of all others, must in its turn be conceived as having evolved from inorganic matter. This conclusion may seem hazardous from the experimental point of view, since the results of micro-biological research tend to make us reject spontaneous generation; it constitutes, however, the necessary completion and crowning of the edifice, as eminent evolutionists have proclaimed it.

If at a glance we take in the whole progress of science, we cannot refuse to acknowledge that teleology has a tendency to recede constantly before causality, as Laplace (64) had already affirmed and as Sully-Prudhomme (65) has clearly shown. This is because our mind never hesitates between the two modes of explanation: every time that a "causal" explanation is offered, even one that is remote and obscure, the "teleological" explanation immediately gives way to it. That the future is determined by the present seems doubtless obscure to our reason, which is obliged to formulate this postulate in order to live and act. But that the present should be determined by a future which does not yet exist, which may never exist, if I admit my free will, if I do not conceive of the course of the universe as entirely determined, this is what is absolutely repugnant to reason. The only way of decreasing this repugnance consists in confounding cause and end, and in supposing the absolute determination of everything. Then, indeed, the world appears to us a solid block rigorously determined in every detail, by every particular detail. This is the point of view which the encyclopædists loved to develop. "The universe for one who could encompass it from a single point of view would only be, if it is permitted to say so, a unique fact and a great truth," wrote d'Alembert. "The absolute independence of a single fact," said Diderot, "is incompatible with the idea of the whole."(66) In the universe thus conceived it becomes indifferent whether we wish to determine the future by the present or, on the contrary, the present by the future. But we are absolutely in ignorance whether in reality the universe does constitute such a block. If it exists, our mind does not permit us to know it; in order to perceive we are obliged contrariwise to break it up into isolated phenomena, and in order to act we are also forced to believe that it does not exist, that the course of the world is not determined in advance, and that we are free to influence it.

It is true, moreover, that teleology implies prescience, and prescience in turn presupposes consciousness. If I do a certain thing in order to attain a certain end, it is because I foresee that the act will lead to the consequence which I desire. Doubtless, in appeasing my hunger and thirst, in accomplishing a sexual act, I am conscious only of following an immediate need, an obscure instinct, whereas after reflection I arrive at the idea that these are teleological acts directed toward the conservation of the individual or the species. But, in that case, I suppose a superior knowledge (Nature or God) which knows of these ends, how otherwise could it will them? Unless, of course, I succeed, as does the theory of evolution, in turning toward causality by imagining that only the species have been able to persist where these needs and these instincts were formed and perfected, in which case teleology is only apparent and immediately vanishes. But if I affirm that a ray of light goes from one point to another by the shortest way, and if I wish to see in this statement something other than an empirical rule, I attribute, it would seem, to the ray not only the choice of ways to follow, but also the anticipated knowledge of the result to be obtained. This is assuredly a view, which, as Poincaré said, "involves something which is shocking to the mind,"(67) and from which our imagination will always try to free itself. It has done this in this particular case, as we know, and the pretended "economy" of nature is transformed for us into a sort of prodigality, since we suppose that undulations would surge forth in every direction if they did not mutually cancel one another.

Lange declared that all intrusion of final causes, in addition to forces acting according to necessity, could have no other meaning than that of arbitrarily closing to investigation a part of the domain of science.(68) It would be to fail to recognize that teleological considerations can merely be provisional. It seems evident to us, on the contrary, that they are capable of rendering immense service where causality as yet has not been able to penetrate. It is certain that before the day of evolutionary theories, they alone were able to permit of general ideas in the biological sciences. And even now, while professing in theory the purest evolutionism, the biologist, who studies the functioning of an organ, will always reason for the most part as if this organ had been especially adapted to this function by a conscious and prescient will. And there is no contradiction here; the scientist has simply the feeling, as has every man, that the causal explanation is something distant and difficult, while he believes the teleological explanation to be provisional—a preliminary step.(69)

Certain very general statements of science, such as the principle of least action and Carnot's principle, have an appearance of teleology; but we can see precisely from the latter that teleological considerations, if they can aid us in discovering general views of nature, are incapable of satisfying our need of explanation. It is, it seems, indeed to considerations of a purposive order that one can reduce the very remarkable attempt of Lalande to give to Carnot's principle the appearance of conformity to the laws of our reason. The transformations operating in virtue of the principle are considered by him as reasonable because, having for a law progress toward equality, they tend by that very fact to satisfy the human intelligence more and more.(70) Indeed, as we have seen, the ultimate end of the universe, in virtue of the principle, would be a state of perfect and infinitely stable equilibrium. This would be not only a state of absolute repose, but also of absolute indifferentiation; and it is evident that this state of complete annihilation would also be entirely rational, for we have arrived again at the sphere of Parmenides. Let us state at once to what extent the result of this deduction, in virtue of the method which we follow, is inadmissible to us. It is enough to envisage real science, present and past, to be convinced that Carnot's principle is irrational—that is, that our reason accepts it with difficulty, as something which penetrates it from without; that it does not appear to it as a statement justifying itself, as do the principles of conservation, but as one which our reason invincibly attempts to justify by reducing it to conceptions which are appropriate to it, explaining it, for instance, by mechanical theories, or again, subordinating it to hypotheses of cyclic return. Thus the irrationality of the principle seems a fact to us. But it is possible, we believe, to show the reasons for it. The Eleatic *unity of Being* is supposed to represent entire reality, past, present, and future. Even its diminished image, Laplace's nebula, seems to us to possess an explicative virtue because it is placed at the beginning, and consequently lends itself to a causal development. Here, on the contrary, undifferentiated chaos is transferred to the end, and, therefore, can no longer explain anything. We are going toward a condition in which there will be no longer any possible change in time and in space; but while waiting, in order to attain it, the present state must become modified in time, to the furtherance of this future state, and this we must consider inadmissible.

But could not causality and teleology exist side by side as an explanation of the same phenomena? It has been imagined that above the groups of facts bound together by causality, there might be a leading idea holding these groups together. Let us consider as an example masons who are constructing a house. Apparently it is their acts which determine the construction; and yet they are only executing the architect's plans. Let us fix at once the limits of this hypothesis; it is inapplicable within the limits of the series of facts governed by laws. Masons, being men, have free will; they have the choice of the acts which they perform, and consequently if they have not themselves conceived an end, they can very easily try to attain an end indicated to them by another. But in the case of inorganic agents, whose actions are obedient to inflexible laws, there is no choice, everything being determined. Nowhere, therefore, can teleology enter. It cannot withdraw the phenomenon from the domination of the law, and it can directly control only what does not appear to be governed by the law—that is, what is outside of science.

On the other hand, nothing prevents the laws themselves, in so far as they are not explained by causality, from being conceived as governed by teleology. Every purely empirical rule, from the very fact that it appears to us as contingent, may be considered as having emanated from a will envisaging an end. As long as I do not know why water has a maximum density at four degrees, as long as that constant seems arbitrary to me, it is perfectly legitimate for me to imagine that it results from a decree of divine free will—in order, for instance, to prevent rivers and ponds from freezing in winter to their very depths and thus to conserve the life of the animals dwelling therein. But if some day we succeed in explaining this constant, with the help of considerations about the arrangement of atoms of hydrogen and oxygen, the supposition on this point will become inadmissible and I shall be obliged to set it farther back.

The extreme limits of this enforced retreat can, even at the present moment, be indicated. They evidently coincide with those of a possible causal explanation. Thus, that which is irrational—transitive action, sensation—always, and no matter what the future development of science is, may be conceived of as teleological, as due to divine intervention, and as instituted by it for an end otherwise undefined. Occasionalism from the scientific point of view will remain irrefutable.

NOTES

1. H. POINCARÉ: *La science et l'hypothèse, p.* 193.
2. D. F. STRAUSS: *Gesammelte Werke.* Bonn, 1876, Vol. VI, p. 269.
3. A. HERZEN: *La cerveau et l'activité cérébrale.* Lausanne, 1887, p. 34.
4. LEIBNIZ: *Monadologie. Opera,* ed. Erdmann, § 17.
5. MULLACH: *Fragmenta philosophorum graecorum.* Paris, 1860, p. 357.
6. BERGSON: *Matière et mémoire.* Paris, F. Alcan, 1903, p. 66.
7. DESCARTES: *Le monde. Œuvres,* Vol. XI. Paris, 1909, p. 7.
8. Cf. BINET: *L'âme et le corps.* Paris, s.d., p. 262. According to recent studies, the same spots in our epidermis are not susceptible of feeling sensations of different kinds. There are really four cutaneous senses—contact, cold, heat, and pain—with special peripheral organs, special means of conduction, particular centres, etc. Cf. Ioteyko and Stepanowska, *Psychohysiologie de la douleur. Compte rendu dans la Revue de métaphysique,* March 1909, p. 7.
9. HELMHOLTZ: *Wissenschaftliche Abhandlungen.* Leipzig, 1882, Vol. II, p. 602.
10. Id., *Populaere wissenschaftliche Vortraege.* Brunswick, 1876, II, p. 53.
11. Cf. RUBENS: *Le spectre infra-rouge. Congrès international de physique de 1900,* Vol. II, p. 142.
12. MELLONI: *Sur l'identité de diverses radiations. Comptes rendus de l'Académie des sciences,* XV, 1842, p. 454 and ff. Cf. ABRIA: *Observations,* etc. *Travaux de la Société de Bordeaux,* Vol. IV, p. 78 and ff.
13. HELMHOLTZ: *Vortraege,* 4th ed. Brunswick, 1896, Vol. II, p. 220.
14. TYNDALL: *Fragments of Science.* London, 1871, pp. 137 and 195.
15. COURNOT: *Matérialisme,* etc. Paris, 1875, p. 398.
16. KOZLOWSKI (*Sur la nature des combinaisons chimiques. Congrès de philosophie de 1900,* Vol. III, pp. 553, 540), by an ingenious hypothesis connects the difference between hearing and sight with the fact that the sensations of this last organ have a spatial character which is lacking in sounds.
17. CONDILLAC: *Logique. Œuvres.* Paris, 1778, Vol. XXII, p. 77.
18. HAECKEL: *The Riddle of the Universe,* trans. McCabe. New York, 1900, p. 341. LE DANTEC: *Les limites du connaissable.* Paris, F. Alcan, 1903, p. 112.
19. Cf. LANGE: *Geschichte des Materialismus,* 4th ed. Iserlohn, 1882, p. 459 and ff.
20. LOTZE: *Metaphysik.* Leipzig, 1898, pp. 506–507.
21. BOUTROUX: *De la contingence des lois de la nature.* Paris, 1874, p. 73.

22. BERGSON: *Matière et mémoire.* Paris, 1903, p. 41.

23. Certain discussions which have taken place in this domain seem to us due precisely to this misunderstanding. Cf. especially, Fouillée, *L'abus de l'inconnaissable. Revue philosophique,* XXXVI, 1893, p. 365.

24. LEIBNIZ: *De scientia universali,* ed. Erdmann, p. 83.

25. Id., *Philosophische Schriften,* ed. Gerhardt, Vol. VII, p. 265. We have translated *percipi* by *to be seized,* because of the context. The doctrine of Leibniz has been admirably summarized by Couturat, *La logique de Leibniz,* Paris, 1901, pp. 256, 257, 261. Cf., however, Appendix I, p. 451.

26. SCHOPENHAUER: *Die Welt als Wille und Vorstellung. Saemmtliche Werke,* ed. Frauenstaedt, Vol. III, p. 206.

27. SPIR: *Pensée et réalité,* p. 9 and ff. Cf. preface of PENJON, p. vii.

28. Cf. p. 82.

29. ROSENBERGER: *Geschichte,* Vol. II, p. 175.

30. COURNOT: *Traité de l'enchainement,* Vol. I, p. 246.

31. STALLO: *l.c.,* p. 88.

32. Cf. p. 72 and Appendix I, p. 447 and ff.

33. SCHOPENHAUER: *Die Welt als Wille und Vorstellung,* Vol. I, pp. 12–13.

34. H. LOTZE: *Grundzuege der Naturphilosophie,* 2nd ed. Leipzig, 1889, p. 17.

35. *Ib.,* p. 35.

36. HUME: *An Inquiry Concerning Human Understanding,* Part II.

37. Cf. GONZALEZ: *Histoire de la philosophie.* Paris, 1890, p. 408.

38. LOCKE: *An Essay Concerning Human Understanding.* London, 1759, Vol. I, Cap. XXIII, p. 135.

39. MALEBRANCHE: *De la recherche de la vérité.* Paris, 1712, Vol. III, p. 113.

40. Cf. DUNAN: *L'espace visuel et l'espace tactile. Revue philosophique,* Vol. XXV, p. 136, and LALANDE, *Bull. de la Société française de philosophie,* 3rd year, 1903, p. 60.

41. BERKELEY: *An Essay towards a New Theory of Vision. Works,* ed. Fraser. Oxford, 1871, Vol. I, more particularly § 45 and ff.

42. HARTMANN believed that the importance of touch as "a sense of reality" is limited to the adult, whereas in the child it is taste and in certain animals the olfactory sense which play this rôle (*Das Grundproblem der Erkenntnisstheorie.* Leipzig, s.d., p. 5).

43. BERKELEY: *l.c.,* § 8.

44. Cf. DUNAN: *l.c.,* p. 355.

45. *Ib.,* pp. 152–153.

46. LALANDE: *Revue philosophique,* Vol. LIII, 1902.

47. *Bulletin de la Société française de philosophie,* 3rd year, 1903, p. 58 and ff. It may be the case that as Kozlowski supposes (*Psychologiczne zrodla.* Warsaw, 1899, pp. 43, 57 and ff.; *Zasady.* Warsaw, 1903, pp. 234, 251), the difficulty of coming to an agreement in this matter is due especially to the fact that one tries to reduce all spatial sensations to one source, either of sight, or of touch, or of muscular sense, and that it is necessary in the case of people who see to attribute the sensation of space of two dimensions to sight and the sensation of the third dimension to other senses.

48. LUCRETIUS: *De rerum natura*, Book I, line 305. Cf. Book II, line 434:

> "*Tactus enim, tactus, pro Divom numina sancta
> Corporis est sensus.*"

49. *Ib.*, Book I, lines 296–299.

50. BERGSON: *Matière et mémoire*. Paris, F. Alcan, 1903, p. 22.

51. HUME: *l.c.*, p. 454.

52. It is to be noted, however, that relativism has tried and, it would seem, has succeeded, at least partly, in an operation of this kind. But it is in profoundly modifying the essence of the instrument—that is, of reason itself, the limit between the rational and the irrational being, quite evidently, a function of this essence. Cf. on the subject *La Déduction Relativiste*, Chap. XXIII.

53. SCHOPENHAUER: *Ueber die vierfache Wurzel*, ed. Frauenstaedt. Leipzig, 1877, p. 145.

54. SPINOZA: *Opera*. The Hague, 1883, Vol. II, p. 208. "*Hic sane lapis quandoquidem sui tantummodo conatus est conscius, et minime indifferens, se liberrimum esse, et nulla alia de causa in motu perseverare, credet, quam quia vult.*"

55. Cf. Appendix I, p. 451.

56. MORELLET, *Mémoires inédits de l'abbé*, etc., 2nd ed. Paris 1822, Vol. I, p. 135 and ff.

57. KANT: *Critique of Judgment*. Bernard, London, 1914, Part II, Div. II, § 76. In spite of what has been said on this subject by Renouvier (*Esquisse d'une classification*, etc., p. 195) we believe that Haeckel (*History of the Creation*, trans. Lankester. New York, 1876, p. 90 and ff.) was right and that this passage is contradicted by what Kant said a few pages later (*l.c.*, § 97, p. 111). But if one cannot remove the logical contradiction one can understand, if necessary, from a psychological point of view how Kant was brought to it. Kant was, doubtless, from an abstract point of view, convinced that everything ought to be explicable "by mechanical reasons," as Leibniz used to say. But for the organized being, the evidence of purpose appeared to him, at the very moment when he was examining this question, as so very overwhelming that the causal problem seemed to him radically insoluble.

58. E. LE ROY: *La nouvelle philosphie*. *Revue de métaphysique*, IX, 1901, p. 294.

59. J. PERRIN: *Traité de chimie physique*. Paris, 1903, p. 141. Cf. Chap. VIII, p. 265.

60. Cf. also on this subject earlier, p. 317.

61. J. WILBOIS: *L'esprit positif*. *Revue de métaphysique*, X, 1902, p. 335.

62. Cf., for example, JACQUES LOEB: *Zur neueren Entwicklung der Biologie*. *Annalen der Naturphilosophie*, Vol. IV, fasc. 2. This conception is, moreover, also that of numerous philosophers. Cf. RENÉ BERTHELOT, *Bulletin de la Société française de philosophie*, 5th year, 1905, p. 250 and ff., and HERMANN COHEN, *Logik der reinen Erkenntniss*. Berlin, 1902, p. 247.

63. I have recently somewhat changed my opinions on this point. Cf. *De l'explication dans les sciences*, Chap. VII.

64. LAPLACE: *Théorie analytique des probabilites*. *Œuvres*, Paris, 1886, Vol. VII, p. 6.

65. SULLY-PRUDHOMME and RICHET: *Le problème des causes finales*. Paris, 1903, p. 90.

66. DIDEROT: *Pensées sur l'interpretation de la nature*. *Œuvres*. Paris, 1875. Vol. II, § 11. Leibniz had already said: "For we must know that everything is bound together in each one of the possible worlds. The Universe, whatever it may be, is of one whole piece, like an ocean" (ed. Erdmann, p. 506).

67. H. POINCARÉ: *La science et l'hypothèse*, p. 154. One may compare with this opinion that of Descartes which we quoted, p. 78.

68. F. LANGE: *Geschichte des Materialismus*, p. 14.

69. It is in this conception of the *provisional* value of teleological explanation that the remarkable observations of Goblet seem to culminate also. *Fonction et finalité*. *Revue philosophique*, XLVII, 1899 ; *La finalité sans intelligence*. *Revue de métaphysique*, VIII, 1900; *La finalité en biologie*. *Revue philosophique*, LVIII, 1904.

70. A. LALANDE: *La dissolution oppsoée á l'évolution dans les sciences physiques et morales*. Paris, F. Alcan, pp. 66, 67, 117.

CHAPTER X

NON-MECHANICAL THEORIES

IN discussing a possible explanation for the change of state of a body by displacement (p. 93) we saw that two ways are open to us. We can suppose that the arrangement or the motion of the parts of the body was modified—this is the mechanical explanation—but we can also claim that to the substance of the body another substance is added, invisible but pre-existing elsewhere. If we apply this method of explanation to the phenomenon of heat, we shall arrive at the theory of heat-fluid. In general, we shall build up theories of a class different from that of mechanical theories and which may be designated by the generic term of "theories of quality."

We have just seen from the preceding chapter that the true quality, the *quid proprium*, of sensation has no place in mechanism. In it sensation remains unexplained no matter what one does. Is it possible to proceed otherwise than do the atomic theories? It will evidently be necessary to start from sensation and objectify it. We do this constantly and instinctively. We have the sensation of redness, but instead of treating it as something belonging to us, we place it outside of ourselves; we attach it to other sensations, thus forming what we call an object, of which we affirm the existence: thus what was in the first place our sensation becomes a quality of the object—the object is red. We name this "common sense"—philosophers call it "naïve realism"—and, in fact, it is a metaphysical system, an aggregate of conceptions of the causes of our sensations, of "the thing in itself."

Now it is easy to prove that common sense admits that an object may change a part of its qualities and yet remain the same. This dog, now grown, is little like what it was four years ago, when it was just born; we consider, however, that it is the *same* dog. The red paint has been scraped off the table and it has been painted black, yet we shall not hesitate to say that it is still the same table. In the case of the dog, we easily see where this conviction comes from. Men—I know through myself, I have the immediate conviction of it—preserve their identity in spite of very profound changes. I remember quite distinctly my looks at the age of ten, and I do not hesitate to declare that that little boy was I: I may some day be completely disfigured by a sickness or an accident, but it will still be I. The man who believes in fairy tales admits that he can be changed into an animal, while retaining consciousness of the continuity of his ego. This is because the animal appears to us as a being which we suppose to possess sensations and volitions analogous to those of men; it is, therefore, natural to admit that there is in it a principle of individuation, completely different from its exterior aspect. In other words, if I believe that the dog is the same as four years ago, it is because I am convinced that it is a *subject* in very much the same way as I am. This is not true in the case of the table; but it may well be that an unconscious assimilation of this object with living beings influences our belief. It is certain also that the crudeness of our senses is a help. The object at first sight appears to us really the same—identical with what it was before—and it is only in considering it more closely that we perceive that slight differences have come about: the dog has grown fat, the paint of the table is not so fresh. At any rate, this conviction of a fundamental identity exists even for inanimate objects; it is a fact: only it fluctuates, for in this case, I no longer have a definite criterion. What changes shall I allow without ceasing to declare that the table has remained the same? I should find it very difficult to state them, as is indicated by the classical joke about the identity of the much-mended knife. But, more or less consciously, I divide the qualities of the table into the more essential ones, such as the material of which it is made or its dimensions, and the less essential, such as its colour and the fact of its being provided with castors. What guides me, evidently, is the greater or less facility of acting upon either one or the other of them; there are properties I know which it is almost impossible to modify. If, in examining the table, I find that a crack in the top, which I had noticed before, no longer exists, I shall have doubts about its identity.

Applying these notions to the variation of things in time, it may be admitted that there is in them a substance that is immutable and accidents that are changing.

It seems at first sight that we have thus come to the very foundations of peripateticism. But let us beware; the true doctrine of Aristotle, according to Malebranche, is not physics but logic. In this respect it here escapes our criticism. But it can be proved, we believe, that in speaking of physical phenomena, peripateticism, particularly in the Middle Ages, had a tendency to depart from this purely logical limit—thus, in fact, giving rise to theories analogous to those to which we have just referred.

We have seen that the atomist, by a mental operation preceding every theoretical research, excludes from reality a large part of sensation, declaring that there is nothing beyond matter and motion. The peripatetic—we use this term with the reservations which we have just indicated—is not obliged to proceed in this way. He is, from this point of view, incontestably nearer common sense. No one can better characterize the distinctive features of this method than Paul Tannery has done: "On the one hand, a tendency to attach oneself to phenomena, as the senses reveal them to a superficial and naïve observation, one may even say a marked respect for common beliefs, if only they are not visibly erroneous; on the other hand, a tendency to go back as far as possible and as quickly as possible in the series of causes, and to do this by a simple analysis of the concept and without new recourse to experience."(1) To this picture, destined to mark the distinctive characteristics of the Stagirite's own philosophy, only a touch is necessary to make it correspond exactly to the tendencies which dominated the doctrines of the philosophers of whom we have spoken; this is because the number of known facts having increased, the emphasis is placed more on experience and less on facts pertaining to common sense proper. But it is preferably with the help of a logical process and following as far as possible the traces of Aristotle himself that one tries to make a distinction between the substance and the accident, between that which remains and that which is modified. It is clear, consequently, that, starting from the notion of the object as common sense presents it to us—that is to say, from a group of qualities— there is no motive for attributing purely mechanical qualities to the substance; one can, on the contrary, choose freely from among the qualities of the bodies those which one shall propose to consider as "substantial." Indeed, all the qualities of objects cannot remain, certain ones are purely accidental; when a body ceases to be round, who in the world, according to Condillac's very just remark, will ask what has become of its roundness?(2) But when a body ceases to be hot or becomes moist, we may very well ask what has become of its heat and whence comes its moisture. These two qualities, heat and moisture, are those Aristotle considered as the most essential in bodies, with the addition, naturally, of coldness and dryness, which are only their opposites. These four qualities, associated in pairs, characterized the four elements: hot-dry (fire), hot-moist (air), cold-moist (water), cold-dry (earth).

Setting aside again the logical and metaphysical import of the doctrine and keeping to its purely physical aspect, it is clear that these four qualities appear as real substances—that is, in a way, as elements of the elements. Aristotle himself has sometimes expressed himself accordingly. Thus in the Second Book of *De generatione et corruptione*, when engaged in deducing the fundamental concept of his four elements, he searches for what may be the "principles of the body perceptible to our senses." "This is why," he says, "neither whiteness nor blackness, neither sweetness nor bitterness, nor any of the opposite sensibles are an element of the bodies"(Chapter II). After having limited these principles to four, he continues: "Since there are four elements, and the possible combinations for four terms are six, but since also the opposites cannot be coupled together . . . it is evident that there will remain but four combinations of the elements" (Chapter III). What Aristotle is speaking of here as elements are therefore not the substances which he elsewhere designates by this term, but qualities.

Hippocrates (3) also believed that the human body is composed of four elements—dryness, moisture, cold, and heat. These four elements form the aliments which in their turn are transformed into humours—Hippocrates recognized four of them also—and these last are the essential components of bodies.

In the Middle Ages we continually see theories of this kind breaking through the purely logical apparatus of Aristotelianism. In the East, at the beginning of the tenth century, Saadia, one of the great Jewish initiators, who had such an important influence on the intellectual movement of that period, in speaking of the destruction of a body by fire, declares that in this case the parts of the body destroyed are separated, but, being elements, remain without change and return simply to their original place, "the heat which was in the body reverting to the element of fire, its moisture and its coldness to their respective elements."(4) In the West, in the ninth century, Scotus Erigena states that bodies are constituted by the union, not of substantial elements themselves, but of their qualitative accidents; and yet these accidents are in a way themselves substances— since they remain indestructible, they can only separate in order to unite again in new combinations and thus create new bodies.(5) In the twelfth century William of Conches teaches that the four elements were created at the beginning of the world and have since been used to create bodies. In these latter the material particles of the elements are simply juxtaposed. These particles are in fact the true elements. "All bodies are composed of elements. An element, as it is defined by philosophers, is a simple and minute particle of any body whatever, simple in what concerns its quality, minute in what concerns its quantity."(6) The bodies which we call earth, water, air, and fire are not elements in themselves; the earth which we know is a body where dry and cold particles predominate. But the earth is porous and surrounded by water, air, and fire. It is, therefore, natural that what we designate by the name of earth also contains particles of the three other elements: those of the element earth prevail; they are there "naturally," the others being there only "accidentally."

The distinctive feature of these doctrines is the manner in which the mixture of elements is conceived, and from Lasswitz's splendid book (7) we see how this question troubled the philosophy of the Middle Ages. The representatives of scholasticism tried to render precise what Aristotle had left somewhat vague. Avicenna and Averroes amongst the Arabians, Albertus Magnus and Saint Thomas in Europe constructed antagonistic theories. That is because with some the purely logical aspect of Aristotelianism prevails, whereas with others its properly scientific theoretical aspect dominates. Those who are interested in practical science, who observe and experiment, lean naturally rather to this latter doctrine. Amongst them are the alchemists for whom the theory of the combination and separation of bodies is of particular importance. To an alchemist of the

Middle Ages, an element is a body endowed with certain qualities, which it preserves in combining and communicates to the combination into which it enters. Yet given the nature of the phenomena to which the alchemists devoted their attention, Aristotle's four cardinal qualities could be of but little help to them. What interested them was not to know whether a body should be considered dry or moist, hot or cold, but whether it was combustible or volatile, or whether, on the contrary, it resisted fire, whether it was of a metallic nature, etc. From this arose the assumption of elements differing from those of the Aristotelians. The relation of these new fundamental substances—which were generally supposed to be three: salt, sulphur, mercury—to the former elements of Aristotle, the existence of which was not denied by the alchemists, has never been well defined,(8) but their rôle as bearers of qualities is entirely clear. Paracelsus, who was wholly imbued with these theories,(9) states that, in analysing, one always finds again the same three elements. What burns is sulphur, what smokes and sublimates is mercury, what remains as residuum after the combustion is salt. Nothing save sulphur burns (10) and it is inversely inferred, from the combustibility of a body, that it contains sulphur.

It is hardly necessary to show how closely this conception is allied to the very foundation of the philosophic doctrine of that time. Because combustible bodies constitute a class or genus, it is concluded that they should contain a common element, and this element, hypostasis of combustibility, the common quality, which unites the different species, is for that very reason a hypostasis of the "idea" of the genus "combustible." This genus is a subdivision of a superior class of concepts as appears from the term "combustible matter"; this particular concept is thus formed from another more general one, *matter*, to which a determinant is added. If this latter is not something arising and disappearing, without any reason for it being required, but, on the contrary, as for Scotus Erigena, is something which persists and only changes place, it becomes itself a sort of substance.

In following out this doctrine to the end, we arrive at a representation of the material world as a whole composed, apart from a fundamental substance which represents the most general concept of *matter*, of an entire series of secondary substances or hypostatizations of the qualities. The most complete system which has been imagined in this realm of ideas had as its author a philosopher of the seventeenth century, Claude Guillermet de Berigard. But although, as we have just seen, these ideas of substantialized qualities are derived by a legitimate evolution from peripatetic conceptions, Berigard's system is no longer merely tributary to peripateticism. It is, on the contrary, atomistic, though qualitatively atomistic according to the expression of Lasswitz, who has drawn attention to this theory and whom we shall follow in this analysis. Berigard supposes an infinite variety of atoms, which, though spherical corpuscles, represent each an elementary quality; he shows that the four fundamental qualities of Aristotle are not enough to explain the perceptible world, which, being infinitely diverse, presupposes an infinite diversity of qualities and consequently of elements.(11) The atom-qualities (Berigard himself characterizes them as corporeal qualities, *qualitates corporatae*) penetrate the pores (*meatus*) of matter and thus confer upon it corresponding properties.(12) Every modification of the material world consists of nothing but the movement of these substances which sometimes are added to the body, thereby determining its species, and we call this its origin (*generatio*), sometimes are separated from it and constitute its corruption. Alteration is produced when following a movement of substances, the properties of the body are not sufficiently modified to produce a new species.(13) It is to be noted, however, that Berigard has not remained, in his deductions, entirely consistent with himself; he has yielded to the attraction of atomism, attributing certain qualities not to elementary substances, but to the process of their grouping. Thus he believes that liquidness results from the fact that the "principles" of the body do not adhere very strongly together, which accounts for their being mobile; and that all elementary substances must be liquid.(14)

Apart from these anomalies, Berigard's doctrine furnishes us with the most perfect example of a purely qualitative physical hypothesis. It helps us thus to understand what would have been, in a certain sense, the result of the alchemists' theories. Yet these latter, precisely because they are much more faithful to the spirit of peripateticism, stop well on this side of the limit. They suppose, in agreement with the Aristotelian doctrine, that between the substratum of the body, the primary matter, and the body clothed with its qualities, the relation is the same as between matter (such as iron) and an object which is formed from it (such as a key or a knife). Therefore matter can change its *form;* alchemists sometimes say, its clothing.

The alchemists did not consider all qualities as substantial, but only a very small number, the others appearing to them as purely accidental. For this reason their affirmations, from the point of view of modern science, seem to us frequently tainted with a certain ambiguity. Thus sulphur, mercury, and salt which compose the bodies are not elements in the sense we give to this word, for they are not always identical with themselves. Paracelsus expressly declares that the different bodies are made of particular *mercurii, sulfura et sales.*(15) Another ambiguity results from the fact that soon a distinction is drawn between the elements and the known bodies bearing the same name. This differentiation increases as science advances. Homberg, in the seventeenth century, believes that ordinary sulphur is composed of earth, an acid, and elementary sulphur, which is the principle of combustibility.(16)

Thus, besides the essential properties which really characterize it, a body has still others which can be modified without its inmost nature being changed. The metals which at first sight are considered as a clearly limited class of bodies, having a great number of properties in common, are supposed to contain the same "primary matter"; while the properties in which they differ can only be of secondary importance.(17) One can hope to transmute one metal into another, either by reducing the first in the beginning to that *materia prima,*(18) or, as the alchemists generally supposed, by acting directly upon its properties. For example, in successively removing from pewter its sound, its softness, its fusibility—those characteristics which distinguish it from silver—one will transform it into silver (19), to which it is supposed to be closely related, doubtless because of the common colour. For certain other metals, in order to change them into silver or gold, one will have first of all to modify their colour—*leucosis* or *xanthosis*, depending upon whether it is a question of whitening or making yellow—and forthwith every chemical operation which seems to modify the colour of a metal assumes immediately importance in the eyes of the investigators.(20) Mercury, doubtless because of its fluidity, which appears paradoxical, seemed to some an excellent starting-point for changes of properties. They spoke of "hardening" it, and many were the recipes given for this : Boyle believed that it could be transformed, without any addition of metal, into a substance like silver ;(21) and Macquer, in the *Dictionnaire de chimie* of 1778, insisted upon the "hardening" of mercury by phosphorous vapours or by boiling linseed oil.(22) When alchemists wish to transform an ordinary metal into a precious metal, they speak in imaginative language of "clothing it with a royal mantle." The phenomenon of the precipitation of copper by iron in blue vitriol is considered an indubitable fact of transmutation;(23) the metal is said to "take off the armour of Mars and put on the robe of Venus."

During the seventeenth century the prestige of peripateticism, as a philosophical and scientific doctrine, diminishes little by little. But the theories of quality which had sprung from it continue to dominate chemistry perhaps in a still more absolute fashion precisely because they are free from the purely logical equipment of Aristotle's doctrine. Toward the middle of the eighteenth century, there is an important change, of which we have spoken in Chapter VII (p. 235). The very multiplicity of the experiments in transmutation has brought about the ruin of that hypothesis. And then as one learned little by little to recognize that the modifications of colour such as that produced by orpiment (*auri pigmentum*) were only apparent, and the futility of all so-called recipes was acknowledged, one began to conceive that there might be elementary substances differing essentially from one another. It is not the metals themselves which are considered as elements, but their "*limes*." The fact that these latter in our atmospheric conditions are very often more stable than the metals themselves had probably contributed to it. But doubtless we ought to look for the principal reason for this in the need which was felt to attribute the many common traits of metals to a common element. This hypothetical element of which the existence is supposed, not only in metals, but also in all inflammable bodies, is phlogiston, which inherited the properties which chemists in other days attributed to their different elements. "They make it the principle of odours, of colours, of flavour, of volatility, of fusibility, of dissolubility,(24) etc.," says an author contemporary with Lavoisier (perhaps, indeed, Lavoisier himself); and the fact, observed by Stahl,(25) that inflammability is susceptible of being transmitted from one body to another seems to confirm directly this point of view. In the same way it is believed that all acids contain a "primary acid,"(26) all salts "a fossil salt,"(27) all earthy calces a single "earthy substance."(28)

We have already seen (p. 234) how slowly the new notion of the chemical element was elaborated. Phlogiston seems at first to have escaped it; Kopp states, with a certain surprise, that chemists, while firmly believing in its existence, do not seem to make any attempt at isolating it.(29) This was because phlogiston was at bottom a heritage of previous ages; it was not an element in the sense in which we use that word, but a kind of quality-bearing principle, and the idea of isolating it would have appeared to a chemist of that age almost as bold as the idea of trying to isolate *heat* to Saadia. The evolution, however, which we have tried to trace still continuing, phlogiston came to be considered, little by little, as an element like others,(30) and from that time on its isolation appeared less paradoxical, to such a degree that toward the end of that period phlogiston is identified with inflammable air (hydrogen).

How deeply rooted was this tendency of which we have been speaking is evident from the history of the celebrated *acidum pingue*. From the fact that calx, soda, and potash may become caustic, and that causticity may be transmitted from one to the other, the chemist Meyer had inferred the existence of a special acid, a support of causticity, as phlogiston was of inflammability; and this hypothesis was accepted with enthusiasm by the whole scientific world.

Before Meyer, Black had formulated the opinion that caustic alkalis were distinguished from others by the loss of a substance, "fixed air" (carbonic acid). Black had clearly proved that in becoming caustic the alkalis lost an important part of their weight.(31) But this did not prevent the majority of chemists from adhering to Meyer's theory. Lavoisier himself at first spoke of Meyer only with great praise.(32)

There is no doubt that these ideas had much to do with the strong opposition which Lavoisier's theory encountered. To sacrifice phlogiston was to abandon definitely a conception which in the first place had seemed evident and indisputable— to wit, that the likeness of properties indicated the presence of a common element, the bearer of these properties.

It is truly astonishing to ascertain what a mass of facts were known before Lavoisier about the increase of weight of oxidized bodies, and about the rôle of the air in this operation(33)— facts which were unexplained or very poorly explained by the theory of "something which leaves," whereas the explanation by "something which is added" was very clear and was suggested, moreover, long before by Jean Rey. The chemists' obstinacy in preferring the theory of phlogiston is explained only by the fact that combustibility, in so far as it is a striking and definitely characterized phenomenon, could not in their opinion dispense with a qualitative material substratum. When the phlogisticians reproached Lavoisier for not having explained why certain bodies burn and others do not,(34) they revealed the true foundation on which their faith rested.

And so in 1788, at the moment when the new school's triumph seemed complete, apparently it is from that side that the last resistance came. The commentary on Kirwan's *Essay* brings its principal effort to bear on this point, and Lavoisier himself, after having properly praised Stahl's discovery, feels called upon to make known with much insistence that "it is unnecessary to suppose that there exists in these substances a principle common to all, that they all contain the base of inflammable air—that is, hydrogen."(35) Moreover, like all great revolutionists, Lavoisier had not completely freed himself from all attachment to the old ideas. The name of oxygen indicates that he considered the new element the bearer of a quality;(36) and it is well known that this conception resulted in the erroneous theory of "murium," and that many efforts were necessary to put that spectre to flight.(37) In the same way Berthelot sets forth rightly that Lavoisier believed that oxygen coloured the blood as it coloured the metallic oxides, and that this correlation "had a tendency to make oxygen the generator of coloured matters, as was formerly supposed of phlogiston."(38)

In another branch of the physical sciences, theories of quality have persisted for a still longer time. It is, in fact, amongst them, as we have seen, that we must classify hypotheses of fluids and of emission. The "caloric," semi-material fluid, bearer of a quality, belongs to the same family as phlogiston, and the relation of Newton's luminous corpuscles to the qualitative atoms of Berigard is equally obvious.

Is it astonishing that in this region of ideas science has so slowly evolved, and that it has abandoned doctrines which appear to us as entirely untenable only step by step and, as it were, against its will, as, for instance, in the case of phlogiston? It is enough, on the other hand, to reflect upon the true nature of our conceptions of quality to understand to what a degree these doctrines conformed to the fundamental postulates of our mind. When, starting either from an immediate impression of our senses, or from a series of observed phenomena, we succeed in endowing a body with a property, when we say this body is red or is inflammable, and when we see this property appear and disappear in the body, we certainly feel the tendency, if this quality seems sufficiently important to us, to ask the question, Where does it come from—where has it gone? Doubtless, as we have already said, this question will not be asked about roundness; but it will be asked about heat. Now, in stating it, we indicate that we are inclined to consider heat as something which persists in time and which consequently only brings about changes by altering its position. This is hypostatizing the quality and attributing to it the character of a substance, and this is the kind of explanation of the phenomenon which our causal tendency will inevitably suggest to us, unless previously we have purposely destroyed the quality by the conception of a universal mechanism, which itself is an emanation of the causal principle. Moreover, the explanation by the transmission of a quality has about it something immediate, complete, and satisfying—advantages which are not found to the same degree in mechanical explanations. This becomes evident by comparing the manner in which the relations between properties of elements and those of compounds are treated by contemporary chemistry with the procedure which the theories of quality used in this respect.

We stated (Chapter VII, p. 238) that the study of the relations between the properties of elements and those of their compounds constitutes the principal task of theoretical chemistry. But this is only to formulate the side of the problem referring to law. But on this point, as on others, law alone is not enough for our understanding. We wish to know not only how things change, but also why they change. When it is a question of bodies entering into a combination, we are very careful to state that we ought not to expect them to preserve their properties; we even make of this the very criterion of the real chemical combination which is defined as the union of bodies whose properties are modified.(39) From a purely empirical point of view this definition is irreproachable; when I place together that silvery and soft metal which I call sodium and the greenish and irritant gas which I designate as chlorine, I shall see finally appear in their place the uncoloured crystals of a well-known substance, sea-salt. But *how* could this happen, where do the properties of sea-salt come from, and what has become of those of the chlorine and the sodium, if, as chemistry correctly teaches us, these two elements continue to exist in the chloride of sodium? "It is at first difficult to conceive," says Berthelot, "how bodies endowed with properties so little like those of sea-salt, are yet the only and true elements of it; one would be inclined to believe in the intervention of some other component which analysis has been powerless to reveal to us."(40) Berthelot rightly states that chemistry possesses sufficient means, from the experimental point of view, to reassure us on this point, to prove to us that these components are really the only ones. Is there need to show that after this demonstration the phenomenon remains as incomprehensible as before? If chemistry is not a purely empirical science, if there exists a "theoretical" or " rational" chemistry, if only we have the hope of constructing one—it evidently has, or ought to have, as its task to explain, as Huxley has stated, why properties of matter result from those of the elements which compose it.(41)

It is curious to notice that Comte was of the same opinion. "Chemistry," he said in defining this science, "has, as its final object, given the properties of all simple bodies, to find those of all the compounds which they may form,"(42) which apparently indicates that the second must be deducible from the first. One might in truth find this affirmation equivocal. Comte, it is well known, admitted in science only empirical rules; might he not have imagined that deduction would take place with the aid of rules of this kind? But here is another passage: "All the fundamental data of chemistry ought, in the last analysis, to be reducible to the knowledge of the essential properties of the only simple bodies."(43) Here there is no longer any doubt, since every empirical rule is excluded. Comte evidently, in making these statements, no longer thought of his definition of science and yielded to an instinctive need of explanation.

Doubtless theoretical chemistry has not yet made much progress in the direction of these ideas. We only know a small number of properties by the combination of which, according to van't Hoff's expression, "The linkage with the chemical formula is so surely established that they are deducible from that formula as a necessary consequence of adopted atomistic and molecular conceptions."(44) But it is enough to open a manual of physical chemistry, such as the splendid works of van't Hoff or of Ostwald, or even an ordinary manual of chemistry, to be convinced that efforts are really being turned in that direction. The end envisaged is obviously to attach *all* properties to the chemical formula, starting with the fundamental properties of elementary atoms, notably with atomic weight—that is, by deducing them either from the number and the nature of grouped atoms or from the manner in which they are grouped. The relations of the first order, those which can be deduced from the simple consideration of molecular weights, manifest themselves with great precision when the bodies are in a gaseous condition or in diluted solutions; those of the second order find their expression in formulae called *constitutional formulae*. It is because the same atoms of carbon, hydrogen, and nitrogen are combined in two different ways that ammonium cyanate and urea—to choose the well-known example of the famous synthesis of Woehler— possess such different properties, and it is because their atoms or groups are placed around an atom of carbon in an asymmetrical manner that the body rotates the plane of polarization. We see that the scope of these researches includes really almost the whole of modern chemistry, and we also see that it is in no way a question of seeking for simple empirical rules, but for real explanations. Doubtless chemical atoms are still far from being identified with physical atoms, although notable progress has been made in that direction, especially in the theory of *ions* of Svante Arrhenius; but the fact that, even when the conceptions of the two sciences seemed to be separated by an abyss, one spoke in chemistry of the atom and the molecule, proves decisively that a true mechanical theory has always been in view. When Sully-Prudhomme proclaims that "the specific properties of bodies tend more and more to be explained by . . . the architecture of the ultimate parts . . . —that is, at bottom, mechanically"(45)—his affirmation may be contested in so far as it refers to the facts, but it is irreproachable in so far as it is the expression of a postulate. Some, doubtless, have found that the theory has been long in coming; that is because of illusions about the facility of the task. Disillusionment has followed, one of the most eminent theorists of chemistry has admitted it in bitter terms;(46) it is the source from which have come those violent attacks which that scientist has directed against mechanical theories in general as well as a new non-mechanical theory, which we shall discuss later on. But this does not alter the fact that the general tendencies of chemistry have been until now such as we have just characterized them.(47) Moreover, there appears to be no doubt that these tendencies are directly due to the principle of causality —that is, to the desire to establish identity in time. Further, we have seen, in discussing unity of matter, that chemistry has not only the tendency to explain the properties of components by those of elements, but also to reduce to a minimum the properties with which it is obliged to endow its elementary atoms. One would like to reduce everything to considerations of atomic weights, because evidently in this way the single matter is more nearly approached; and it is felt to be a serious inconvenience that this reduction has not yet taken place for valence, and that this latter must remain an "occult quality."

But these are very remote prospects; at present we not only do not know how to explain the properties of elements, but even in assuming these latter, those of compounds appear enigmatic to us. One is apt to be astonished that chemical theory seems to accept placidly, even though provisionally, such a state of things, and Huxley, in the passage to which we referred (p. 335), has vigorously expressed this astonishment. After having noted the strange change of properties which we observe when oxygen and hydrogen combine to form water, the great biologist continues: "Nevertheless, we call these, and many other strange phenomena, the properties of the water, and we do not hesitate to believe that, in some way or another, they result from the properties of the component elements of the water." This is because Huxley had never really weighed the wealth of good will which is shown by us every time the causal explanation is resorted to. It is, no doubt, very "strange" that water contains hydrogen and oxygen. What we designate by the terms hydrogen and oxygen are bodies having each one a collection of well-known properties. It is by these that we define them, and they are an integral part of the concept. We obviously cannot affirm that they remain unchanged in water, but we believe that "in some way or another"—we leave to the future the task of achieving the necessary precision on this point—they are hidden in it. This is the same subterfuge which, on a like occasion, Black's theory of heat employed, and which, moreover, we also employ under certain circumstances more openly, notably in the concept of "potential energy"(p. 192).

Chemistry, of course, does not entirely ignore this difficulty, a difficulty all the more apparent since we sometimes recognize an element under several equivalent forms called allotropic states. Supposing it really were contained in a compound, which of its different states does it assume? The theorists get out of all these difficulties with the help of an ambiguity. The element contained in a combination is "atomic." As soon as they are disengaged the atoms reunite in molecules; it is, therefore, not at all astonishing that the element then shows entirely different properties. This subterfuge shows us clearly that it really is a question of a pure metaphysical concept, since it is understood that this "atomic element," which is the true element, being the only one which enters into combinations and which persists, is radically different from the body which we know under the same name and which never can be really isolated, and consequently never can be perceived. It is, therefore, something analogous, from this point of view, to *sulphur* or to *mercury*, as they were conceived by the chemists of the seventeenth century.

It is certain that our present hypothesis applies to an infinitely larger number of facts and is adapted to them in a much more precise way, following matter and energy closely in their transformation, and controlling the data with the help of measuring instruments; but the explanations which it gives, or, rather, which it promises, are much less precise. Let us come back to the three equations of the oxide of mercury (Chapter VI, p. 222). A phlogistician would find it quite natural that the mercury precipitated *per se* should give metallic mercury, since the phlogiston, a principle of "metallicity," was added to it. At present we have the choice between two sorts of conceptions. Either we admit the chemical elements as ultimates; there then exists no real relation between the different metals, and the analogy between their properties is essentially inexplicable, and all the more is it inexplicable since these properties appear at a given moment. Or else we suppose that they are the compounds of a particular order, and we can then hope that we shall some day learn why the matter which composes them manifests in them these *metallic* qualities; but this explanation seems to us vague and far off. The qualitative explanation of perfect simplicity and clearness is replaced by an hypothesis which from the point of view of quality explains obviously very little, as Huxley and Berthelot show in the passages just cited. It is evident, moreover, that this insufficiency of mechanical theories is due to their very essence; they completely and intentionally set aside quality as sensation, and in respect to other properties they tend doubtless to explain them, but the elements which they employ have so little variety that this explanation seems extraordinarily difficult. One must not, therefore, be too astonished at the vitality which these qualitative theories have manifested in chemistry. If one forgets momentarily that chemical equations symbolize a phenomenon which takes place in a determined sense, it is certain that, as far as equality between the two members is concerned, representation according to the theory of phlogiston was more complete, since it presupposed a real pre-existence of the most striking property which appeared in the course of the phenomenon, *metallicity*.

We are thus finally brought back to the doctrines of quality by a somewhat long detour, which we, nevertheless, felt unavoidable: this past, withal a rather recent one, has become so foreign to us that to illuminate it we cannot use too freely the elements of comparison offered by the present. At least we hope that we have proved by what precedes that the problem which these doctrines sought to solve is the same as that with which contemporary science is wrestling—how to *explain* the appearance or the disappearance of properties? Mechanical theories postulate that all must be reduced to arrangements and movements of elements to which one attributes in advance but a minimum of properties—the ideal being, as we know, to strip them completely of such; the theories of quality, on the contrary (we can reunite under this denomination Aristotelianism conceived in its scientific aspect, and the theories which issue from it up to and including that of phlogiston, and also the theory of fluids in physics), presuppose more directly that the quality itself has pre-existed, that it has been displaced under a more or less hypostatized form, that it has united itself with the body or that it has left it. It is the dry and moist, the hot and cold, forming the human body according to Hippocrates: it is, in Saadia, the heat of the body returning, after the destruction of this latter, to the element of fire; it is also, in Stahl, phlogiston, inflammability, and, in Black, the caloric fluid passing from one body to another. And through all these doctrines we clearly see that the causal tendency shows itself with great vigour.

The deduction just undertaken brings to light another problem. If, indeed, it is true that the theories of quality are tributaries of the same tendencies, born of the same principle as mechanism, what advantage, then, does the latter system present, how explain that it tends more and more to dominate science?

Let us attempt in the first place to imagine what a purely qualitative science might be. Quality, we have seen, is only a hypostatized sensation. Two sensations, however similar we may conceive them—from the moment that they do not appear to us as absolutely identical, as are, for instance, the sensations of two pieces of cloth of the same colour, or the tones of two tuning-forks played in unison—can only be distinguished by a qualitative sign; this is also true of the sensations of two billiard balls of different size (p. 305). Remaining, therefore, in the domain of pure quality, we may easily identify a sensation;(48) we can also create a numerical scale in order to be able to judge as we do for temperature or for examination marks, but we cannot go farther than that. The fact that, in the case of the three notes or the three samples (lighter or darker) of the same red colour, or, again, the three billiard balls of different size, I can always indicate the note or the sample or the ball which must be placed between the other two, will not help me in the least. For even when I have set up a complete scale, such as a scale of notes or of colours or a series of billiard balls, I cannot by any artifice pass from one tone, from one shade, from one ball to those which border on it. For example, it will be impossible to declare that two notes are equivalent to a third; they cannot be added. This seems particularly clear in this case because a combination of two notes forms a chord and not a single note. But at bottom it is the same for colour or for size conceived as a pure tactile sensation; the fact that two shades are capable of furnishing a third, and the same for two billiard balls, has nothing to do with immediate sensation. Not only each quality, as Hume said,(49) but each shade of quality, or rather of sensation (the quality being already a transposition, a hypostasis) is something complete and does not suggest anything else.

In what way does a sensation of quantity, of size, become superposed upon this purely qualitative sensation? That depends evidently, as the very term quantity suggests, on substantialistic conceptions. I consider that the cause of my sensation *ball* is the existence of a definite object, formed of a certain material. If I unite the material of two equal balls, and give to it the form of a single ball, I shall obtain a sensation which, a little while ago, seemed to me similar but different qualitatively. And now, considering that the material has only changed place, that it has only undergone a modification through which its identity seems to me to be assured, I shall declare that between one of the two original balls and the one which I have just formed, there is only a difference of more or less, a difference of quantity. I can also succeed in thus reducing to quantity shades and notes, by observing that the same chord shortened or lengthened will give tones of different pitch, and that a sample dyed with double the same colour will have a determined shade. It is well known, moreover, that we have even found numerical relations between different colours by introducing the consideration of wave-lengths; but in this case the relation between the modification of the object and my sensation is less immediate, and that is why I am less inclined to lose from sight that this latter knows nothing directly of these considerations of quantity. But this is just as certain for the balls. In order to strengthen our conviction on this important point we have only to consider the sensation of quantity under its most elementary form and to substitute sight for touch. Let us suppose a hundred oranges arranged in a square of ten on a side. Doubtless I can look at them one by one, and in that case I shall have one hundred similar sensations. But if, at the very outset, I glance at them all, I shall have the sensation of a "square of oranges"—that is, a single sensation. By saying that this square is made of one hundred oranges, I affirm that if I place in a certain way one hundred objects of which each one in particular gives me the sensation "orange" I shall obtain that of the square in question; but in itself this latter is as primitive as the first. A stick of 6 metres will not give me twice the sensation of a stick of 3 metres, I simply know that if I place end to end two sticks of 3 metres I shall have the sensation of a stick of 6 metres.

This substitution of the external object, its supposed cause, in place of the pure sensation, presents, therefore, the great advantage of attaching one sensation to another, of explaining one sensation by another, that of the six-metre stick by that of the three, and so on. The possibility of this addition, inapplicable as long as we remain in the domain of pure qualitative sensation, involves evidently that of all analogous operations. Thereafter we shall continue this operation in the strictly scientific domain, where, moreover, sensation will inconvenience us less and less. To be able to affirm that mass and energy are conserved (which will permit explanations by identity, as in the case of the stick) we must evidently have transformed them beforehand into quantities. And thus it is that for the quality is substituted a magnitude capable of being added. The advantage resulting from this, from the point of view of science, even when science is concerned merely with laws rather than causes, is enormous. Indeed, this conception permits the application of mathematics; in all languages of the world, to calculate and to foresee are synonyms.

In the case of the stick and the ball the substitution of the object for the sensation is done unconsciously; it is the effect of what is called common sense, the functioning of which we shall study a little later. This substitution is so rapid that we must make an effort to come back to pure sensation. Language is, so to speak, incapable of expressing the pure sensation; it is, as has been observed, entirely modelled on common sense, and refers constantly, not to the sensation, but to the external object. In substituting for sound or colour, vibrations, a quantitative phenomenon, we also introduce mathematics into a domain of qualitative sensation; but since we are acting consciously, the substitution is less complete, the quantitative element, we have seen, does not intermingle with our sensation.

Remaining strictly in the domain of quality, the science which can be built up will be extremely limited, since the number of different sensations is infinite and the repetition of actually identical sensations is very rare. In truth, no one has ever tried to build up a science of this kind; that of Aristotle is already very remote. He really tried to treat "hot" as a pure and simple quality; and from the fruitlessness of the effort attempted by this great mind, it is now clearly seen how impractical is that way. By the side of "hot" Aristotle was obliged to establish "cold" as a distinct quality, since, indeed, these are two totally different sensations.(50) But even using these two opposite qualities, he could reach no clear conception of a gradation of heat, a conception which appears to us of the greatest simplicity. He never could have succeeded, indeed, except by considering hot and cold as real substances which are mixed in varying proportions; this would have meant, of course, departing still farther from the qualitative point of view. His expressions, moreover, are sufficiently ambiguous for his disciples in the Middle Ages to have understood him at times in this way.

But if hot and cold become substances, it is easier to do away with one of the two, somewhat as in the science of electricity the theory of two fluids has had to yield to that of a single fluid. We then come to the conception of heat-substance or heat-fluid, which, indeed, was prevalent for a long time in science. It is also clearly allied to the theories of quality, and under this aspect we considered it earlier; but it is a qualitative theory strongly diluted by considerations of quantity, since it is by this means that the different gradations of heat are connected with each other.

It is seen, moreover, that if purely qualitative theories are condemned to remain entirely sterile from a scientific point of view, it is not the same for these intermediary theories. The conception of heat-fluid rendered great service to the physicists of the eighteenth century; it permitted the establishment of laws of mixture, the study of conditions of change in the state of aggregation, etc. Carnot also was known to have used it in his celebrated monograph. Since, in a note, he admitted that he considered heat to be a movement, it has sometimes been inferred that he only used the notion of heat-fluid to conform to the general opinion of the learned public of his times. This is drawing too rapid a conclusion. One may easily suspect, in carefully reading the *Considérations*, that the conception of heat as a fluid in the process of spreading was not entirely useless to him. It is certain that mechanistic conceptions could have been of no use to him for this; they would rather have embarrassed him, for it is difficult to make strict mechanism agree with Carnot's principle (Chapter VIII, p. 264). Such qualitative conceptions as these still remain, as we have seen, in science and notably in chemistry; who will say that they are not destined still to render considerable service? They stop at the explanation of "becoming" and do not aspire to give that of "being." They are, therefore, the expression of a less rigorous application of the principle of identity than the mechanical theories; they may sometimes guide scientific thought precisely where, as in the case of Carnot's principle, the principle of absolute identity is necessarily in default.

A distinctive feature of qualitative, compared with mechanical theories, is that they admit of continuity; as long as heat and electricity were believed to be fluids, an atomic constitution did not seem necessary for either one or the other. This, let us remark in passing, is an argument against the thesis according to which mathematics introduced the discrete into physics. For us the basis of this distinction lies in the deduction which we presented previously (Chapter II, p. 93 f.). The discrete atom becomes necessary when we attribute change to the arrangement of parts, which must be immutable in time; and being essentially extended, must preserve indefinitely their spatial properties which cannot therefore be other than definite. The hypostatized qualities, on the contrary, are in no wise spatial in essence. If I suppose heat to be a fluid, I shall not attribute to it a definite volume, the same quantity may occupy any volume. Identity will be here assured, not, as for the atom, by the persistence of spatial limits, but by that of a sign of intensity, primarily based upon the consideration of a sensation —the same heat being that which appears such to the touch —for which we shall substitute next a derived concept, such as that based upon the thermometric scale. Consequently the discrete will no longer be necessary.

But, of course, all qualitative theories, however diluted they may be, present the same essential inconvenience, owing to the fact that the domain of the supposed quality appears absolutely delimited, surrounded somehow by an impassable barrier and without any possible relation to the rest of the phenomena of nature. So long as heat was a fluid and electricity another fluid different from the first, no transition between the two was possible; or to be more precise, one might have been able to imagine, if necessary, that one was transformed into the other by a sort of rearrangement of the molecules, somewhat as white phosphorus becomes red phosphorus; but in that case the fluid would cease to be specifically caloric, this characteristic becoming an attribute of the mode of arrangement of its particles. In other words, the fluid would no longer be the hypostasis of a sensation and the theory would cease to be qualitative. Ideas of this kind may be sometimes detected in the eighteenth century. But science has clearly conceived the existence of diverse forms of energy only by the transformation of mechanical into heat-energy, etc.; moreover, even before this the likeness between heat and light, on the one hand, and vibratory motion, on the other, had been clearly established; the idea existed, therefore, that it was everywhere a question not of arrangement but of modes of movement.

In the same line of thought the establishment of clear relations between different chemical elements would lead directly to the prevalence of the concept of the unity of matter—that is, the qualitative, specific differences which we are obliged to suppose at the present moment would disappear to make room for differences of arrangement or of movement.

Thus, starting from a qualitative theory, science as it progresses comes more and more to substitute quantity for quality. It must be noted that the principle of law alone, the permanent interest in establishing relations between things, suffices as the motive of this progress. But it must not be forgotten that the point of departure, the qualitative theory, is already a causal conception, in this sense that it postulates the persistence of something (which is in this case a hypostatized sensation). Moreover, this advance, which ends in the replacement of one causal concept by another, occurs also in the direction of causality. Indeed, every time that we pass from a quality to a quantity we move away from the sensation and substitute for it more and more a hypothetical concept. When instead of Aristotle's hot and cold, we introduce, first, *heat*, and then caloric fluid, we have already created a highly abstract concept; this fluid is very different from our sensation, since it creates in us at least three highly characteristic sensations—*cold, hot, burn*. The difference is still more accentuated when heat becomes a movement. Now all these concepts have not and cannot have any relation to our sensation other than that of being a supposed cause of this sensation. It is, therefore, by substituting for the sensation what is supposed to be its cause that progress has been brought about. It is also in this sense, and not only because it does not stop at becoming but pretends also to explain the cause of being, that mechanism constitutes a more complete expression of the causal principle.

Conceptions analogous to the theories of quality constitute in great part the foundation of a group of doctrines which arose in the first half of the nineteenth century. However, the speculations of the German *Naturphilosophen*, to which we here allude, have taken place rather on the border-line of science; if they were not absolutely without influence upon its development—we must not forget that they inspired Oersted, to whom is due the discovery of electro-magnetism—yet they do not seem at any time to have formed real scientific theories. We need not, therefore, examine them. But another theory has recently been formulated which, though connected in certain ways with these older doctrines, is none the less essentially scientific. The name of its author, Ostwald, the celebrated chemical theorist, is alone enough to draw attention to these conceptions, remarkable for more than one reason.

Ostwald believes that the external world constitutes the manifestation of a single principle—energy. We know the world only through our sensations; now these latter are nothing but differences of energy.(51) One can subordinate all phenomena to the concept of energy; this alone determines all of them.(52) The concept of energy includes that of cause.(53) Even space is known to us only by the energy necessary to penetrate it.(54) If we suppose it to be immutable, if we postulate its conservation—it is because it is a question of the conservation of a particular form of energy, the energy of volume.(55) Energy is at the same time the most general of substances and the most general of accidents.(56) It is a reality, whereas matter is an invention "rather imperfect moreover, which we have forged in order to represent what permanency there is in all vicissitudes."(57) If one separates energy from matter, the latter vanishes.(58) Energy, in a word, is, to a greater degree than the ether of certain atomistic physicists, the ultimate element, the single substratum of all reality. It goes without saying that we could never dream of really decomposing it; but in our minds we attempt this operation, since we decompose it into factors in different ways. Certain of these factors belong to the class which Ostwald designates by the name of "factors of intensity," such as, for instance, velocity or temperature. These are not real magnitudes, since they cannot be added together; two bodies of identical weight form together a body of double weight, but two bodies of the same velocity or of the same temperature will only furnish one body of identical velocity or of identical temperature. Ostwald observes that if energy is divided by a factor of intensity, magnitudes are obtained which remain constant—that is, which can only be modified if the system receives energy from the outside; such are mass, quantity of motion, quantity of electricity. The principle of the conservation of matter ceases to appear, as it had appeared until now, as a fundamental statement of science and becomes a particular case of the conservation of those magnitudes which Ostwald calls "capacities."(59)

It must be recognized that Ostwald's system is in many ways extremely alluring. The deduction of the "capacities"—this general concept that appears to include everything which, among phenomena, ought to be conserved, this process which permits it to be grasped *a priori*—favours, at first sight, the supposition that we have really discovered one of the fundamental secrets of nature, perhaps the most general principle directing it. As we look closer, grave doubts arise.

Let us set aside the astonishment provoked by the deduction of the immutability of space—a notion which we feel to be, if not prior to, at least simultaneous with the very origin of every experience—from a conception as complicated as the energy of volume: that is, in the last analysis, from the conservation of energy. This affirmation may not be an essential part of the system, and Ostwald might surrender it without jeopardizing his theory. Let us not insist either upon a certain illogicalness of detail, which, if necessary, might be removed.(60) Let us consider the very heart of the system, the concept of energy and the principle of its conservation. We have seen that Ostwald believes that it is something which dominates and determines our entire experience; yet he does not think that this principle is *a priori* (in this he is evidently quite right), but he assigns to it an empirical origin.(61) It would seem that it would have to be, therefore, at least an observation of continuous and daily experience, being established from all eternity. But, as we have seen, it is quite recent. Before the seventeenth century, not only had no one ever stated it (contrary to what took place in the case of the conservation of matter), but no one had ever even had a presentiment of it; and its formula is so difficult to understand that when it was stated for the first time (by Descartes) it was stated erroneously. Even at the present moment it remains, in so far as it is an empirical law, not only difficult, but in many cases impossible to verify; not to speak of recent discoveries, notably the discovery of radio-active bodies, which certainly tend to invalidate it in so far as it is a notion directly deduced from experience.

In fact, Hertz tells us that energy is in no way a substance: its conservation is simply *plausible*; and in that case must be deduced from the principle of causality, and not inversely, as Ostwald declares.

On the other hand, the exceedingly ingenious system of *intensities* and of *capacities* leads to an anomaly menacing it in its most essential part. Temperature, according to the definition of Ostwald, is incontestably one of the most characteristic factors of intensity, since two bodies having the same temperature, when united, do not change it. Dividing heat energy by temperature results in entropy. Entropy ought, therefore, according to Ostwald, to enter into the class of *capacities*—that is, to remain constant. But we know that its essential characteristic (except in the limiting case, unrealizable in the physical world) is, on the contrary, to increase constantly. Ostwald has tried to brush aside this difficulty so destructive of his system. With the help of certain experimental data, and notably, it seems, those of Landolt, he deduces that mass might not be constant, but subject to incessant modifications in one and the same direction.(62) Evidently this supposition entirely modifies the notion of capacities established by Ostwald himself; all capacities are assimilated to entropy. Who does not see the artificiality of such a system? That matter may be dissociated is assuredly admissible; but the facts by which this dissociation is shown, taking things at their best, are rare and meagre. What analogy is there between this situation and the manner in which entropy behaves whose manifest and incessant tendency to increase appears to us as the great spring regulating the becoming of phenomena, as, moreover, Ostwald himself recognizes? Is it not evident, on the contrary, that instead of behaving like entropy, mass behaves rather like energy; that the principle of conservation of mass in no way resembles that of Carnot and is entirely analogous to the principle of the conservation of energy? The experimental anomalies discovered for the first of these principles are certainly not less than those ascertained for the last. Not to speak of the fact that, as Etard justly observes,(63) the concepts of matter and of energy are so indissolubly linked in our thought that the destruction of one engenders the disappearance of the other; for when $m = o$, mv^2 equally becomes null, velocity evidently remaining finite. And how can one imagine energy not having mass as a substratum? Under these circumstances to set up the conservation of energy as the immovable basis for a theory of the world and to suppose that the conservation of mass is only an appearance which facts will eventually refute, seems truly contrary to all the rules of logic.

It may, moreover, be said that Ostwald, in forming his theory of energy, contradicts the general principles which he himself had proclaimed. These principles, we have seen from a passage cited at the beginning of this book (Chapter I, p. 17), are those of Auguste Comte. They are summed up in the affirmation that the law alone is enough for the explanation of the phenomenon; this is, therefore, the *hypotheses non fingo* carried to the last extremity, the proscription of all that goes beyond the law. Is there need to show that the hypothesis of energy as conceived by Ostwald does not confine itself within these limits? More, and better than the atoms of whatever mechanistic theorist, the energy of the Leipzig scientist is a true ontological being, a thing in itself.(64) It exists absolutely, independently of any other thing, encompassing substance and accident, space and cause, being itself its own cause, *causa sui*, and causing the whole phenomenal world. The fact that such an eminent mind as Ostwald, in spite of his clear profession of faith, was unable to remain within the domain of pure law, that he had sought, outside of this latter, to construct a veritable system of *explanations* is certainly most significant. It is equally worthy of note that once having left the concept of conformity to strict law, he immediately adopted as the basis of his theory a notion of something immutable in time, a *constant*. Finally it is curious to observe to what a degree in this system, just as in the atomic theory, Carnot's principle appears as an anomaly.(65) Ostwald, we have just seen, sought to get round the difficulty by supposing that the other "capacities" shared the same fate. But really the logic of his system demands rather an assimilation in the opposite sense; it is entropy which ought to behave like mass and quantity of motion, and be indefinitely preserved. In other words, the growth of entropy being the main spring of change, *there must be no modification in time*. This is indeed, as we have seen, the formula of all "explanations." Perhaps it will even be found that from this point of view the kinetic theories are still superior to the theory of Ostwald. It is certainly less paradoxical to try to explain Carnot's principle by statistics than to seek, while maintaining the constancy of energy, to establish an analogy between mass and entropy.

NOTES

1. P. TANNERY: *Les principes de la science de la nature chez Aristote. Congrès de philosophie de 1900*, Vol. IV, p. 214.

2. CONDILLAC: *Logique. Œuvres*. Paris, an IV, Vol. XXI, p. 83.

3. GALENUS: *De elementis secundum Hippocratem*, Book I. *Opera*, ed. Kuehn, Vol. I, pp. 457, 477, 479, 480, 487. Cf. LASSWITZ, *Geschichte*, Vol. I, p. 229.

4. Cf. LASSWITZ, *ib.*, p. 156.

5. SCOTUS ERIGENA: *De divisione naturae*. Oxford, 1681, I, Chaps. XXXI, XXXII. Cf. Lasswitz, *l.c.*, Vol. I, p. 39.

6. *Elementa philosophiae*, in BEDA. *Opera*. Cologne, 1688, Vol. II, p. 209. Cf. LASSWITZ, *l.c.*, vol. I., p. 74.

7. LASSWITZ: *l.c.*, Vol. I, p. 235 and ff.

8. For PARACELSUS, as for most alchemists, Aristotle's elements are found beneath the chemical elements; here there are, so to speak, two degrees of simplicity (Kopp, *Die Alchemie*, Vol. I, p. 35). A little later, Nicolas le Fevre identifies, on the contrary, Aristotle's elements and those of the chemists: phlegm is water, the spirituous or mercurial principle is air, the sulphurous or oily principle is fire, the salty principle earth.

9. PARACELSUS was the initiator of iatrochemistry. We saw (p. 228 and ff.) that theories about elements remain about the same. Only the goal of chemistry is modified.

10. PARACELSUS: *Opera*, ed. Huser. Bâle, 1589, *Paramirum*, Book I, p. 74.

11. Circulus Pisanus Claudii BERIGARDI Molinensis *De veteri et peripatetica philosophia*. Udine, 1643, Book IV, Circulus XX, p. 125. Cf. LASSWITZ, *l.c.*, Vol. I, p. 491.

12. *Ib.*, Circulus II, p. 17. LASSWITZ, p. 490.

13. *Ib.*, Circulus II, p. 6. LASSWITZ, *ib.*

14. *Ib.*, Circulus XVIII, p. 115. LASSWITZ, p. 497.

15. KOPP: *Geschichte*, Vol. I, p. 97.

16. *Ib.*, p. 182.

17. Libavius expresses a general belief in affirming that metals *distare videntur, non tam substantia, quam accidentium absolutione* (KOPP, *Alchemie*, Vol. I, p. 46). It is this belief in the facility of transmutation which later constituted the most serious obstacle in the progress of analytical chemistry— cf. id., *Geschichte*, Vol. III, p. 56. Differences between metals appearing quite insignificant, it was supposed that they could be made to disappear by a sort of fermentation, which led to attributing to the philosopher's stone, considered as a ferment, properties which appear to us so chimerical. In the same way it was thought that metals could multiply themselves, that copper coloured white with arsenic and added to silver actually

increased the quantity of this last metal (Kopp, *Alchemie*, Vol. I, p. 166), which, moreover, was conformable to Aristotle's theory of mixture.

18. Cf. BERTHELOT: *Les origines de l'Alchimie*. Paris, 1885, p. 282.

19. *Ib.*, p. 208.

20. KUNCKEL, also in the eighteenth century, based his belief in transmutation on the change of colour which gold undergoes when it is subjected to the action of salammoniac or borax (Kopp, *Alchemie*, Vol. I, p. 61 and ff.).

21. *Ib.*, Vol. I, pp. 53, 249.

22. *Ib.*, p. 250.

23. KOPP (*ib.*, p. 46) believes it to be the only really efficacious receipt for metallic transmutation; the true nature of the reaction has been explained by Angelo Sala, at the beginning of the seventeenth century.

24. Cf. BERTHELOT: *La révolution chimique*. Paris, 1902, p. 54.

25. Cf. KOPP: *Geschichte*, Vol. III, p. 307. This was the fundamental experiment for the theory of phlogiston, an experiment which had for this conception the same importance as that of the oxidation of metals in an enclosed vessel had later for the antiphlogisticians.

26. KOPP: *Geschichte*, Vol. II, p. 15. Stahl even claims to have transmuted sulphuric acid into muriatic and nitric acid; cf. *ib.*, p. 352.

27. *Ib.*, Vol. III, p. 75.

28. *Ib.*, Vol. III, p. 144.

29. *Ib.*, Vol. I, p. 150.

30. *Ib.*, pp. 151, 152, 222. Cf. LAVOISIER: *Œuvres*, Vol. I, p. 154.

31. LAVOISIER: *Œuvres*, Vol. I, p. 468.

32. "Few works on modern chemistry show more genius than that of Meyer's" (*ib.*, p. 482). Later Lavoisier, on the contrary, celebrated the merit of Black (*Essai sur le phlogistique de Kirwan*. Paris, 1788, p. 23).

33. A summary of this will be found in KOPP: *Geschichte*, Vol. III, p. 119 and ff.

34. KOPP: *Geschichte*, Vol. III, p. 155.

35. *Essai sur le phlogistique*, p. 23.

36. LAVOISIER: *Traité élémentaire de chimie. Œuvres*. Paris, 1864, Vol. I, pp. 9, 48, 57.

37. *Ib.*, Vol. I, p. 61; cf. DAVY, *Works*. London, 1839, Vol. V, p. 513.

38. BERTHELOT: *Lavoisier*, p. 180. Cf. LAVOISIER, *Œuvres*, Vol. II, p. 180.

39. It is very characteristic from this point of view that in the theory of *ions* the fact that in an aqueous solution all the physical properties of the salts are additive is considered as a proof that there is complete dissociation—that is, no combination at all. Cf. Arrhenius, *La dissociation électrolytique*. *Congrès international de physique de 1900*, Vol. II, p. 377.

40. BERTHELOT: *La Synthèse chimique*. Paris, F. Alcan, 1876, p. 7.

41. HUXLEY: *Lay Sermons*. London, 1887, p. 118.

42. COMTE: *Cours*, Vol. III, p. 18.

43. *Ib.*, p. 15.

44. VAN'T HOFF: *Leçons de chimie physique*, trans. Corvisy, 3rd Part. Paris, 1900, p. 3.

45. SULLY-PRUDHOMME AND RICHET: *Le problème des causes finales*. Paris, F. Alcan, p. 91.

46. OSTWALD: *Lettre sur l'énergétique. Revue générale des sciences*, VI, 1895, p. 1071.

47. The tendencies which we mention in the text have been strongly accentuated since I wrote these lines. Cf. on this subject *La Déduction Relativiste*, § 198 and ff.

48. This supposes evidently that my sensation under analogous conditions will be the same, for it may be, indeed, that the material appears to me to be of a more or less vivid colour, according to the predispositions of my eyes. But this implicit postulate admitted, one does not well see why Lasswitz affirms (*Geschichte der Atomistik*, Vol. I, p. 498) that one cannot recognize a quality as identical unless it is transformed into quantity. It seems sufficient in a somewhat prolonged observation to acquire the conviction that a tuning-fork or a material coloured with Turkey red (a coloured glass may be substituted for it) does not become sensibly modified during a relatively long lapse of time and that one may, therefore, judge by comparing the sensation with that of the type which has already been established.

49. Cf. p. 307.

50. It is known that Gassendi also assumed the existence of a matter that is cold side by side with calorific matter. Cf. Rosenberger, *Geschichte*, Vol. II, p. 118. Cf. also Chap. IX, p. 319, Note 8, the observations on the transmission of sensations of cold or heat through the different peripheral organs.

51. OSTWALD: *La déroute de l'atomisme contemporain. Revue générale des sciences*, VI, p. 956.

52. I., *Vorlesungen ueber Naturphilosophie*, 2nd ed. Leipzig, 1902, p. 152.

53. *Ib.*, p. 153.

54. *La déroute*, etc., p. 957.

55. *Vorlesungen*, etc., p. 285.

56. *Ib.*, p. 146.

57. *La déroute*, etc., p. 956. It may be that on this particular point Ostwald's ideas have been somewhat modified, as seems to be shown in passages we shall quote later.

58. *Ib.*, p. 957.

59. *Vorlesungen*, etc., pp. 281–282.

60. HOEFLER: *Zur gegenwaertigen Naturphilosophie*. Berlin, 1906, p. 37, has attracted attention to this anomaly. Ostwald admits the undulations; but can energy itself vibrate, when under its mechanical form (because of V^2) it can have neither negative value nor direction?

61. *Vorlesungen*, etc., pp. 173 and 186.

62. *Ib.*, p. 281.

63. ETARD: *Les nouvelles théories chimiques*. Paris. s.d., p. 12.

64. Cf. especially, *Vorlesungen*, etc., p. 242, where Ostwald, protesting against any other supposition for "the thing in itself," shows that energy should be considered as such. Driesch (*Naturbegriffe und Natururtheile*. Leipzig, 1904, p. 106) quite justly calls Ostwald's theory "metamorphosed materialism."

65. OSTWALD (*Vorlesungen*, p. 281) calls it an "irregularity in our image of the world."

CHAPTER XI

COMMON SENSE

IN this chapter we shall try to show that while it is true that what we call concepts of common sense are fashioned by an unconscious process, the process is otherwise strictly analogous to the operation by which we form scientific theories; that here, too, the causal tendency, the principle of identity in time, plays a preponderant rôle, and that from this point of view common sense is an integral part of science; or, inversely, that science is, as has been said, but with perhaps a slightly different meaning—only a prolongation of common sense. In preceding chapters we were obliged to discuss briefly by anticipation certain particular aspects of the problem. We are now going to examine it a little more closely.

As I open my eyes I perceive objects, and this perception seems to be something simple and primitive. But this is not so. When a man born blind gains his sight—this statement has become a common-place in psychology—he has at first only confused sensations; it is only by use that he relates them to the tactile sensations which have been familiar to him for a long time, and thenceforth he succeeds in really perceiving "objects" by sight. Perception is, therefore, a complicated operation. Memory plays a considerable rôle in it: "consciousness means memory,"(1) "there is no perception which is not mingled with recollections,"(2) says Bergson, and mingled to such a degree that "perceiving ends in being only an occasion for remembering."(3) These memories, moreover, are often those of several senses: this is why people who see have spatial perceptions that are always composed of memories, of visual and tactile sensations, mutually evoked. Yet it is important to remember that these recollections are distinguished in the last analysis from those designated ordinarily by this name, in the sense that we are not conscious that they are recollections, but that they appear to be an integral part of the actual sensation which evoked them. These evoked sensations and their synthesis—their "concretion," to use the singularly expressive term coined by Ampère(4)—are so rapid, so instantaneous, that it is only with the help of a very arduous analysis that we succeed in certain cases in unravelling these associations and in reaching, with Bergson, "the immediate data of consciousness." Without pretending to fathom this subject, let us try, with the aid of a few simple analyses of concrete facts, to throw light upon several points which particularly interest us.

In the distance I see a tree. I see (or I think I see, which is the same thing here) a host of details—branches, leaves, ruggedness of bark, etc. It is entirely certain that my real sensation has only a few vague marks and that all the rest belongs to the concretion of memory.(5) To be convinced of this, I need only look closely at a scene on the stage or at an impressionistic picture, either of which, at the right distance, gives me the impression of the real thing. The very colours which are the object of my direct sensation are very different from those I think I perceive. For many long years the pictures of impressionists have provoked exclamations or laughter from the great majority of the public, enlightened connoisseurs as well as the mob, and even from the generality of painters. It was considered absurd that a forest should be violet in the distance. And yet we have no doubt to-day that it actually *is so;* but our memory immediately transforms this image, with the help of the memory of the same forest seen close by, and consequently we swear that we see it green, which means that we really see it such. The work of impressionism has consisted precisely in partly retracing this work of transformation and in approaching more closely the immediate, the fugitive sensation.

Let us note that memory which intervenes so rapidly and so efficaciously is very often a generalized memory. It is not necessary for me to have seen near by the tree or the forest at which I am looking from afar; any tree, any forest, not too unlike those that I know well, will suffice to put my memory in movement at the first vague but characteristic specks of colour which I see; this is because I know that a tree, a forest, look like this from afar. This knowledge which I have evidently acquired by experience is a generalized experience—in other words, a law. Thus my perception is not only influenced by what I remember, but also by the way in which I have generalized it—that is, *by what I know.* But perhaps it will be wise to illustrate this statement by still another example.

I am in a train that is standing still. Through the left window

I see another train standing still also, through the right window I see the station. I look to the left; at a certain moment I have a distinct sensation that my train, without a jolt, has started to move. I look out of the right window; the station building is not moving. Instantly my sensation is modified, my train is not moving; if I look to the left again, it is the other train which is going. That may happen at a station absolutely unknown to me, which I see for the first time as I try to verify things by a glance through the right window. This fact will not make me hesitate, my sensation will be modified just as rapidly; apparently because I *know*, at the first glance, that it is a building and that buildings are generally rooted to the ground. This is a generalized experience, a law. But it goes without saying that the intellectual process of which we are speaking does not reach my consciousness : it is like the action of memory itself, entirely unconscious; it is an integral part of what I judge to be my pure and simple perception.

If we now try to remount this stream, strip perception of all that memory brings to it, we shall evidently, in the last analysis, end at consecutive states of consciousness that may be divided between different senses, but which will contain no element not ours—since they will be states of our consciousness, and which, therefore, will include no trace of that division into distinct objects which characterizes the data of common sense.

What is the source of this "segmentation of reality"? Bergson (6) tells us that it takes place because of the exigencies of practical life, and this thesis is certainly right. Nothing is so important as to be capable of foreseeing these states of consciousness. Indeed, I soon see that they are essentially variable, variable in time, which means, in this case, variable as a function of other states of consciousness, of which I know and foresee the periodicity, such as the return of day and night or that of the seasons. Moreover, I feel immediately that this variation is independent of my will and that if I am not able to foresee it in order to react, the states of consciousness which will follow will be disagreeable. This is why, in order to establish laws allowing me to exercise this prevision, I have the greatest interest in subdividing these states of consciousness into particular sensations, especially those among them which usually accompany or follow one another, succeeding thus in associating themselves and in evoking each other by the effect of memory. Thus the appearance of a white spot of a determined nature coming within the field of my vision makes me believe that in combining my actions in an appropriate manner I shall succeed in procuring that agreeable sensation which I call "the taste of sugar."

What I thus constitute is the phenomenon, considered, of course, as belonging exclusively to me, as taking place solely in my consciousness. There is nothing, it seems, which can suggest the notion of something outside me. Assuredly these sensations are independent of my will; but they are always *my* sensations. How conceive that there is an element in them which does not come from me? And yet this is what we continually do (Chapter X, p. 323 f.). The sensation of red, which belongs to me, I transform into the quality of an external object by affirming: this object is red. Is this not an inexplicable leap? Philosophers, no doubt, have maintained that there is no leap there. According to their belief, common sense, in affirming the existence of the table and its red quality, claims to announce nothing which is external to my consciousness. It simply predicts that, under certain conditions, I shall apprehend the group of sensations which I designate as table and as red. All would end, therefore, with the sensation or the possibility of a sensation. It is enough to question any man whose understanding has been preserved from "metaphysical doubt" or even to probe one's own consciousness to perceive to what a degree this explanation is at variance with reality. Common sense is certainly an ontology; it clearly affirms the existence of external objects and is very far from supposing that the existence depends on our consciousness.

Thus I feel no hesitation in affirming the existence of objects of which I have no sensation. I am quite convinced that that table which I no longer see still exists. Shall one say that it is because I have preserved the memory of it? But the room where I spent my childhood, its one window, its blue walls, the curtains and my little bed—my memory of these is so precise that I only have to close my eyes to see them again; and that friend whom I lost a few years ago, and who was the better part of myself, my thought has only to touch lightly upon that dear likeness to make his presence become painfully real to me, almost palpable. And yet I am convinced that all of that has ceased to exist, whereas other objects which have entirely disappeared from my memory, or which have never even been a part of my direct sensation, yet appear to me, if I ask myself, as existing. There is, therefore, no concomitant variation and, therefore, no real relation.

It is also quite clear, it seems, that the question of simple utility cannot furnish the explanation sought for. Doubtless, when I have once formed the whole concept of an external world and of objects which move in it, this concept will help enormously to classify my sensations and consequently to predict them also. But the problem is to know how I was able to take the first step, to conceive even the possibility that something can exist outside of me, outside of my consciousness; how, supposing even that the concept of "an outside" comes to me from another source, I had the paradoxical idea of placing in it what is my own sensation, what belongs incontestably to me.

Let us note at once that though the external world, as it is conceived by common sense, does not depend on direct sensation, it is, nevertheless, entirely constructed with the help of elements borrowed from it. In this sense it is exact to say that it is the result of my memory, and also that it represents a possibility of sensation. The table which I no longer see, which is in no way bound to my actual sensation, was, however, a part of my state of consciousness some moments previously; and although I have never been to the city of Lucknow, I can nevertheless conceive it as existing, because I imagine that in going there—that is, in putting into execution a determined series of actions—I shall have a more or less determined sensation, of which the elements are furnished without any doubt by sensations I have really felt, since they could not have come to me in any other way.

Certain philosophers have tried to assimilate memories of sensations, or images constructed with the aid of more or less transformed memories, to real sensations, maintaining that between the two there is only a difference of intensity, the first being strong states of consciousness, and the second, weak ones. But this is surely unjustifiable. When I see the table through a more and more heavy fog, or in the growing dusk, or when I am shown on a screen a view of Lucknow which becomes dimmer and dimmer, can I at any moment really confuse these sensations with those of mental images? In other words, as Spir asks,(7) as the actual sensations themselves pass through all the degrees of intensity, from zero to the point where they become intolerable, how, at any degree whatsoever of this scale, can we confuse sensation and memory? Doubtless, I can experience illusions; I can have dreams or hallucinations. But, then, I am myself conscious that it is a question of facts having nothing in common with the normal functioning of my mind. The case is a little more embarrassing, if I suppose that I am simply mistaken, when, for instance, at dusk in the country, I think I see a man where really it is only a tree-trunk. Indeed, it is certain that at a given moment I saw the man, I had a real sensation; but this error comes evidently from the fact that my memories recalled to me that I had previously seen men whose silhouette resembled that of this tree-trunk. Is this not a confusion of memory and real sensation? Not at all. Every actual sensation, we have seen, is largely composed of memories, but these latter differ from real memories. We might correctly say, in speaking of an error of this kind, that memory disturbed us, but we should never compare it to a real memory.

Thus an object of which I affirm the existence when I have not the sensation of it is still composed of my sensations, but of sensations which I do not experience at the very moment. I therefore affirm, literally, the actual existence of sensations which are mine and yet of which I am not conscious.

This affirmation seems contradictory, and it is so indeed. To affirm the existence of objects when they are no longer evident to our senses constitutes, as Hume rightly says, "a contradiction in terms, and supposes that the senses continue to operate even after they have ceased all manner of operation."(8) Consequently, to attenuate this contradiction it is most often stated that we affirm the existence, not of the sensation itself, but of its *cause*. It was in this sense that Schopenhauer declared that matter is wholly (*durch und durch*) causality, (9) and that Huxley defined it as "a name for the unknown and hypothetical cause of our own states of consciousness."(10)

But here we must remember that causality means identity—
causa aequat effectum. When we affirm that an object which is
not part of our actual sensation constitutes a possibility of
sensation, we simply have recourse to the eternal subterfuge
we employ every time that identity is manifestly lacking, and
where we want it most. This possibility of sensation, as its
etymology indicates, moreover, is a being of the same order as
Aristotle's quality of *potentiality*,(11) or as the potential energy
of the physicists. It is something which manifests itself in no
way and which consequently does not exist, but of which we
are obliged, nevertheless, to suppose the existence to satisfy
our need of identity, because we know that it *may* manifest
itself (cf. pp. 192 f., 385).

What is, indeed, most remarkable about this possibility of
sensation is the permanency which I attribute to it and which
clashes with my immediate sensation. "This idea of something
which is distinguished from our fleeting impressions by what,
in Kantian language, is called *Perdurability;* something which
is fixed and the same, while our impressions vary; something
which exists whether we are aware of it or not, and which
is always square (or of some other given figure) whether it
appears to us square or round, constitutes altogether our idea
of external substance," says Mill.(12) Ostwald, starting from an
entirely different point of view, comes also to the conclusion
that what is essential in a concept expressed by a substantive
—that is, the concept of an object—is that it represents something durable and independent of time.(13) The procedure of
unconscious reasoning which we here suppose would then be
the following. I have had a mixture of sensations which I
call the red table: I know that these sensations may come back;
consequently, to satisfy my causal tendency, I suppose that these
sensations exist during the interval. Now since, by hypothesis,
they do not exist within me, they must exist somewhere else;
there must be, therefore, a "somewhere else," a non-ego, a
world exterior to my consciousness.

The fact that we have an irresistible tendency to hypostatize
our sensations—that is, to detach them from ourselves and to
assume their existence outside of ourselves—is incontestable;
we have had sufficient examples of it in the development of this
book. Let us think of Leibniz's "mill"; what does this reasoning

show? That sensation is something unintelligible, irrational. And what would be necessary to make the sensation intelligible, rational? There would have to be identity between what the mill produces and what it receives, between the external world and the sensation. Leibniz represented the brain as a mechanism; that is because it constitutes a simple prolongation of the external world (Chapter IX, p. 305). But between the sensation and the external world there is no doubt that the former is the primordial element, the existence of the latter being only the result of a deduction. If, therefore, there must be identity, it is because we had supposed that our sensations really can exist, wander around (if we dare express ourselves thus) outside of ourselves. This is so true that we feel the greatest repugnance to admit that the reasoning of the physicist and of the physiologist is really valid under these circumstances. This is why Bergson requires (p. 295) that light (of course, the light-sensation) be recognized as a component of electricity and not inversely; and Lotze, having reached the conviction that there must be a subject for this sensation, since, as he amusingly says, "a splendour whose brightness no one saw, the sound of a note which no one heard, sweetness which no one tasted," would be "just as impossible as a toothache which no one felt,"(14) finally asks himself whether things themselves would not experience the sensations which they make us experience; this would be, indeed, the most complete and the most logical formula of the hypostasis of sensation, and of its persistency outside of us. Moreover, this formula would lead straight to a purely qualitative physics.

Let us remark that common sense does not proceed absolutely thus. Sensations have, indeed, really helped to constitute the object, but they have not remained entirely intact. When it is a question of sound and colour, it is understood that what I place outside of me, by virtue of common sense, is a simple hypostasis of my sensation. But if we think of the concept of matter, which is the most important one of the external world (one might speak of the *material* world, and this would be a synonym), the situation changes. Matter is not a hypostasis, pure and simple, of sensation—if it were, it would be, like colour or sound, a purely qualitative concept—but it is a quantity, or at least it admits the application of the category of quantity.

Matter is a complicated concept in the elaboration of which all our senses participate, the most important being, at least in the case of normal men, sight and touch. We have no intention of attempting a complete deduction of this concept with the help of sensation alone; this, perhaps, is not possible, for it is not quite certain whether, the concept of matter being closely allied to that of space, there are not purely *a priori* elements involved depending on the very constitution of our reason. But the analysis already furnished (p. 341 f.) clearly shows, in our opinion, that the relation between the concept of material quantity and our corresponding qualitative sensations is analogous to that which unites the concept of light vibration with the sensation of colour or that of sound vibration with the sensation of sound.

We shall leave aside completely, as being outside of our subject, the question of how, to this image of the external world, resulting from our sensation, or, in Schopenhauer's words, from our representation, is attached that which we can deduce from our will. Even if one postulates that this latter is primitive and that our conception of the non-ego comes primarily from the assumption of a will foreign to ours, or that one adopts even for the origin of the concept of the non-ego whatever metaphysical hypothesis one wishes, our demonstration remains unassailable in its essential parts. It is enough, indeed, to recognize that common sense constitutes the concept of a present object with the help of (more or less transformed) hypostatized sensations, and that consequently the concept of an absent object is made up of the same sensations of which the persistence is supposed. Consequently it becomes evident that, in forming these concepts of external objects according to the system of common sense, our understanding has followed no other rules than those which we recognize in scrutinizing the operations of science. It is always the principle of causality, the tendency to see, under the pressure of a need for explanation, everything persisting without change; there is also, in answer to this need, the same procedure in substituting a quantitative cause for a qualitative sensation.(15) And since, of course, the point of departure can be no other than our sensation, it is natural that the first system to adopt be that of making these sensations undergo the minimum of transformation, of hypostatizing them as much as possible as they are; this is what we call common sense.

The word is, moreover, well chosen. The system simplifies relations with our fellow-men. It is of little importance, from this point of view, whether our concepts are more or less adequate to things; since errors are the same in the case of other men, they are eliminated when we communicate with them. "Amongst men nothing is equal, nothing is similar, except the names of things," says Euripides(16); and d'Alembert, in the *Discours préliminaire à l'Encyclopédie*, asks, "whether this reciprocal communication (between men), added to the resemblance which we perceive between our sensations and those of our fellow-beings, does not contribute greatly toward forming the invincible leaning we have to suppose the existence of all objects which strike us."(17) Without going as far as d'Alembert, since, indeed, we suppose that the concept of the object is formed in a different way, we admit that the agreement of others and the usefulness of the communication confirm our inclination.

And yet the system also renders great service in our relations with things. There are really, as Mach formulates it, following Mill,(18) "groups of sensations,"(19) which, if they have not absolute immutability, change, however, so little and so slowly that it is advantageous for us to suppose their persistence in time and in space—that is, the existence of objects. Poincaré expresses himself similarly, qualifying sensations as "united together by I know not what indestructible cement and not by a day's chance."(20)

Ostwald, whose theory, we have seen, tends to set aside entirely the concept of matter, explains that only different forms of energy united in a single and identical space act upon our senses and our instruments, whereas one energy presented separately could affect neither one nor the other.(21) Very striking proofs would be necessary, evidently, to establish such a thesis. What is certain is that our sensations follow each other in such a way that the constitution of this world of *objects* is possible. And it is also certain, as we have said, that once this world is constituted, prevision is facilitated. In other words, in the field of common sense, just as in that of science, conceptions created by the causal principle (or, if you prefer, with its aid) favour the application of the principle of conformity to law. And since, on the other hand, generalized experience—that is, conformity to law—concurs in the formation of the common-sense reality, the result is that, from the beginning of the operations of our understanding, the two principles of causality and conformity to law collaborate and that their operations become inextricably entangled, just as they do later on in science.

Yet, since it is a question in the latter of our relations with things, errors no longer become eliminated, and, as soon as we advance a little in research, the world of common sense immediately appears to us what it is in reality—to wit, an introductory and very imperfect sketch of a scientific and metaphysical system. Indeed, at the very first step we are forced to abandon the supposition that things are what to us they seem to be; and as soon as we have made that first concession, we are immediately and irresistibly drawn toward the complete dissolution of this conception, which at first seemed so indubitable. Here is a stick. I see its double in the looking-glass without believing that the image is a real stick. I plunge it into water and it appears to me bent, but immediately "my reason straightens it," according to La Fontaine's admirable expression. Now my reason can only do this by reasoning. I am, therefore, led to talk about reflection and refraction, about light rays and undulations. Light becomes a movement, the stick is decomposed into a nebula of atoms, and the same reasoning which "straightened" it when it was plunged into the water constrains me afterward to affirm that its matter or its substance must persist even when I burn it.

What must be especially noted here is that the same procedure which served to form the concept of common sense serves also to dissolve it. *Causalism*—if it is permitted to use this term—is not a privilege of the scientist. It is the characteristic of man. It will help in no way to try to brush aside this "ontology." Hertz saw this clearly when he declared that "every thinking person experiences herein difficulties which the scientist ordinarily qualifies as metaphysical," and when he drew from it this conclusion, "that no scruple which, in any fashion whatever, has made an impression on our mind, can be brushed aside by the fact that it is qualified as metaphysical."(22) Thus this dissolution of reality operates both in an irresistible and an insensible fashion. Common sense is only a more or less artificial halting-place on a constantly sloping decline. From the moment the stick ceased to be a pure visual sensation to me, calling up the possibility of a tactile sensation, I can no longer stop, I am pushed on from experience to experience and from reasoning to reasoning until it vanishes completely in the ether.

Another halting-place, equally factitious, on the same road is represented by mechanism. A conception infinitely more perfect than that of common sense, it shows also to a greater extent its agreement with reality and consequently is capable of aiding us in the discovery of a much larger number of relations. Moreover, mechanism is also like common sense in this respect, as Renouvier (23) admirably perceived, that in reducing sensibility to certain elements, the most abstract of all, such as movement, resistance, penetrability, elements no doubt incompletely determined, but of which the concept is, nevertheless, constituted in somewhat the same way in all men, it becomes by this fact a means of facilitating communications, a kind of "scientific common sense."

But it goes without saying that mechanism, being a more advanced product of our thought, is for the very reason more logical than common sense because it is more differentiated. It, therefore, construes in a more exclusive manner our tendency to suppose persistence in time, and is consequently opposed in a certain measure to the group of conceptions resulting from Carnot's principle where variation in time is affirmed. In common sense, on the contrary, these two tendencies are entirely mingled. When I think, for instance, of a being whom I know endowed with life, such as a child or a dog, the idea of the modification which he will undergo in time is an integral part of my concept of this external object. It is the same to a certain point for objects deprived of life of which the change in time has struck us; for example, a building or a picture of which we foresee the senescence and of which the absolute conservation, if we were to see it again without change after many years, would appear as an abnormal fact. This is why an appeal made, in regard to scientific theories, to notions of common sense is apt to introduce into our reasoning an element of confusion. And this is the profound source of the fundamental error which we have discovered in Helmholtz and in Hertz, an error which consists in establishing perfect identification between laws and properties of bodies. It is certain, as we have shown, that at first sight the former appear simply as a more precise translation of the latter. But, looking more closely, we see that in forming this concept of property we have retained precisely this possibility of change in time which cannot be applied to the concept of law.

What we have stated about the genesis of the notions of common sense will make us understand better the futility of the effort to exclude causality from science. What would be the point of departure of a science strictly conformable to the idea of Comte and of Mach—that is, solely inspired by the principle of conformity to law, setting aside, to cite Renouvier, all substantialistic conceptions in favour of an absolute pheno-menalism? It would have to start apparently from our sensa-tions, for Mach himself says: "Not things, but colours, sounds, pressures, spaces, durations (what we call generally sensations), are the real elements of the world."(24) In truth, one would have to go still farther and take as a point of departure those "im-mediate data of consciousness," which Bergson has disengaged. Does science proceed in this way? Not in the least. It leaves at first this problem completely aside. When it does speak of it, it is to relegate its solution to one of its most backward and complex branches, physiology; sometimes science discards it completely, declaring it to be metaphysical in essence. The point of departure of science is, on the contrary, solely from data of common sense; this is quite easy to verify, and, moreover, eminent scientists have expressly stated it. Duhem thinks that "our most sublime scientific knowledge has, in the last analysis, no other foundation than the data of common sense"(25); and Mach warns us that "the scientist for his routine work (*den Handgebrauch*) cannot get along without the most palpable conceptions of substance."(26) The physicist, indeed, begins by believing blindly, as does every man, in the conceptions of common sense. He modifies them afterward, but how does he modify them? Solely by proceeding from reality to reality. When he has decomposed the stick into a nebula of atoms, or even, if you prefer, of electric ions, these atoms or these ions are as *real* to him as the stick was; he has never, indeed, "reduced" anything but substantive to substantive, object to object. At no time, unless it is a question of "errors of observation," or of phenomena expressly qualified as "subjective," will the physicist permit the consideration of the subject to intervene. At no moment in the course of his deductions will he substitute for an object something manifestly unreal.(27) "Ask your imagination," exclaimed Tyndall, in speaking of the hypotheses concerning the nature of light, "if it will accept a vibrating multiple proportion."(28) And Hartmann declares that only the inhabitants of a lunatic asylum would attempt to explain physics with the help of concepts wittingly unreal.(29)

But this question seems so important to us that we ask to be allowed to dwell on it a little more, lest any doubt exist. Indeed, the matter has been so admirably elucidated by Duhem that if we cannot always adopt the views of this eminent scientist, at least his analysis will be of constant service to us. Duhem describes an experiment in physics in these words: "Go into this laboratory; approach this table encumbered with a lot of apparatus, an electric battery, copper wires covered with silk, small cups full of mercury, coils, an iron bar supporting a mirror; the observer puts into little holes the metallic stem of a hook, the head of which is of ebony; the iron swings and the mirror, bound to it, casts upon a celluloid ruler a band of light of which the observer follows the movements; indisputably this is an experiment; by means of the movement of this spot of light the physicist observes minutely the oscillations of the piece of iron. Now ask him what he is doing. Will he reply: I am studying the oscillations of the iron bar which supports the mirror? No, he will reply that he is measuring the electric resistance of a coil. If you show your amazement, if you ask him what sense these words have and what their relation is to the phenomena which he has ascertained, and which you have ascertained at the same time—he will tell you that your question would demand many long explanations and he will advise you to take a course in electricity."(30) Whoever has the least idea of physical researches will immediately recognize that this description, scrupulously exact, characterizes an entirely general case. Not only experiments in electricity, but almost all experiments in physics performed in a laboratory of to-day are of this type. Everything would remain a sealed book to the man unacquainted with the special chapter of physics to which the experiments belong, no matter what trouble he may take to observe them. Duhem establishes, with great exactness, that the theoretical interpretation to which phenomena are subjected by the physicist is only possible through the use of instruments.(31) He concludes that between phenomena really observed and the result of an experiment formulated by a physicist a very complex intellectual elaboration intervenes.(32) In a word, "an experiment in physics is not simply the observation of a phenomenon; it is, in addition, the theoretical interpretation of this phenomenon,"(33) and since it is impossible to give even an account of an experiment in physics without using theoretical language,(34) "the statement of the result of an experiment implies, in general, an act of faith concerning a whole group of theories."(35)

Duhem believes that these deductions indicate that there is a close solidarity between the scientific facts of an entire division of physics and even of several divisions. We believe that they show us, in addition, to what a degree the physicist is closely attached to the concept of *thing*. What, as a matter of fact, does the electrician study during the experiment described? He studies an electric current; to him this current and the "resistance" which the coil opposes to it are certainly *real*. A man, unacquainted with physics, seeing the experiment, understands nothing. He thinks that what happens is a phenomenon which involves an iron bar, mirror, etc.—all *objects* of common sense; but since he is unacquainted with electrical theories, he cannot perceive the *object*—that is, the current, which alone is really observed by the physicist. And it is easy to see why it is impossible to state this experiment without speaking of the hypothesis. This is because the experiment has to do with something created by this latter; and, of course, the statement when formulated will imply an act of faith in a theory, for it will have to do with the object the existence of which is the basis of the hypothesis in question or even of a group of hypotheses.

Will it be said that the theory does not really imply the existence of these objects, that they are simply terms used to indicate a group of phenomena? We saw (Chapter I, p. 52 f.)

that the entire attitude of science is a protest against a supposition of this kind. Let us observe, moreover, that this supposition
is entirely analogous to that formulated by philosophers, who
deny that common sense denotes the affirmation of anything
whatsoever outside our consciousness (p. 357) and to whom
the electric current, therefore, will still be a "permanent
possibility of sensation." But the conception will be, in this
case, just as insufficient as in the case of an object of common
sense; it will mean doing violence to the profound feeling of
the electrician, as it did a moment before to that of the naïve
man. Hide the galvanometer behind a screen and ask the
electrician if the current is passing. He will, perhaps, believe
that you are asking whether a switch has not been turned by
mistake, and he will verify it; but it may be that he will
have doubts about the functioning of his battery, and, in that
case, he will want to see the galvanometer. But insist; explain
to him that you are asking him whether he believes that the
current has ceased to flow because of the single fact that he cannot see the galvanometer. If the man you are addressing has
no philosophical background, if he has been preserved from
"metaphysical doubt," and if you have made him understand
the import of your question (which will not be easy, so strange
will it sound to him), well, then, if he is an honest man he
will laugh in your face. Doubt, in this case, will appear to him
as unjustifiable as if you asked him whether he doubted the
existence of his wife or of his workshop simply because he
perceives neither of them at that moment. His belief in the
objects of the two kinds is evidently analogous and flows
from the same source. And even the scientist, accessible to
philosophic doubt, when, in his laboratory, he works with the
help of the current, and as long as he works with it, believes
in it "with all his heart," as the popular expression goes.
He is forced to believe in it, forced to make use of "the most
naïve conceptions of substance," to quote Mach. Doubtless,
his faith is neither absolute nor immutable, but such is the
case also with his belief in common sense, which he abandons
when he gives himself up to metaphysical speculation and
which he takes up again as soon as he enters everyday life.
Electricians have at all times so thoroughly believed in the
current—they have *seen* it so much—that they have ended by

"materializing" it, in very much the same way as a spiritualist medium pretends to materialize his thought. Whoever asks whether the current is, in truth, a real object need only be referred to the most recent theories, where the current consists of a true flux of electrons; it is, indeed, impossible to doubt that these latter are conceived as real, since it is they that constitute matter and are supposed to be, consequently, the source of all reality.

To strengthen our conviction in this respect it will be enough to note to what a degree this creation of *objects* constitutes a general and common process in the physical sciences. Thus discoveries made with the help of such instruments of research as the microscope or the telescope are expressed quite naturally under this form. This is so true, the analogy we have just spoken of is so complete, that one would have great difficulty, probably, in explaining to a biologist, accustomed to observe under the microscope the evolutions of a particular micro-organism, that this micro-organism was not absolutely *real* to the same degree as any animal whatsoever seen with the naked eye. Now it is certain that the *consensus omnium*, the consensus of opinion of the immense majority of mankind about the existence of the real world, is an integral part of the concept of common sense; whereas the microbe in question is certainly unknown to a great part of humanity, and most of those who believe in its existence do so only on the word of scientists. One might, indeed, object that some rare animal, such as the okapi, has, only been seen up to this day by a privileged few, but the case at bottom is very different. To be convinced of this it is enough to have observed a man who, for the first time, has been shown a drop of putrid water under the microscope. As soon as he removes his eye from the microscope, he evidently conceives doubts about the *reality* of the image he has just seen; he asks himself whether it is the same drop which he now sees with his naked eye, stripped of all appearance of organic life, and whether there was not a little fraud somewhere or an error on the part of the instrument. These doubts are known to have been shared, at the beginning of microscopic or telescopic studies, by many eminent minds; Comte again believed that he ought to protest.(36)

But, in a more direct and therefore a more conclusive way,

it can be shown that *reality* for the two sorts of objects, those seen with the naked eye and those perceived under the microscope, is not entirely of the same order. We have already spoken (p. 303) of the "supremacy of touch," and we gave the reasons why we felt it should not be accepted. But it seems undeniable to us, that in all that concerns space and the occupation of space, the sense of touch and its memory play a most important rôle. Now there can be no question of touching a microbe; its size is much too small for its form to make an impression upon the termini of our tactile nerves. When we think of that organism and of the space which it occupies, we imagine as the subject of the sensation a minute being, but one endowed with senses analogous to ours; it is to this being that a microbe would appear as really occupying a space—to this being it would seem *real* in the same degree that our animals are to us. This is so true that a student is apt to forget the true scale of images he is looking at and to transpose them simply into the world of sizes perceptible to the naked eye, and this, as has been recently stated by an eminent histologist, can engender errors of a peculiar kind.(37)

Perhaps we shall see better still the nature of objects of this kind by observing certain of those we know both by direct sensation and scientific observation. Descartes had already remarked that we have "two entirely diverse ideas of the Sun": one which "draws its origin from the senses," and the other "which is based on reasons of Astronomy."(38) To our immediate sensation, the sun is a spot of light; it might be, if necessary, only an ephemeral phenomenon. Heraclitus assumed that a new sun began every day at dawn and perished at dusk. Scientific reasoning, based upon telescopic observations, has transformed it into a stellar body the size of which far surpasses that of our earth. And so science, where common sense was not enough for the constitution of a true material object, has come to its help and has worked entirely in the same direction, by affirming the permanence of the *thing* even when it remains invisible, and in giving to it reality or *corporeity*, if one may say so, forming it according to models furnished by naïve realism: the sun is an incandescent mass somewhat like those masses which emanate from a Bessemer converter. Moreover, when once this image of the sun is formed, science keeps to it; it never returns to direct sensation. Whenever it is a question of the sun in astronomy, you will have to think of the immense incandescent stellar body; you will never hear of the little ephemeral spot of light.

Let us now recall what we stated about scientific concepts of a very different order, such as *mass, force, energy*. These concepts in the beginning are evidently only relations. Mass is the coefficient which bodies manifest at the moment of mechanical action; force is only the cause of the acceleration, which is a difference of two velocities; energy is a concept still more complicated, impossible in certain cases to define in its entirety. It is, moreover, a simple integral, characterizing not a body but a system, and of which only the variations are studied. This does not prevent physics from manifesting the tendency to treat these concepts as real things. In certain respects the reality which is attributed to them is even superior to that which common sense assumes in objects created by it. Indeed the distinctive character of these last, perdurability, is here intensified. All objects of the external world which we know are modified in time and by the action of time; of this we have an immediate and absolute conviction—a conviction, moreover, which is an integral part of our concept of the object or of time itself. But mass, force, and energy persist; they are entirely independent of the action of time.

It is almost useless to show that the situation is the same with regard to the atom—a concept still nearer the concepts of common sense than those we have just discussed, since the notion of mechanism of which it forms the basis can be considered as a sort of scientific common sense (p. 365). The principal function of the atom also is to be eternal, immutable.

We can corroborate in still another way the result we have just reached. Perdurability, if it is the most apparent distinctive feature of objects created by common sense with respect to our sensations, is, however, not the only one. Another distinction, at least as essential, it seems, is clearly perceived if we refer to considerations of quantity, as we have stated them (p. 341 f.). The world of common sense, we saw, is qualitative in part; but only in part: for all that has to do with space and with the occupation of space appears to us as distinctly quantitative, whereas our immediate sensation can only be purely qualitative.

Does science reverse this evolution of common sense? Does it penetrate through quantitative perception as far as the qualitative sensation? On the contrary, it accentuates the evolution and forces it to its utmost limits. This attitude is so striking that it has often been noticed even by superficial observers, and this progressive substitution of quantity for quality has been made one of the characteristic features of science in general, or at least of modern science. This is because physics, improving on common sense, introduces considerations of quantity where this latter ignored them. It declares that two lights of different colour are only distinguishable by the wave-length, which is incontestably a purely quantitative concept; it even ends by reducing to considerations of quantity, distinctions as fundamental as those existing between electricity and light.

Thus science creates new objects which resemble entirely those of naïve realism, and even entities of a particular order, where the distinctive feature of the object, perdurability, is pushed to the extreme. It brings out the concept of quantity where common sense has been powerless to accomplish this task; and when it transforms the image of naïve realism, it is only in substituting for the *object* another *object*, the first condition of which is to exist independently of our sensation. Therefore, in the advance which separates it from common sense, science never returns toward sensation; on the contrary, it pushes on, always forward, in the way and in the direction which have led thought from sensation to common sense.

This general proposition may be directly verified in the case of Duhem's electrician. The electric current is certainly in no way an object of common sense. Indeed, what characterizes clearly objects of common sense is that they are composed of hypostatized sensations; now we have no specific sensations of electricity, since we possess no organ sensitive to that form of energy. A wire through which a current of 10,000 volts passes does not change in aspect when the switch is turned on; and when the current or the spark passes through our bodies all that we experience is a simple mechanical shock. This is why it is very difficult to speak about the current in common-sense terms as we do, for instance, about the animalcules in the drop of putrid water, or about the sun, for both being visible with the aid of optical instruments become immediately, as we have seen, objects of a sort of enlarged common sense. However this difficulty is not absolutely insurmountable, and it is important to note in what way we can, if necessary, succeed in overcoming it. Duhem's electrician, who sent the spectator to take a course in electricity, was satisfied to state that it would take very long to explain, which is perfectly true. And yet if the questioner had insisted, if he had constrained him to attempt a short explanation, there is no doubt that the explanation would have been conceived in terms of common sense; it would have involved objects as they are conceived generally by common sense. In doing this, the electrician would simply have retraced in the opposite direction the way followed by science in forming the concept of the electric current: it started from the data of common sense, it can therefore, if necessary, return to them. Evidently this will necessitate a great deal of circumlocution. But, note carefully, if, starting from the electric current and its properties, one wishes to return to the immediate sensation, there is no other way than by these concepts of common sense, since between the current and the sensation there exists no direct bond. Thus the current in so far as it is an object independent of us, though not belonging to common sense proper, nor even to common sense extended to microscopic or telescopic objects, is none the less dependent wholly on this conception. It is, indeed, the product of a double transposition: in the first place, the transposition which hypostatizes the sensations into objects of common sense, and secondly, that which, using these objects as a basis, creates concepts of scientific theory, which are in their turn new realities, new objects.

It is further to be noted that this is no mysterious peculiarity of our imagination. The scientist obeys only two principles, that of conformity to law and that of causality. The first, it is clear, can only serve to establish relations between concepts already pre-existing. It is, therefore, powerless by itself alone to modify these concepts; when it shows their insufficiency (p. 346) the principle of causality which has created them must intervene to modify them. Now this principle proceeds from identity to identity or what is supposed to be such. It cannot,

therefore, replace one concept by another which is heterogeneous to it and consequently, if we start from an object
considered as real, we shall naturally arrive at an object of
the same kind. There is undoubtedly somewhere, at the beginning (or at the end, if you wish), between the sensation and
the object, a kind of gulf which the principle of causality
readily crosses; but the leap is forced upon us and, moreover,
we make it unconsciously. The work of science is, on the
contrary, conscious, the scientist proceeds with slow steps,
the length of which he may change to suit himself, and consequently any deviation, any rupture of continuity, would
immediately become apparent.

We may also see why in certain respects, and especially in
respect to perdurability, the concepts created by science, such
as the atom, mass, or energy, seem to be *things*, as it were, in a
higher degree than objects of common sense. Indeed, *how*
does the scientist succeed in showing the insufficiency of
common sense? In looking for the cause, in equating the
antecedent with the consequent—that is, in trying to find what,
in one and in the other, might have remained identical. Let
us recall the example of the stick; when seeing it bent in the
water, I affirm that it has nevertheless remained straight—
I evoke the persistence of something which is incontestably a
concept of common sense; but when, having burned it, I
maintain that its "matter" has not perished, I have recourse
to concepts which are no longer a part of it. I do this because,
the stick as such manifestly not persisting, I wish to imagine
something the existence of which I may suppose both in the
burned object and in the gases which arise from combustion.
It is, therefore, because the perdurability of common sense
objects is not sufficient that we abandon them, that we create
a series of new objects which then appear necessarily endowed
with a superior perdurability and thereby are more detached,
and still more independent of us, participating more in the
character of the thing in itself.(39) It is evident, moreover,
that this deduction does not apply solely to science as we know
it to-day, but to science in general. Indeed, the peripatetic
system, so different from ours, employed, nevertheless, in this
respect quite analogous processes. Aristotle's hot may claim
to be a pure quality, but its true destiny is to explain changes by

displacement, it has, therefore, a perdurability superior to that of a simple object of perception. It is almost needless to show that this community of method comes from the fact that it is a question of the direct consequences of the causal principle.

We see how inapplicable is the injunction one might be tempted to give to the scientist, of limiting himself to the destruction of the reality of common sense without creating a new one. He has created in destroying, and it is only in behalf of the new reality that he has abolished the old one.

One may also advise him to abolish all reality at once, and by decree, so to speak. Indeed, to escape from common sense there is still another way than that of scientific thought: the way of metaphysical thought. The physicist, if only he professes idealistic opinions in philosophy, will have no difficulty, apparently, in effecting this escape; but in appearance only. The most determined solipsist, when he opens his eyes in the morning, *sees* matter, and *touches* it when he stretches out his hand. This "metaphysics" is operating in us without our consent, instantaneously, irresistibly, to such a degree that we believe in a simple passive reception of our senses where really there is a very complicated effort in our brain. "I know, moreover," says Reid, "that this belief (in the reality of the outside world) is not the effect of argumentation and reasoning; it is the immediate effect of my constitution." And before this "philosopher of common sense," as he has been called,(40) a metaphysician who professed opinions diametrically opposed, perhaps the most extreme Pyrrhonist ever known in the history of modern philosophy, Huet, Bishop of Avranches, wrote: "When it is a question of guiding one's life, of accomplishing one's duties, we cease to be philosophers, to be doubtful, uncertain; we become idiots, simple-minded, credulous, we call things by their names. . . ."(41)

Huet, without doubt, meant simply that we need common sense in order to act. But the prodigious facility with which the concepts of common sense, which we believed were abolished, return, shows that that abolition was only apparent, that we were not entirely freed from them, and that we were always dominated by the "ontological" need.(42)

Of course, according to the theory of common sense, which we have discussed, this need has nothing mysterious or primordial about it. It is simply an expression of the tendency to see our sensations persist in time. They vary without ceasing, and this seems unreasonable to us. They *must* remain, and since they cannot remain in us, we place them outside; we perhaps even create the outside wherein to lodge them. If, now, by the intervention of science, this first series of created objects is shown to be contradictory, non-existent, we must immediately create others. Indeed, our sensations cannot subsist by themselves independently, for their variation in time would be without cause; that cause, therefore, *must* be created, a permanent cause, and if it cannot be the objects endowed with the qualities of common sense, it will be the atoms and electrons. It is this which finally convinces us that the scientist can never disengage himself from the *object*, that he can only replace one reality by another, a little less illogical, but at bottom just as chimerical and destined, moreover, to sink in its turn into the abyss of ether, or rather of non-differentiated space.

If, on the contrary, the scientist ceases his causal deductions, or if he eliminates them completely from science, the simple result will be that the conception of common sense will remain standing, a conception just as ontological as any other, but the complete inconsistency of which is revealed by the slightest scientific reasoning. Let us suppress every atomic and mechanical hypothesis from a given chapter of science. There will still remain laws—that is, statements of relations, not between the phenomena of our consciousness, but between material objects, that is, between causal images. We shall, therefore, have gained absolutely nothing, from a philosophical point of view, in eliminating the "metaphysics" of theories, nor in giving to these latter, by more or less complicated artifices, a form such that their ontological content, the hypothesis on the nature of reality, should be, so to speak, obliterated.(43)

As to abstaining from all metaphysics, that would be a vain pretence indeed. Metaphysics penetrates all science, for the very simple reason that it is contained in its point of departure. We cannot even isolate it in a precise region. *Primum vivere, deinde philosophari* seems to be a precept dictated by wisdom. It is really a chimerical rule almost as inapplicable as if we were advised to rid ourselves of the force of gravitation. *Vivere est philosophari.*

From what precedes we perceive that there is not the great difference sometimes supposed between common sense and science. We believe literally, as Le Roy has stated, that science corresponds to the same attitude as common sense.(44) When this philosopher tells us that the scientist *makes* scientific facts and not brute facts,(45) we agree with him, since the scientific fact appears to us related to an object which the scientist has created. But it is on condition that we are assured that in doing so he has exactly followed the same process which common sense employed in creating the brute fact. When Le Roy affirms (46) that in the phenomenon of the eclipse there are two facts—one a common-sense fact, the other a fact of the scientist—we beg to explain. There is, in the first place, in the phenomenon of the eclipse a series of "immediate data of consciousness," according to Bergson, infinitely difficult to attain, because our consciousness transforms them instantly, infinitely difficult also to state, because all language has been made in view of the "realities" created by common sense and scientific theories. But what is certain is that these immediate data contain only subjective states and nothing which resembles an external fact. The external fact, the brute fact, comes into existence with common sense. But once in existence it is attacked by scientific criticism. Or rather brute fact and scientific fact are one; between the two there is no breach of continuity. When I look at the sun about to be eclipsed, what do I see? Is it brilliant and plane or something convex? It is not easy to say. It is quite certain that our ancestors saw a plane spot, but since our childhood we have been so often told that it is a sphere, that we think we see it; and surely the astronomer, who looks at the sun every day, watching the spots move and change their aspect according to their situation as the sun turns, *sees* the sun as a sphere. He sees it still better in the moon, which is nearer us, and of which the relief is much sharper. No one can doubt that if he is accustomed to seeing it as a spherical body in the telescope, he will *see* it so also when he looks at it with the naked eye, and the vision of a plane spot is no longer possible for him; just as we think we see a man in the dark but are quite incapable of seeing him again when we are convinced that it is only a tree.(47) As to the sky, certainly we are quite incapable of *seeing* the crystal vault of our ancestors. This expression which designated a reality for them, something they thought they saw, is a pure metaphor for us. In looking toward the sky we no longer see a limit, so to speak; we have the impression of looking into infinite space without a limit. Moreover, all these facts come without any doubt from the fundamental statement which we formulated a little while ago: *generalized* memory—that is, our knowledge—enters into our perception, is a constitutive part of it. Le Roy concedes that between common sense and science there is no precise limit, between them there exists a vague zone.(48) This, we think, is an insufficient concession; we affirm absolute continuity, common sense being only a scientific and metaphysical system, and being transformed under the influence of science, with much greater slowness, however, than the properly called scientific theories.

Our conception is much nearer that of Duhem, from whom, especially at the beginning of this exposition, we have borrowed so freely. However we are not quite sure that we have understood the difference which this eminent scientist has established between common sense and scientific theories. Duhem compares a naval officer giving an order in technical language to his sailors with a physicist speaking of batteries, pressure, and electric-motive force, and points out that the officer's commands correspond in his men's minds to determinate acts, whereas the physicist's statement can be realized in infinitely different ways.(49) But cannot the physicist, in his turn, speak in a less general, more definite manner? And cannot the naval officer express himself in more general terms so as to indicate simply the end to be attained? When a captain, before entering port, indicates to the pilot the part of the harbour in which he wishes to anchor, has not the pilot the choice of infinitely varied movements, manœuvrings, by which he can attain the desired anchorage? The very order, moreover, of the officer, looking at it closely, leaves a vast field of indetermination. The sailor knows that he must pull such a rope, but to do this he can place his left leg in front of his right one, or inversely, and so on; in a word, he has the choice between a really unlimited multiplicity of different movements which

will only have in common, just like the different operations of
the physicist corresponding to the same statement, the consummation of a result considered as one and the same. Duhem,
we think, more nearly approaches reality by opposing the
spontaneous abstractions of common sense to the slow, complicated, conscious abstractions of physical theories.(50) This,
we believe, is the real difference; common sense acts unconsciously, and even when it has been modified by science (as in
the case of the moon, which the astronomer sees convex), its
action is instantaneous. Moreover, it acts almost identically
in the great majority of men; thus its decrees, because of their
spontaneity and the general consensus by which they benefit,
appear to acquire a superior certainty. But really they are
of the same nature, engendered by the same process as those
of science.

NOTES

1. BERGSON: *Introduction à la métaphysique. Revue de métaphysique*, XI, 1903,
p. 5.

2. Id., *Matière et mémoire*. Paris, 1903, p. 20.

3. *Ib.*, p. 59.

4. A. M. AMPÈRE: *Essai sur la philosophie des sciences*. Paris, 1834–43.
Vol. I, p. 51.

5. The very curious psychological observations on *cerebral* deafness or
blindness seem to be related to considerations of this kind. The organ of
sensation being intact, the sick person hears or sees, but, auditory or visual
memory being abolished, he no longer recognizes sensations which were
familiar to him. Cf. Mach, *La connaissance et l'erreur*, trans. Dufour. Paris,
1908, pp. 59–60.

6. BERGSON: *Perception et matière. Revue de métaphysique*, IV, 1896, p. 272.
Matière et mémoire, p. 202.

7. SPIR: *Pensée et réalité*. Paris, 1896, p. 34.

8. HUME: *A Treatise of Human Nature*. Oxford, 1896, Book I, Part IV,
§ 2. Cf. *Psychologie* trans. RENOUVIER ET PILON. Paris, 1878, p. 249.

9. SCHOPENHAUER: *Ueber die vierfache Wurzel*, etc. *Werke*, ed. Frauenstaedt. Leipzig, 1877, p. 82. Cf. *Die Welt als Wille und Vorstellung*, Vol. I,
p. 10.

10. HUXLEY: *Lay Sermons*. London, 1887, p. 124.

11. ARISTOTLE: *De Caelo*, Book III, Chap. III, § 1. "An element, we
take it, is a body into which other bodies may be analysed, present in them
potentially or in actuality."

12. J. S. MILL: *Examination of Sir William Hamilton's Philosophy*. New
York, 1873, pp. 236–237.

13. Ostwald: *Vorlesungen*, p. 40.

14. Lotze: *Metaphysik*. Leipzig, 1879, pp. 506–507.

15. We believe that it is the more or less conscious but very powerful feeling for this analogy, which is found at the base of affirmations of the continuity of common sense and of science. We may mention especially on this subject the declaration at which Painlevé arrives in the conclusion of his work on the principle of energy. "If it is a convention to say that the earth rotates, it is equally a convention to say that it exists, and these two conventions are justified by identical reasons" (*Bull. Soc. phil.*, 5th year, 1905, p. 50). Let us add, however, that, according to Painlevé, both *conventions* have their sole source in what he calls "the principle of causality," which is only the conviction that the laws of nature are not modifiable in space and time (cf. also *ib.*, p. 31 and ff.) ; this is, therefore, the statement which we have qualified as the principle of conformity to *law*. Hermann Cohen (*Logik der reinen Erkenntnis*. Berlin, 1902, p. 379), after having declared that matter and ether are two equivalent hypotheses, adds : "It is the prejudice of sensation which makes matter appear less under the aspect of an hypothesis."

16. Euripides: *Phoenissae*, p. 501.

17. D'Alembert: *Discours préliminaire à l'Encyclopédie*, p. 21. An analogous theory concerning the rôle of the social element in conceptions of common sense has been recently formulated by Lalande (*La Dissolution*, Paris. 1899, p. 175, and *Bulletin de la Société française de philosophie*, 3rd year, 1903, p. 58 and ff.).

18. J. S. Mill: *Examination of Sir William Hamilton's Philosophy*. New York, 1873, p. 238.

19. E. Mach: *Die oekonomische Natur der physikalischen Forschung. Almanach der Akademie der Wissenschaften*. Vienne, 1882, p. 307.

20. H. Poincaré: *La valeur de la science*, p. 270.

21. Ostwald: *Vorlesungen*. Leipzig, 1902, p. 181.

22. H. Hertz: *Gesammelte Werke*. Leipzig, 1895, Vol. III, p. 27 and ff.

23. Renouvier: *Critique philosophique*, IX, p. 349.

24. E. Mach: *La mécanique*, trans. E. Bertrand. Paris, 1904, p. 451.

25. Duhem: *L'évolution de la mécanique*, p. 179.

26. Mach: *Die Principien der Waermelehre*. Leipzig, 1896, p. 420.

27. The point of view developed in the text appears as the exact counterpart of Spir's opinion, according to which science proceeds from change to change, but never arrives at a real object (*Pensée et réalité*, pp. 89–99). Yet it seems that the divergence is one of terms rather than of real content in the two theses. But Spir, doubtless, has been influenced by his confusion between lawfulness and causality.

28. Tyndall: *Fragments of Science*. London, 1871, p. 136.

29. Hartmann: *Das Grundproblem der Erkennstnistheorie*, p. 22.

30. Duhem: *La théorie physique*. Paris, 1906, pp. 234–235.

31. *Ib.*, p. 248.

32. *Ib.*, p. 247.

33. *Ib.*, p. 233.

34. *Ib.* pp. 266–267.

35. DUHEM: *La théorie physique*. Paris, 1906, p. 300. LAVOISIER already stated "the impossibility of separating nomenclature from science and science from nomenclature" (*Traité élémentaire de chimie. Œuvres*. Paris, 1864, Vol. I, p. 2). Lavoisier's *nomenclature* is evidently the expression of a theory.

36. Cf. earlier, Chap. I, p. 21.

37. "It is evident that since the microscopic world differs greatly from the one familiar to us, the histologist is subject to certain characteristic errors. Within the visual field he has representations as large as ordinary objects, but these are only pure phantoms, which correspond to structures entirely subject to the laws of molecular physics. This antinomy must always be borne in mind by anyone who wishes to understand the architecture and the mechanism of anatomic elements. In my last study on the nervous fibre I had occasion to state that this precept has not always been followed." *Notice sur les travaux scientifiques de M. J. Nageotte*. Paris, 1911, p. 9; cf. *ib.*, p. 59.

38. DESCARTES: *Méditations. Œuvres*, Vol. IX. Paris, 1904, p. 31.

39. PLANCK has admirably seen that that which forces us to introduce certain considerations of molecular movement, even into domains which at first seem inaccessible to them, such as that of irreversible phenomena, is the necessity of detaching science from what he calls "anthropomorphic considerations"—that is, considerations relative to the personality of the observer—and that it is this progressive emancipation which constitutes the true characteristic of the evolution of theoretical science. He recognizes equally that this evolution is in opposition to the positivistic conception, which would demand a return to sensation, and a science establishing direct relations between elements of sensation. (*Acht Vorlesungen ueber theoretische Physik*. Leipzig, 1910, pp. 3–7.) Wundt, on his part, understood perfectly that it was this necessity of supposing a substratum mobile in space (that is, unmodifiable in time), a necessity made pressing because of the progress of electromagnetic theories, which brought about the ruin of the energetic conception (*Die Prinzipien der mechanischen Naturlehre*, p. 3).

40. T. REID: *Works*, ed. Hamilton. Edinburgh, 1846. *Of the Human Mind*, p. 183.

41. HUET: *Traité philosophique de la faiblesse de l'esprit humain*. Amsterdam, 1723, p. 242.

42. HARTMANN (*Das Grundproblem der Erkenntnistheorie*, p. 14 and ff.) maliciously points out with what deplorable ease idealistic philosophers, even in the course of their most apparently abstract reasonings, fall again into naïve realism.

43. HARTMANN, amongst others, has well brought to light that what is generally embellished with the name of positivism is, from a metaphysical standpoint, only a scarcely transformed naïve realism (*l.c.*, p. 55).

44. E. LE ROY: *Science et Philosophie. Revue de métaphysique*, VII, 1899, p. 511.

45. Id., *La science positive et la liberté. Congrès de philosophie de 1900*, Vol. I, p. 333.

46. Id., *Bulletin de la société française de philosophie*, 1901, p. 17.

47. HELMHOLTZ (*Vortraege und Reden*, 4th ed. Brunswick, 1896, p. 114)

recounts that as a child he saw, as he was passing a tower, some little dolls on the upper balcony and that one day he asked his mother to put up her arm and take a few of them. "Later," he adds, "I have often looked toward the balcony of that tower, where there were men, but they no longer consented to be transformed, by my more wary eyes, into pretty dolls." This is an excellent example of the impossibility of return to primitive perception, when it has been modified by more recent knowledge.

48. E. le Roy: *Bull. soc. phil.*, 1901, p. 20.
49. Duhem: *l.c.*, p. 240.
50. Id., *l.c.*, p. 272.

CHAPTER XII

CONCLUSIONS

FROM the preceding pages this conclusion, it seems, stands out: it is not true that the sole end of science is action, nor that it is solely governed by the desire for economy in this action. Science also wishes to make us *understand* nature. It tends, indeed, according to Le Roy's expression, toward the "progressive rationalization of reality."(1)

Science has, in truth, been established with the almost complete certainty that nature is regulated, but also with the tenacious hope that it will manifest itself as intelligible. In every chapter of science these two principles have been applied simultaneously and continue to be so applied. Their action is irrevocably entangled, because they pass and repass their acquisitions to each other; not only, as has been said, do empirical facts serve to establish theories which bring about the discovery of new facts, but also considerations of conservation, of identity, intervene at every step in empirical science, which is, in spite of appearances, saturated with these *a priori* elements.

Science is not *positive* and does not even contain positive data in the precise meaning which Auguste Comte and his adherents have given to this term—that is, data "stripped of all ontology." Ontology is of a piece with science itself and cannot be separated from it. Those who pretend to separate them are unconsciously using a current metaphysical system, a common sense more or less transformed by science of the past, which is familiar to them. The positivist plan is, therefore, truly chimerical. Not only does it correspond neither to modern science nor to any which humanity has known at any epoch of evolution, but it implies and demands such a modification, such an unsettling of our habits of thought, that we have infinite difficulty in conceiving it and especially in measuring all of its consequences. Indeed, the only means of doing away with every ontology would consist in accomplishing that operation at the very beginning of physics, by dissolving the object and returning to the immediate data of Bergson, in order to try afterwards to establish direct relations between these data, without passing through the hypothesis of an objective existence. Is such a science possible? Malebranche expressly denied it. He attempted to show that in no case could one pretend to measure sensations directly by one another, as subjective phenomena; and that all comparison of these presupposes a preliminary reduction to objective causes, and therefore a subjection of them to fixation in time and space.(2) This seems to be an impregnable deduction. We saw (p. 341) that a purely qualitative science, which was still substantialistic, though capable of setting up *scales*, could no longer *measure*. With still greater reason would this be so in the science that is truly phenomenalistic, from which the very quality itself, viewed as substratum, would be excluded. And yet must the possibility of a science of this kind be radically denied, and its entire uselessness from the point of view of prevision be asserted? What makes one hesitate before this absolute negation is precisely the novelty, the unknown factor in the proposed method. Without further attempt to go to the bottom of this question, which would be too great a digression from the subject of this book, let us observe, once again, how greatly science thus constituted, supposing even that it were possible, would depart from all that we know. It would certainly no longer be physics, but rather a sort of psycho-physics pushed to the extreme; it would, indeed, be infinitely more than all we know under this name, removed from physics, since modern psycho-physics, it is easily understood, presupposes physics as a basis, and consequently the whole ontological world of common sense and of science.—The ontological character of scientific explanation is ineffaceable. Doubtless, through the unity of matter it finally ends in uniform and empty space. But here there is destruction of reality, of the whole external world; and in this destruction, it goes without saying, law also has been abolished, for there being no longer any diversity either in time or in space, there is no longer any phenomenon, and therefore nothing which law may rule.(3) Therefore, and contrary to what is sometimes supposed believable, there is not, there cannot be, in the natural evolution of scientific theories, any phase where ontological reality would disappear, and at the same time the concept of conformity to law remain standing. Their disappearance is certainly *simultaneous*, and if we take the world of scientific theory at the moment, so to speak, when it is going to evolve into non-entity, we shall find it as ontological as that of the reality of common sense; the singular points of the ether, in so far as we differentiate them from their medium by any means whatsoever, will be just as real, just as much *objects*, and even more fundamentally independent of us and our sensation than anything in our perception. Explanatory science, indeed, rejoins absolute idealism or solipsism, but it is only in complete acosmism that these two ways encounter each other. Between these two parallel lines, along which science and philosophy, each one by itself, tend to destroy reality, one cannot imagine any point in common, except one situated in infinity.

This explains a peculiar characteristic of physicists' research into the constitution of matter, a characteristic which is certainly of a nature to strike the attention of the philosopher— to wit, the unconscious certainty, one might almost say the alacrity, which the scientist shows in this domain, whereas to the philosopher, his conclusions appear formidable, extravagant in the literal sense of the word, completely departing from the ordinary plan of experimental research. How does it happen, then, that the physicist does not possess this feeling at all, that he has, on the contrary, the very distinct impression of being in his own domain and of following his customary methods? It is because, starting from a conception of the world such as our naïve perception offers, he has never transformed it except by putting into play the very rules according to which this conception was constituted. He has continually substituted the invisible for the visible, but what he has created is of the same order as what he has destroyed. He simply treats the atom as the biologist treats the microbe, the first is compared to a billiard ball as the second is compared to an animal.

With all the more reason the scientist feels himself protected from doubt in less extreme, less exposed parts of his domain; and it is not astonishing that this security has at times been envied by the philosopher. This is why frequently renewed attempts have been made to extract a real philosophy from science with the help of processes of extrapolation and generalization. The progress and ultimate end of this kind of enterprise may be traced in advance to a certain extent. Indeed, in

creating science, man has constantly obeyed his causal instinct;
starting from sensation, he has unceasingly tried to explain it,
to make it yield to the exigencies of his reason. Therefore,
what will be most general in science will necessarily be also
a form of these exigencies, and, consequently, a conception
saturated with the *a priori:* a causal hypothesis such as that of
the persistence of qualities and especially the atomic or
mechanical theory. And so it is that believing to generalize
the results of experience we succeed paradoxically in liberating
our conceptions, prior to experience, from the restrictions
imposed by experience.

It goes without saying that in pressing his thought into the
ontological mould, in giving to it the form of an hypothesis
about the reality of things, the scientist, just like the common-
sense man, acts in an entirely unconscious manner. It is not
astonishing, therefore, to see him unacquainted with the process
which he is applying—nay, even with the metaphysical tendency
which is pushing him on. No more than any other man does
the scientist see himself thinking. Doubtless, if he has peculiarly
powerful gifts, he may succeed, by a slow and patient analysis,
in sometimes recognizing the true path which his thought
has followed; but the fact of being a scientist, nay, even a
great scientist, has nothing to do with it. Indeed, the distinctive
quality of a great scientist is a powerful scientific instinct, a
sort of divination which allows him to touch the high places
only. The discovery, it has often been noticed, comes to him
suddenly—after long labour, of course; it is a flash, a revelation:
is it astonishing that he has not been able to trace its genesis?
And so it follows that we must not look to the scientist for
the principles which have really guided his thought; we must not
even believe him on his word when he tries to state them. He
may have discovered these principles in almost any other way
than by a patient analysis of his own thought. He has most
often found them already fashioned in some book; they penetrated him without his knowledge, because they pervaded the
intellectual atmosphere surrounding him.

This explains how one can go astray in searching for the
principles of science, even on the supposition that one is
following closely the scientists; their methodical ways are
cheerfully accepted, without questioning whether the aforesaid

methods had ever really been applied by the scientists themselves. It is this error, we think, which is at the bottom of the affirmation according to which, as a very eminent contemporary philosopher says, "Mathematical physics turns aside from the essence of things and their inner substantiality in order to turn toward their numerical order and connection, and their functional and mathematical structure."(4)

Declarations of this sort may certainly be found in the creators of modern physical science—in Kepler, in Newton, even in Descartes, in Boyle, and in Boscovich. But if, on the other hand, we consider without prejudice and on its merits their work as scientists, we easily perceive that it offers a quite different picture. Thus Boscovich seems, indeed, according to the title of his *Theoria*, to reduce the concept of force to that of law. But it is clear, when one reaches the heart of the work, that he considers this force to be, on the contrary, a real being, a *thing*, the true essence of nature, which he has sought for and found; his argumentation against the corpuscular theory would have no meaning if this were not so. Boyle, we have seen, was one of the strictest atomists known to the history of science at any time; he invented the term "corpuscular" for the particular form of the theory which he adopted and which he constantly used. His foregone conclusion from this point of view greatly impressed his contemporaries, such as Spinoza and Leibniz;(5) and it is clear that in attempting to reduce a change of colour to the displacement of molecules, as he did many times, he was not concerned simply with the rule of a phenomenon, but with its true nature, its essence, and its cause. And as to Descartes, it is certain that he sought for the essence of things as eagerly as the scholastics, but, unlike these latter, he found it in space; surely no one has been more affirmative, more apodictic than he in this respect. In spite of appearances the situation was the same with Kepler and with Newton. Kepler, while seeking for the laws of planetary attraction, sought at the same time for its cause, and formulated a whole theory on this subject. Newton, in spite of the *hypotheses non fingo*, based his *Opticks* on the theory of emission. His famous definition of mass by density can only be explained, as Rosenberger has justly shown,(6) by strongly entrenched atomistic convictions. And it is reasonable to doubt whether, in eliminating every real hypothesis, he ever conceived the action of gravitation as a pure and simple law; on the contrary, he openly accepted in the first place the partly theological hypothesis of More, attempting to give it a more scientific appearance by the assumption of a particular medium, and afterward allowed Cotes, in the preface to the second edition of *Principia*, to speak of force acting at a distance as of a real being.(7)

This situation is so apparent that, in building up antisubstantialistic conceptions of science, it could not be entirely ignored. The difficulty has generally been avoided by treating the works and the attempts in question as simple digressions, by pretending to believe that it was a question of parts which were not essential to the whole of the work and which could be easily detached. Now it is certain that, on the contrary, such an operation would be extremely difficult, even for Newton, whose *Opticks* and *Principia* would be deprived of some of their most essential chapters. And if one tried to do it for Descartes, all his *Principia* would have to be effaced. Evidently the scientific work of these great scientists holds together and is ordered in quite a different sense from the statements of method which are cited.

We saw at the beginning of this book(8) that the primitive source of what might be called the positivist error lies in the confusion between law and cause, in the misunderstanding of the truth, that in explaining a phenomenon by a law we are only using a synecdoche. The fact, however, that many scientists have made statements condemning all search for essence and for cause is susceptible, we believe, of more direct psychological explanations. It must be noted that it is a very simple principle, which can be expressed under a precise form like that finally given it by Comte, and for that very reason it is tempting in itself. Moreover, it flatters the scientist's pride, since it makes his chosen field appear to be in a manner sovereign, and entirely independent of the other pursuits of human thought. It is conceivable that it was on these last grounds that positivism conquered the nineteenth century, an epoch distinguished for the fruitfulness of experimental research. But it is not at all astonishing that this conception in a way surreptitiously seduced many minds before that time. One should rather be astonished at the contrary, and, indeed, if this conception did not appear sooner, if, when sometimes formulated very distinctly (as it was, for instance, by Berkeley) it again disappeared, immediately forgotten, it is not, as has frequently been said, because of a kind of vicious propensity of the human mind toward ontology, but rather because it is entirely contrary to the real advance of the intellect as much in the individual thinker as in the whole evolution of science. What would have happened in the past if humanity, seeking the impossible, had adopted Berkeley's or Comte's point of view and considered that there is no cause beyond law or that it ought not to be sought for? The great idealistic philosopher prudently abstained from applying his principle. But Auguste Comte expressed himself with greater precision. Thus he praised Fourier for having dealt with heat without trying to know whether it was matter or movement.(9) He denied that the undulatory theory or any other could ever possess "any real usefulness in guiding our minds in the effective study of optics";(10) he considered that the "pretended optical interferences or the analogous crossings in acoustics" were "essentially subjective phenomena," the contrary opinion of physicists being "a serious illusion";(11) he affirmed that all comparison between light, sound, or motion will always be "an arbitrary assumption";(12) he condemned in general as due "to the prolonged preponderance of the old philosophical mind" all tendencies attempting to establish relations between what to-day we call the different forms of energy.(13) Moreover, it is easy to ascertain that these errors of the founder of positivism are in no way accidental. Starting from the utilitarian concept of science, as we saw in Chapter I, one can justify explicative hypotheses, if necessary. However, it becomes difficult to explain the physicist's predilection for atomic conceptions; and we see that Comte's anathema against the undulatory theory, etc., is really a part of his doctrine.

Principles of positivism, or, at any rate, analogous principles, have since been adopted, at least in appearance, by many scientists, who have often felt bound to protest, like Comte, against atomic theories; but, as a matter of fact, and in spite of the aid given to this tendency by the great and legitimate authority of Mach, it remains to-day, as it did during the nineteenth century, without the least influence on the progress of science. The scientists of the beginning of the twentieth century continue to build up atomic theories just as their predecessors have done. All, doubtless, do not believe in the truth of the theories which they imagine or which they follow; but all believe in their utility. All see in them, for want of something better, an instrument of research of great value, "working hypotheses." These play an extremely important rôle. Bacon believed that one could arrive at scientific discoveries by mechanical processes of induction, so to speak; he went to great lengths in elaborating detailed plans the use of which would leave little to be attributed "to the penetration and vigour of minds," making them, on the contrary, "all nearly equal."(14) It is incontestable that certain rules stated by Bacon (such as, for example, those of concomitant variations) are useful in scientific reasoning. But his tables or schemes, one may boldly affirm, have never been employed in a constant manner by a scientist worthy of that name; at any rate, no scientific discovery, great or small, is due to their application.(15) It would seem that one cannot better refute Bacon's opinions than by citing those of three eminent men, counted amongst the creators of that especially experimental science, the chemistry of the end of the eighteenth century and the first half of the nineteenth. "To attempt an experiment," says Berthollet, "one must have an end, be guided by an hypothesis."(16) Humphry Davy affirms that "it is only in forming theories and in comparing them with facts that we can hope to discover the true system of nature."(17) And Liebig, after having declared that between experiments in Bacon's sense and true scientific research "there is the same relation as between the noise a child produces by striking on a drum and music,"(18) shows that, on the contrary, it is the scientific imagination which plays the most important rôle in discoveries, and that experiment, like the calculus, only aids in the process of thought.

Among our contemporaries, Poincaré, in his Report to the *Congrès International de Physique de 1900*, stated that to wish to experiment without preconceived ideas would be to render all experiment sterile, and, moreover, that it is impossible to free oneself from ideas of this kind;(19) and Duhem showed the close dependence of experiments upon scientific theories,(20) and made clear the impossibility of the famous *experimentum crucis*, which plays such an important part in the Baconian theory.(21)

As to the "working hypotheses," the only point of view which directly interests the scientist is their fertility, their aptitude for making him discover relations between phenomena which he had not suspected. What assumptions have ever equalled from this point of view the utility of mechanical hypotheses? In the entire domain of science, which they fill, they have produced, and are producing, a prodigious harvest of discoveries of the highest value. Where scientists in the first place have thought there was only a quite superficial similitude, subsequent research has sometimes brought to light in a most unexpected manner a more profound analogy. Let us recall how sceptical people were at first about Kekulé's hypothesis concerning the structure of the components of carbon and the position of atoms in the molecule; and even when it was proved that this description explained admirably an immense series of phenomena, which, until then, constituted a kind of impenetrable jungle, to many it still seemed grossly inadequate. And yet what an astonishing extension and verification of these theories were Le Bel's and van't Hoff's discoveries about the asymmetric atom of carbon!(22) Who does not marvel at the rôle of the atomic hypotheses in the recent progress of electricity and at the alliance of chemistry with it through the efforts of Svante Arrhenius? And is it not surprising to notice that the greater part of irreversible phenomena, which by their nature seem to elude causal explanations, appear traced, so to speak, to a mechanical phenomenon, viz. friction, to the point that physicists are now convinced that it is more than a simple analogy—something which reveals the intimate nature of things?(23) We have cited only recent, almost contemporary, examples, but there were just as many in the past, as, for instance, only to mention one illustrious example, the so brilliantly realized previsions which were deduced from Fresnel's theorem.(24)

So also the history of sciences shows us that, thanks to atomic conceptions, humanity has really foreseen to some extent certain important scientific truths, and developed a kind of prescience. When the Greek atomists affirmed that air, like any other substance, must be composed of discrete parts, it was a pure *a priori* conception. No fact was known at that time to confirm this opinion; on the contrary, everything seemed to show that air is a continuum. But we can now prove experimentally that this last opinion is untenable, that the gases really have a structure, are discontinuous.(25) So also the chemists of the nineteenth century, by attaching a tenacious hope to the hypothesis of the unity of matter, were in opposition to the best established experimental facts which formed the very basis of their own doctrine. And yet phenomena relating to cathode rays, to radiant matter, etc., are tending to furnish an experimental foundation to this hypothesis. What is taking place as regards the reversibility of chemical reactions is of the same order. It is certain (Berthollet's ideas on this having had almost no influence on the progress of science) that this notion was absolutely foreign to the mind of a chemist in the middle of the nineteenth century; and nothing was less justifiable from this point of view than the use of the sign of equality to unite the two terms of what is called a "chemical equation" (p. 225). This sign, a palpable manifestation of the causal tendency, expressed a postulate or, if you will, a hope, which, in the light of the then prevailing theories, was unrealizable or rather absurd, since it was understood that the two sides of the equation indicated, one the initial state and the other the final state of the phenomenon, which always had to take place in the same direction, without hope of return. It is all the more astonishing to state that this almost chimerical hope has, in a certain measure, been realized: chemical reactions appear to us to-day as generally reversible and we can, in fact, replace the equation sign (the meaning of which was distorted), by van't Hoff's two arrows.

But the most striking, the most marvellous phenomenon of this order, is the existence of the principles of conservation. In virtue of the causal tendency, humanity had a presentiment of them; it had formed the concept of the atom-substance long before any experiment on the conservation of matter, and it vaguely conceived mechanical systems as implying the persistence of motion before inertia and the conservation of energy. So if, on the one hand, these principles seem simply to formulate a knowledge that humanity had always possessed, on the other hand, they surpass, so to speak, the very limits of the hope it had a right to conceive. Thus heat and light might well have been movements, conforming to the postulate of universal mechanism, without any possibility of converting these movements of particles into movements of mass, or vice versa. This was approximately the conception of Leibniz and Huygens, and, in general, of most mechanistic physicists before the establishment of the conservation of energy. This last discovery is a quite unexpected confirmation. In the same way the most determined mechanist would never have dared to hope in the nineteenth century, before the work of Gouy, that the agitation of molecules could ever be made directly visible by its most immediate mechanical effects. These surprising agreements attracted the attention of thinkers. We saw (Chapter II, p. 91) that Cournot, in stating the perennial character of atomic theories, had concluded that it was possible that its inventors had "immediately fallen on the very key of natural phenomena." At other times he thought that he could infer from the conservation of the weight of matter that the idea of substance is not merely a logical abstraction, but that it has "its foundation in the essence of bodies."(26) Many remarks of contemporary physicists may be cited in which they express their astonishment at the agreement between the conceptions of the mind and the results of experimental research. Poincaré's observation on irreversible phenomena, which we have noted earlier, belongs to this region of ideas. At another time this eminent theorist marvels rightly at the surprising analogy between electric oscillation and the motion of the pendulum.(27) Boltzmann states that "all the consequences of the mechanical theory of heat, even those belonging to the most incongruous domains, have been confirmed by experiment; it may even be said that they agree most strangely, even in their finest shades, with the pulse of nature."(28) Hertz, in the beginning of his mechanics, declares that in a general manner, in order that we may form images of things, the logical consequences of these images must indeed be images of the consequences which things really produce in nature. There must, therefore, be agreement between nature and our minds.(29)

It was consequently wrong to have called, as we did, causal hypotheses, simple instruments of research, "working" hypotheses. They are more than the scaffolding destined to disappear when the building is constructed. They have their own value; they correspond certainly to something very profound and very essential in nature itself.

And so, and this is very important to notice, the agreement between the postulates of our mind and phenomena goes beyond pure conformity to law. Nature not only shows itself to be ordered, but, even to a certain point, really intelligible. This point of view has sometimes been misunderstood. Spir himself, although on many points he had clearly recognized the action of the principle of identity in science, and had deduced from it atomism and the principles of conservation, insisted, on the other hand, upon the fact that only the order of phenomena, and not any real object or any plurality of objects, remains immutable in the world, and that scientific explanation will have reached its highest aim in the determination of laws.(30)

People have sometimes feigned to see in the atomism of contemporary science a kind of historical accident; this is assuredly an error, atomism has its root in the depth of our spirit. It is certain that the agreements which we discover between these theories and the results of experiment fortify the hold they have upon us; but our faith does not rest exclusively on this agreement, it is prior to it. If this is not recognized, we must deny all analogy between modern atomic theories and those of the ancients, for what facts could the Jainas or Democritus allege? But this analogy is, on the contrary, flagrant. One may even ask, taking everything into consideration, whether our faith can be stronger than that of the ancients. For we see difficulties and contradictions of which they were ignorant. According to Lucretius, hard bodies, such as the diamond or rock, contain interlaced atoms; those of liquids are round, whereas smoke and flame are composed of pointed, but not curved atoms. Milk and honey have round and polished atoms; those of absinthe are, on the contrary, hooked. In the same way pleasant images are transmitted by polished atoms and disagreeable ones by atoms of great roughness.(31) Still in the seventeenth and eighteenth centuries physicists and chemists advanced mechanical theories which appear to us stupefying in their boldness. Lémery believed that acids are composed of pointed particles;(32) Boyle, that the particles of the air are small springs;(33) Boerhaave compares the different organs of the human body to pumps, springs, and sieves.(34) We are, alas, far from being able to give explanations that are as simple and clear; and we are also sometimes forced to note disagreements. Indeed, the agreement between the rational and the real cannot be complete. However surprising it may be to state that, with the help of the "statistical" method, irreversible phenomena are in a certain measure explainable by mechanism (another example of those agreements just mentioned), this statement has not the importance which we are tempted to attribute to it. Indeed, even if the explanation were complete, it would not satisfy us. For mechanism has no explicative power of its own; it gains all it has from the fact that it is a causal formula which is founded on identity. Now we cannot (of this there is no doubt) completely satisfy our causal tendency, our need of identity, for what it postulates in the last analysis is the annihilation of the phenomenon.

Moreover, if the agreement were complete, if nature were, indeed, entirely explicable, intelligible, it ought to be capable of being constructed *a priori*. For the term *intelligible* can mean nothing else than reducible to purely rational elements. This would not imply, need we say, the impossibility of progress in the knowledge of nature. Humanity has waited centuries for the revelation of certain properties of the circle and of the ellipse which we know were, nevertheless, implicitly contained in the definition of these curves, since we can deduce them from it by syllogisms and with the help of a small number of postulates and of axioms recognized as valid at all times. But for the circle and ellipse we use no experiments. Of what avail would they be since it is a question of purely rational deduction? That it was possible to proceed in the same way in regard to nature, to arrive at a knowledge of it through pure deduction, was thought, certainly, by many great minds. Probably many of the ancient atomists were of this opinion. Descartes also seems to have believed it. He demands openly an absolute certainty for the principles stated by him, and guarantees to deduce all nature from them. No doubt his powerful scientific instinct suggested to him that it was not possible to dispense completely with experiments. And so he has given them a small place in his system; but he has introduced them there by a sort of illogicalness. He affirms that in approaching reality one will find that, from principles laid down by him, many consequences result; and the experiment will decide which of these consequences will be realized.(35) But if the principles and deductions must be entirely rational, one does not see how, from syllogism to syllogism, everything is not connected in an absolutely unique, rigorous manner, leaving no room for choice, and consequently for experiment. After Descartes, Spinoza, starting from the Cartesian principles and proceeding with that pitiless logic and that "metaphysical rapture" which was the characteristic of that prodigious mind, states this formula, the most absolute expression of the postulate of intelligibility: "The order and the connection of ideas are the same as the order and the connection of things";(36) he proves this proposition by using an "axiom" which compares effect to necessary, logical consequence. But Spinoza, who knew mathematics, was not a physicist and wisely abstained from applying this principle to science. Leibniz, we have seen, was strongly convinced that everything in the physical world must take place *mechanice*. He believed also in the absolute domination of sufficient reason, and the formula in which he states this opinion and which we cited (p. 28) is at bottom that of Spinoza; but, being of a more comprehensive and less absolute genius than the latter, he affirms, on the other hand, that there are contingent truths which demand an infinite analysis, and that for that reason God alone can know them to be necessary.(37)

In the nineteenth century Hegel, though proclaiming by a sort of illogicalness that metaphysics must follow experience and not precede it, comes back, nevertheless, to Spinoza's postulate as far as intelligibility is concerned and tries to deduce really *a priori* the entire system of the productive ideas of nature;(38) and it is well known that Taine openly proclaimed himself to be his disciple at least in so far as the postulate of intelligibility is concerned.

From the point of view of science, what have been the results of the efforts of deduction, attempted by so many and

such powerful minds? Let us put aside the principles of kinetic
theories which we have seen must be attributed to a deduction;
there remains only that kind of presentiment for the principles
of conservation of which we have spoken and which seems
indeed to have led, since the time of antiquity, to the affirmation
of the conservation of the weight of matter. But every attempt
at the total deduction of nature has remained lamentably
vain. The work of Descartes constitutes, no doubt, the most
prodigious effort humanity has attempted in that line of
thought. Before this colossal, cyclopic construction we are
imbued with an almost religious respect. But, alas, this
palace is an irretrievable ruin. Who believes to-day in Cartesian
vortices, in the three elementary matters, in channelled parts—
all things for which he claimed "a more than moral certitude"?
Doubtless, some partial deductions of Descartes, the principle
of inertia and that of the conservation of motion, must be
counted (although the expression of the second was erroneous)
amongst the highest conquests of science; but they belong
precisely to the outline that we have traced above. Leibniz
abstained from all general deductive construction, even while
applying his principle of the equality of cause and effect, with
a marvellous scientific instinct, where it became necessary, to
the discovery and demonstration of the principle of the conservation of *vis viva*. The impotence of pure deduction stands
out also in Kant's work. Kant, we shall presently see, did
not believe in the entire intelligibility of nature and applied
himself to the task of tracing a limit between what in science
is derived from deduction and what is due to experience.
Yet he was led to ascribe too much power to the first. His
formulæ are in agreement with the science of his times and
with the consequences which such a vigorous mind could
draw from them. Thus he deduces gravitation proportional
to the mass and inversely proportional to the square of the
distance as a part of the essential concept of matter, but the
same deduction leads him to establish a repulsion inversely
proportional to the cube of the distance.(39) But doubtless the
work of the German metaphysicians of the period immediately
following offers the best demonstration of the sterility of *a priori*
speculations in science. Nothing is more instructive in this
respect (to choose only a few very striking examples) than

Schelling's deductions on the evaporation and condensation of water (40) and on the ellipse as a trajectory of the heavenly bodies;(41) Hegel's deductions on reflection and polarization,(42) on the nature of light,(43) on the retardation of the oscillations of the pendulum on the equator (44), on the carbonic acid which potash "produces in the air to be afterward saturated with it,"(45) or on the necessity of a void in the planetary system between Mars and Jupiter,(46) a necessity shown at the very moment when Piazzi discovered the first minor planet, Ceres. But the metaphysicians have not been the only ones to attempt deductions, scientists themselves have sometimes believed that they could reason about abstract principles, and they, too, have made serious mistakes. Fouillée (47) has brought some of these to light, the authors of which are seen to be such distinguished men of science as Prévost and Dumas, J. Müller, Magendie, Pasteur.

This defeat of the deductive effort does not surprise us. We know that reason proceeds only from identity to identity; it cannot, therefore, draw from itself the diversity of nature. "Blind metaphysical necessity, which is certainly the same always and everywhere, could produce no variety of things," says Newton.(48) Contrary to Spinoza's postulate, the order of nature cannot be entirely conformable to that of thought. If it were, there would be complete identity in time and space —that is to say, nature would not exist. In other words, the very existence of nature is a decisive proof that it cannot be entirely intelligible.

The principle of identity is the vastest hypothesis we can formulate, since it applies to the whole of the sensible world; but its action, as an hypothesis, resembles that of no other. Indeed, in forming any other hypothesis we can at least have the illusion that it will apply to all the phenomena which it has undertaken to explain. But here we know in advance that we are condemned to fail, and fail, not only in what concerns the entire domain of facts belonging to that hypothesis, which is in this case the universe, but in the explanation of each particular fact. No phenomenon, even the most insignificant, is completely explainable. We may try in vain to "reduce" the phenomenon to others, to substitute for it more and more simple ones; each reduction is a rent in identity, at each one we leave a shred of it, and finally there remain on each side of our explanation these two enigmas, which, however, are only two aspects of a single one—sensation and transitive action. In order to explain this double enigma which constitutes apparently the very essence of nature, we ought to understand efficient causality, the "communication of substances"; but we know that it is inaccessible to our understanding, "irrational." The opposite has been affirmed: this is because it was confused with scientific causality, which is quite another thing, which is identity, and which constitutes, on the contrary, the essence of our understanding. Some have tried, on the other hand, to exclude even this scientific causality from the domain of science—that is, the same mistake has been made in the opposite direction, scientific causality was identified with efficient causality. The first mistake was that of Descartes and Spinoza; the second that of Berkeley and Comte. The first believed in universal intelligibility, whereas the latter, limiting science to law, affirmed by it that intelligibility ought in no way to intervene in science, or, in other words, that nothing was intelligible.

The true way was shown by Kant: there, is indeed, agreement between our understanding and reality, but this agreement is partial, since in the end we run against contradictions which we call antinomies. Reality is partially intelligible, and our scientific knowledge is mixed with *a priori* elements and with others that are *a posteriori*.

But, when it is a question of separating these elements from each other, a task Kant undertook in two admirable works, *Metaphysische Anfangsgründe der Naturwissenschaft* and *Vom Uebergange von den metaphysischen Anfangsgründen der Naturwissenschaft zur Physik*, we can no longer follow the great philosopher to the very end. We have already mentioned some of the results he obtained. They clearly show that in general he assigned too large a part to deduction. Thus, in speaking of the conservation of matter, he says: "From general metaphysics this principle is borrowed and taken as a basis: that in all changes of nature no substance is lost or created. Here we do nothing but show what is substance in matter."(49) This, indeed, as we have seen, is the real foundation of the statement. But, for Kant, the last part of his proposition is equally *a priori;* the concept of matter, he believes, includes not only that of mass, but also that of weight, just as the concept of motion includes that of uniform and rectilinear motion—that is, inertia.

Kant thinks that science admits of a *pure* part—that is, a part purely rational, and which consequently is entirely *a priori*. This part includes not only what, since the time of Ampère, has been called kinematics (and which corresponds to what Kant designated as *phoronomy*), but also a part of mechanics. Now, this is not so. There exists no pure mechanics nor even pure kinematics. Our kinematics of to-day presupposes the principle of inertia, including the composition of motion. For of what use would it be to compound rectilinear "segments," as has been proposed,(50) if it were not understood that bodies move in a straight line and that motions are combined in that manner? Let us suppose that we are dealing with celestial bodies and let us try to adopt for them the theory which was still that of Copernicus, the theory of "natural" motion in a circle. Evidently we shall no longer find our *a priori* kinematics. If we desire to make a purely rational science of kinematics, without any recourse to experiment, our only resource is to present it as hypothetical. On that condition it can be deduced quite rigorously, and all that need be done afterward is to show that these results agree with experience. But such was not Kant's idea.

Kant's merit in this field is none the less important. It was in following his steps that Whewell succeeded in specifying correctly the manner in which we ought to represent the rôle of deduction and empiricism in certain declarations of science: "It is a *Paradox* that experience should lead us to truths confessedly universal and apparently necessary, such as the Laws of Motion are. The *Solution* of this paradox is that these laws are interpretations of the axioms of causation. The axioms are universally and necessarily true, but the right interpretation of the terms which they involve is learnt by experience. Our Idea of Cause supplies the *Form;* experience, the *Matter*, of these Laws."(51) In another passage Whewell, after having expounded the same theory, insists that "without this teaching (of experience) the laws of motion could never have been distinctly known."(52) Although he has expressed himself sometimes in rather a contradictory fashion (53) and has not applied this method to the conservation of weight (which he considered, as we have already indicated, as entirely *a priori*, because he thought, as did Kant, that the concept of weight was included in that of substance) (54), one cannot apparently deny Whewell the merit of having been the first clearly to indicate the peculiar nature of the statements which are deducible from the principle of identity. His thesis has often been revived, with the necessary corrections. (55) This solution, however, has not attracted all the attention it merits. Even doubts on the subject of the origin of the principles of conservation persist. Poincaré certainly expresses the general opinion of contemporary scientists when, wishing to show why the principle of the conservation of energy "occupies a sort of privileged place"—that is, why we attribute to it a value surpassing its experimental foundations—he looks for "the little reasons" of this apparent anomaly. (56) Helm, too, with regard to the constancy of energy, declares that all considerations based on the principle of causality must be banished from science and confined to metaphysics. (57)

As has been shown, we believe that the fact that the principles of conservation constitute a class of peculiar propositions derived from the principle of causality, is of capital importance, since it appears to us as being of a nature to throw an important light on the manner in which science and even our entire knowledge of the external world are constituted. And so we have done our utmost to base this conception of principles upon a study of their history and a logical analysis of their content.

Thus what is really *a priori* in science is in the first place the series of postulates which we need for empirical science—that is, in order to be able to formulate this proposition: nature is ordered and we can know its course. Nevertheless, this rigorously empirical science is an artificial creation, and *science* is not exclusively empirical; it is also the application to nature, in successive phases, of the principle of identity, the essence of our understanding. But from this principle we can draw no precise proposition by deduction; this is why there can be no *pure* science, contrary to what Kant supposed. In trying to explain phenomena we attempt to make them comply with what this principle postulates, and that is why its intervention in science shows itself as a tendency, the causal tendency.

We see that nature shows itself in a great measure to be *plastic*, according to the expression of William James;(58) it submits to this tendency of our reason. We know also that in going to the extremity we shall arrive at an insuperable barrier. But within this limit nothing permits us to indicate in advance where and how we shall be able to apply this principle and to give satisfaction to our causal tendency. In other words, if we know where the analogy between the order of ideas and that of things, to use Spinoza's language, no longer exists, no *a priori* reasoning permits us to indicate where it exists. Whether it is a question of explaining phenomena by mechanism, of finding formulæ of conservation, of eliminating time, or of reducing matter to ether, everywhere we can only proceed by studying reality, by observing, by experimenting, and by trying to adapt our reasonings to the results of these observations and of these experiments. Every proposition which is causal, explicative—that is, having in view reduction to identity —finds our understanding marvellously ready to accept it; every proposition of this kind appears plausible: but it is this preparation which constitutes the sole *a priori* element of these propositions, all the rest is empirical. And although he entirely misunderstood, or rather expressly denied, the importance in science of the non-empirical elements, the fact of having eloquently proclaimed the necessity of experimental research at an epoch when deduction alone was in favour is Bacon's imperishable merit.

The manner in which our understanding proceeds in applying the principle of identity explains why it is subject to errors in this matter. Principles of conservation have been formulated which science has had to abandon completely later on, or again it was necessary to transform greatly their tenor, to modify the expression of what is conserved. In the course of our investigations we have come upon examples of both. Black's principle of the conservation of heat belongs to the first category; this proposition appears to us now as manifestly erroneous, and, what is more, as contradicted by facts of common experience, such as the production of heat by friction. Black's principle, however, was for a long time considered as firmly established and as one of the most solid bases of physics. Descartes' principle of the conservation of motion is

an example of the second category. Descartes had the feeling
that in the communication of motion something must be
conserved. Of course, we see now that even under this indeterminate form the proposition is already far from being
purely *a priori*, for the faculty which a body in motion possesses
of transmitting this motion is a fact, and a fact impossible to
prove by deduction since it is unintelligible. But deduction in
this domain is so little able to lead us to the goal that, seeking
for what is conserved, Descartes went astray, and his error was
shared by his contemporaries.

Other examples may be cited. In the beginning of the
seventeenth century Quercetanus (Du Chêne) assumed that
with the ashes of a plant one could reproduce the plant in
solution, or at least its essential form. This meant affirming
to a certain extent the persistence of the specificity of the
plant after combustion. The theory, designated under the
name of *palingenesis*, although based on observations obviously
erroneous, had immediately many partisans and for a long
time held its own in spite of the refutations of Van Helmont
and Kunckel.(59) In the eighteenth century the hypothesis of
the preformation of germs, formulated, it seems, by Leibniz,(60)
but given its definite form by Haller, enjoyed great prestige.
At first sight one might be tempted to treat as a simple
scientific curiosity a theory according to which in the beginning,
at creation, individuals carried in individualized form in themselves the germs of all those who were to be their descendants in
the course of centuries. But observers who are well informed
tell us that elements of this doctrine are found even in the
most modern conceptions of embryology, and, moreover, that
the hypothesis of Haller, as well as later theories, is derived
from this same state of mind—that is, from the desire we feel
to substitute epigenesis for genesis; in other words, to treat the
becoming as an appearance hiding a real identity in time.(61)

Approaching our times, about 1872, Preyer, a physiologist
of renown, formulated a principle which he called "the law
of the constancy of organic life," a principle which caused
many lively discussions, but which was finally almost unanimously rejected, because it was too contrary to facts.(62)
Manifestly, therefore, the causal tendency, the avidity with
which our mind seizes upon everything which has the

appearance of a proposition of identity, may lead us into error, and there may arise on that side a certain danger, albeit a slight one, and one which the control exercised by experience is sufficient to correct.

From the theoretical considerations which precede, is it possible to draw any indications concerning the methods science ought to follow? It seems to us that, on the whole, our results end in confirming the processes which scientists have applied more or less consciously up to the present time; and this is but natural, seeing that our special desire has been to extract rules from these very processes. We believe that we have shown that the methods of science hold together better than is generally supposed and that their basis is not that usually attributed to them; and in this way we have come to understand better the necessity of certain developments. Thus atomic theories must be maintained in science. Certainly the treatises of mathematical physics are full of them at the present time. But at times one detects a sort of discomfort in the authors; feeling that their spatial representations end in contradictions, they excuse themselves for using them. Van't Hoff, for example, one of the authors of the theory of the asymmetric atom of carbon, seems to regret that one is obliged to use the molecular conception, upon whose hypothetical character he lays stress. This necessity, however, appears provisional to him.(63) Maxwell, who has done so much for the development of mechanical conceptions, whose principal work —his treatise on electricity—is, as Poincaré states,(64) dominated by the desire to show in each particular case the possibility of mechanical explanations, and who has at least partially succeeded in introducing them into the domain of Carnot's principle, which until then seemed closed to them, Maxwell himself sometimes yields to this tendency. In his communication to the Mathematical and Physical Section of the British Association, before giving a brief and brilliant exposition of the kinetic theory of gases, he warns his hearers that this is only a metaphor, an illustration, and is only useful as such. There are men who can get along without this help, and Maxwell admits implicitly that this is a mark of superiority; but the majority have need of it, and science must satisfy both.(65) Duhem, who has so clearly recognized the essential character of the theories (cf.

Chapter XI, p. 367), declares also that the use of mechanical
theories is a question of personal convenience.(66) These
reservations seem unjustified. No doubt, it is possible, by
completely neglecting the natural development of science, to
give to certain of its parts the appearance of pure empiricism.
Attempts of this kind will always be interesting, as is everything
which proceeds logically from a single point of view. Such
an exposition will also have the additional advantage of
making us see clearly the results that have been reached. But
it involves inconveniences also.

The principle of inertia, we have seen, can be proved experimentally; the entire branch of mechanics depending upon it
can consequently be treated, conformably to the programme
of Kirchhoff, as a "descriptive science." But for the conservation of energy we have found experimental demonstrations to
be insufficient; if, therefore, one makes these proofs its basis,
starting from the work of Joule and neglecting all prior
developments, not only is a heresy committed from an historical
point of view,(67) but one runs the risk of completely perverting
the signification and import of the principle. Moreover,
expounded without hypotheses, the experimental results appear
to us as something definite, finished, without our having seen
the way which has led us to them, nor the way which can
lead us farther; for science is not Baconian, and experiment
alone, without the help of hypothesis, cannot lead far. That
is why the image of science or of a part of science, offered us
thus, will be in a sense static. Whereas as a matter of fact
science is in perpetual flux, is dynamic.

We have seen (p. 20 f.) that Comte believed that certain
laws possessed this character of definiteness, which led him to
veto any research capable of modifying them; and it is clear
that this conception would have been impossible except for
his horror of all explanatory theory.

Without wishing consequently to proscribe the attempts of
which we have been speaking, especially in the exposition of
chapters of science in a very advanced phase of evolution, we
believe that the scientist ought, every time that the development
demands it, to use to a great extent kinetic considerations. It is
certain that from the point of view even of the strictest experimental science, we have an interest in following causal deduc-

tions to the end, even though they are the most abstract in appearance. Boltzmann, in stating the speculations of which we have spoken concerning Carnot's principle, has very rightly insisted upon this fact, that they ought not to be considered as unimportant, for they may suggest experiments about the limits of the divisibility of matter, the size of the spheres of action, etc.

The scientist in building up his hypotheses ought not even to be too much afraid of ultimate contradictions. The agreement between the causal image and the phenomenon, between thought and nature, cannot be complete; but there is a real and profound analogy. Every mechanical theory of a series of phenomena constitutes an immense scientific advance; it will lead surely to discoveries, for it contains a revelation of the essence of these phenomena. However perfect in many respects Fresnel's theory was, it would certainly have been wrong to take literally the affirmation of the existence of the luminiferous ether endowed with the contradictory properties we know. But that there was similarity, more than that, an identity of properties between light and the mode of spatial motion called undulation, that was certain, and this truth has remained even when Fresnel's conceptions have given place to those of Maxwell. Now these undulations could only be conceived of in a medium; it was, therefore, wise to accept the luminiferous ether in spite of its irreconcilable properties.(68) One must be resigned to these contradictions which result from the limitations of our understanding. Doubtless, one should try to reduce them to a minimum and a great progress will have been made every time an agreement has been found in the theory of two distinct parts of science. But no theory, however perfect it may be, will ever be logical or intelligible to the very end. Scientists have been very much concerned with certain fundamental problems of mechanism. Must the elementary particles be considered as infinitely elastic or as infinitely hard? Leibniz and Huygens have earnestly discussed this question. In the same way we have seen that an explanation has been sought for the elasticity of atoms by motions of all kinds. Finally, there have been great discussions on the question whether we ought to consider the atom as a corpuscle or as a centre of forces. This research and these discussions have been very useful; there would evidently be an advantage in definitely putting aside action at a distance, which is too repugnant to our understanding. By reducing all transitive action to a single type, we should have, in the first place, a minimum of the irrational, which is always satisfactory from a theoretical point of view; and besides, this hypothesis would without doubt be truer—that is, would present a greater analogy with reality, and would better than any other enable us to discover more relations between phenomena. This would be a real advance and would have its immediate repercussion even on the part of science devoted solely to law: it is probable that our calculations would be simplified by it, for it is less complicated to suppose that a particle is only influenced by what is contiguous to it than to admit that it is directly under the influence of the entire universe. An eminent theorist has shown in this respect that Maxwell's equations, which are based upon the exclusion of action at a distance, are only a particular case, a simplification, of those of Helmholtz, where such action, on the contrary, is postulated;(69) and another scientist, while declaring that he would consider the corpuscular and dynamic conceptions as equivalent, confesses nevertheless to have been surprised by the simplicity and elegance of certain formulæ of Hertz.(70)

As to the ultimate end which these theories have in view, an end essentially unattainable, it lies in the explanation of phenomena by an element differentiated to the least possible extent from space, or, if you will, it lies in the reduction of matter to space. From this point of view science can never turn aside from the path traced for it by perhaps the most powerful mind humanity can boast of—Descartes. (Descartes' mistake was in believing that deductions could produce anything but hypothetical constructions.) Never will any theory whatsoever be simply true. We saw that the superiority of corpuscular mechanism over dynamism resides in the fact that it corresponds more nearly to a postulate relative to space; and that the virtue, the "explicative force," of mechanism in general comes solely from the causal principle—that is, from the fact that the persistence of something is stipulated—and not from the fact that the thing of which the conservation is postulated, the dynamic or corpuscular atom, can ever be rendered comprehensible, its essential function, transitive action, being fundamentally inaccessible to our intelligence. The end of the reduction can only be irrational. It may very well be that in this respect electric theories, which presuppose an action from place to place, the mechanical nature of which is not determined, constitute the best solution. But while waiting for that solution to be firmly established and universally accepted, scientists are right in using in their theories, without too many scruples, both corpuscles and actions at a distance, neglecting momentarily the contradictions in which they end.

So scientists are wise in not wrangling too much over the unconscious "deceits" of the theories we have noted, such as the theory which considers the ether both as identical and differentiated (p. 251). These are simple consequences of the causal instinct which ends in the causal illusion, and they are justified by the partial agreement between our thought and reality. As Duhem has said: "No teaching of physics can (and we add *ever* could) be given under a form which leaves nothing to be desired from a logical point of view."(71) In the same line of thought one must not be too surprised if physicists are led to use, side by side, two or even several contradictory theories or incongruous mechanical models, as Maxwell has done amongst others. No doubt, this is rather inconvenient; a theory well regulated and logical would be infinitely preferable, because, being *truer*, it would have much more chance of rendering us service. Duhem is right, therefore, in protesting against the abuse of these procedures;(72) but perhaps too much rigour in this matter is not advisable. In a science like that of electricity, which is in a state of rapid development, somewhat irregular procedures of this kind may render great service. And it must also be added that since common sense can here be of no direct help to us (lacking as we do for electricity the organ of immediate sensation), material images, whatever they be, are often indispensable to uphold our wavering imagination.

Yet, in using atomic theories, it would be wise for the scientist to see clearly the nature of these conceptions, and the nature of the *a priori* elements which they conceal. He will then understand better that their basis is immutable, because they rest upon what constitutes the foundations of the human mind. Very great scientists at times have been turned aside from the right path on this point. Thus Boltzmann admitted that there might be a question of changing atoms.(73) There would have been nothing to say against this hypothesis if this physicist had conceived the atoms (or what supposedly were such) as composed of smaller particles which remained immutable. But, according to all appearances, he wished to speak of ultimate particles of matter, and hence his supposition is inadmissible. Atoms which should simply change in time (nothing else could be imagined) would change without cause; they could not, therefore, explain anything—that is, they would lose their reason for being, and being only creatures of reason they would cease to exist. Nor must we ever lose sight of the fact that we do not know where the analogy between mechanism, or, better still, between the causal conception of the world and nature ceases. The only thing of which we are sure is that it must cease somewhere. If, then, we come upon a phenomenon which does not seem to conform to this conception, we doubtless have the right to try every way of making it conform; but we are not permitted to throw it aside, or reject it, if it appears unruly. It may be precisely that the future has many ideas of this kind in store for us. After having sought a long time for what especially persists, science, since the importance of Carnot's principle has been clearly recognized, is turning its attention more and more toward that which is modified, toward perpetual flux, and it is clear that on this ground causal considerations will always be more or less at fault.

Within these limits we would say with Ostwald (74) that the identity of thought and being postulated by Spinoza, Schelling, and Hegel, remains the programme of science, a programme toward the realization of which its efforts tend. This tendency shows itself through the influence of the causal considerations of which mechanical theories constitute a particular expression.

It is permissible, therefore, to state that science really tends toward the reduction of all phenomena to a universal mechanism or atomism, defining these terms so as to include electrical theories, and remembering that the causality of being, so near a relative of the causality of becoming, demands that the elementary particles be made of a single matter possessing only a minimum of qualities, in such a way that it may be, to a certain extent, identified with space or its hypostasis, ether. Not that this reduction is really possible, nor that we can believe that this atomism constitutes the essence of things, nor that it is capable of offering a system free from contradiction—but because it is, amongst all the images which our intellect is capable of conceiving, the only one, which, satisfying at least to a certain degree our tendency in the direction of identity, offers at the same time real and sometimes surprising agreements with phenomena. It is, therefore, in following up this image, in rendering it more and more adequate to the facts, that we have the greatest chance of knowing these latter better. In other words, reduction to mechanism and atomism is not in itself an end but a means. It is a rule which guides the progress of science, as Lange has shown.(75)

It cannot be said that science approaches indefinitely reduction to mechanism, if by this last term is meant a logical, coherent hypothesis, free from contradictions. Science only accomplishes finite progress, and all the mechanical hypotheses which it forms being contradictory in themselves—that is, absurd at bottom—it always remains separated by an infinite distance from that logical conception toward which it seems to tend.

It is as a guide, as the directing principle, that mechanism has rendered invaluable services to science and—the past being a sure guarantee for the future—will doubtless render still more. Adopting it frankly as such, we shall have, moreover, the advantage of ridding theoretical science of certain phantoms (as Bacon would say) which haunt it, such as the "tendency to unity" or the "tendency to simplicity." In a certain sense the tendency to unity exists, since our understanding, denying all diversity in time and space, tends to reduce finally the totality of phenomena to an indistinct whole. But this tendency is not an independent principle and it is not at all mysterious. It is a direct consequence of the principle of identity. In regard to simplicity we must make distinctions. Science surely tends to simplify acquired knowledge—that is, to summarize it by formulating more and more general laws and theories; this is a consequence of the principle of the economy of effort, which is the source of empirical science. But it is not true to say that as science advances our conception of a real phenomenon gains in simplicity; for if science often discovers the simple beneath the complex, at other times, as Poincaré shows, it is, on the contrary, the complex which science discovers beneath the appearances of simplicity. Thus the simplicity of Newton's law might very well be only apparent. "Who knows whether it is not due to some mechanism, to the impact of some subtile matter . . . and whether it did not become simple only through the play of averages and large numbers."(76) And if of two formulæ, of two theoretical solutions, we ought always, the merits being equal, to adopt the simplest, it is not correct that of two eventualities the one which corresponds to the simplest theory must be realized. It was simple to suppose that the planets turn around the sun in circles, and since Copernicus had at his disposal only crude observations, he acted logically in adopting this hypothesis. An ellipse is, as a matter of fact, a more complicated line than a circle, and the fact that the sun is in one of its foci, the other remaining empty, shocks our sense of symmetry at first; but this did not prevent Kepler, in his turn, from being right in not hesitating in this case. In the same way the laws of Mariotte and Gay-Lussac on the volume of gases are very simple; does this prove that they are correct—that is, that they are laws really followed by nature itself? In the present state of science the question is no longer even asked; we know very well that no gas exactly follows the laws of which we are speaking, and in stating them or in applying them we are extremely careful to specify that we are dealing with an entirely hypothetical thing which we designate as "perfect gas." We saw, however, that the question presented itself to Comte (cf. p. 20 f.), and that he settled it in the opposite sense. Milhaud, in a remarkable analysis, has shown that the source of Comte's inspiration was a real dogma, and he has disclosed its foundations.(77) They are quite foreign to the philosophy of the physical sciences, having their origin in a sociological conception. Comte was extremely preoccupied with the idea of order; he had placed it at the very centre of his system. Having put aside theological traditions, he could establish order only on the basis of experience. Experience, therefore, must needs set up definite principles and laws, which should remain immovable for all time.

Law, such as science really understands it, is an ideal construction, an image transformed by our understanding of the ordering of nature; it cannot, therefore, directly express reality or be truly adequate to it. It did not exist before we had formulated it, and it will no longer exist when we shall have merged it in a wider law. To suppose that an empirical rule conceived by us will no longer be modifiable in the future is to affirm, on the contrary, that that rule exists objectively in nature itself; for no one could pretend that in the knowledge of rules we shall ever be able to pass definite limits, since there is no possibility of tracing these limits, or even of conceiving their existence. In this respect, it is asserted that nature is in agreement with thought. The latter, in formulating laws, must allow itself to be guided by considerations of simplicity. Thus, in the last instance, we attribute these same considerations to nature. Let us observe, moreover, that every definition of simplicity can only be relative to the faculties of our mind, to the means it has at its disposal and to its habits. As Le Roy has shown,(78) the sine function which enters, for instance, into the law of refraction appears simple to us, because we are accustomed to use it, and we even possess tables for it; but if we were obliged to express it under a purely arithmetical form, by a polynomial, it would be very complicated. To-morrow, perhaps, we shall discover a new process for the mathematical calculus which will make the problems now embarrassing us seem simple. We have here most evidently an accidental element which it seems difficult to attribute to nature. Moreover, we never really do so. When an astronomer, laboriously, by successive approximations, calculates the "perturbations" which the planets cause one another, he has not the least doubt that nature solves this same problem instantaneously with an absolute exactitude and without any difficulty. As Fresnel has said: "Nature is not embarrassed by difficulties of analysis."(79) This is why Poincaré believes that nature "has too often given the lie" to those who proclaim that it loves simplicity,(80) and why Duhem also comes to the conclusion that simplicity, "so ardently sought for, is an unattainable chimera."(81)

Let us add, as Poincaré indicated in the passage quoted a little before, that even where nature may appear to us as simple, this may be purely an appearance. This simplicity may easily cover a real diversity of very numerous facts; it would then be *statistical*. When we watch from some distance the movement of a crowd emerging from a gateway, we discover without difficulty that the phenomenon has an entirely regular aspect; yet each one of the individuals which compose it is making very different movements. In the same way the regularity of births and deaths in important aggregates covers a group of facts peculiar to each individual.

Upon this same postulate of the simplicity of nature is based a fundamental objection which is sometimes brought against atomism, and to which notably Stallo seems to give much importance.(82) In formulating the kinetic theory of gases, one evidently seeks to explain that state of matter by the solid state, or, if you will, by the ultra-solid (p. 71 f.). Now it is easy to be convinced, that everywhere and always—whether it is a question of purely physical phenomena, such as the change of volume as a function of the pressure and the temperature, diffusion, specific heat, or even of chemical reactions (the law of Gay-Lussac)—the laws which regulate the gaseous state are simpler than the laws applicable to the solid state of matter. Therefore, it is concluded, "if there be a typical and primary state of matter, it is not the solid, but the gaseous," and consequently "the gaseous form is the true basis for the explanation of the solid form, and not, conversely, the solid for the explanation of the gas."(83)

This objection, in the light of what we have just established, appears to us as purely specious. It presupposes that the simpler phenomenon must be, by that very fact, more fundamental. Now, we have just seen, simplicity here may only be *statistical*, and as the number of molecules in one cubic centimetre of gas is incomparably larger than the number of human individuals in any aggregate of which we know, or the existence of which we can even suppose in the future, and as the regularity of phenomena evidently increases as a function of this number, it is not astonishing that the laws which gases obey are much more regular than those of human statistics.

So also it is certain that if we do not adopt mechanism as a guide our analogical reasoning will wander, so to speak, without a compass on the limitless ocean of possibilities. This is clearly seen in the strange hypotheses of the *Natur-Philosophen*, and it is this which has rendered their reasonings so sterile.

And yet one cannot pass too absolute a judgment. The analogies between nature and our understanding are many and profound. A vigorous mind may, therefore, by simple analogical reasoning arrive at important scientific discoveries. Indeed, there is no doubt but that many great discoveries are due to reasonings of this kind.(84) It is not, therefore, astonishing that Oersted, starting from the doctrines of "the philosophy of nature," discovered electro-magnetism; and it may very well be that the relations formulated by Ostwald, which seem at present to be rather numerical combinations, may bring us to generalizations of great value.

It may, however, be predicted apparently without too great a risk of error that the theories and the hypotheses which will be at the basis of this kind of reasoning will be ephemeral. Only the foundation of mechanism, the explanation of phenomena by motion, is and will be really eternal.

As long as humanity attempts to develop science, mechanism will continue to be developed with it. The return to peripateticism, extolled with such force and learning by Duhem,(85) appears impossible to us. Indeed, it does not seem to us that the pure doctrine of Aristotle was a truly scientific doctrine. It became so, as in the case of the alchemists, only by deviation from it. Nor do we believe that the recent developments of theoretical physics and chemistry, as, for instance, in the work of Gibbs, constitute really an advance in the direction of Aristotelian physics. The analogies are thin and superficial. The similarity established between change of state and motions is probably the only real one; and even on this point the resemblance is perhaps more in the expressions than in the conceptions of the two doctrines. When we are told that the modern theory contemplates change "in itself," as Aristotle did, it seems to us that at bottom the analogy holds especially of a kind of negative fact, namely that neither regards atoms as intervening, the intrusion of which, being the expression of a strict causality, ends in re-establishing identity, that is in denying change itself. But modern theories of change pretend in no way to penetrate to the bottom of it; they are not explicative, as Aristotle's conceptions were believed to be. Duhem himself recognizes this difference. It follows that these theories do not exclude mechanism as an explanation. Gibbs himself used mechanistic conceptions, and no one pretends that the most recent development of physics, which, we have seen, seems entirely directed toward atomism, has entered into conflict at any point whatsoever with his theories.(86) The two kinds of conception seem to live together peacefully.— But as to the process itself of analogical reasoning, it must be clearly understood that it is still more indestructible, if that is possible, than mechanism, for by it alone can we approach reality. Whatever we do we are always obliged to suppose—at least momentarily—that nature proceeds, as does our reasoning. The error of Descartes and the *Natur-Philosophen*, as also of Comte, consisted solely in using analogy, not to formulate assumptions to verify, but for apodictic affirmations.

It is only just, however, to point out that something of this spirit subsists in our present physics. When we assign a peculiar place to the principles of conservation, and when in general we attribute to every proposition emanating from the principle of identity an importance surpassing its experimental basis, we evidently assume in nature a tendency analogous to that of our mind. Are we wrong? We have already replied to that question; the analogy between our intelligence and nature cannot be denied. Moreover, it seems evident that the fundamental opinions of humanity have not varied much in that respect. Anaxagoras, and before him Hermotimus, Aristotle tells us, "proclaimed that it is intelligence which, in nature as well as in animate beings, is the cause of order and regularity everywhere in the world."(87) But we are forced to go farther than these ancient philosophers, since beyond order we again perceive the plasticity of nature with respect to the causal principle. Unless we suppose, as did Spir, that there is in this agreement an "organized deception,"(88) planned in advance, we are indeed forced to assume this analogy and to admit a partial harmony.

Should we wonder at it? Doubtless, if we oppose the world of consciousness to that of the noumenon. But it must not be forgotten that this, on the whole, is only a metaphysical theory; that it is we who have created the conception of the noumenon, and that we created it in order that it may act. If it remains without action it vanishes immediately, just like the gods of Epicurus, or the ether of physicists when we deprive it of mass.

We therefore postulate action at the same time as the concept, and consequently also the analogy. If, therefore, in this dualistic concept, the analogy appears as a miracle, it is a miracle of the same order as sensation.

But this conception is not the only one. It is equally allowable for me to consider my ego as a part of the great whole or to judge, on the contrary, that the entire world is only my sensation.

> Are not the mountains, waves and skies a part
> Of me and of my soul, as I of them?

says Byron in verses Schopenhauer loved to cite.(89) If we adopt a conception of this kind, wonder disappears, or rather the difficulty will then consist in understanding how it happens that the analogy is not more complete, that there remain unknowable, transcendent elements.

Here again we are on the ground of metaphysics proper. We cannot, indeed, evade a reply to this question: Are the results at which theoretical science has arrived of a nature to determine our choice between the different systems which metaphysics offers us? To this question von Hartmann, in a remarkable book,(90) appears to give an affirmative answer. He states that science, with the help of experience and of observation, and starting from common-sense notions, arrives finally at substituting for them an entirely different conception, mechanism. But, on the other hand, science, though destroying the reality of common sense, maintains time and space. It culminates, therefore, in a noumenon subject to the conditions of time and of space—that is, in a determined, metaphysical system, called "transcendental realism."

In the light of the results at which we have arrived we cannot evidently recognize this conclusion as valid. Let us state in the first place that, contrary to what Hartmann seems to suppose, mechanism in its turn is not an end; it is only a stage, just like common sense, a somewhat artificial resting-place upon a road which does not admit of such. We have put aside the greater part of sensible qualities, declaring them, with Democritus, conventional; we only wish to retain what is strictly necessary to define a body. It is here that the difficulty arises. What can we logically retain? According to the reply which we give to this question, the form of the mechanical system which we adopt will vary; but in scrutinizing things profoundly we shall soon come to the conviction that we can retain no sensible quality, the atom cannot even "harbour" its impenetrability, which is manifestly an "occult quality," and the body vanishes into space, which has for a logical corollary the disappearance of space itself and of time. Consequently, in applying the reasoning of Hartmann, one would conclude that science leads us not to his "transcendental realism," but to idealism, or, if you wish, to the most absolutely negative dogmatism, since its formula would be: Nothing exists or can exist. But we know that mechanism is not a *result* of science. Science confirms it to a certain extent, just as experience of ordinary life seems to confirm the naïve realism of common sense; it is invariably the agreement between reason and reality, evidently a partial agreement. But mechanism is itself prior to science, or, at least, coeval with it. The fact that theoretical science, constructed with the aid of mechanism, conserves the notions of time and space is not at all enigmatic. It is like those numerical games made for the amusement of children, who marvel at finding their initial number after a whole series of complicated operations. Finally, as a last argument against Hartmann's reasoning, it cannot even be said that mechanism really conserves intact the concepts of space and time. For we have seen that mechanical theories notably suppose time to be reversible, which assuredly clears the way for its elimination, and enables us to see once more that mechanism is only a stage.

And yet does not the very process of this elimination suggest to us that there might be something justified in the argument in question? Indeed, if our understanding postulates elimination, reality resists it, and its resistance is shown by Carnot's principle (p. 286). We therefore have but to change the point of departure of the reasoning and substitute Carnot's principle for mechanism: does not the generality of this formula prove that reality cannot be conceived independently of time? No doubt, in a certain measure. What we see clearly, indeed, in this is that we cannot exclude conditions of time in the consideration of a phenomenon. But we knew that from the beginning; we knew that every external phenomenon was inconceivable for us outside of the conditions of time and space. Carnot's principle simply expresses this truth in a clearer way. Science, on this point also, teaches us nothing about the noumenon; it only states precisely that there is a partial agreement between our intelligence and the external world. One may start from the fact of this agreement to arrive at the existence of the external world, as Leibniz (91) did amongst others; but one may also use, as do idealistic philosophers, the fact that this agreement is only partial, that there is also disagreement, to prove the impossibility of the same external world. One may finally, like Kant, attempt a conciliation by supposing that the agreement is due to intuitive elements indissolubly mixed with our sensation. These are matters which are the exclusive property of metaphysics.

A study of the history of philosophy readily assures us of this truth. If the solutions which the moderns have proposed for these problems differ from those formulated in antiquity or during the Middle Ages, it is rather in form than in substance, and it seems that the progress of the physical sciences can only definitely influence this form of the solution. The agreement and the disagreement of which we are speaking are manifest with the advent of common sense. Our sensations really present themselves in groups, and render possible the constitution of a world of persistent objects (p. 363); but as soon as we seek to penetrate a little more deeply into the nature of things, we see this world dissolve (p. 364 f.). Shall we say that this second evolution already belongs to science? No doubt, but we have seen that, from this point of view, there is an absolute continuity between science and common sense. As a matter of fact, atomism belongs to the dawn of human thought; common sense, science, and metaphysics are, so to speak, blended in it.

Science in progressing does not abolish atomism; on the contrary, it develops it and renders it more precise. But at the same time it posits the antagonistic conception in Carnot's principle. In other words, its tendency is toward both the abolition of reality and its affirmation. In it the two opposite philosophical tendencies exist together peacefully. Therefore, from the metaphysical point of view one can draw from it no conclusion going beyond Hermotimus' statement as properly modified.

We may remark that we are here repeating, in slightly different terms, a proposition which we have already expressed. In fact, since theory is in search of a reality behind that of the world of common sense, the affirmation: "no theory will ever be simply true" (p. 408) amounts to this: "one cannot consider the entity created by a theory as a thing in itself." A very different meaning, however, is sometimes attributed to statements of this kind. By declaring that hypotheses could not be transformed into realities, that in their nature they were neither true nor false, that they were unverifiable in their essence—propositions perfectly correct if applied to the totality of our assumptions about the external world—one has sought to affirm a fundamental difference between the world of theory and that of common sense. Now the difference, we have seen, does not exist from this point of view; and if by the term *reality* we understand not that of the thing in itself, but that of the sensible object, as common sense conceives it, the proposition becomes certainly incorrect. In the first place, from the historical point of view it is easy to show that some theories must have passed into common sense. Sound certainly did not appear to our far-off ancestors as a vibration; but men have learned a long time since to see and to feel these vibrations under certain conditions, and it cannot, it would seem, be contested that, for a large part of humanity at present, the concept of these vibrations is a part of sound considered as a real object. The transformation which the sun, the moon, the sky have undergone considered as objects is of the same order. Moreover, from a philosophical point of view, we saw that as soon as we admit of the intervention of memory in our perception, we are, in fact, forced to admit also that of our *knowledge*, which leads us equally to affirm the evolution of common sense. Thus it is possible that what was an hypothesis, an assumption, agrees so well, in the consequences that we draw from it, with our sensations, that a connection, an association more and more intimate becomes established, and that finally the latter is instantaneously and automatically called forth by the former. At that moment the hypothesis will be a part of the reality of common sense; it will become, in Le Roy's terminology, a brute fact. But from the logical point of view, little will be changed; brute facts being at bottom only causal hypotheses, just like scientific facts and theories.

The elaboration of scientific hypotheses is the continuation of the process which creates the realities of common sense; but the work being conscious, their authority is thereby lessened. We feel that between the hypotheses and the facts there are the laws; these latter, while not expected, like hypotheses, to penetrate into the secret of nature's work, appear to us because of this as nearer to the facts themselves. So when the law, stipulating the conservation of a concept, seems to create a veritable object, almost a thing in itself,(92) this rule exercises upon our mind the double authority of laws and hypotheses. This is evidently only a slightly different form of the explanation which we gave before (p. 215), but perhaps it will seem more direct under this new aspect. It seems also to point out more clearly the peculiar nature of the propositions in question, the reason why, in spite of what we have learned about the rôle of causality in science, about its incessant intervention at the moment of the latter's genesis, they constitute, nevertheless, quite evidently a well-defined class, that of *plausible* statements. This is because in this case the influence of the causal tendency attains its culminating point, shows itself in the very heart of the domain which appears to belong to pure law alone; the statement appears to be deducible directly from the causal principle and yet it is susceptible of being treated as an experimental law.

To a less degree, because less immediately derived from the causal principle, all those laws which are susceptible of a mechanical or spatial interpretation, like those which regulate the radiation of heat or like Newton's law, partake of this authority. Poincaré, speaking of the law of attraction, attributes a particular dignity to the constant 2, which is there in the quality of exponent; he declares it *essential*, whereas the greater part of the others would only be *accidental*. It seems to us that no other foundation can be found for this distinction than the fact that in the first case there exists a possible spatial interpretation.

In the light of the results obtained in our work, we now propose to return to the point of departure and once again attack the important problem with which we dealt at the beginning, namely, that of the relation between the two principles of conformity to law and causality. We there established that the second could not be deduced from the first, and what we have since learned can only confirm this conclusion. The principle of conformity to law, indeed, dominates all science; as science stretches out its domain, that of conformity to law increases, since the limits of both coincide. This is not so with the principle of scientific causality, which is a form of the principle of identity. In postulating the intelligibility of nature it ends in its complete destruction.

We have just stated, however, that nature lends itself also to the exigencies of the causal principle, that there is harmony there, partial it is true, but real just the same. May it not be that these two propositions are in reality but one? That entire obedience to pure law and partial obedience to causality are at bottom one and the same thing, or at least are involved in each other? To state the problem in a slightly different form, may not the very fact of the existence of rules have as its corollary that certain concepts, certain expressions, must remain constant? Many thinkers seem to have admitted, more or less explicitly, that one must reply in the affirmative to that question, and this is again, we believe, one of the sources of the confusion between the two principles of conformity to law and causality. Assuredly this confusion is impossible if the principle of causality is taken in its strict sense; it, indeed, postulates the conservation of everything, whereas conformity to law implies change. But not for a single instant can we apply causality with that rigour. Nature exists, and this fact alone suffices to keep us from doing so. Therefore, even while pretending to make a profession of faith in favour of the causal principle, we also make a kind of mental reservation; it will be applicable not totally but partially. Hence the confusion spoken of becomes possible.

It is doubtless somewhat in this way that Lucretius reasoned. After having solemnly proclaimed that "nothing comes from nothing," and that "nothing can be resolved into nothing"— which is the principle of causality in its most absolute form— he adds also that this rule is necessary in order that "trees may always bear the same fruit." Does he mean to affirm that these fruits are always there? Not at all; he knows very well that they ripen and perish. What he postulates is that something in them—the germs, the atoms—persists; so that as soon as he stated the principle, he tacitly renounced applying it with all its force. But, on the other hand, the partial application seemed indispensable to him in safe-guarding order in nature—that is, as we have just indicated, that the absolute rule of conformity to law involves the partial rule of causality.

This thesis has found but few to contradict it. Newton plainly adopted it in adding to it a very remarkable sort of demonstration to which we shall return later. Kant seems to have shared this way of looking at things.(93) Hartmann considers, as demonstrated, that the lawfulness of phenomena can only be observed if the latter have immutable substances as substrata.(94) Contemporary thinkers seem also to be of the same opinion. "It is clear," says Milhaud, "that if the world is governed by law, there will be quantities which will remain constant."(95) Kozlowski adopts almost textually the declaration of Lucretius; after having pointed out that the persistence of matter is "a postulate of purely rational origin," he adds: "It is a *conditio sine qua non* of regularity in the phenomenal world. In a world where *everything might give birth to everything*, no regularity, no prevision, and consequently no science would be possible."(96)

In other cases a somewhat subjective form is given to this thesis (which evidently modifies its content). Thus Bergson believes that "stable visions about the instability of reality" are forced upon us by our concern for the practical knowledge of reality—in other words, that to be able to formulate rules permitting us to act, we are forced to suppose the conservation of certain concepts. And it may be said that an analogous affirmation forms logically, in a certain sense, one of the corner-stones of the system of the Marburg school. We know, indeed, that these philosophers, whose work constitutes an incomparable whole, profess that the concept of mathematical function is the foundation of our reason; the concept of substance is subordinated to it, and its rôle to science and in philosophy would in a way be limited to preparing for the accession, the penetration of the first; identity would only be an instrument of knowledge.(97) Consequently, just as Bergson says, understanding would create the constant in its concern to seize the variable.

Let us examine, first of all, the thesis under its objectivistic form. In order to refute this opinion easily, we must be able to show that conformity to law could reign alone—that is, that we can imagine a universe (not ours, of course) which would be so ordered as to suggest the idea of rule to an intelligence contemplating it, but from which, nevertheless, everything which might suggest the idea of a persistence, of an identity of things in time, would be absent. It would seem to be enough to formulate clearly this proposition, to perceive how difficult is its demonstration. It is, indeed, a question of reasoning *in abstracto* upon the nature and properties of the universe. Now, since the universe includes everything, terms of comparison are lacking. Can one even say that it exists? can one affirm that it has properties? This only has sense if I oppose it to the ego. In reasoning about these properties, I shall necessarily be led to compare the universe with what is only a part of it; who knows, then, whether my conclusions will not be infected with error? We know but one universe. It *alone is*, and is what it is. Such as it is, it admits at the same time the application of the principle of conformity to law and that of causality. The two in it are indissolubly linked. How separate them?

Happily the analysis we have just made concerning the action of the principle of causality in science will permit us to descend from the heights of the most quintessential abstraction, where we are led infallibly by considerations upon universes, possible or impossible to conceive of, into regions enjoying a slightly less rarefied atmosphere. Let us, then, take up one by one the different manifestations of the causal principle in science.

We have, in the first place, the atomic theory. It was of this, we have just seen, that Lucretius thought. Sixteen centuries afterward, Newton, with more insistence, developed the same thought. After having summarized, with a few strokes of great precision what constitutes the eternal foundation of corpuscular atomism, he writes: "God in the Beginning form'd Matter in solid, massy, hard, impenetrable, moveable Particles, . . . and these primitive Particles being Solids, are incomparably harder than any porous Bodies compounded of them; even so very hard as never to wear or break in pieces. . . . While the

Particles continue entire, they may compose Bodies of one and the same Nature and Texture in all Ages. But should they wear away, or break in pieces, the Nature of Things depending on them would be changed. Water and Earth composed of old worn Particles and Fragments of Particles would not be the same Nature and Texture now, with Water and Earth composed of entire Particles, in the Beginning. And, therefore, that Nature may be lasting, the Changes of corporeal Things are to be placed only in the various Separations and new Associations and Motions of these permanent Particles."(98) In other words, the fact that bodies at all times obey the same laws shows that they are composed of imperishable particles: this is exactly what Lucretius said.

What is the import of this reasoning? At first sight one has the illusion that it tends to establish a real logical bond between the qualities of objects and the nature of the particles of which they are composed; but it is not so. If Newton had been asked what was the size and the form of the particles of water or earth (he was thinking, doubtless, of Aristotelian elements), and how one could deduce from them the qualities of these bodies, he would have certainly declined to reply. And if Lucretius had been more affirmative about the atoms with which he meant to compose his trees and fruits, it is certain that his assumptions would not appear very conclusive to us; in fact, both relied on a statement that can be formulated in these terms: We cannot imagine qualities of bodies being derived from anything but those of the elementary particles which compose them.

Under this aspect the reasoning reveals its true nature to us. It is a causal reasoning, an hypothesis about the nature of external things, about the supposed causes of phenomena. Newton's exposition confirms it: far from attempting to deduce the atomic theory by this reasoning, Newton lays it down as a premise. Now the atomic theory is derived from the postulate: there is no change other than displacement. It is implicitly assumed, therefore, that what is displaced must remain without change; if it is a material atom, it must, of course, be eternal. Hence there is no difficulty in deducing as a consequence that which was contained in the premises. The persistence of laws really plays no rôle in this deduction;

it is a pure superfluity, and the entire reasoning constitutes simply one more proof of the difficulty we have in limiting ourselves to the phenomenon, in abstaining from all causal reasoning, this reasoning being the foundation of our intellect. This is so true that after all there remains a sort of doubt: Is not something else there? Does there not exist between law and causality a more profound bond which has escaped our analysis?

Let us try to probe more deeply this reasoning of Lucretius and Newton. We are in a much better position to discuss this matter than the contemporaries of either of them. Where these, speaking of the composition of bodies, could reason only upon vague conjectures, we can use the infinitely more precise concepts of contemporary chemistry. Now a glance is enough to show that similarity of properties does not necessarily involve similarity of substances. Cæsium bromide and potassium iodide are two bodies resembling each other from many points of view, and yet we must suppose, according to prevalent theories, (99) that they have nothing in common as substances— that not a single atom of the first body is identical with an atom of the second. Yet these are very simple combinations, the simplest we know. As we pass to more complex bodies, like those which belong to the subject of organic chemistry, we see the nature of the component atom influence the qualities of the compound less and less. When, in a slightly complicated organic molecule, we replace an atom of hydrogen by an atom of chlorine, its properties are scarcely modified, even though chlorine and hydrogen are elements endowed with extremely different qualities. The modification is still less marked if we put in the place of this atom of hydrogen a group composed of carbon and of hydrogen, as CH_3, or in place of the chlorine the group NO_2; in both cases, however, the thing substituted and the substitute differ greatly. Contrari-wise, the same atoms, being differently grouped, may constitute unities manifesting properties as distinct as possible. The elements themselves, in what is called their "allotropic modifica-tions," furnish convincing examples of this: oxygen and ozone, charcoal and diamond, yellow phosphorus and red phosphorus, are doubtless very different bodies; yet we are obliged to suppose that the matter has remained the same and that its grouping alone has changed. This is, perhaps, still more evident if we examine combinations, especially those of organic chemistry. At the very origin of that science, Woehler's celebrated synthesis gave a striking example of this; it is hard to imagine two bodies more different than cyanate of ammonium and urea. Let us suppose a slightly complicated organic molecule, say (to be definite), of rosanaline hydrochloride, which is, we know, the colouring matter known under the name of fuchsine. The atoms which compose this body may, especially if we are not satisfied with simple isomerism, and consent to divide the molecule, constitute bodies which will be acids, bases, alcohols, aldehydes, acetones, etc. In fact, since all organic bodies have about the same elementary composition, when we place in a cup a piece of chalk, water, and nitrate of soda, we can with its contents reproduce almost all of them, and when we add to them a little sulphur and phosphorus, we may obtain the substances which compose the human brain. Evidently the peculiar character, the *quid proprium*, of these substances appears to us as much less conditioned by the elements of which they are composed than by their grouping.

If we mount still higher, to organized beings, to the "trees and fruits" of Lucretius, we shall, no doubt, be obliged to leave somewhat the solid domain of facts: physiology is only at its beginning, and science can scarcely formulate the vaguest assumptions about the true nature of the chemical reactions which go on within animals and plants. Yet the few data it offers us are enough to indicate what the progress of scientific thought on this subject is. Here is a plant which has grown inland; it contains a certain quantity of potash salts, as we are easily assured by analysing its ashes. We carry it to the seashore, to a spot where the soil is poor in potash and rich in soda. At first the plant will suffer, but with appropriate care we shall succeed in making it grow again, and in analysing its ashes we observe that a notable part of the potash salts has been replaced by salts of soda. Doubtless, replacing the potash by the soda has not been absolutely without influence on the other properties, the plant differs a little even externally from what it was in the first place; but let us not forget that the *type* of the species is only an abstract concept. The individuals

which compose it—we are sure of this in advance, because of
"the principle of indiscernibles"—are really all different; the
problem is to know whether these divergences are sufficiently accentuated to oblige us to make a new classification.
They are not in the present case: botanists have not even
designated the plant thus transformed as a variety. We can,
therefore, say with Lucretius, that it is still the same plant and
that it bears the same fruits. Yet the change which we have
produced in its composition is considerable; we cannot for
an instant doubt that the potash and the soda play an important
rôle in its development, for if we do not give it the necessary
alkali it cannot live. We are, no doubt, much less advanced
on the question of the organic substances which the plant
contains; but since we know that they are of an extremely
complicated constitution, we can at least conceive (and that
alone concerns us for the moment) that if by some artifice
we succeed in replacing a substance playing a considerable
rôle in its economy by its superior homologue (that is, by a
substance having the same constitution, but where for an
atom of hydrogen would be substituted a CH_3 group), the
properties of the substance being but little modified, it would
play the same rôle—that is, it would still be *the same plant*.

This reasoning, valid for Lucretius, does not seem to be
entirely so for Newton; it is certain, indeed, that if we are
able with different materials to constitute unities that are
similar, we do not succeed in making them *identical*. However
complicated we imagine the organic substance, the substitution
for an atom of hydrogen of an atom of chlorine or of a group
CH_3 will provoke a change of properties which may be slightly
apparent, but which *ought*, nevertheless, to be clearly denoted;
that is because chemical bodies, according to prevalent theories,
due to the fixity of the elements and the law of multiple
proportions, appear to us absolutely defined species without
any transition. But do these assumptions correspond to reality?
It is perhaps possible to doubt it.

One easily discovers, in closely scrutinizing chemical phenomena, that theory confers upon them greater regularity than
they really possess. When I affirm that silver has such and
such a property, I know very well that if my statement is not
entirely crude, it will not be completely true for the immense

majority of pieces of this metal which fall under my hand and yet which constitute in their entirety the species "silver." What the chemist generally means by this name is what he more exactly designates by the term "pure silver." We have already spoken of the important work which Stas and those who have verified his data have been obliged to undertake to arrive at this substance; evidently whenever one wishes to verify the affirmations of those who have held the substance in their hands, one must have recourse to long and minute preparations. The atomic theory explains these difficulties by the immense number of atoms of silver contained in a gramme of this metal and the strong attraction which these atoms exercise upon others of a different sort (for instance, upon atoms of oxygen), whence it results that it must be extremely difficult to prepare a gramme of matter containing only silver. The explanation is plausible. But what one is trying to explain here is the fact that the silver which I encounter corresponds so little to the scheme which I have formed—that is to say, precisely the lack of identity in its properties; one cannot, therefore, use this pretended identity of properties to deduce from it the necessity of atomism.

Without wishing to return to Berthollet's ideas it may well be asked whether the enormous 'difficulties encountered by chemists in determining atomic weights, however approximately, do not come from the fact that these constants are not really immutable, but vary within certain limits. Crookes,(100) amongst others, seems to be of this opinion, which may well be illustrated by reference to the new theories on the constitution of matter. Let us suppose that the chemical atom is composed of a great number of particles (nearly a thousand, we are told) of sub-atoms. This would be a sort of molecule, but an infinitely more complex molecule than any of those we know. Consequently, according to what we know about this kind of construction, the nature of the sub-atom would only have a slight influence on the properties of the whole. If one of these sub-atoms were to be replaced by another, more or less analogous, the whole would still have properties entirely similar; the situation is the same as for the trees and fruits of Lucretius.

We know, moreover, that what is supposed to constitute these sub-atoms, these ions or electrons, to give them their true name, is nothing but the ether. The properties of the compound cannot, therefore, be derived from those of the component, since it is understood that this latter is single and self-identical throughout. Shall we say that it is at least the fixity of the properties of the ether which guarantees that of the atoms, of the molecules, and consequently the persistence of the laws? But the ether, we know, ought not to have properties, or rather it should only have negative ones, since it is nothing but an hypostasis of space. We thus come to this conclusion that the constancy of laws has no other guarantee than the fixity of the properties of space; under its paradoxical appearance this is a pure truism, since we know, by preliminary convention, that law is independent of displacement in space.

Moreover, we might have come to the same result by a road more rapid but perhaps less sure. Let us observe, indeed, that the ancient atomists, and very probably Newton, believed in the unity of matter. Therefore, they thought also that the properties of different bodies, if they had to be derived from those of atoms, could not be deduced from those of the matter of atoms, but from their shape. Thus, to choose a concrete example, Lémery attributes the particular qualities of acids to the fact that they contain "pointed parts."(101) Now, shape is a spatial function, so that the properties that are brought into play are those of space.

It is not, therefore, legitimate to suppose that the resemblance of properties must necessarily have its source in a fundamental identity of primary matter. This would mean returning to the scholastic conception, according to which there must be in every individual of the species dog a common principle of *dogness* or to the theory, prevalent before the time of Lavoisier, which supposed in metals a common principle of *metallicity*. It is certain that nature contains a great number of objects which resemble one another, and that we have the gift of noticing this resemblance, of generalizing, and of thus deducing rules. If we stop there, if we abstain from "explaining" them, from wishing to find the causes, we shall never arrive at atomic conceptions; if, however, we throw ourselves into this search we shall succeed more and more in attributing the properties of the compound to the qualities resulting from the manner of grouping, and not to the properties of the components which, on the contrary, we gradually strip of every quality;(102) the primary element which we seem to be pursuing always escapes us, and is finally dissolved into space: it is a procedure the legitimacy of which we have sufficiently established; it is in strict correlation with the tendency which guides us in these researches, since it flows directly from a principle, analogous to and the logical continuation of that of causality proper.

After atomic theories, the principles of conservation constitute the most important manifestation of causality in science. May it be supposed that there is an intimate bond between these statements and the reign of law?—in other words, does not the very fact that we can submit events to calculation demand that certain expressions remain constant? Milhaud seems to affirm this; but this thesis, far from being evident, appears to us to be very difficult to establish. It is rightly assumed that, in order to study a phenomenon, we are obliged to set it apart artificially from the great whole, to isolate it, to make it as "pure" as this may be done; we only follow as far as possible the variation of a single element at a time, while we suppose that, during this time, all others remain without change. But it does not follow that these elements, the constancy of which we momentarily suppose, are really immutable; on the contrary, we have a very distinct feeling that the "pure" phenomenon thus created is an abstraction, that the natural phenomenon is infinitely complex, and that when, in a short time, we pass to phenomena of a different kind, in the next chapter of science, what we laid down as constant will appear to us as variable, and vice versa. If in mechanics m appears constant, that only means that we are studying the motions of bodies, assuming that during the duration of the phenomena in which we are interested the mass will not vary, or what is the same thing, assuming that purely mechanical phenomena exist. We are not occupied with the thermal, electric, or chemical state of the bodies we are dealing with; we lay this down as invariable. But really we do not doubt for a single instant that the mechanical phenomenon is accompanied by thermal, electric, or chemical phenomena. It in no way follows that, when we study these phenomena in their turn, m must remain constant. Were it otherwise one could directly prove the conservation of mass by mechanics. Now from all evidence this demonstration is impossible; there is, indeed, a certain connection between the two ideas, but it works with the help of the postulate: Every phenomenon is mechanical. Hence every accessory phenomenon, every cause of trouble, disappearing by hypothesis, it is evident that the condition which we impose upon the mechanical phenomenon becomes general. In the seventeenth and eighteenth centuries, when mechanics was already well developed, no one evidently believed in the conservation of mass in chemical phenomena, and there was no contradiction in this; in the same way, if, to-morrow, Landolt's observations are confirmed and generalized our mechanics will remain intact. To summarize: if the existence of an order in nature must demand the constancy of certain terms, one ought to be able to deduce the principles of conservation from the very concept of this order. But we only have to refer to our analysis of the three principles: None has ever been or can be deduced *a priori*—all require experiment; therefore, if experiment had pointed clearly in the opposite direction, we should not have stated them; nature, however, we cannot doubt, would have continued to appear to us as ordered. Indeed, it so appeared to our ancestors; and humanity lived many centuries before conceiving these principles. Humanity, nevertheless, acted—that is, predicted, which could not be done without postulating conformity to law.

Finally, the causal principle creates in science the tendency to eliminate time, and, by its extension to space, flowing equally from the principle of identity, the tendency toward the unification of matter. But these are conceptions which have not the least connection with the principle of conformity to law. Law, while stipulating definite relations between antecedent and consequent, diversifies them clearly by that very fact, instead of confusing them: we here again find antagonism between the principle of conformity to law and the principle of causality in its integral sense—the elimination of time being, indeed, a very advanced form of this principle. This is still more true for the unification of matter and its ultimate end, the dissolution of matter in space; this complete disappearance of reality constitutes evidently the conception which is the most opposed to that of a real world governed by inexorable laws.

We are, therefore, led to conclude that from the very fact of the existence of law in nature one cannot deduce any of the consequences which we have attributed to the action of the principle of identity. The phenomenal world might appear to us as subject to laws, without anything outside of these laws persisting. As Cournot has said: "If it were proved that under the right circumstances bodies could be destroyed without anything remaining . . . the bodies on that account would not cease to show us the spectacle of linked and well-ordered phenomena."(103) Moreover, may it not be that "the constants," the existence of which we believe we establish, are only a more or less naïve appearance? Carnot's principle affirms a continued progress in time, and we may reasonably presume that the world is ruled solely by principles of this kind. Were we to suppose that evolution in certain cases was infinitely slow, that would give us a world of *real* constants, as our present principles of conservation admit. But we can also suppose it simply *very slow*, and hence our constants would only be approximate, evolving constantly in a determined direction.

Let us observe, however, that the results to which we have just come have only to do with science. If we were to try to push our investigations still farther and to attain identity as it shows itself in the conception of common sense, it is certain that we should come against an insurmountable barrier. Nor is it difficult to see the reason why. A world which would not suggest to me the concept of something persistent could not give birth in me to the concept of object; an object is created by us solely as a first sketch of an explanation of variable sensation, and perdurability is its essential quality (p. 359 f.). Thus such a world, in so far as it is real and objective, constitutes a contradiction and vanishes. If by the term *sensation* we designate anything but the "immediate datum" of Bergson, if we think of a sensation of an *object*—it is certain that causal deduction is an integral part of it and cannot be separated from it. But this is not true, we have seen, of scientific causal deductions, which have nothing to do with our immediate sensation (except, of course, in cases where they succeed in influencing the conception of common sense, p. 359 f.). It is precisely this circumstance which has permitted us to indulge in the preceding reasonings.

The world of which we can thus to a certain extent form an

image nearly resembles the world of Heraclitus (or rather the one commonly attributed to him, for it may be that really the great Ephesian was neither so very far from scepticism nor so attached to the conception of order, nor even so hostile to every concept of persistency).(104) It would be a world of apparent persistencies, permitting us to conceive it as exterior to us (or, if you prefer, forcing us to do so), but from which a somewhat more careful examination would immediately make every idea of persistence disappear. In such a world science would not be ontological, as is ours, but truly positivistic or idealistic, in the sense that it would encounter the acosmism of absolute idealism, immediately at the beginning, not at the end of its route. It would resemble ours in so far as it would dissolve the object of common sense, but it would differ from it in the fact that it would not accomplish this labour to the advantage of a new reality; that it would not put anything *objective* in the place of the *object*, neither atom, nor mass, nor force, nor energy, nor any hypostatized quality. This seems very difficult to accept wholesale, whatever the positivist theory may say. But on particular points, making use of our analysis, we can pursue the question farther. Thus what is called *force* is in the beginning from the conceptual point of view something very complex, since it is an hypostasis of acceleration, of relation between two velocities—velocity itself being a derived concept, composed with the help of the concepts of time and space. It is because the acceleration is constant in time that we succeed in hypostatizing it, in transforming it into a *thing*, and, on the other hand, we are distinctly aided by the fact that we can, up to a certain point, compare this hypostasis, force, with our sensation of effort (just as we are aided in the case of the atom by the fact that we can assimilate it to a solid body—that is, to an object of common sense). Consequently in order to prevent phenomena of this group from giving rise to the concept of a thing, it is necessary that the relation regarded as constant in time (which is the very essence of law) should not lend itself either to being simplified or to being assimilated, however remotely, to our immediate sensation or to the objects of common sense. This second condition is not indispensable, of this we have proof in energy and better still in the electron. But the first seems really essential in the sense that if the relation remains too complicated, our imagination seems powerless to transform it into *a thing*. We have proof of this in the concept of force. No doubt we are so accustomed to consider the laws of falling terrestrial bodies from the point of view of acceleration that we should have great difficulty in avoiding this manner of regarding them. But for celestial bodies, the discovery of laws in themselves very complicated, which govern their motions, and the simplification of these laws, their deduction with the aid of the composition of a velocity and an acceleration, have been separated we know by a long lapse of time. One might, therefore, imagine without apparently too much trouble that this Newtonian simplification was not at all possible, and that Kepler's laws remained ultimate; and it seems that henceforth in this chapter of science a new concept of thing could hardly have arisen.

Is there need to indicate how imperfect is this image to which we have come with so much difficulty? It would certainly be difficult to trace any limit as regards this simplicity. We need only think of energy, of the complicated abstract relation which it constitutes in reality, to be convinced that our intellect shows in this respect an extreme good will. And there is no doubt that this is an essential condition of its functioning. For we have made it sufficiently clear that the scientific intellect imperiously demands an ontological reality, and if science did not permit the creation of a new one, it would certainly be powerless to destroy the old one—that of common sense. The science which we are trying to find is, therefore, strictly unimaginable; because, our intellect being what it is, there is a contradiction between the data of the problem. Thus one can affirm the impossibility of a law-conforming world void of constant quantities. But the source of this impossibility does not lie in the fact that this world is conceived as law-conforming; this is implied in the term *world*, which designates something external to our consciousness, a unity which can only be composed of substances (as has been confirmed precisely by the examples of Lucretius and Newton). In other words, substantiality cannot be deduced from the existence of law. The persistence of the relation, implied in the very concept of law, is not enough to give rise to the concept of substance; there must be added the tendency, prior to common sense and creator of this latter, to see our sensations persist in time.

But, besides this, the analysis just made shows us once more that the world in which we live is not that of Heraclitus. Nature really offers us relations susceptible of being simplified, of being transformed into things; this is the agreement between nature and our intellect that we have observed (p. 395).

Let us notice again that this affirmation of the persistence of certain concepts is not the only one that we can formulate in respect to the universe. Indeed, side by side with the action of causality, and in opposition, if not to this action itself, at least to the fundamental ideas of our intellect whence this conception is derived, we have the intervention of Carnot's principle, which forces us to assume an inevitable advance of the world in one direction, always the same and without a possible return. Nor can this be deduced from the conception of a simple interdependence of phenomena, which evidently admits cessation, inverse motion, and cyclic return.

In summary and with the aid of mathematical language, since the concept of interdependence finds its most precise expression in that of mathematical function, we may say that the formula $Y = f(X)$ can doubtless be applied to all that happens, to all phenomena without exception (as far, of course, as they are conceived to be subject to science—that is, to law); but no one could pretend to make our present conception of the world, with all we believe we know about it, enter entirely into this formula, for we know that whatever may be the modification undergone by X and, consequently, by Y, certain terms on the two sides of the equation will remain invariable, and we know also that X, at bottom, is or contains the measure of time, the only true independent variable, which is subject to a continual increase. Thus X will never be able to resume its value, and it will be the same necessarily with Y. In other words, conceived as the image of the world, as *Weltbild*, according to the German expression, the formula $Y = f(X)$ is incomplete, because it is too lax.

Certain of the arguments just brought against Milhaud's contention obviously affect Bergson's thesis also. However, for the sake of greater certainty, let us try to determine more precisely the import of the reasoning under its subjective form. We have stated, in the course of our investigation, that causal suppositions facilitate the application of rules; with the advent of common sense it is clear that the hypothesis of discrete bodies, that first and naïve approximations to substance, was an integral part of all reasoning with a view to prevision; and as to science we saw that one can reasonably doubt even its possibility in a state where it would be totally stripped of every causal hypothesis. But may it not be possible, therefore, that it was this very necessity which created the concept of causality; that we create discrete objects solely *because* we can, in assuming their displacement, better foresee the future; and that we suppose a fundamental identity in what science calls at present the diverse forms of energy solely because that will permit us to foresee better the appearance of each one of them, and that the conception of the atom is due solely to the obscure but powerful conviction that we shall succeed by this means in establishing a mathematical bond between all phenomena?

Thus presented, this reasoning seems to have an unusual force. Yet if it were true that persistence was only an auxiliary construction permitting the establishment of a law of connection or of a functional relation (according to the terminology of the Marburg school), how does it happen that the prestige of the mechanical or atomic explanation, the explanation *per substantiam*, seems to take precedence over that of law or the purely functional relation to such an extent? These should be equivalent ways of comprehension, or rather, mathematical comprehension, being the veritable end, ought constantly and from the very beginning to take precedence over the other; whereas we have seen from the example of Newton's law of gravitation, a purely functional conception never remains in its purity, but, on the contrary, has an invincible tendency to engender an explicative or substantialistic theory. How explain that strange tendency to eliminate time if we pursue only knowledge of the variation, when time is manifestly the independent variable indicated by nature? And how much stranger is the reduction of the phenomenal world to space, to nothing, a reduction which (as we think we have proved) withdraws all substratum from mathematical dependence.

In the principles of conservation, in which the search for constancy and the establishment of a functional dependence seem to come in contact with each other, we saw that they cannot be deduced from one another. Examining Milhaud's thesis, we found that the conservation of mass cannot be deduced from mechanics; we may say here that it is hardly likely that, in laying down this conservation, the intellect has made an effort, even unconsciously, to construct mechanics.

Moreover, if atomism has really value for the understanding only in proportion to its mathematical content, would not a bond be necessary, if not manifest, at least powerful and essential, always and everywhere, between the two? Now it is the contrary which certainly has taken place in history. There seems to be but little mathematics in Hindoo atomism; there is none in the atomism of Democritus. Doubtless, Democritus was preceded by Pythagoras, and it is allowable consequently to establish a connection between the two conceptions; but atomism, Aristotle assures us, took its origin from the conception of Parmenides, from the theory of persistence, and not from that of an arithmetical constitution of the universe. It cannot even be said that atomism and quantitative conceptions are terms necessarily connected, for we have seen that qualitative atomic theories have existed. Finally, it is incontestable that humanity, during long centuries, has explained and understood by the aid of quality; this is further attested by certain elements, the persistence of which in science has been prolonged for ages, and it is surely very difficult to force conceptions of this sort into the plan of a mathematical idealism.

May it not be, however, that our intellect, having recognized from the very beginning, from the birth of common sense, the services which the assumption of persistence renders, from the point of view of the perception of functional dependence of phenomena, has transformed this hypothesis into a principle to the point of making of it an almost independent statement? Let us remark at once that this theory, in its application to science, is very near to our own. As soon as it could be proved by evidence that our reason, by a kind of impulse capable of surpassing its end, is preoccupied with persistence even where its application surpasses the need of the establishment of mathematical relations, the action of this tendency would evidently have to be sought for in science and its effect carefully noted, whatever be the idea, which might be formed of the genesis of the tendency in question. But it is sufficient, we think, to envisage the consequences of the theory to perceive its enormous difficulties. To prove that common sense is not profoundly ontological is doubtless not a task to frighten the ingenuity of a philosopher, given our ignorance of the real ways of our understanding and the plasticity of our reason, but science and its history are more refractory. Is it possible to admit that the impulse, supposing it capable of leading reason to continue its functioning after its goal has been reached, will succeed also in driving away reason from its goal to the extent of bringing about the elimination of time and the assimilation of matter to space? And as for qualitative theories, they would constitute thus an enigma for which evidently a particular explanation must be sought.

Thus in order to refute these theories we have only had to renew each time, the direction being somewhat modified, the course of the demonstration which is the foundation of our work. The reader has doubtless found in the preceding pages an inclination at times toward tiresome repetition. It is an inconvenience that our method could scarcely avoid, but, on the other hand, the conviction perhaps has been acquired that this method, preached but not practised by Auguste Comte, and consisting in penetrating the functioning of thought by analysing its action in science, presents some advantages over that, more immediate in appearance, which pretends to proceed by direct introspection.

Finally, there remains one last hypothesis to consider, that in which the principle of conformity to law would be deduced from the principle of identity, would be a sort of abridged edition of it, a short cut. We saw that we sometimes use the concept of law when really we are thinking of the cause. This is a synecdoche: we consider the establishment of law as a preliminary step toward that of the causal relation. Now the principle of causality is deduced from identity, the foundation of our reason; may it not be, therefore, that our belief in the order of nature comes from the fact that at bottom we believe that it is subject to identity?(105) This hypothesis, at first sight, seems difficult to accept. Identity, we know, appears to us as something desirable, but far off, as a flexible principle which adjusts itself to circumstances, admits of explanations, engenders illusions. Conformity to law, on the contrary, is rigid; it claims to govern all that is not subject to the free will of terrestrial or superterrestrial volition, it admits of no exception. How could the latter have been derived from the former, and that at the very dawn of human intelligence, since we saw that primitive man (not to speak of the animals) conceives without any doubt numerous phenomena, such as those of gravitation, as subject to law? Once again, this supposition seems hardly admissible, and yet one does not dare to affirm that it is inacceptable. Our individuality being for us the type of all unity, there is in us a sort of secret longing to believe in the unity of our intellect, a longing which is somewhat disturbed by the duality of the guiding principle, which we have admitted for our scientific thought. Let us, therefore, not exclude absolutely the idea of unification on this point. Let us insist rather on this fact, that, at least where contemporary man is concerned, in so far as he applies himself to the knowledge of reality, the two principles must be considered as functioning separately, although their action is unceasingly intermingled.

NOTES

1. E. LE ROY: *Science et Philosophie. Revue de métaphysique*, VII, 1899, p. 534.

2. MALEBRANCHE: *De la recherche de la vérité*. Paris, 1721, XIth *Eclaircissement*, Vol. IV, p. 277 and ff.

3. Cf. earlier, p. 252.

4. ERNST CASSIRER: *Das Erkenntnisproblem in der Philosophie und Wissenschaft der neuern Zeit*. Berlin, 1906–1907, Vol. II, p. 530. Cf. my article, *Revue de métaphysique*, January 1911, p. 122 and ff.

5. Cf. earlier, p. 253.

6. F. ROSENBERGER: *Isaak Newton*. Leipzig, 1895, pp. 173, 192. The same author points out the contradiction between the title *Philosophiae naturalis principia mathematica* and the content of the writing, which, in fact, constitutes only an exposition of the principles of *mechanics* (*ib.*, p. 172); but this is because Newton, like Descartes and like Leibniz, had the firm conviction that everything in physics should be reduced to mechanics.

7. Cf. on this subject, Appendix I, p. 452 and ff.

8. Cf. Chapter I, pp. 18, 39.

9. COMTE: *Cours de philosophie positive*, 4th ed. Paris, 1877, Vol. I, p. 18.

10. *Ib.*, Vol. II, p. 453.

11. COMTE: *Politique positive*, Vol. I, p. 531. The date at which he expresses this opinion (1851) only renders it the more curious.

12. *Cours*, Vol. II, p. 445.

13. *Ib.*, Vol. III, p. 152. He maintained this opinion in 1851, cf. *Politique positive*, Vol. I, p. 528: "Six irreducible branches" of physics, "perhaps seven." It is at least probable that other errors of Comte are connected, a little less directly, with the same tendency; such as his opinion on Lamarck's theory of the variability of species which he characterizes as an "irrational hypothesis" (*Pol. pos.* Vol. I, p. 665); his enthusiasm for the mediocre conceptions of Gall (*Cours*, Vol. II, pp. 513, 534–587), an enthusiasm which, even to the end of his life, he only partially got over (cf. *Pol. pos.*, Vol. I, p. 669 and ff.); his hostility toward organic chemistry, which appeared to him "a heterogeneous and factitious assemblage," which must be "destroyed" (*Cours*, III, p. 174) and against which he renewed his attacks even in 1851 (*Pol. pos.*, Vol. I, p. 550), more than twenty years after Woehler's synthesis (1828), after the discovery of compound ammonia by Wurtz (1849), and on the very eve of the appearance of Gerhardt's theory of types (1853); finally his misunderstanding of the development of general chemistry, on which he wished to impose a peculiar theory of binary composition (*Cours*, III, p. 81 and ff.; VI, p. 614), a theory which was probably only a clumsy generalization of Berzelius's conceptions, which the chemists about that time were gradually abandoning; with the result that Comte, noticing the small success of his theory, accused them of a "metaphysical spirit" (*Pol. pos.*, Vol. I, p. 551).

14. BACON: *Novum Organon*, Book I, Aph. 61. It is very curious to observe that, just like Comte and evidently for analogous reasons, Bacon was strangely mistaken in his judgment about the great conquests of science. Thus he severely blamed Copernicus (*Glob. int.*, Cap. VI), and Gilbert, whose works on electricity are a veritable monument to the purest scientific thought, was his pet aversion (*Novum Org.*, I, § 54; II, Aph. 48). Naturally we in no wise mean to attribute to Comte, on this question, opinions analogous to those of Bacon. On the contrary, Comte constantly insisted upon the necessity of hypothesis; absolute empiricism, according to him, is "not only entirely sterile, but even radically impossible for our understanding" (*Cours*, Vol. VI, p. 471). He only protested against hypotheses characterized by him as "metaphysical." But this attitude, although less absolute than that of Bacon, was enough to lead him into erorrs of the same kind.

15. ROSENBERGER: *Geschichte*, II, p. 191, remarks on Bacon's little real influence on the progress of science. Boyle seems to have allowed himself to be tempted to apply, not, indeed, Bacon's schemes (that would probably have been impossible), but certain of his principles. Rosenberger thinks that this circumstance was the reason why, having in hand all the experimental data of Mariotte's law, it slipped from him in the end.

16. BERTHOLLET: *Essai de statique chimique*. Paris, 1803, p. 5.

17. *Encyclopaedia Britannica*, 9th ed., article *Davy*, p. 847.

18. LIEBIG: *Reden und Abhandlungen*. Leipzig. 1874, p. 249.

19. *Congrès international de physique*, Vol. I, p. 3.

20. DUHEM: *La théorie physique*, p. 300; cf. earlier, p. 368.

21. Id., *La théorie physique*, p. 308.

22. VAN'T HOFF has recalled, with just pride, that Emile Fischer, in his researches which ended in the synthesis of glucose, was guided by considerations of stereochemistry (*Revue générale des sciences*, V, 1894, p. 272). It is known that this theory was applied also to pentavalent nitrogen and quadrivalent tin and sulphur.

23. H. POINCARÉ: *La science et l'hypothèse*, p. 208.

24. Cf. DUHEM: *La théorie physique*, p. 43.

25. Cf. O. REYNOLDS: *Proceedings of the Royal Society*, Vol. XXVIII, February 6, 1879.

26. COURNOT: *Traité de l'enchaînement*. Paris, 1861, p. 157.

27. H. POINCARÉ: *La science et l'hypothèse*, p. 191.

28. BOLTZMANN: *Ueber die Unentbehrlichkeit der Atomistik, Wiedemann's Annalen*, Vol. LX, 1897, p. 243. Cf. also id., *Leçons sur la théorie des gaz*. Trans. GALOTTI and BENARD, 2nd Part. Paris, 1905, p. 8.

29. H. HERTZ: *Gesammelte Werke*. Leipzig, 1895, Vol. I, p. 1.

30. SPIR: *l.c.*, pp. 225, 271. It is probably because he believed that these deductions could be complete that there entered into them only *a priori* elements, that, the confirmation by experiment appearing useless to him, the agreement between this latter and our reason did not strike him.

31. LUCRETIUS: Book II, line 388 and ff.

32. DUHEM: *Le mixte*, p. 20. Cf. Kopp, *Geschichte*, Vol. III, p. 31.

33. *Ib.*, p. 28.

34. DASTRE: *La vie et la mort*, p. 32.

35. DESCARTES: *Discours de la méthode. Œuvres*, Vol. VI. Paris, 1902, p. 64 and ff.

36. SPINOZA: *Ethics*, 2nd Part, Prop. 7: "*Ordo et connexio idearum idem est ac ordo et connexio rerum.*" This was incontestably in Cartesian logic, but, of course, we do not mean to affirm that Spinoza had not drawn from other sources. Giordano Bruno had already said: "*Primo dunque voglio che notiate essere una e medesima scala per la quale la natura discende a la produzion de le cose e l'inteletto ascende a la cognizion di quelle*" (*De la causa*, ed. Wagner. Leipzig, 1890, p. 285).

37. LEIBNIZ: *De scientia universali. Opera*, ed. Erdmann, p. 83.

38. HEGEL: *Vorlesungen ueber die Naturphilosophie. Werke*. Berlin, 1842, Vol. VII, Preface by MICHELET, p. 15.

39. KANT: *Metaphysiche* Anfangsgründe, p. 54.

40. SCHELLING: *Werke*. Stuttgart, 1856, Vol. IV, p. 501.

41. *Ib.*, p. 271.

42. HEGEL: *Vorlesungen ueber die Naturphilosophie. Werke*. Berlin, 1842, Vol. VII, § 278.

43. *Ib.*, § 276.

44. *Ib.*, § 270.

45. *Ib.*, § 332.

46. Id., *De orbitis planetarum*. Iena, 1801. Piazzi's discovery dates from January 1st of the same year.

47. FOUILLÉE: *Le mouvement positiviste*. Paris, 1896, p. 19.

48. NEWTON: *Principia*, trans. Motte. New York, 1848, p. 506. The context makes clear that he is speaking of the diversity which rules everything "as to times and places."

49. KANT: *Metaphysiche Anfangsgründe*, p. 74.

50. Cf. CALINON: *Étude critique sur la mécanique*. Nancy, 1885, p. 12 and ff.

51. WHEWELL: *The Philosophy of the Inductive Sciences*. London, 1840, p. 28.

52. *Ib.*, p. 239.

53. Cf. for example, *ib.*, p. 213, where he appears to affirm that inertia could have been discovered independently of experiment, and p. 24 where the kinematics appears as entirely *a priori*.

54. Cf. earlier, p. 177.

55. Cf. earlier, p. 146 and ff.

56. H. POINCARÉ: *La science et l'hypothèse*. Paris, s.d., p. 157.

57. HELM: *Die Lehre von der Energie*. Leipzig, 1889, p. 41.

58. W. JAMES: "The Dilemma of Determinism." *The Will to Believe*. New York, 1877, p. 145.

59. Cf. KOPP: *Geschichte*, Vol. I, p. 111; Vol. II, p. 243 and ff.

60. Cf. COUTURAT: *Revue de métaphysique*, XI, 1903, p. 92.

61. Cf. LE DANTEC: *Les Neo-Darwiniens*. *Revue philosophique*, XLVIII, 1899. F. HOUSSAY: *Les théories atomiques en biologie*. *Congrès de philosophie de 1900*, Vol. III; and APPUHN: *La théorie de l'epigenèse*. *Congrès de philosophie de Genève*, 1904, *compte rendu de* COUTURAT *dans la Revue de métaphysique*, XII, 1904, p. 1059. Haller, moreover, had himself indicated as the foundation of his theory the principle: "There is no becoming." *Es gibt kein Werden* (ib.).

62. Cf. DASTRE. La vie et la mort, p. 245.

63. VAN'T HOFF: *Leçons de chimie physique*, trans. CORVISY, 1st Part. Paris, 1898, p. 9.

64. H. POINCARÉ: *Electricité et Optique*. Paris, 1901, p. IV–VIII. Cf. *La science et l'hypothèse*, p. 249.

65. MAXWELL: *Scientific Papers*, Vol. II, p. 219.

66. DUHEM: *L'évolution de la mécanique*, p. 186.

67. HELMHOLTZ (*Vortraege und Reden*. Brunswick, 1896, p. 407) insists particularly on the fact that the leading principles which had inspired him in his work of 1847 on the conservation of energy did not seem to him "new but, on the contrary, very old."

68. MACH, whose impartiality on this question can in no way be doubted, declares that if Young and Fresnel had abandoned the undulatory hypothesis (because of the difficulties experienced in imagining them in a fluid) the loss to science would have been as great as if Newton had abandoned the theory of gravitation (*Erkenntnis und Irrtum*. Leipzig, 1905, p. 251).

69. PLANCK: *Die Maxwell'sche Theorie*. *Wiedemann's Annalen*, 1899, Spl.

70. L. LANGE: *Das Inertialsystem*. *Philosophische Studien*, 1902, p. 55.

71. DUHEM: *La théorie physique*, p. 424.

72. *Ib.*, p. 145 and ff.

73. BOLTZMANN: *Wiedemann's Annalen*, Vol. LX, 1897, p. 240.

74. OSTWALD: *Vorlesungen*, p. 6.

75. LANGE: *Geschichte des Materialismus*, 4th ed. Iserlohn, 1882. Preface, HERMANN COHEN, p. ix.

76. H. POINCARÉ: *La science et l'hypothèse*, p. 176; cf. *Thermodynamique*, p. vii.

77. MILHAUD: *L'idée d'ordre chez Auguste Comte*. *Revue de métaphysique*, IX, 1901, p. 539. LÉVY-BRUHL, *La philosophie d'Auguste Comte*, 2nd ed. Paris, also remarks that in Comte "the scientific interest, however intense it may be, is subordinated to the social interest." Cf. *ib.*, pp. 5, 25. It seems, indeed, that this particular conviction of Comte's flows in no way from his conception of science, which would end rather by considering laws as the ephemeral expression of a momentary condition of the science of a period (cf. *Cours*, Vol. VI, pp. 600–601, 622, 630, 642), the restrictions (*ib.*, pp. 601, 623) appearing as something foreign to the very substance of the doctrine. It is true nevertheless, as we have already indicated (p. 398 f.), that the error could not have taken place if Comte had not proscribed all theoretical research.

78. E. LE ROY: *Un positivisme nouveau*. *Revue de métaphysique*, IX, 1901, p. 146.

79. A. FRESNEL: *Mémoire sur la diffraction de la lumière*. *Mémoires de l'Académie royale des sciences*, Years 1821–1822, Vol. V, p. 340.

80. H. POINCARÉ: *Thermodynamique*, p. vii.

81. DUHEM: *L'évolution de la mécanique*, p. 343.

82. STALLO: *l.c.*, p. 132 and ff.

83. *Ib.*, p. 134.

84. DUHEM: *La théorie physique*, p. 50 and ff. Duhem's thesis goes still farther: he wishes to establish that "search for explanations was not Ariadne's clew." The services rendered by mechanism seem to us, however, very difficult to deny.

85. It is but right to state, however, that Duhem toward the end of his life seems to have somewhat changed his opinion on this subject. Thus in his important book on the *Système du Monde* (Paris, 1913 and following years, Vol. I, pp. 194, 196, 240, 284), after having brought out that none of the notions of peripatetic mechanism "has the least analogy with the notion of mass" of modern physics, and that Aristotle's theory of motion is open to an objection which "ruins" it, he praises the University of Paris for having, in the fourteenth century, "begun to substitute a sensible dynamics for Aristotle's dynamics," and states that in the years to come "there will not rest one stone upon another" in the edifice erected by this latter. [Addition to the 3rd ed.]

86. BOLTZMANN: *Leçons sur la théorie des gaz*, 2nd Part. Paris 1905, p. 206, establishes "that Gibbs had continually on his mind this idea of molecular theory, even when he did not use equations of molecular mechanics."

87. ARISTOTLE: *Metaphysics*, Book I, Chap. III, § 28.

88. SPIR: *l.c.*, pp. 9, 18, 317.

89. BYRON: *Manfred;* cf. SCHOPENHAUER, *Die Welt als Wille und Vorstellung*, Vol. I, p. 213.

90. ED. VON HARTMANN: *Das Grundproblem der Erkenntnistheorie*. Leipzig, s.d., p. 21 and ff.

91. Cf. COUTURAT: *La logique de Leibniz*. Paris, F. Alcan, 1901, p. 258.

92. It is right to recall that Ostwald's system resulted in elevating energy to this dignity (p. 349 f.).

93. KANT: (*Kritik der reinen Vernunft*, ed. Rosenkranz und Schubert p. 157), declares that persistence of substance is "the substratum of the empirical representation of time itself, which renders alone possible all determination of time" (*an welchem alle Zeitbestimmung allein moeglich ist*). Therefore, in his opinion, without the persistence of substance, uni ormity of time and consequently all regularity of phenomena would disappear.

94. HARTMANN: *l.c.*, pp. 1, 9.

95. G. MILHAUD: *Science et hypothèse*. *Revue de métaphysique*. XI, 1903, p. 786.

96. KOZLOWSKI: *Sur la notion de combinaison chimique*. *Congrès de philosophie de 1900*, Vol. III, p. 536.

97. CASSIRER: *Substanzbegriff und Funktionsbegriff*. Berlin, 1910, p. 404. Cf. NATORP (*Die logischen Grundlagen der exakten Wissenschaften*. Leipzig, and Berlin, 1910, pp. 70–72): "*Liesse ueberhaupt nichts sich als konstant festhalten, so waere alle Moeglichkeit dahin, die Veraenderung selbst zur Bestimmung zu bringen. Unumgaenglich bleibt doch, irgendein Letztes zu supponiren, ein Letztes nicht an sich, sondern fuer die Rechnung, die uns die Natur wissenschaftlich darstellt.*"

98. NEWTON: *Opticks*, 3rd ed. London, 1721, p. 375. A very analogous development is found also in Lucretius, Book I, lines 552–565, 584–598. We cannot say whether Newton had often read the *De rerum natura*. But the reasoning of Lucretius is found reproduced in Gassendi, *Opera*, Lyon, 1658, Vol. I, p. 261, from which he might also have borrowed it.

99. Naturally setting aside for the moment recent developments of electric theories (cf. p. 97 and ff.).

100. W. CROOKES: *La genèse des elements*. *Revue scientifique*, 1887, p. 203.

101. Cf. p. 279. Lémery's contemporary, Sylvius (*De la Boë*) deduced, on the contrary, the properties of the acids from the fact that they contained "igneous matter." It is thus clearly seen that the procedure of mechanism, which consists in attributing properties resulting from the manner of grouping, is opposed to that of qualitative theories which place the property in the component.

102. "In a group, the matter does not interest us; it is the form alone which is important," said H. Poincaré while showing how the ancient mathematicians, considering forms of matter differing in appearance, suddenly found themselves united without knowing why: they had considered isomorphous groups (*Science et méthode*. Paris, 1908, p. 30). It is because he entirely misunderstood this "manner of grouping," which is a fundamental conception of explanatory science, that Hannequin (*Essai critique*, pp. 22(, 237) succeeds in affirming that science always carries over to the atom the qualities required by the whole which it constitutes—which is as much as to deny to the mechanical theory all possible utility and all possible sense.

103. Cournot: *Traité de l'enchaînement*. Paris, 1861, p. 156.

104. Cf. on this subject, Appendix IV.

105. It is thus that Spir conceives the relation between the two principles (*l.c.*, pp. 72, 211, 217), and it is doubtless because this deduction seems evident to him that he sometimes succeeds in confusing them.

APPENDICES

I

LEIBNIZ, NEWTON, AND ACTION AT A DISTANCE

As soon as Newton had discovered the law of universal gravitation, the question of action at a distance became inevitable, and was immediately discussed; it was the occasion for bitter and famous quarrels (see, for example, in the *Recueil de lettres entre Leibniz et Clarke, 1ᵉʳ écrit, § 1, et 5ᵉ écrit, § 114,* allusions which have an unfortunate air of appealing to the secular arm, but it is only just to note that Leibniz had been preceded in this path by the Newtonians, Cotes, in his famous preface to the *Principia,* having declared that the search for the causes of gravity was a sign of atheism).

It is strange, indeed, that doubts could have arisen about the true opinions of the protagonists. Was Newton really Newtonian, as the eighteenth century used to say? Did he not, on the contrary, disapprove at bottom of the hypothesis of action at a distance, formulated by those who invoked him? And did not Leibniz, "starting from a system in which he rejected attraction" change his opinion, in the end, "sharing, concerning the nature of this property—the opinion of Newton's close disciples," as Duhem states (*L'évolution de la mécanique,* p. 39)? Certainly, the different texts cited may thus be interpreted. And yet we think that in considering the opinions of these two great men as a whole we must confirm the ideas of their contemporaries.

1. LEIBNIZ.—Let us note in the first place that if anyone insists on his having changed his opinion, it could not be in the sense which we have just indicated. Indeed, it is especially in the work of his maturity (after 1700) that he speaks against Newtonian ideas with a clearness that leaves nothing to be desired. Thus, in his *Nouveaux Essais,* 1703, he says: "*On peut juger que la matière n'aura pas naturellement l'attraction mentionnée ci-dessus, et n'ira pas d'elle-même en ligne courbe, parce qu'il n'est pas possible de concevoir comment cela s'y fait, c'est-à-dire de l'expliquer mécaniquement";* and later he qualifies this hypothesis as *fainéante,* and accuses it of destroying "*également notre Philosophie qui cherche les raisons, et la divine sagesse qui les fournit*" (ed. Erdmann, p. 203). In his correspondence with Clarke, which dates from the years 1715–16 and forms the last of Leibniz's important writings (it is certainly later than the passages upon force, etc., which are cited), he expresses himself with still more energy, if that is possible. Let us copy the most striking passages, *4ᵉ écrit, § 45:* "*Il est surnaturel aussi que les corps s'attirent de loin, sans aucun moyen; et qu'un corps aille en rond, sans s'écarter par la tangente, quoique rien ne l'empêchât de s'écarter ainsi. Car ces effets ne sont point explicables par les natures des choses.*" *5ᵉ écrit, § 35:* "*Car c'est une étrange fiction que de faire toute la matière pesante, et même vers toute autre matière; comme si tout corps attiroit également tout autre corps selon les masses et les distances; et cela par une attraction proprement dite, qui ne soit pas dérivéed'une impulsion occulte des corps; au lieu que la pesanteur des corps*

sensibles vers le centre de la Terre, doit être produite par le mouvement de quelque fluide. Et il en sera de même d'autres pesanteurs, comme de celles des planètes vers le Soleil, ou entre elles. Un corps n'est jamais mû naturellement, que par un autre corps qui le pousse en le touchant; et après cela il continue jusqu'à ce qu'il soit empêché par un autre corps qui le touche. Toute autre opération sur le corps est ou miraculeuse ou imaginaire." 5e *écrit*, § 113: "*C'est par là que tombent les Attractions proprement dites, et autres opérations inexplicables par les natures des créatures, qu'il faut faire effectuer par miracle, ou recourir aux absurdités, c'est-à-dire aux qualités occultes scholastiques, qu'on commence à nous débiter sous le spécieux nom de forces, mais qui nous ramènent dans le royaume des ténèbres. C'est inventa fruge, glandibus vesci.* § 114. "*Du temps de Mr Boyle, et d'autres excellens hommes qui fleurissoient en Angleterre sous les commencements de Charles II, on n'auroit pas osé nous débiter des notions si creuses. J'espère que ce beau temps reviendra sous un aussi bon gouvernement que celui d'à présent, et que les esprits un peu trop divertis par le malheur des temps, retourneront à mieux cultiver les connoissances solides. Le capital de Mr Boyle étoit d'inculquer que tout se faisoit mécaniquement dans la Physique. Mais c'est un malheur des hommes de se dégoûter enfin de la raison même, et de s'ennuyer de la lumière.*" Therefore, to be in agreement with the facts it ought to be supposed that Leibniz, at first favourable to action at a distance, was finally converted to the opposite side, or else he must twice have changed his opinion and toward the end of his life he must have returned to the opinions he professed at the beginning. These suppositions certainly are not at all unlikely in themselves. What makes them rather difficult to maintain is a somewhat psychological argument suggested by the correspondence with Clarke. Writings in which Leibniz speaks of force had been published long before this. It is hardly likely, in view of the celebrity of their author, that Clarke should have been unaware of them, if, indeed, he did not expressly peruse his critic's works in order to find weapons. Doubtless Clarke's tone is a little more moderate than that of his illustrious adversary. And yet is it believable that, had he been able to place Leibniz in contradiction with himself, he would have allowed this *argumentum ad hominem* to escape? However there is not a trace of this in the *Recueil de lettres*. But we believe that, by an examination of the aforesaid texts, it can be directly established that Leibniz in this question did not change his mind, and that his opinions, rather difficult to understand because of the fragmentary manner with which he loved to express himself and which frequently renders his declarations obscure in spite of the apparent clearness of his sentences, have, nevertheless, been entirely consistent from one end to the other of his scientific career.

Let us note at once that Leibniz, in discussing these matters, generally commences by establishing the principle that "the essence of body" does not consist in extension alone. This seems now quite evident to us (although, as we saw in Chapter VII, modern science really tends equally toward the contrary supposition): but science at that moment was Cartesian, and Descartes, as is well known, had absolutely confused the two concepts of matter and space. The first in date of the writings cited by Duhem (it was published in 1691) has precisely the title, *Lettre sur la question si l'essence du corps consiste dans l'étendue* (ed. Erdmann, pp. 112–113). To quote: "*Tout cela fait connaître qu'il y a dans la matière quelque autre chose, que ce qui est purement Géométrique, c'est-à-dire, que l'étendue et son changement, et son changement tout nud. Et à le bien considérer, on s'aperçoit qu'il y faut joindre quelque notion supérieure ou métaphysique, sçavoir celle de la substance, action, et force; et ces notions portent que tout ce qui pâtit doit agir réciproquement, et que tout ce qui agit doit pâtir quelque réaction; et par conséquent qu'un corps en repos ne doit pas être emporté par un autre en mouvement sans changer quelque chose de la direction et de la vitesse de l'agent. Je demeure d'accord que naturellement tout corps est étendu, et qu'il n'y a point d'étendue sans corps. Il ne faut pas néanmoins confondre les notions du lieu, de l'espace, ou de l'étendue toute pure, avec la notion de la substance, qui outre l'étendue, renferme la résistance, c'est-à-dire, l'action et la passion.*" And before this in the *Réplique à l'abbé de Conti* (1687, ed. Dutens, Vol. III, p. 199), he affirms, "*qu'il faudra admettre dans les corps quelque chose de différent de la grandeur et de la vitesse, à moins qu'on veuille refuser aux corps toute la puissance d'agir.*" Likewise in the *De primae philosophiae emendatione et de notione substantiae* (which appeared in 1694, Erdmann, p. 122), after having insisted on his notion of substance, he continues: "*Quod illi non satis percepisse videntur, qui essentian ejus* [*sc. corporis*] *in sola extensione . . . collacaverunt.*" In the short *Lettre à un ami sur le cartésianisme*, we read: "*C'est depuis quelque temps que j'ai des démêlés avec Messieurs les Cartésiens. . . . Car quoique je demeure d'accord que le détail de la nature se doit expliquer mécaniquement, il faut, qu'outre l'étendue on conçoive dans le corps une force primitive, qui explique intelligiblement tout ce qu'il y a de solide dans les formes des écoles* (Erdmann, p. 123). He also says in the *Supplément à la lettre à Fabri* (dated in 1702, *Mathem. Schriften*, ed. Gerhardt, Vol. VI, p. 98): "*Nempe corporis essentiam Cartesiani collocant in sola extensione, ego vero, etsi cum Aristotele et Cartesio contra Democritum Gassendumque Vacuum nullum admittam . . . puto tamen cum Democrito et Aristotele contra Cartesium aliquid in corpore esse passivum praeter extensionem, id scilicet quo corpus resistit penetratione.*" And again in the *Commentatio de anima brutorum* (1870, Erdmann, p. 463) he comes back to the idea that extension alone does not suffice for the conception of body.

But from the moment that this "superior metaphysical notion" of "substance, action, and force" is to be taken primarily as differentiating body from space, and furthermore, as we have seen, action at a distance is to be rejected, it remains then that it is a principle of action manifesting itself in contact—in other words, as a synonym of our notion of *mass*, as it is understood, of course, by physicists, who exclude action at a distance. What appears to contradict this conception, and what has doubtless been one of the principal sources of error for commentators, is the fact that Leibniz seems sometimes to state that the notion of mass is not sufficient. The apparently most conclusive passage from this point of view is found in *Système Nouveau de la Nature* (1695, Erdmann, p. 124): "*Mais depuis ayant taché d'approfondir les principes mêmes de la Mécanique, pour rendre raison des lois de la Nature que l'expérience faisoit connaître, je m'aperçus que la seule considération d'une masse étendue ne suffisoit pas et qu'il falloit employer encore la notion de la force, qui est très intelligible quoiqu'elle soit de ressort de la Métaphysique.*"

This difficulty is solved if one is mindful that the term mass has not here the same signification as in modern mechanics. This is clearly shown in the following passage (*Supplément à la lettre à Fabri*, already cited, p. 100): "*Porro, τὸ δυναμιχὸν seu potentia in corpore duplex est, Passiva et Activa. Vis passiva proprie constituit Materiam seu Massam, Active ἐντελέχειαν seu formam.*" The same distinction between the passive and active power of matter appears in the *Lettre à Wagner* (1710, Erdmann, p. 466, § II): "*Respondeo primo, principium activum non tribui a me materiae nudae sive primae, quae mere passiva est, et in sola antitypia et extensione consistit; sed corpori seu materiae vestitae sive secundae, quae praeterea Entelechiam primitivam seu principium activum continet.*" The following explains still more clearly this distinction: "*Respondeo secundo, resistentiam materiae nudae non esse actionem, sed meram passionem, dum nempe habet antitypiam, seu impenetrabilitatem, qua quidem resistit penetraturo, sed non repercutit, nisi accedat vis elastica.*" And so also in the *Commentatio de anima brutorum*: "*Materia in se sumta seu nuda constituitur per Antitypiam et Extensionem. Antitypiam voco illud attributum, per quod materia quod sit . . . principium . . . motus seu actionis externae. Et tale principium appellamus substantiale, item vim primitivan ἐντελέχειαν τὴν πρώτην . . . quod activum cum passivo conjunctum substantiam completam constitutit* (Erdmann, p. 463).

This active principle appears, moreover, as an intensive magnitude, the cause of change in nature: *Activum vel Potentia praeditum est Thema (vel rerum status) ex quo sequetur mutatio certis quibusdam praeterea positis inertibus, seu quae talia sunt, ut ex ipsis solis positis utcunque nulla mutatio sequatur* (CASSIRER, *Leibniz's System*, Marburg, 1902, p. 336). It is the principle which creates the laws of motion, since it is the cause of the fact that the sum of the *vis viva* cannot increase, one body not being able to push another except at the expense of its own *vis viva*, as appears from the continuation of the *Supplément à la lettre à Fabri* (we cite this passage in Appendix III with reference to Kepler's concept of inertia).

Thus the difference between the modern conception of mass and that of Leibniz is in the fact that in using this term we think both of the passive and the active side of the phenomenon; whereas Leibniz, although he was aware, of course, that the two are inseparably linked together (see the passage from the *Lettre sur la question*, etc.) separated them, nevertheless, in thought, and called the faculty of suffering *alone*, *antitypy*, impenetrability or mass, attributing it to *primary* or *bare* matter, whereas he thought that the faculty of acting was *form*, *entelechy* or *force* and, added to the first, constituted *invested matter*. Assuming bodies which were endowed with antitypy alone, they would have been in a way hard bodies, but deprived of all elasticity; these expressions are not correct in the sense that the concept of hardness includes, as far as we are concerned, a faculty of acting, whereas Leibniz thought really of a sort of purely passive hardness having need, in order to manifest itself in action, of the accession of an elastic force. This is seen in the passage already cited from the *Lettre à Wagner*, and still more clearly in the continuation of the *Supplément à la lettre à Fabri*, where he deduces the fact that every body is essentially elastic. But this *vis elastica* is not force or entelechy itself; it must be explained by this force (which he calls this time *active force*) and motion, *quae ex motu, adeoque et vi activa materiae superaddita, derivari debet*, he adds in the *Lettre à Wagner* after the words *vis elastica*, and in the *Supplément à la lettre à Fabri* he says the same (*l.c.*, p. 103): "*Hinc autem intelligitur, etsi admittatur vis illa primitiva seu Forma substantiae, tamen in vi elastica aliisque phaenomenis explicandis semper procedendum esse Mechanice, nempe per figuras quae sunt modificationes materiae, et per impetus qui sunt modificationes formae,*" the word *mechanice* having here, and in general with Leibniz, the meaning of action by contact—that is, to the exclusion of action at a distance; sometimes, however, he uses it to indicate that which has to do with primary or bare matter alone, as when he says (*Commentatio de anima brutorum*, Erdmann, p. 463): *Itaque pro certo habendum est, ex solo mechanismo, seu materia nuda ejusque modificationibus perceptionem explicari non posse, non magis, quam principium actionis et motus.* There is here evidently a certain vacillation in vocabulary which has contributed to the misunderstanding of which we have spoken. (Concerning Leibniz's double concept of mass, compare also CASSIRER, *l.c.*, p. 333–342, 515.)

The passage which we have just cited shows, moreover, that Leibniz also attached to this concept of force the perception as well as the soul of an animal. This is a point of view on which he strongly insists in the greater part of the writings which we have mentioned in this Appendix. We have sometimes had to mutilate the quotations, replacing with dots all that relates to that aspect of the question in order not to interrupt our deduction. The clearest exposition is in the *Lettre à Wagner: Respondeo tertio: Hoc principium activum, hanc Entelechiam primam, esse revera principium vitale, etiam percipiendi facultate praeditum, et indefectibile, ob rationes dudum a me allegatas. Idque ipsum est, quod in brutis pro anima ipsorum habeo.* If one observes that Leibniz in his *Système Nouveau* (cf. p. 352 and 517) introduces the notion of *force*, declaring it, without any other explanation, to be "*très intelligible quoi qu'elle soit du ressort de la Métaphysique*"—in an analogous passage of the treatise *De primae philosophae emendatione* (Erdmann, p. 122) he adds after the words *vis seu virtus* the parenthesis: "*quam Germani vocant Kraft, Galli la force,*" which clearly shows that he was referring not to a scientific abstraction, but to a common-sense notion, one comes to the conclusion that Leibniz was thinking of what we call the *sensation of effort*. Moreover, he uses this term in one of his other writings (*Lettre à Pélisson*, ed. Dutens, Vol. III, p. 718): "*La notion de force est aussi claire que celle de l'action et de la passion. Car c'est ce dont l'action s'ensuit, lorsque rien ne l'empêche; l'effort,* conatus: *et au lieu que le mouvement est une chose successive, laquelle par conséquent n'existe jamais, non plus que le temps parce que toutes les parties n'existent jamais ensemble; au lieu de cela, la force ou l'effort existe tout entier à chaque moment, il doit être quelque chose de véritable et de réel.*" Consequently it does not seem too bold to establish a relationship between his conceptions and those of Schopenhauer, who says that in exerting an act of will we find ourselves "behind the scenes of nature" (cf. Chap. IX, p. 308).

If one admits that Leibniz used the term *intelligible* in the sense which we have just indicated, his declaration relative to the complete intelligibility of nature (see Chapter IX, p. 298) assumes a very different signification. It seems, moreover, as if one had to have recourse to this interpretation, for we have seen that Leibniz conceived sensation as inexplicable by mechanism (p. 291), and the concept of pre-established harmony (p. 302) proves that he placed transitive action in the same category; both taking place apparently in a sphere superior to things which "the angel" might explain, and which are only to be reached by an "infinite analysis." We may remark, to avoid all misunderstanding, that even when we interpret him thus, Leibniz's postulate differs from our conception, for he supposes that mechanism (neglecting the irrational which it contains) can entirely explain nature (with the exception of sensation), whereas we believe that this "explication" by mechanism aims really only at an identity, which is unrealizable, as Carnot's principle shows.

In the text we have preferred to take literally Leibniz's affirmation, because it offered us the opportunity of making our thought clear. Indeed, it seems that Schopenhauer understood it thus; the statement cited by us (although Leibniz's name is not mentioned) certainly alludes to it; it is, moreover, more than probable that Schopenhauer was not aware of the relationship of the conceptions which we have stated.

Leibniz is known to have superposed a metaphysical world of monads on the physical world of mechanism; and the difficulty which one encounters in trying to grasp his thought becomes particularly acute when one seeks to understand, as in the question just discussed, how this superposition operates.

2. NEWTON.—It is certain that Newton never expressly affirmed that gravitation was due to a genuine action at a distance. But the second edition of *Principia*, which appeared in 1713, is preceded by a preface by Roger Cotes, which contains very decided declarations on this subject. Gravitation is an essential quality of matter, in the same degree as extension, mobility, and impenetrability; it is not an occult quality, since its existence can be directly proved *ex Phaenomenis ostensum est hanc virtutem revera existere*. Can it be supposed that concerning this very essential question Newton was in absolute disagreement with his disciple, and that he yet allowed him free play at the risk of being compromised by him? We know that Newton cordially detested and systematically fled from anything which resembled discussion, or polemic. Is it believable that he would have allowed opinions necessarily shocking to his contemporaries to pass as his, involving him in contradictions and contentions, if these opinions were diametrically opposed to those which he really professed? Is it not infinitely more likely that he approved of them tacitly, to use Rosenberger's apt expression (*Geschichte*, III, p. 2)?

In regard to these deductions, and to the unanimous sentiment of his contemporaries and of immediate posterity, a certain number of texts are cited. The most precise in appearance is a passage from a letter to Bentley (dated February 25, 1692, *Opera*, ed. Horsley, London, 1785, p. 438): "That gravity should be innate, inherent, and essential to matter, so that one body may act upon another through a *vacuum*, without the mediation of anything else, by and through which their action and force may be conveyed from one to another, is to me so great an absurdity, that I believe no man who has in philosophical matters a competent faculty of thinking can ever fall into it." But, looking at it more

closely, one perceives that this declaration is much less conclusive than
it seems to be. We shall see a little later that Clarke, with somewhat less
emphasis, expressed himself in an almost analogous manner; and yet we
cannot doubt that, from our point of view, he was a partisan of action at a
distance. Newton does not at all say that action seems possible to him only
by the contact of two bodies; he is content to declare that one body, in
order to act upon another, has need of an intermediary; he leaves undetermined the nature of this "something" and more particularly does not
affirm that it must be something of a material nature. Moreover, we need
only notice how these declarations were understood by his correspondent.
Bentley, who was a Hellenist, but well versed in scientific things, and, moreover, evidently endowed with great assimilative powers, had been charged
to give the first series of eight annual lectures devoted to the defence of
Christianity which Robert Boyle, the celebrated scientist, who was at the
same time a rigid Protestant, had founded with a legacy. This was the
reason why he wrote to Newton, whose letters were replies to Bentley's
request for information. The lectures were given that same year, 1692,
and were printed soon after. They were very successful, going through
several editions. The passages which we cite are extracts from the seventh
lecture entitled *A Confutation of Atheism from the Origin and Frame of the
World;* it was delivered on November 7th. "'Tis utterly inconceivable,"
says Bentley, "that inanimate brute Matter, without the mediation of
some Immaterial Being, should operate upon and affect other Matter
without mutual contact; that distant Bodies should act upon each other
through a *Vacuum* without the intervention of something else by and through
which the action may be conveyed from one to the other." And he adds:
"Now if these things be repugnant to Human Reason, we have great reason
to affirm that Universal Gravitation, a thing certainly existent in Nature,
is above all Mechanism and material Causes, and proceeds from a higher
principle, a Divine energy and impression" (Richard Bentley, *Eight Sermons
Preach'd at the Honourable Robert Boyle's Lecture,* 5th ed, Cambridge, 1724,
pp. 277, 281). The general tenor of this explanation was certainly congenial
to Newton; it is known that from that time on the most intimate relations
existed between the two men, relations which lasted until the death of
Newton. And yet perhaps the latter leaned rather toward a less direct
action of divinity, and the intervention of some sort of medium or of an
immaterial or spiritual principle, the idea of which he had borrowed
from the semi-theological doctrine of Henry More, a philosopher of the
second half of the seventeenth century, whose doctrines seem to have
enjoyed a considerable authority at that time. The outline of this is to
be found in Lasswitz (*Wirklichkeiten,* 2nd ed., p. 42 and ff.), where one
sees how, with the help of Newton's religious tendencies, that which at the
beginning was a sort of article of theological faith was transformed by him
into a scientific theory, which, because of his prestige, was accepted by those
around him. From a strictly physical point of view, it is clear that these
conceptions amount to pure and simple action at a distance. Clarke, in his
discussion with Leibniz (4ᵉ *réplique,* § 45, Erdmann, p. 762), again makes
allusion to an immaterial principle: "*Il est vrai que si un corps en attirait un*

autre, sans l'intervention d'aucun moyen, ce ne serait pas un miracle, mais une contra-diction; car ce serait supposer qu'une chose agit où elle n'est pas. Mais le moyen par lequel deux corps s'attirent l'un l'autre peut être invisible et intangible et d'une nature différente de mécanisme." Cotes, on the contrary, sets it aside; if Newton permitted the theory to be stated in this manner, it was probably because, having come to the conviction that from a scientific point of view these two kinds of conception amounted to the same thing, he judged it preferable to separate what was really a theological hypothesis from a book on physics. It is clear also that one can conceive of *force* as that "something" inter-mediary, which is spoken of in the letter to Bentley; but it must be noticed that this very term force is there evidently applied not to action at a distance, but, as in Leibniz, to action by contact.

There are, apart from the letter to Bentley, several more or less ambiguous passages here and there in the *Principia* and *Opticks*. One of the most explicit follows, in the *Principia*, the famous *hypotheses non fingo*. But the quotation should be reproduced in its entirety : *Rationem vero harum Gravitatis proprietatum ex Phaenomenis nondum potui deducere, et Hypotheses non fingo. Quicquid enim ex Phaenomenis non deducitur*, Hypothesis *vocanda est; et Hypotheses seu Metaphysicae, seu Physicae, seu Qualitatum occultarum, seu Mechanicae, in* Philosophia Experi-mentali *locum non habent. In hac Philosophia Propositiones deducuntur ex Phaeno-menis, et redduntur generales per Inductionem. Sic impenetrabilitas, mobilitas, et impetus corporum et leges motuum et gravitatis innotuerunt. Et satis est quod Gravitas revera existat, et agat secundum leges a nobis expositas, et ad corporum coelestium et maris nostri motus omnes sufficiat* (*Principia*, Amsterdam, 1714, p. 487).

Surely, if one isolates the sentences *in hac philosophia*, etc., they have the appearance of a Comtian profession of faith. But in this respect it is sufficient to go back to the first phrase: *Nondum potui*, etc. What Newton meant was that in the exposition of results of scientific research, one must refrain from formulating assumptions which would not be confirmed by facts; but he did not distinguish, in this respect, between assumptions relative to laws and those concerning the mode of production. Especially, he did not intend to deny that these assumptions were useful in guiding the scientist, and still less did he think of forbidding research on the mode of production. The continuation of the same passage proves this abundantly. It is a slightly nebulous exposition in which there is a question *de Spiritu quodam subtilissimo corpora crassa pervadente et in iisdem latente*. Newton attributes to this hypothetical being the phenomena of cohesion, electricity, light; in the same way *Sensatio omnis excitatur et membra Animalium ad voluntatem moventur, vibrationibus scilicet hujus Spiritus per solida nervorum capillamenta ab externis sensorum organis ad cerebrum et a cerebro in musculos propagatis*. Newton adds : *Sed haec paucis exponi non possunt; neque adest sufficiens copia Experimentorum quibus leges actionum hujus Spiritus accurate determinari et monstrari debent*. Evidently we have here to do with a genuine hypothesis about the mode of production, and if Newton refrains from developing it, it is solely because his research is not far enough advanced. As to the nature of this hypothesis it is no doubt derived from More's conceptions, and it is hardly likely that action by contact would have gained by a more ample exposition.

A declaration analogous to the *hypotheses non fingo* was inserted by Newton in the *Opticks* amongst the *Questions* added to the first Latin edition (1706). But here again it is better to quote the entire passage. After having rejected every attempt to explain gravitation by the action of a universal medium, Newton continues: "And for rejecting such a Medium we have the Authority of those of the oldest and most celebrated Philosophers of *Greece* and *Phenicia*, who made a *Vacuum* and Atoms, and the Gravity of Atoms, the first Principles of their Philosophy; tacitly attributing Gravity to some other Cause than dense Matter. Later Philosophers banish the Consideration of such a Cause out of Natural Philosophy, feigning Hypotheses for explaining all things mechanically and referring other Causes to Metaphysicks: Whereas the main Business of Natural Philosophy is to argue from Phaenomena without feigning Hypotheses, and to deduce Causes from Effects, till we come to the very first Cause, which certainly is not mechanical" (*Opticks*, 3rd ed. London, 1721, p. 343). It is seen that the hostility toward hypotheses (evidently expecially Cartesian hypotheses) is here allied with the search for causes, as far as and including the First Cause (conceived, it seems, somewhat as in Bentley, in the passage already cited).

On the other hand, we find in the *Opticks* passages which seem to show that Newton at a certain moment had really thought of reducing gravitation to the mechanical action of a medium. In Advertisement II to the XXIst Question (*ib.*, 1721, p. 325), Newton expressly defends himself against having assumed action at a distance: "And to shew that I do not take Gravity for an Essential Property of Bodies I have added one Question concerning its Cause, chusing to propose it by way of a question, because I am not yet satisfied about it for want of Experiments." In the *Question* itself, he, indeed, speaks of a medium, conceived evidently as material, which would be rarer in the interior of the sun, of the stars, of the planets, and of the comets than in the empty celestial spaces; this medium, becoming more and more dense as one moves away from these bodies, would be the cause of the gravitation of celestial bodies towards each other and of parts of these bodies towards the bodies themselves. The very form of this passage as an interrogation and the guarded wording of the *Advertisement* show that Newton did not take these declarations too seriously and if, in the preface to the second edition of the *Opticks*, he inserted several sentences where he seems still to protest against the opinion attributed to him of a direct action at a distance, he, nevertheless, did not think of suppressing the passages of the XXXIst Question, where he traced the programme of a physics which would reduce all phenomena to actions at a distance exerted by particles of bodies.

These were apparently only stylistic phrasings inserted as a precaution and destined to anticipate polemics from which Newton willingly fled. His contemporaries certainly understood that to be his true thought, and everything seems to indicate that they were right. One may suppose that Newton before reaching the concept of action at a distance must have groped in the dark; it is probably at this time that he made certain efforts with a view to explaining the action of gravitation by that of a material medium; later he made a clever use of these vague attempts to give a semblance of satisfaction to his adversaries.

It must, however, be recognized that this way of looking at the matter of Newton's fundamental opinions cannot be supported by direct proof. We see in the *Correspondence* with Cotes (*Correspondence of Sir Isaac Newton with Professor Cotes,* etc., by J. EDDLESTON. London, 1850, p. 158) that Newton, who carefully went over the proofs of the second edition, which were sent to him as they came out, had expressly refused to go through those of Cotes's preface. "I must not see it, for I find I shall be examined on it," he wrote to his disciple. (Cotes, in the first place, had rather curiously proposed that Newton alone, or with Bentley, should write this preface, promising in advance to sign it and to defend it afterward, but Bentley, in Newton's name and in his own, had immediately repelled this proposition, *ib.,* p. 150). Eddleston thinks that Newton's refusal was due to the attacks directed by Cotes against Leibniz with regard to the infinitesimal calculus, Newton wishing to leave to his disciple the entire responsibility for these attacks. But it may be supposed, if need be, that the cut and dried opinions formulated by Cotes with regard to gravitation, had something to do with this and that Newton did not entirely approve of them. It remains much more likely, however, that this disapproval (supposing it to be real) was directed rather to the form than to the contents of Cotes's conceptions (cf. on Newton's habit of having his opinions dogmatically stated by his disciples and making use of them to fight his adversaries, all the while preserving an apparent neutrality, F. Rosenberger, *Isaak Newton und seine physikalischen Prinzipien,* Leipzig, 1895, pp. 6, 260, 287).

It is curious to notice that Cotes himself wrote later in such a way as to weaken his declarations concerning the essential nature of gravitation (EDDLESTON, *Correspondence,* p. 158).

II

THE PASSAGES FROM PLUTARCH AND SIMPLICIUS

For the passage from Plutarch we made use in our French text (p. 114) of Bétolaud's translation (Paris, 1870, p. 139). The very approximative manner in which certain expressions are rendered seems to facilitate the confusion. Here is a version which we attempted to render as literally as possible: "And what helps the moon not to fall is its motion and the rapidity of its revolution. Thus objects placed in a sling cannot fall because of the turning in a circle. For motion which is in conformity with nature moves each thing if it is not diverted by something else. That is why weight does not move the moon, because circular motion repels the inclination downward."

The word translated by Bétolaud by *neutralize* is ἐγχρονόμενον; it signifies *chases, diverts, pushes back*. DUEBNER in his Latin translation (Paris 1856) expressed it by *excutit*. The term ῥοπή, which we have expressed by *inclination downward*, is used currently to designate the force which makes the beam of a balance incline; it may, therefore, be translated also by *gravity*, as Bétolaud has done; we, however, have preferred a less precise term, to distinguish it from βάρος, which precedes it.

The passage from Simplicius has been designated by WOHLWILL (*Archiv fuer Voelkerpsychologie*, Vol. XV) and summarized by VAILATI (*Le speculazioni di Giovanni Benedetti*, etc., *Ac de Turin*, 1897–98, p. 23). We know of no translation, so we have attempted the following:

"Hipparchus, in his περὶ τῶν διὰ βαρύτητα κάτω φερομένων, in regard to objects thrown upward, above the earth, says that the impulse (ἰσχύς) with which an object is thrown upward, as long as it predominates over the force (δύναμις, *potentia*) is the cause of the ascent, and that the velocity of the ascent of the thrown object is proportional to that predominance; but when the former (ἰσχύς) diminishes, the object is no longer carried upward with the same velocity and afterwards the object thrown is carried downwards because of its inclination (ῥοπή, weight) when there still exists something of the force (δύναμις) which causes ascent, then this latter gradually vanishing, the object carried downward is carried more and more quickly and attains the highest degree of velocity when the force which has projected upward ceases. He gives the same cause for objects dropped from above; for there subsists in them to a certain degree the force of that which has held them back, and this force acting in a contrary direction determines at the beginning the slowness of the descent." Aristotle, *Opera*, ed. Bekker, Vol. IV; *Scholia*, ed. Brandis, p. 485.

III

THE COPERNICANS AND THE PRINCIPLE OF INERTIA

WE saw (p. 149, Note 14) that according to Rosenberger the triumph of geocentric theories in antiquity is connected with the absence of the concept of inertia.

This remark is certainly quite correct. Our immediate sensation seems at first sight to give us an absolute certainty concerning motion and rest; the principle of inertia destroys this certainty by convincing us that the phenomena which we should consider as characterizing rest are in reality those of rectilinear and uniform motion; and we can therefore envisage the motion of that which appears to us in *apparent rest*.

This opinion, however, entails an immense historical difficulty. Logically the principle of inertia would have to be anterior in time to the heliocentric theory or the two must at least have been stated simultaneously. Now Rosenberger himself attributes the principle of inertia to Galileo. What, then, could be the opinion of Copernicus himself and of those who adhered to his doctrine in the interval which separates the appearance of the *De revolutionibus* (1543) from the publications of Galileo and even in certain respects we have seen from the publications of Descartes? The historians of physics, in speaking of the men of this period, do not seem to have cast all the light that is desirable upon the problem we have just formulated.

It is doubtless because he was conscious of this difficulty that Painlevé formulated a curious theory as to the origin of the principle of inertia (*Bulletin de la Société française de philosophie*, 5th year, 1905, p. 36–37). This eminent mathematician supposes that Copernicus and the *Copernicans* conceived of the principle in its generality; if they did not state it, it is only because of the material danger which such an affirmation would have presented. It would seem, however, that in the theological discussions which arose concerning these theories (as, for example, in the trial of Galileo), it was solely a question of the earth's motion. After Galileo's condemnation, Descartes, whose prudence is well known, stated the principle of inertia without apparently having the least consciousness of expressing a daring opinion from a religious point of view; whereas in speaking of the earth's motion he, on the contrary, uses endless precaution.

We believe, nevertheless, that there is a great portion of truth in Painlevé's theory, that Copernicus and his immediate successors really depended upon a principle implicitly understood and relative to motion. This principle, however, was not our principle of inertia, but a much less precise idea, partly erroneous moreover, which might be called the *principle of relative motion*.

In the first place it may be stated that according to Copernicus the planetary bodies are in no wise moved by inertia. We have mentioned in the text his opinion on the subject of natural circular motion and the absence of centrifugal force resulting from the earth's rotation. In the same context may be cited what he said about the famous "third motion" of the terrestrial axis. Copernicus apparently would have considered it natural that the axis of the earth should describe a cone around the axis of the ecliptic; he therefore believed that he must endow the earth, besides the two motions of rotation and revolution, with still another motion, destined to maintain its axis at the same inclination in relation to the plane of the ecliptic: *Sequitur ergo tertius declinationis motus annua quoque revolutione, sed in praecedentia, hoc est contra motum centri reflectens. Sicque ambobus invicem aequalibus fere et obviis mutuo evenit, ut axis terrae, et in ipso maximus parellelorum aequinoctialis in eamdem fere mundi partem spectent, ac si immobiles permanent* (*De revolutionibus orbium coelestium,* Thorn, 1873, Chap. XI, p. 31).

These theories do not constitute an absolute proof: we have, indeed, seen that even Descartes did not always correctly deal with the motion of rotation of the planets. Copernicus was not directly engaged in mechanics; he only discussed the phenomena of the motion of terrestrial bodies to explain their relation to the motion of the earth itself. We shall, therefore, ask in the first place what was the statement that he needed for his theory.

From this point of view, the opinions of Nicolas de Cusa, which we summarized in the text, are of great help to us. Doubtless, Cusa was only a precursor; his vague affirmations are far from the lucid theory of planetary motions formulated by the great Polish astronomer. But it is, nevertheless, true that Cusa had envisaged the possibility of the earth's motion. Of course, in doing this, he was conscious of offending the conviction resulting from our immediate sensation that the earth is something stable. What did he do to remove this serious objection? He emphasized the example of the ship which, to those on board, seems immovable if they do not see the shore. At first sight it might be said that this was simply our principle of inertia. But let us be careful: no more than Sextus Empiricus did Cusa indicate that his statement was limited to rectilinear and uniform motion. On the contrary, he applied his idea to whatever motion there might be. If we had to state precisely its tenor we should formulate it in about the following terms: *it is impossible to determine by immediate sensation or by the direct observation of mechanical phenomena whether a body is in motion or not.* It was, therefore, an almost purely negative statement, simply denying mechanical control as far as the theory of terrestrial motion is concerned, a negation quite understandable, indeed, if one realizes that the physics of those days was entirely under the influence of peripateticism. But it is clear that a proposition like this could not be of great worth in mechanics, and that it was notably impossible to deduce from it the resolution of the motion of a projectile, which was the real point of departure for the principle of inertia. This explains why Cusa, when he conceived persistent motion in a horizontal plane, in no way attached it to his conception of the relativity of motion.

Everything indicates that Copernicus professed analogous opinions from these different points of view. Like Cusa, he used the example of the ship; he cites for this purpose a verse from Virgil, a very appropriate quotation, since the poet there depicts immediate sensation, evidently illusory in this case: *Provehimur portu, terraeque urbesque recedunt* (*De revolutionibus,* Thorn, 1873, p. 22). He thus refutes the evidence of our senses in what concerns the reality of motion: *Quamquam in medio mundi terram quiescere inter autores plerumque convenit, ut inopinabile putent, sive etiam ridiculum contrarium sentire.*

Si tamen attentius rem consideremus, videbitur haec quaestio nondum absoluta et idcirco minime contemnenda. Omnis enim quae videtur secundum locum mutatio, aut est propter spectatae rei motum, aut videntis, aut certe disparem utriusque mutationem. Nam inter mota aequaliter ad eadem, non percipitur motus, inter visum dico et videns (Ib., p. 16).

One might suppose that Copernicus was conscious that it was in this case a question of a particular kind of motion, of what we call inertial motion; the expression *mota aequaliter ad eadem* seems in a way to justify an intepretation of this kind (the German version of MENZER, Thorn, 1877, translates *ad eadem* by *in gleicher Richtung,* which is a little more precise than the Latin text and seems to be nearer our modern conceptions). But it is clear from the context that Copernicus meant quite simply that if the observer and the object observed do not possess the same motion, since there is relative displacement, motion becomes evident. He not only made no difference, from this point of view, between rectilinear and curvilinear motions, but the latter in certain cases seemed privileged to him; it especially gave the sensation of rest: *Igitur quod aiunt simplicis corporis esse motum simplicem (de circulari in primis verificatur), quamdiu corpus simplex in loco suo naturali ac unitate sua permanserit. In loco siquidem non alius, quam circularis est motus, qui manet in se totus quiescenti similis. Rectus autem supervenit iis, quae a loco suo naturali peregrinantur, vel extraduntur, vel quomodolibet extra ipsum sunt. Nihil autem ordinationi totius et formae mundi tantum repugnat, quandum extra locum suum quidquam esse. Rectus ergo motus non accidit, nisi rebus non recte se habentibus, neque perfectis secundem naturam, dum separantur a suo toto et ejus deserunt unitatem (Ib.,* p. 23).

It is not very difficult, it seems, to understand how Copernicus was led to conceive these theories. The principle of relative motion, as we have stated it, is in itself a rather paradoxical conception; as we have said, it is not only impossible to draw a mechanical conception from it, but it is contradicted by facts from common experience, such as the stone placed in a sling. To be sure, nothing indicates that Copernicus had made a more profound study of the motions of terrestrial bodies; but we know that he must have been preoccupied with the question of centrifugal motion, notably when he had to explain the (supposed) absence of this motion following terrestrial rotation (cf. p. 118 f.).

He probably had the feeling that the principle did not quite sufficiently explain phenomena as we perceive them on the earth. This is why he has recourse to the distinction between natural motion and violent motion, established by Aristotle and firmly anchored in the minds of his contemporaries. Aristotle, it is true, believed that natural circular motion only belonged to celestial bodies; but since with Copernicus the earth becomes a celestial body, similar to other planets, it is quite easy to attribute the same privilege to it as well as to the terrestrial objects which it carries with it in so far as they participate in its motion. Aristotle assumed terrestrial bodies to have a natural rectilinear motion, downward (heavy bodies) and upward (light bodies). Copernicus preserved this notion, so that with him terrestrial objects possess natural motions of two sorts—on the one hand, circular; on the other, rectilinear (downward and upward). But since he doubtless hesitated to make rectilinear motion (more especially that which takes place because of weight) participate in the same privilege as that of natural circular motion, he devised a distinction between them. Circular motion becomes, in a way, the pre-eminently natural or simple motion, since the body "persists in its natural place and in its unity," and since the motion "remains entirely within itself." Motion, upward and downward, is inferior to it in the sense that the body "has left its natural place or has been forced outside of it." Copernicus knew, moreover, that the motion of falling bodies is not uniform; but this pecularity, which we believe to be fundamental from the point of view of the characteristic of the motion in question, seems secondary to him; he only mentions it in the passage following that which we have just cited, the distinctions between the motions accomplished in their place and outside their proper place appearing much more important to him.

Evidently this whole system has only astronomy in view; as we have said, Copernicus is solely interested in this, only discussing terrestrial problems in order to brush aside more readily the objections which might be formulated against his theory. Moreover, even from this point of view, the system is very imperfect, as is seen from the objections of his adversaries, who constantly emphasize arguments drawn from the motion of terrestrial bodies, such as that of a stone falling from the top of a tower. It would seem in particular that arguments of this kind in great part prevented Tycho Brahé from adhering to the Copernican theory, although in other ways he admitted the convenience of this conception for purposes of calculation and highly praised its author (ROSENBERGER, *Geschichte*, Vol. I, p. 135).

Kepler's ideas on this subject are also very curious. Kepler had a great admiration for the author of the heliocentric theory, and on every occasion invoked his thought; but this did not prevent him from profoundly modifying one of the principal features of its doctrine, by substituting ellipses for circles. He also modified its mechanical basis. It may be, moreover, that these two changes are closely correlative. Indeed, the conception of natural circular motion issued from ideas upon the particular virtue of the circle's figure considered as *simple* and *perfect*. Now it was difficult to assign the same privileges to the ellipse, in which, therefore, it could not be pretended that bodies moved *naturally*.

According to Kepler, every body has a tendency to remain in the place in space where it is found, a tendency independent of the motion with which it is endowed. The passages in which he applies this theory to celestial bodies are extremely numerous. Let us cite a few of the most striking ones: *Tertius interveniens*. (*Opera omnia*, ed. Frisch, Frankfort, 1870, Vol. I, p. 590): "*Für mein Person sage ich, dass die Sternkugeln diesse Art haben, dass sie an einem jeden Ort des Himmels, da sie jedesmal angetroffen werden, stillstehen würden, wann sie nicht getrieben werden solten. Sie werden aber getrieben per speciem immateriatam Solis, in gyrum rapidissime circumactam. Item werden sie getrieben von jhrer selbst eygnen Magnetischen Krafft, dürch welche sie einhalb der Sonnen zuschiffen, andertheils von der Sonnen hinweg ziehlen. Epitome Astronomiae, ib., Vol. VI, p. 341 : (Globus aliquid coelestis) habet tamen ratione suae materiae naturalem ἀδυναμίαν transeundi de loco in locum, habet naturalem inertiam seu quietem, qua quiescit in omni loci, ubi solitarius collocatur.* Ib., p. 345: *Dictum est hactenus, praeter hanc vim Solis vectoriam esse etiam naturalem inertiam in planetis ipsis ad motum, qua fit, ut inclinati sint, materiae ratione ad manendum loco suo. Pugnant igitur inter se potentia Solis vectoria et impotentia planetae seu inertia materialis.*

Thus *inertia*, if it could predominate, would put an end to the displacement of a body which is in motion and would lead it to rest; it is *repugnans motui* and constitutes, as Kepler himself has defined it with precision, a *causa privativa motus* (*ib.*, p. 174).

What must be noticed, also, especially in the quotations just given, is that, according to Kepler, this property is not limited to celestial bodies; on the contrary, it belongs to them only because they are composed of matter, *materiae ratione*—in other words, it is a property general to all matter as such. And this he has clearly formulated in other passages: Vol. VII, p. 746: *Es hat aber aller koerperliche zeug oder materia aller ding in der gantzen Welt dise art, oder vilmehr dise tode vnart, dass er plump ist und ungeschickt, von sich selber auss einem Ort in den andern zu wandern und müssen derhalben von einem Leben, oder sonsten von aussen hero gezogen und getrieben werden.* Ib.: *Auf diese Weise sage auch ich, nit nur von dem mittelen sondern von eim jedem Ort, wann etwas drein gesetzt werde, das da ein toder Körper ist wann es nit von dannen durch etwas anderes ausserhalb seiner gezogen werde, so koennt es auch von sich selbst nit von dannen kommen, darum dieweil es tod ist oder träg und unartig.*

Under these conditions evidently the persistent motions of celestial bodies need persistent causes in order to overcome the *inertia* which continually tends to suppress them. As to what concerns revolution, Kepler sees the cause for that in a magnetic fluid emanating from the sun, as is indicated by the passage which we first cited (cf. also amongst others, *ib.*, Vol. VI, pp. 311, 342, 343). As to the rotation of the earth, he supposes many causes for it (*ib.*, pp. 175–177), the principal one consisting, it would seem, in a particular property of circular fibres placed around the terrestrial axis. But he also takes the example of the top, and the expressions which he employs on this occasion are somewhat like those we use in cases of this kind (as, for instance, *quantum vero materialem inertiam attinet, subjecti loco sit ad concipiendum impetum continuandamque rotationem*). However, it must be remembered that this particular manner of considering bodies in rotation had been current since the days of antiquity (cf. p. 115). Cusa had even gone farther than Kepler, since he had conceived the perpetuity of this motion of rotation by purely mechanical causes (p. 117 f.), whereas it seemed to Kepler that it must diminish of itself with time (*temporis diuturnitate debilitata paulatim emoriatur*). This is why this *species motus* cannot be exactly the same for the earth as for the top: *non jam hospes amplius in Terra ut illa in turbine sed inquilina plane seu materiae suae victrix et domitrix existens.*

Let us note, nevertheless, that Kepler drew from these considerations a very important conclusion, which, in the opinion of physicists of to-day, appears related also to the concept of inertia. We saw that Copernicus believed that he must assume a particular motion of the terrestrial axis, destined to preserve its direction in space. Kepler regards this assumption as useless. This correction is ordinarily attributed to Gassendi (cf., for instance, *De revolutionibus*, Thorn, 1873, Notes p. 10), but it is already clearly indicated in Kepler's youthful work, the *Mysterium cosmographicum* (ed. Frisch, Vol. I, p. 121) : *Secundum motum in meram axis quietem redegimus, tertius jam ad secundum est reducendus et cum eo in unum conflandus.* Kepler seeks for the cause of this parallel position of the terrestrial axis, in "a natural and magnetic inclination of its fibres at rest," and this *inclinatio* (as is seen in a passage from the *Epitome*, p. 176) appeared to him under the aspect of a *forma* analogous to the properties of circular fibres in the motion of rotation of which we have just spoken. Yet he adds immediately: *vel etiam propter continuitatem diurnae convolutionis circa hanc axem quae illum tenet erectum, ut fit in turbine incitato et discursitante.* In the *Epitome astronomiae*, he even uses, referring to the maintenance of the direction of the terrestrial axis, the term *inertia;* this is the passage which we quoted before in which the latter is defined as the *causa privativa motus.*

Concerning bodies which are on the earth, Kepler, like his illustrious predecessor, makes use of the implicit statement, which we have called the "principle of relative motion," in order to shake the direct evidence of the senses: *Motus enim non est proprium visus objectum, nec habet peculiarem sensum quo percipiatur, sed senso communi dejudiciatur* (Vol. VI, p. 181). He also quotes the motion of the ship and cites to this effect the same verse from Virgil. But, like Copernicus, he undoubtedly feels that this is not enough, and, having no longer at his disposal the resource of "natural motion," he invents a special theory. If terrestrial objects are carried along influenced by the motion of the globe, it is because of the action which the earth exerts on them. This action is not simply attractive, or at least not solely so: the earth also carries the object along in its circular motion, and Kepler seems to believe that this influence can be explained by attraction alone: *Cum autem gravia petant terrae corpus per se petanturque ab illo, fortius itaque movebuntur versus partes viciniores Terrae, quam versus remotiores. Quare transeuntibus illis partibus vicinis perpendiculariter subjectis, gravia inter decidendum versus superficiem transeuntem illam insuper etiam circulariter sequentur, perinde ac si essent alligata loco, cui imminent, per ipsam perpendicularem, adeoque per infinitas circum lineas, seu nervos quosdam obliquos minus illa fortes, qui omnes in sese paulatim contrahi soleant.* It is evidently rather difficult to depict the mechanism of this action and to understand how these "oblique nerves" could exert a horizontal push upon a body projected in the air, in order to force it to follow the motion of the earth, whereas it should have, in virtue of its *inertia,* remained at least behind the terrestrial motion. At first sight it seems strange that Kepler could have been content with a conception of this kind. But it must not be forgotten that this latter corresponds to his theory of the revolution of the solar system: the earth makes neighbouring bodies rotate, just as the sun, because of its rotation, makes the planets move. If we wish to know to what extent Kepler's theory differs from ours, not only in regard to the causes which both invoke, but also in regard to the phenomena which must result from them, we have only to refer to the example given by Kepler himself; that of the stone which would arrive on the earth from the depths of space (Kepler, in this case, as in many others, is solely occupied with the terrestrial rotation, neglecting revolution). The assumed motion is very strange from our modern point of view: the stone which moves at first in a straight line toward the centre of the earth undergoes in approaching it a greater and greater deviation in the direction of the rotation, until at a given moment it is completely absorbed in this latter and ends by falling vertically upon a point of the terrestrial surface (cf. the diagram, *ib.*, p. 182).

In the presence of these conceptions one cannot but feel that it was high time for Galileo and Descartes to extricate the Copernicans from embarrassment. Admiration increases for the authors of the heliocentric theory, who knew how, in the midst of obscurity, to distinguish truth, and for their adherents, on whose minds arguments, principally astronomical—that is, in a word, based on considerations of simplicity—were powerful enough to make them overlook grave physical difficulties (an excellent summary of these arguments will be found in LECHALAS, *Etudes sur l'espace et le temps*, 2nd ed., Paris, 1910, p. 143 and ff.). But one is inclined also to show a little more indulgence toward the attitude of those who did not have the courage to adopt these novelties.

Let us state, moreover, that Kepler seems in no way to have been influenced by Galileo, which is strange if we compare dates.

The *Epitome astronomiae copernicanae* from which we have taken our quotations dates from 1618 and 1621. Galileo seems to have conceived the resolution of the motion of the horizontal throw as early as 1610; the theory is indicated, at least partially, in the treatise bearing the title *Istoria e dimostrazioni intorno alle macchie solari*, published in 1613, and other communications seem to have circulated amongst scientists at about that time or a little after (cf. Wohlwill, *l.c.*, XV, p. 267). Now Kepler had certainly followed the writings and discoveries of Galileo with great care. As early as 1597 he had corresponded with him (ed. Frisch, Vol. I, pp. 40–41), and we have five letters of Kepler's dating from the years 1610 and 1611, as well as Galileo's replies (*ib.*, Vol. I, p. 454 and ff.). Can it be possible that he was unaware that the latter, in the treatise which we have mentioned, had clearly explained that a body would preserve its motion indefinitely in any direction upon a spherical surface concentric to the earth? (GALILEO, *Opere*. Florence, 1842, Vol. III, p. 418.)

Evidently, if Kepler had adopted these ideas, there would have been no need for the strange theories of the *Epitome*. Must we suppose, therefore, that these latter had acquired such power over his mind that it had become inaccessible to considerations which appear to us to-day so manifestly evident? What is certain is that even in Kepler's writings posterior to the *Epitome* nothing permits us to conclude that at any moment he had changed his mind about the phenomena of motion. It is true that the last part of his life was particularly troubled by external circumstances; he died in 1630— that is, before the publication of Galileo's *Discorsi*.

Auguste Comte habitually designated the principle of inertia as "Kepler's law" (cf., for example, *Cours*, Vol. VI, p. 682), and this attribution has not yet completely disappeared from the history of physics. The error has been due in great part to the fact that the terms used by Kepler (*inertia*, *Traegheit* in German) have become established in science, thanks very probably to Newton. But this *inertia*, which is the property of matter to remain in the place where it is, a tendency to remain at rest, requiring constantly renewed forces in order to be overcome, was a conception very different from our modern ideas.

The confusion has doubtless been furthered by the fact that Leibniz has declared several times that the concept of inertia was due to Kepler and that Descartes had borrowed it from the latter. As Leibniz certainly had a very clear notion of what to-day we call the principle of inertia, it seemed logical to conclude that he had found it in Kepler's writings. But he really meant something quite different. This is evident from the most explicit of the declarations which refer to this attribution: *Duae insunt Resistentiae sive Massae: primum Antitypia ut vocant seu impenetrabilitas, deinde resistentia seu quod Keplerus vocat corporum inertiam naturalem quam et Cartesius in Epistolis alicubi ex eo agnovit, ut scilicet novum motum non nisi per vim recipiant corpora adeoque imprimenti resistant et vim ejus infringant. Quod non fieret, si in corpore praeter extensionem non inesset τὸ δυναμικὸν seu principium legum motus quo fit ut virium quantitas augeri non possit neque adeo corpus ab alio nisi refracta ejus vi queat impelli* (*Supplément à la lettre à Fabri. Mathematische Schriften*, ed. Gerhardt, Vol. VI, p. 100).

Thus what Leibniz means to attribute to Kepler is the notion of inertia in so far as it is a synonym of *mass*. This affirmation is certainly justified in great part. Kepler frequently stated that, as a result of its *inertia*, matter resisted the force (*virtus*) which attempted to displace it, and that the motion which resulted from it must be regulated in proportion to this inertia and the moving force. This meant attributing to matter, as we should say to-day, a numerical coefficient which is really the essential part of our notion of mass. Kepler knew that the concept thus created was analogous to that of weight, without being entirely identical with it: *quae sit ei velut pondus*, he says, in speaking of the necessity of attributing *inertia* to a celestial body (*l.c.*, Vol. VI, p. 342). This opinion seems to have come to him from the theorists, who toward the end of the Middle Ages had developed the theory of *impetus* (cf. p. 117). We still occasionally use the word inertia in the same sense as Leibniz. Thus, when one speaks of explaining the inertia of bodies by electric theories, one is thinking especially of their mass. However the two ideas may certainly be separated. When we state the *principle of inertia*, we are not occupied with the setting of the body in motion nor with the numerical coefficient which it manifests on this occasion, we imagine it to be already in a certain state and we stipulate the persistency of this latter. Yet the two ideas are connected, and that is why the concept of mass cannot be entirely attributed to Kepler. Descartes may have received the idea from him, but he understood its contents better since he connected it with the principle of inertia.

IV

THE ΠΑΝΤΑ ΡΕΙ OF HERACLITUS

EVEN in Greek antiquity Heraclitus was called obscure; it is, therefore, not surprising that moderns dispute about the real meaning of his doctrine. And yet in the end it seems to us that SCHUSTER (*Heraklit von Ephesus, Acta Soc. philologae Lipsiensis*, Vol. III. Leipzig, 1873, p. 8) is right and that the importance of the passages on the πάντα ρεῖ have been exaggerated. The conception according to which Heraclitus considered that the only thing permanent was an *order* of things, an order which he symbolized by fire, was first asserted by FERDINAND LASSALLE. ZELLER seems to reject this (*Philosophie der Grich*, trans. Boutroux. Paris, 1887, p. 120); and yet in numerous passages he so nearly approaches it (cf., for instance, pp. 121, 136, 145, 188–189) that one hardly perceives the difference. Consequently this way of understanding the doctrine of Heraclitus has become almost current. It, however, seems evident to us in the great number of passages where Aristotle counts Heraclitus amongst those who deduced the whole of reality from one single substance, a substance conceived evidently as material (cf., for instance, *De Caelo*, Book III, Chap. I, 3; *Metaphysics*, Book I, Chap. III, §§ 7, 9, 10, 11, 18, 22 ; Chap. V, 18 ; Chap. VII, §§ 1, 6; cf.; also, on this subject, TANNERY, *Pour l'histoire de la science hellène*, p. 193 ff., fragm. 26, 28, 31, 46, 49, equivalent to SCHUSTER, 12, 44, 47, 57, 59, and to DIELS, *Die Fragmente der Vorsokratiker*. Berlin, 1903, p. 66 ff., fragm. 7, 31, 88, 90) that Heraclitus assumed at least the persistence of something, a substratum, a support, like that which he attributed to the sun renewing itself every day (ZELLER, *l.c.*, p. 147, note). It is thus, it seems, that the doctrine was understood in ancient times, as Lucretius witnesses, who, although he thought it *mad* (*perdelirum*), summarizes it and discusses it at length (Book I, lines 646–693). One cannot doubt that Lucretius conceived Heraclitus's fire as material. The passages like those from Plato's *Cratylus* (*Dialogi*, ed. Wohlrab. Leipzig, 1887, Vol. I, p. 204), which we cited in the text, do not necessarily contradict this opinion. They must be understood as the affirmation that nothing persists as it is—that is, that fire, the substratum and eternal substance, carries in itself the principle of its change. This would be something like Ostwald's energy, both "the most general of substances and the most general of accidents" (cf. p. 347). It is to be noted that Aristotle affirms that Heraclitus supposes that all sensible objects are in a state of perpetual flow and that "there is no science possible for things thus made" (*Metaph.* Book II, Chap. VI, 1). It may be that the term *science* is here taken in its narrow sense of *science of the cause, of the persistent*. However, the fact that immediately after Heraclitus, his doctrine had turned into a sort of absolute scepticism (Cratylus blaming his master for having said that one did not enter twice into the same river; according to him one did not even enter once), seems to show that in spite of the statement frequently cited about the world which "had not been made by any god nor by any man, it has always been and always will be eternally living fire, lighting itself and extinguishing itself regularly" (TANNERY, fragm. 27 ; SCHUSTER, fragm. 46 ; DIELS, fragm. 30), Heraclitus insisted much less upon the universal order than is generally supposed. One may also compare with the doctrine of Cratylus certain statements of Heraclitus himself, such as that quoted by Aristotle, *Metaph.*, Book IV, Chap. III, 10: "A thing may, at the same time, both be and not be."

As to the doctrine of the eternal return in Heraclitus, cf. TANNERY, fragm. 44, 46, 49, 59, 86–87, equivalent to Schuster, 49, 59, 57, 89, 67, and to DIELS, 46, 52, 67, 88, 90. Observe the fragment TANNERY, 91 (SCHUSTER, 88 ; DIELS, 59–60): "The straight and winding path are one and the same, the path up and down is one and the same" (Schuster translates the path *upward* and *downward*, which seems to show that Heraclitus did not have a very clear sense of the irreversibility of the particular phenomenon).

Regarding the great year of Heraclitus, cf. SCHUSTER, *l.c.*, p. 375 ; ZELLER, *l.c.*, p. 164.

INDEX

SCHOPENHAUER (*continued*)—
occult qualities, 245
Leibniz's angel, 298
impenetrability, 300
the external world and representation, 362
and Byron, 417
(*see Appendix I*)
SCHUSTER, *see Appendix IV*
SCHUTZENBERGER, atomic theories, 112
n. 131, 255 n. 30
SCHWANN, presumed influence, 56 n. 15
SCIENCE—
rule of action, 21, 22
real advance, 21, 384
its domain, 23–24
progressive evolution, 24 f.
and free will, 25, 308
the miracle, 27 f.
science as an end in itself, 41 f.
science purely that of law, 226–227
and mechanism, 253, 297
and reduction to non-existence, 254
importance of Carnot's principle,
278, 284, 286
disagreement with reality, 282–283
domination of identity, 284
re-establishment of reality, 284–285,
286
relation between conformity to law
and the three concepts of causality,
309–310
and teleology, 311–319
qualitative conceptions, 334
reduction to quantity, 346
continuity of common sense and
science, 361–383
vanity of tendency toward elimination of causality, 366
science creates objects, 368
supplements common sense, 371
does not return toward sensation, 373
and metaphysics, 377–378, 416–419
transformation of perception, 379
distinction: common sense acts unconsciously, 379–380
and positivism, 384 f.
scientist's state of mind, 386 f.
science and hypothesis, 390–395
Kant's conception, 400
Whewell's conception, 401–402
a priori science, 402–403
impossibility of pure science, 402

SCIENCE (*continued*)—
rôle of empiricism, 403
method of science, 403 f.
dynamism, 406
use of kinetic theories, 406–407
perpetual flux, 410
tendency towards universal mechanism or atomism, 410–411
and "simplicity," 411–414
analogous reasoning, 414–415
perennial character of mechanism,
415–416
theories and causal principle, 420
causal manifestations, 424–433
(*see Appendix IV*)
SCOT, M., translation of Al Bitragi
(Alpetragius), 117
SECCHI, A., elasticity of molecules, 71
SÉGUIN—
anticipates the principle of conservation of energy, 193, 202
impossibility of perpetual motion,
202
Tait's attacks, 213 n. 58
SENNERT, atomism, 87
SEXTUS EMPIRICUS—
motion, 116
relativity of motion, 127 f., 130
Democritus, 292
SIEMANS, analogy with Rankine, 288
n. 30
SIMPLICIUS, persistency of rectilinear
motion, 115, 117
(*see Appendix II, The passages from
Plutarch and Simplicius*)
SMITH, ADAM, restriction of conformity
to law, 20
SOMMERFELD, atomic theory, 103 n. 8
SPENCER, HERBERT—
concept of force, 81
inertia, 124 f.
conservation of matter, 177–178; of
energy, 198
unity of matter, 240
the "half-periods," 270; related to
ancient conceptions, 271–272; distinguished from Boltzmann's hypothesis, 274
primacy of touch, 303
SPINOZA—
understanding, 42
ultimate cause, 253
mechanism, 253–254, 292

CATALOGUE OF DOVER BOOKS

Books Explaining Science and Mathematics

WHAT IS SCIENCE?, N. Campbell. The role of experiment and measurement, the function of mathematics, the nature of scientific laws, the difference between laws and theories, the limitations of science, and many similarly provocative topics are treated clearly and without technicalities by an eminent scientist. "Still an excellent introduction to scientific philosophy," H. Margenau in PHYSICS TODAY. "A first-rate primer . . . deserves a wide audience," SCIENTIFIC AMERICAN. 192pp. 5⅜ x 8.   S43 Paperbound **$1.25**

THE NATURE OF PHYSICAL THEORY, P. W. Bridgman. A Nobel Laureate's clear, non-technical lectures on difficulties and paradoxes connected with frontier research on the physical sciences. Concerned with such central concepts as thought, logic, mathematics, relativity, probability, wave mechanics, etc. he analyzes the contributions of such men as Newton, Einstein, Bohr, Heisenberg, and many others. "Lucid and entertaining . . . recommended to anyone who wants to get some insight into current philosophies of science," THE NEW PHILOSOPHY. Index. xi + 138pp. 5⅜ x 8.   S33 Paperbound **$1.25**

EXPERIMENT AND THEORY IN PHYSICS, Max Born. A Nobel Laureate examines the nature of experiment and theory in theoretical physics and analyzes the advances made by the great physicists of our day: Heisenberg, Einstein, Bohr, Planck, Dirac, and others. The actual process of creation is detailed step-by-step by one who participated. A fine examination of the scientific method at work. 44pp. 5⅜ x 8.   S308 Paperbound **75¢**

THE PSYCHOLOGY OF INVENTION IN THE MATHEMATICAL FIELD, J. Hadamard. The reports of such men as Descartes, Pascal, Einstein, Poincaré, and others are considered in this investigation of the method of idea-creation in mathematics and other sciences and the thinking process in general. How do ideas originate? What is the role of the unconscious? What is Poincaré's forgetting hypothesis? are some of the fascinating questions treated. A penetrating analysis of Einstein's thought processes concludes the book. xiii + 145pp. 5⅜ x 8.   T107 Paperbound **$1.25**

THE NATURE OF LIGHT AND COLOUR IN THE OPEN AIR, M. Minnaert. Why are shadows sometimes blue, sometimes green, or other colors depending on the light and surroundings? What causes mirages? Why do multiple suns and moons appear in the sky? Professor Minnaert explains these unusual phenomena and hundreds of others in simple, easy-to-understand terms based on optical laws and the properties of light and color. No mathematics is required but artists, scientists, students, and everyone fascinated by these "tricks" of nature will find thousands of useful and amazing pieces of information. Hundreds of observational experiments are suggested which require no special equipment. 200 illustrations; 42 photos. xvi + 362pp. 5⅜ x 8.   T196 Paperbound **$2.00**

*MATHEMATICS IN ACTION, O. G. Sutton. Everyone with a command of high school algebra will find this book one of the finest possible introductions to the application of mathematics to physical theory. Ballistics, numerical analysis, waves and wavelike phenomena, Fourier series, group concepts, fluid flow and aerodynamics, statistical measures, and meteorology are discussed with unusual clarity. Some calculus and differential equations theory is developed by the author for the reader's help in the more difficult sections. 88 figures. Index. viii + 236pp. 5⅜ x 8.   T440 Clothbound **$3.50**

SOAP-BUBBLES: THEIR COLOURS AND THE FORCES THAT MOULD THEM, C. V. Boys. For continuing popularity and validity as scientific primer, few books can match this volume of easily-followed experiments, explanations. Lucid exposition of complexities of liquid films, surface tension and related phenomena, bubbles' reaction to heat, motion, music, magnetic fields. Experiments with capillary attraction, soap bubbles on frames, composite bubbles, liquid cylinders and jets, bubbles other than soap, etc. Wonderful introduction to scientific method, natural laws that have many ramifications in areas of modern physics. Only complete edition in print. New Introduction by S. Z. Lewin, New York University. 83 illustrations; 1 full-page color plate. xii + 190pp. 5⅜ x 8½.   T542 Paperbound **95¢**

History of Science and
Mathematics

THE STUDY OF THE HISTORY OF MATHEMATICS, THE STUDY OF THE HISTORY OF SCIENCE, G. Sarton. Two books bound as one. Each volume contains a long introduction to the methods and philosophy of each of these historical fields, covering the skills and sympathies of the historian, concepts of history of science, psychology of idea-creation, and the purpose of history of science. Prof. Sarton also provides more than 80 pages of classified bibliography. Complete and unabridged. Indexed. 10 illustrations. 188pp. 5⅜ x 8.   T240 Paperbound **$1.25**

A HISTORY OF PHYSICS, Florian Cajori, Ph.D. First written in 1899, thoroughly revised in 1929, this is still best entry into antecedents of modern theories. Precise non-mathematical discussion of ideas, theories, techniques, apparatus of each period from Greeks to 1920's, analyzing within each period basic topics of matter, mechanics, light, electricity and magnetism, sound, atomic theory, etc. Stress on modern developments, from early 19th century to present. Written with critical eye on historical development, significance. Provides most of needed historical background for student of physics. Reprint of second (1929) edition. Index. Bibliography in footnotes. 16 figures. xv + 424pp. 5⅜ x 8.   T970 Paperbound **$2.00**

A HISTORY OF ASTRONOMY FROM THALES TO KEPLER, J. L. E. Dreyer. Formerly titled A HISTORY OF PLANETARY SYSTEMS FROM THALES TO KEPLER. This is the only work in English which provides a detailed history of man's cosmological views from prehistoric times up through the Renaissance. It covers Egypt, Babylonia, early Greece, Alexandria, the Middle Ages, Copernicus, Tycho Brahe, Kepler, and many others. Epicycles and other complex theories of positional astronomy are explained in terms nearly everyone will find clear and easy to understand. "Standard reference on Greek astronomy and the Copernican revolution," SKY AND TELESCOPE. Bibliography. 21 diagrams. Index. xvii + 430pp. 5⅜ x 8.   S79 Paperbound **$2.25**

A SHORT HISTORY OF ASTRONOMY, A. Berry. A popular standard work for over 50 years, this thorough and accurate volume covers the science from primitive times to the end of the 19th century. After the Greeks and Middle Ages, individual chapters analyze Copernicus, Brahe, Galileo, Kepler, and Newton, and the mixed reception of their startling discoveries. Post-Newtonian achievements are then discussed in unusual detail: Halley, Bradley, Lagrange, Laplace, Herschel, Bessel, etc. 2 indexes. 104 illustrations, 9 portraits. xxxi + 440pp. 5⅜ x 8.   T210 Paperbound **$2.00**

PIONEERS OF SCIENCE, Sir Oliver Lodge. An authoritative, yet elementary history of science by a leading scientist and expositor. Concentrating on individuals—Copernicus, Brahe, Kepler, Galileo, Descartes, Newton, Laplace, Herschel, Lord Kelvin, and other scientists—the author presents their discoveries in historical order, adding biographical material on each man and full, specific explanations of their achievements. The full, clear discussions of the accomplishments of post-Newtonian astronomers are features seldom found in other books on the subject. Index. 120 illustrations. xv + 404pp. 5⅜ x 8.   T716 Paperbound **$1.65**

THE BIRTH AND DEVELOPMENT OF THE GEOLOGICAL SCIENCES, F. D. Adams. The most complete and thorough history of the earth sciences in print. Geological thought from earliest recorded times to the end of the 19th century—covers over 300 early thinkers and systems: fossils and hypothetical explanations of them, vulcanists vs. neptunists, figured stones and paleontology, generation of stones, and similar topics. 91 illustrations, including medieval, renaissance woodcuts, etc. 632 footnotes and bibliographic notes. Index. 511pp. 5⅜ x 8.   T5 Paperbound **$2.25**

THE STORY OF ALCHEMY AND EARLY CHEMISTRY, J. M. Stillman. "Add the blood of a red-haired man"—a recipe typical of the many quoted in this authoritative and readable history of the strange beliefs and practices of the alchemists. Concise studies of every leading figure in alchemy and early chemistry through Lavoisier, in this curious epic of superstition and true science, constructed from scores of rare and difficult Greek, Latin, German, and French texts. Foreword by S. W. Young. 246-item bibliography. Index. xiii + 566pp. 5⅜ x 8.   S628 Paperbound **$2.45**

HISTORY OF MATHEMATICS, D. E. Smith. Most comprehensive non-technical history of math in English. Discusses the lives and works of over a thousand major and minor figures, from Euclid to Descartes, Gauss, and Riemann. Vol. I: A chronological examination, from primitive concepts through Egypt, Babylonia, Greece, the Orient, Rome, the Middle Ages, the Renaissance, and up to 1900. Vol. 2: The development of ideas in specific fields and problems, up through elementary calculus. Two volumes, total of 510 illustrations, 1355pp. 5⅜ x 8. Set boxed in attractive container.   T429,430 Paperbound the set **$5.00**

Classics of Science

THE DIDEROT PICTORIAL ENCYCLOPEDIA OF TRADES AND INDUSTRY, MANUFACTURING AND THE TECHNICAL ARTS IN PLATES SELECTED FROM "L'ENCYCLOPEDIE OU DICTIONNAIRE RAISONNE DES SCIENCES, DES ARTS, ET DES METIERS" OF DENIS DIDEROT, edited with text by C. Gillispie. The first modern selection of plates from the high point of 18th century French engraving, Diderot's famous Encyclopedia. Over 2000 illustrations on 485 full page plates, most of them original size, illustrating the trades and industries of one of the most fascinating periods of modern history, 18th century France. These magnificent engravings provide an invaluable glimpse into the past for the student of early technology, a lively and accurate social document to students of cultures, an outstanding find to the lover of fine engravings. The plates teem with life, with men, women, and children performing all of the thousands of operations necessary to the trades before and during the early stages of the industrial revolution. Plates are in sequence, and show general operations, closeups of difficult operations, and details of complex machinery. Such important and interesting trades and industries are illustrated as sowing, harvesting, beekeeping, cheesemaking, operating windmills, milling flour, charcoal burning, tobacco processing, indigo, fishing, arts of war, salt extraction, mining, smelting iron, casting iron, steel, extracting mercury, zinc, sulphur, copper, etc., slating, tinning, silverplating, gilding, making gunpowder, cannons, bells, shoeing horses, tanning, papermaking, printing, dying, and more than 40 other categories. 920pp. 9 x 12. Heavy library cloth. T421 Two volume set **$18.50**

THE PRINCIPLES OF SCIENCE, A TREATISE ON LOGIC AND THE SCIENTIFIC METHOD, W. Stanley Jevons. Treating such topics as Inductive and Deductive Logic, the Theory of Number, Probability, and the Limits of Scientific Method, this milestone in the development of symbolic logic remains a stimulating contribution to the investigation of inferential validity in the natural and social sciences. It significantly advances Boole's logic, and describes a machine which is a foundation of modern electronic calculators. In his introduction, Ernest Nagel of Columbia University says, "(Jevons) . . . continues to be of interest as an attempt to articulate the logic of scientific inquiry." Index. liii + 786pp. 5⅜ x 8. S446 Paperbound **$2.98**

***DIALOGUES CONCERNING TWO NEW SCIENCES, Galileo Galilei.** A classic of experimental science which has had a profound and enduring influence on the entire history of mechanics and engineering. Galileo based this, his finest work, on 30 years of experimentation. It offers a fascinating and vivid exposition of dynamics, elasticity, sound, ballistics, strength of materials, and the scientific method. Translated by H. Crew and A. de Salvio. 126 diagrams. Index. xxi + 288pp. 5⅜ x 8. S99 Paperbound **$1.75**

DE MAGNETE, William Gilbert. This classic work on magnetism founded a new science. Gilbert was the first to use the word "electricity," to recognize mass as distinct from weight, to discover the effect of heat on magnetic bodies; invented an electroscope, differentiated between static electricity and magnetism, conceived of the earth as a magnet. Written by the first great experimental scientist, this lively work is valuable not only as an historical landmark, but as the delightfully easy-to-follow record of a perpetually searching, ingenious mind. Translated by P. F. Mottelay. 25 page biographical memoir. 90 fix. lix + 368pp. 5⅜ x 8. S470 Paperbound **$2.00**

***OPTICKS, Sir Isaac Newton.** An enormous storehouse of insights and discoveries on light, reflection, color, refraction, theories of wave and corpuscular propagation of light, optical apparatus, and mathematical devices which have recently been reevaluated in terms of modern physics and placed in the top-most ranks of Newton's work! Foreword by Albert Einstein. Preface by I. B. Cohen of Harvard U. 7 pages of portraits, facsimile pages, letters, etc. cxvi + 412pp. 5⅜ x 8. S205 Paperbound **$2.25**

A SURVEY OF PHYSICAL THEORY, M. Planck. Lucid essays on modern physics for the general reader by the Nobel Laureate and creator of the quantum revolution. Planck explains how the new concepts came into being; explores the clash between theories of mechanics, electrodynamics, and thermodynamics; and traces the evolution of the concept of light through Newton, Huygens, Maxwell, and his own quantum theory, providing unparalleled insights into his development of this momentous modern concept. Bibliography. Index. vii + 121pp. 5⅜ x 8. S650 Paperbound **$1.15**

A SOURCE BOOK IN MATHEMATICS, D. E. Smith. English translations of the original papers that announced the great discoveries in mathematics from the Renaissance to the end of the 19th century: succinct selections from 125 different treatises and articles, most of them unavailable elsewhere in English—Newton, Leibniz, Pascal, Riemann, Bernoulli, etc. 24 articles trace developments in the field of number, 18 cover algebra, 36 are on geometry, and 13 on calculus. Biographical-historical introductions to each article. Two volume set. Index in each. Total of 115 illustrations. Total of xxviii + 742pp. 5⅜ x 8. S552 Vol I Paperbound **$2.00**
S553 Vol II Paperbound **$2.00**
The set, boxed **$4.00**

*THE THIRTEEN BOOKS OF EUCLID'S ELEMENTS, edited by T. L. Heath. This is the complete EUCLID — the definitive edition of one of the greatest classics of the western world. Complete English translation of the Heiberg text with spurious Book XIV. Detailed 150-page introduction discusses aspects of Greek and medieval mathematics: Euclid, texts, commentators, etc. Paralleling the text is an elaborate critical exposition analyzing each definition, proposition, postulate, etc., and covering textual matters, mathematical analyses, refutations, extensions, etc. Unabridged reproduction of the Cambridge 2nd edition. 3 volumes. Total of 995. figures, 1426pp. 5⅜ x 8.   S88, 89, 90 — 3 vol. set, Paperbound **$6.75**

*THE GEOMETRY OF RENE DESCARTES. The great work which founded analytic geometry. The renowned Smith-Latham translation faced with the original French text containing all of Descartes' own diagrams! Contains: Problems the Construction of Which Requires Only Straight Lines and Circles; On the Nature of Curved Lines; On the Construction of Solid or Supersolid Problems. Notes. Diagrams. 258pp.   S68 Paperbound **$1.60**

*A PHILOSOPHICAL ESSAY ON PROBABILITIES, P. Laplace. Without recourse to any mathematics above grammar school, Laplace develops a philosophically, mathematically and historically classical exposition of the nature of probability: its functions and limitations, operations in practical affairs, calculations in games of chance, insurance, government, astronomy, and countless other fields. New introduction by E. T. Bell. viii + 196pp. S166 Paperbound **$1.35**

DE RE METALLICA, Georgius Agricola. Written over 400 years ago, for 200 years the most authoritative first-hand account of the production of metals, translated in 1912 by former President Herbert Hoover and his wife, and today still one of the most beautiful and fascinating volumes ever produced in the history of science! 12 books, exhaustively annotated, give a wonderfully lucid and vivid picture of the history of mining, selection of sites, types of deposits, excavating pits, sinking shafts, ventilating, pumps, crushing machinery, assaying, smelting, refining metals, making salt, alum, nitre, glass, and many other topics. This definitive edition contains all 289 of the 16th century woodcuts which made the original an artistic masterpiece. It makes a superb gift for geologists, engineers, libraries, artists, historians, and everyone interested in science and early illustrative art. Biographical, historical introductions. Bibliography, survey of ancient authors. Indices. 289 illustrations. 672pp. 6¾ x 10¾. Deluxe library edition.   S6 Clothbound **$10.00**

GEOGRAPHICAL ESSAYS, W. M. Davis. Modern geography and geomorphology rest on the fundamental work of this scientist. His new concepts of earth-processes revolutionized science and his broad interpretation of the scope of geography created a deeper understanding of the interrelation of the landscape and the forces that mold it. This first inexpensive unabridged edition covers theory of geography, methods of advanced geographic teaching, descriptions of geographic areas, analyses of land-shaping processes, and much besides. Not only a factual and historical classic, it is still widely read for its reflections of modern scientific thought. Introduction. 130 figures. Index. vi + 777pp. 5⅜ x 8.
                                        S383 Paperbound **$3.50**

CHARLES BABBAGE AND HIS CALCULATING ENGINES, edited by P. Morrison and E. Morrison. Friend of Darwin, Humboldt, and Laplace, Babbage was a leading pioneer in large-scale mathematical machines and a prophetic herald of modern operational research—true father of Harvard's relay computer Mark I. His Difference Engine and Analytical Engine were the first successful machines in the field. This volume contains a valuable introduction on his life and work; major excerpts from his fascinating autobiography, revealing his eccentric and unusual personality; and extensive selections from "Babbage's Calculating Engines," a compilation of hard-to-find journal articles, both by Babbage and by such eminent contributors as the Countess of Lovelace, L. F. Menabrea, and Dionysius Lardner. 11 illustrations. Appendix of miscellaneous papers. Index. Bibliography. xxxviii + 400pp. 5⅜ x 8.   T12 Paperbound **$2.00**

*THE WORKS OF ARCHIMEDES WITH THE METHOD OF ARCHIMEDES, edited by T. L. Heath. All the known works of the greatest mathematician of antiquity including the recently discovered METHOD OF ARCHIMEDES. This last is the only work we have which shows exactly how early mathematicians discovered their proofs before setting them down in their final perfection. A 186 page study by the eminent scholar Heath discusses Archimedes and the history of Greek mathematics. Bibliography. 563pp. 5⅜ x 8.   S9 Paperbound **$2.45**

Dover Classical Records

Now available directly to the public exclusively from Dover: top-quality recordings of fine classical music for only $2 per record! Originally released by a major company (except for the previously unreleased Gimpel recording of Bach) to sell for $5 and $6, these records were issued under our imprint only after they had passed a severe critical test. We insisted upon:

First-rate music that is enjoyable, musically important and culturally significant.

First-rate performances, where the artists have carried out the composer's intentions, in which the music is alive, vigorous, played with understanding and sympathy.

First-rate sound—clear, sonorous, fully balanced, crackle-free, whir-free.

Have in your home music by major composers, performed by such gifted musicians as Elsner, Gitlis, Wührer, the Barchet Quartet, Gimpel. Enthusiastically received when first released, many of these performances are definitive. The records are not seconds or remainders, but brand new pressings made on pure vinyl from carefully chosen master tapes. "All purpose" 12" monaural 33⅓ rpm records, they play equally well on hi-fi and stereo equipment. Fine music for discriminating music lovers, superlatively played, flawlessly recorded: there is no better way to build your library of recorded classical music at remarkable savings. There are no strings; this is not a come-on, not a club, forcing you to buy records you may not want in order to get a few at a lower price. Buy whatever records you want in any quantity, and never pay more than $2 each. Your obligation ends with your first purchase. And that's when ours begins. Dover's money-back guarantee allows you to return any record for any reason, even if you don't like the music, for a full, immediate refund, no questions asked.

MOZART: STRING QUARTET IN A MAJOR (K.464); STRING QUARTET IN C MAJOR ("DISSONANT", K.465), Barchet Quartet. The final two of the famed Haydn Quartets, high-points in the history of music. The A Major was accepted with delight by Mozart's contemporaries, but the C Major, with its dissonant opening, aroused strong protest. Today, of course, the remarkable resolutions of the dissonances are recognized as major musical achievements. "Beautiful warm playing," MUSICAL AMERICA. "Two of Mozart's loveliest quartets in a distinguished performance," REV. OF RECORDED MUSIC. (Playing time 58 mins.) HCR 5200 **$2.00**

MOZART: QUARTETS IN G MAJOR (K.80); D MAJOR (K.155); G MAJOR (K.156); C MAJOR (K.157), Barchet Quartet. The early chamber music of Mozart receives unfortunately little attention. First-rate music of the Italian school, it contains all the lightness and charm that belongs only to the youthful Mozart. This is currently the only available source for the composer's work of this time period. "Excellent," HIGH FIDELITY. "Filled with sunshine and youthful joy; played with verve, recorded sound live and brilliant," CHRISTIAN SCI. MONITOR. (Playing time 51 mins.) HCR 5201 **$2.00**

MOZART: SERENADE #9 IN D MAJOR ("POSTHORN", K.320); SERENADE #6 IN D MAJOR ("SERENATA NOTTURNA", K.239), Pro Musica Orch. of Stuttgart, under Edouard van Remoortel. For Mozart, the serenade was a highly effective form, since he could bring to it the immediacy and intimacy of chamber music as well as the free fantasy of larger group music. Both these serenades are distinguished by a playful, mischievous quality, a spirit perfectly captured in this fine performance. "A triumph, polished playing from the orchestra," HI FI MUSIC AT HOME. "Sound is rich and resonant, fidelity is wonderful," REV. OF RECORDED MUSIC. (Playing time 51 mins.) HCR 5202 **$2.00**

MOZART: DIVERTIMENTO IN E FLAT MAJOR FOR STRING TRIO (K.563); ADAGIO AND FUGUE IN F MINOR FOR STRING TRIO (K.404a), Kehr Trio. The Divertimento is one of Mozart's most beloved pieces, called by Einstein "the finest, most perfect trio ever heard." It is difficult to imagine a music lover who will not be delighted by it. This is the only recording of the lesser known Adagio and Fugue, written in 1782 and influenced by Bach's Well-Tempered Clavichord. "Extremely beautiful recording, strongly recommended," THE OBSERVER. "Superior to rival editions," HIGH FIDELITY. (Playing time 51 mins.) HCR 5203 **$2.00**

SCHUMANN: KREISLERIANA (OP.16); FANTASY IN C MAJOR ("FANTASIE," OP.17), Vlado Perlemuter, Piano. The vigorous Romantic imagination and the remarkable emotional qualities of Schumann's piano music raise it to special eminence in 19th century creativity. Both these pieces are rooted in the composer's tortuous romance with his future wife, Clara, and both receive brilliant treatment at the hands of Vlado Perlemuter, Paris Conservatory, proclaimed by Alfred Cortot "not only a great virtuoso but also a great musician." "The best Kreisleriana to date," BILLBOARD. (Playing time 55 mins.) HCR 5204 **$2.00**

SCHUMANN: TRIO #1, D MINOR; TRIO #3, G MINOR, Trio di Bolzano. The fiery, romantic, melodic Trio #1, and the dramatic, seldom heard Trio #3 are both movingly played by a fine chamber ensemble. No one personified Romanticism to the general public of the 1840's more than did Robert Schumann, and among his most romantic works are these trios for cello, violin and piano. "Ensemble and overall interpretation leave little to be desired," HIGH FIDELITY. "An especially understanding performance," REV. OF RECORDED MUSIC. (Playing time 54 mins.) HCR 5205 **$2.00**

SCHUMANN: TRIOS #1 IN D MINOR (OPUS 63) AND #3 IN G MINOR (OPUS 110), Trio di Bolzano. The fiery, romantic, melodic Trio #1 and the dramatic, seldom heard Trio #3 are both movingly played by a fine chamber ensemble. No one personified Romanticism to the general public of the 1840's more than did Robert Schumann, and among his most romantic works are these trios for cello, violin and piano. "Ensemble and overall interpretation leave little to be desired," HIGH FIDELITY. "An especially understanding performance," REV. OF RECORDED MUSIC. (Playing time 54 mins.)   HCR 5205 **$2.00**

SCHUBERT: QUINTET IN A ("TROUT") (OPUS 114), AND NOCTURNE IN E FLAT (OPUS 148), Friedrich Wührer, Piano and Barchet Quartet. If there is a single piece of chamber music that is a universal favorite, it is probably Schubert's "Trout" Quintet. Delightful melody, harmonic resources, musical exuberance are its characteristics. The Nocturne (played by Wührer, Barchet, and Reimann) is an exquisite piece with a deceptively simple theme and harmony. "The best Trout on the market—Wührer is a fine Viennese-style Schubertian, and his spirit infects the Barchets," ATLANTIC MONTHLY. "Exquisitely recorded," ETUDE. (Playing time 44 mins.)   HCR 5206 **$2.00**

SCHUBERT: PIANO SONATAS IN C MINOR AND B (OPUS 147), Friedrich Wührer. Schubert's sonatas retain the structure of the classical form, but delight listeners with romantic freedom and a special melodic richness. The C Minor, one of the Three Grand Sonatas, is a product of the composer's maturity. The B Major was not published until 15 years after his death. "Remarkable interpretation, reproduction of the first rank," DISQUES. "A superb pianist for music like this, musicianship, sweep, power, and an ability to integrate Schubert's measures such as few pianists have had since Schnabel," Harold Schonberg. (Playing time 49 mins.)   HCR 5207 **$2.00**

STRAVINSKY: VIOLIN CONCERTO IN D, Ivry Gitlis, Cologne Orchestra; DUO CONCERTANTE, Ivry Gitlis, Violin, Charlotte Zelka, Piano, Cologne Orchestra; JEU DE CARTES, Bamberg Symphony, under Hollreiser. Igor Stravinsky is probably the most important composer of this century, and these three works are among the most significant of his neoclassical period of the 30's. The Violin Concerto is one of the few modern classics. Jeu de Cartes, a ballet score, bubbles with gaiety, color and melodiousness. "Imaginatively played and beautifully recorded," E. T. Canby, HARPERS MAGAZINE. "Gitlis is excellent, Hollreiser beautifully worked out," HIGH FIDELITY. (Playing time 55 mins.)   HCR 5208 **$2.00**

GEMINIANI: SIX CONCERTI GROSSI, OPUS 3, Helma Elsner, Harpsichord, Barchet Quartet, Pro Musica Orch. of Stuttgart, under Reinhardt. Francesco Geminiani (1687-1762) has been rediscovered in the same musical exploration that revealed Scarlatti, Vivaldi, and Corelli. In form he is more sophisticated than the earlier Italians, but his music delights modern listeners with its combination of contrapuntal techniques and the full harmonies and rich melodies charcteristic of Italian music. This is the only recording of the six 1733 concerti: D Major, B Flat Minor, E Minor, G Minor, E Minor (bis), and D Minor. "I warmly recommend it, spacious, magnificent, I enjoyed every bar," C. Cudworth, RECORD NEWS. "Works of real charm, recorded with understanding and style," ETUDE. (Playing time 52 mins.)   HCR 5209 **$2.00**

MODERN PIANO SONATAS: BARTOK: SONATA FOR PIANO; BLOCH: SONATA FOR PIANO (1935); PROKOFIEV: PIANO SONATA #7 IN B FLAT ("STALINGRAD"); STRAVINSKY: PIANO SONATA (1924), István Nádas, Piano. Shows some of the major forces and directions in modern piano music: Stravinsky's crisp austerity; Bartok's fusion of Hungarian folk motives; incisive diverse rhythms, and driving power; Bloch's distinctive emotional vigor; Prokofiev's brilliance and melodic beauty couched in pre-Romantic forms. "A most interesting documentation of the contemporary piano sonata. Nadas is a very good pianist." HIGH FIDELITY. (Playing time 59 mins.)   HCR 5215 **$2.00**

VIVALDI: CONCERTI FOR FLUTE, VIOLIN, BASSOON, AND HARPSICHORD: #8 IN G MINOR, #21 IN F, #27 IN D, #7 IN D; SONATA #1 IN A MINOR, Gastone Tassinari, Renato Giangrandi, Giorgio Semprini, Arlette Eggmann. More than any other Baroque composer, Vivaldi moved the concerto grosso closer to the solo concert we deem standard today. In these concerti he wrote virtuosi music for the solo instruments, allowing each to introduce new material or expand on musical ideas, creating tone colors unusual even for Vivaldi. As a result, this record displays a new area of his genius, offering some of his most brilliant music. Performed by a top-rank European group. (Playing time 45 mins.)   HCR 5216 **$2.00**

LÜBECK: CANTATAS: HILF DEINEM VOLK; GOTT, WIE DEIN NAME, Stuttgart Choral Society, Swabian Symphony Orch.; PRELUDES AND FUGUES IN C MINOR AND IN E, Eva Hölderlin, Organ. Vincent Lübeck (1654-1740), contemporary of Bach and Buxtehude, was one of the great figures of the 18th-century North German school. These examples of Lübeck's few surviving works indicate his power and brilliance. Voice and instrument lines in the cantatas are strongly reminiscent of the organ: the preludes and fugues show the influence of Bach and Buxtehude. This is the only recording of the superb cantatas. Text and translation included. "Outstanding record," E. T. Canby, SAT. REVIEW. "Hölderlin's playing is exceptional," AM. RECORD REVIEW. "Will make [Lübeck] many new friends," Philip Miller. (Playing time 37 mins.)   HCR 5217 **$2.00**

CATALOGUE OF DOVER BOOKS

DONIZETTI: BETLY (LA CAPANNA SVIZZERA), Soloists of Compagnia del Teatro dell'Opera Comica di Roma, Societa del Quartetto, Rome, Chorus and Orch. Betly, a delightful one-act opera written in 1836, is similar in style and story to one of Donizetti's better-known operas, L'Elisir. Betly is lighthearted and farcical, with bright melodies and a freshness character-istic of the best of Donizetti. Libretto (English and Italian) included. "The chief honors go to Angela Tuccari who sings the title role, and the record is worth having for her alone," M. Rayment, GRAMOPHONE REC. REVIEW. "The interpretation . . . is excellent . . . This is a charming record which we recommend to lovers of little-known works," DISQUES.

HCR 5218 **$2.00**

ROSSINI: L'OCCASIONE FA IL LADRO (IL CAMBIO DELLA VALIGIA), Soloists of Compagnia del Teatro dell'Opera Comica di Roma, Societa del Quartetto, Rome, Chorus and Orch. A charm-ing one-act opera buffa, this is one of the first works of Rossini's maturity, and it is filled with the wit, gaiety and sparkle that make his comic operas second only to Mozart's. Like other Rossini works, L'Occasione makes use of the theme of impersonation and attendant amusing confusions. This is the only recording of this important buffa. Full libretto (English and Italian) included. "A major rebirth, a stylish performance . . . the Roman recording engineers have outdone themselves," H. Weinstock, SAT. REVIEW. (Playing time 53 mins.)

HCR 5219 **$2.00**

DOWLAND: "FIRST BOOKE OF AYRES," Pro Musica Antiqua of Brussels, Safford Cape, Director. This is the first recording to include all 22 of the songs of this great collection, written by John Dowland, one of the most important writers of songs of 16th and 17th century Eng-land. The participation of the Brussels Pro Musica under Safford Cape insures scholarly ac-curacy and musical artistry. "Powerfully expressive and very beautiful," B. Haggin. "The musicianly singers . . . never fall below an impressive standard," Philip Miller. Text included. (Playing time 51 mins.)

HCR 5220 **$2.00**

FRENCH CHANSONS AND DANCES OF THE 16TH CENTURY, Pro Musica Antiqua of Brussels, Safford Cape, Director. A remarkable selection of 26 three- or four-part chansons and de-lightful dances from the French Golden Age—by such composers as Orlando Lasso, Crecquil-lon, Claude Gervaise, etc. Text and translation included. "Delightful, well-varied with respect to mood and to vocal and instrumental color," HIGH FIDELITY. "Performed with . . . dis-crimination and musical taste, full of melodic distinction and harmonic resource," Irving Kolodin. (Playing time 39 mins.)

HCR 5221 **$2.00**

GALUPPI: CONCERTI A QUATRO: #1 IN G MINOR, #2 IN G, #3 IN D, #4 IN C MINOR, #5 IN E FLAT, AND #6 IN B FLAT, Biffoli Quartet. During Baldassare Galuppi's lifetime, his instru-mental music was widely renowned, and his contemporaries Mozart and Haydn thought highly of his work. These 6 concerti reflect his great ability; and they are among the most interesting compositions of the period. They are remarkable for their unusual combinations of timbres and for emotional elements that were only then beginning to be introduced into music. Performed by the well-known Biffoli Quartet, this is the only record devoted exclu-sively to Galuppi. (Playing time 47 mins.)

HCR 5222 **$2.00**

HAYDN: DIVERTIMENTI FOR WIND BAND, IN C; IN F; DIVERTIMENTO A NOVE STROMENTI IN C FOR STRINGS AND WIND INSTRUMENTS, reconstructed by H. C. Robbins Landon, performed by members of Vienna State Opera Orch.; MOZART DIVERTIMENTI IN C, III (K. 187) AND IV (K. 188), Salzburg Wind Ensemble. Robbins Landon discovered Haydn manuscripts in a Bene-dictine monastery in Lower Austria, edited them and restored their original instrumentation The result is this magnificent record. Two little-known divertimenti by Mozart—of great charm and appeal—are also included. None of this music is available elsewhere (Playing time 58 mins.)

HCR 5223 **$2.00**

PURCELL: TRIO SONATAS FROM "SONATAS OF FOUR PARTS" (1697): #9 IN F ("GOLDEN"), #7 IN C, #1 IN B MINOR, #10 IN D, #4 IN D MINOR, #2 IN E FLAT, AND #8 IN G MINOR, Giorgio Ciompi, and Werner Torkanowsky, Violins, Geo. Koutzen, Cello, and Herman Chessid, Harpsichord. These posthumously-published sonatas show Purcell at his most advanced and mature. They are certainly among the finest musical examples of pre-modern chamber music. Those not familiar with his instrumental music are well-advised to hear these outstanding pieces. "Performance sounds excellent," Harold Schonberg. "Some of the most noble and touching music known to anyone," AMERICAN RECORD GUIDE. (Playing time 58 mins.)

HCR 5224 **$2.00**

BARTOK: VIOLIN CONCERTO; SONATA FOR UNACCOMPANIED VIOLIN, Ivry Gitlis, Pro Musica of Vienna, under Hornstein. Both these works are outstanding examples of Bartok's final period, and they show his powers at their fullest. The Violin Concerto is, in the opinion of many authorities, Bartok's finest work, and the Sonata, his last work, is "a masterpiece" (F. Sackville West). "Wonderful, finest performance of both Bartok works I have ever heard," GRAMOPHONE. "Gitlis makes such potent and musical sense out of these works that I suspect many general music lovers (not otherwise in sympathy with modern music) will discover to their amazement that they like it. Exceptionally good sound," AUDITOR. (Playing time 54 mins.)

HCR 5211 **$2.00**

CATALOGUE OF DOVER BOOKS

J. S. BACH: PARTITAS FOR UNACCOMPANIED VIOLIN: #2 in D Minor and #3 in E, Bronislav Gimpel. Bach's works for unaccompanied violin fall within the same area that produced the Brandenburg Concerti, the Orchestral Suites, and the first part of the Well-Tempered Clavichord. The D Minor is considered one of Bach's masterpieces; the E Major is a buoyant work with exceptionally interesting bariolage effects. This is the first release of a truly memorable recording by Bronislav Gimpel, "as a violinist, the equal of the greatest" (P. Leron, in OPERA, Paris). (Playing time 53 mins.)   HCR 5212 **$2.00**

ROSSINI: QUARTETS FOR WOODWINDS: #1 IN F, #4 IN B FLAT, #5 IN D, AND #6 IN F, N. Y. Woodwind Quartet Members: S. Baron, Flute, J. Barrows, French Horn; B. Garfield, Bassoon; D. Glazer, Clarinet. Rossini's great genius was centered in the opera, but he also wrote a small amount of first-rate non-vocal music. Among these instrumental works, first place is usually given to the very interesting quartets. Of the three different surviving arrangements, this wind group version is the original, and this is the first recording of these works. "Each member of the group displays wonderful virtuosity when the music calls for it, at other times blending sensitively into the ensemble," HIGH FIDELITY. "Sheer delight," Philip Miller. (Playing time 45 mins.)   HCR 5214 **$2.00**

TELEMANN: THE GERMAN FANTASIAS FOR HARPSICHORD (#1-12), Helma Elsner. Until recently, Georg Philip Telemann (1681-1767) was one of the mysteriously neglected great men of music. Recently he has received the attention he deserved. He created music that delights modern listeners with its freshness and originality. These fantasias are free in form and reveal the intricacy of thorough bass music, the harmonic wealth of the "new music," and a distinctive melodic beauty. "This is another blessing of the contemporary LP output. Miss Elsner plays with considerable sensitivity and a great deal of understanding," REV. OF RECORDED MUSIC. "Fine recorded sound," Harold Schonberg. "Recommended warmly, very high quality," DISQUES. (Playing time 50 mins.)   HCR 5210 **$2.00**

Nova Recordings

In addition to our reprints of outstanding out-of-print records and American releases of first-rate foreign recordings, we have established our own new records. In order to keep every phase of their production under our own control, we have engaged musicians of world renown to play important music (for the most part unavailable elsewhere), have made use of the finest recording studios in New York, and have produced tapes equal to anything on the market, we believe. The first of these entirely new records are now available.

RAVEL: GASPARD DE LA NUIT, LE TOMBEAU DE COUPERIN, JEUX D'EAU, Beveridge Webster, Piano. Webster studied under Ravel and played his works in European recitals, often with Ravel's personal participation in the program. This record offers examples of the three major periods of Ravel's pianistic work, and is a must for any serious collector or music lover. (Playing time about 50 minutes).   Monaural HCR 5213 **$2.00**
                           Stereo HCR ST 7000 **$2.00**

EIGHTEENTH CENTURY FRENCH FLUTE MUSIC, Jean-Pierre Rampal, Flute, and Robert Veyron-Lacroix, Harpsichord. Contains Concerts Royaux #7 for Flute and Harpsichord in G Minor, Francois Couperin; Sonata. dite l'Inconnue in G for Flute and Harpsichord, Michel de la Barre; Sonata #6 in A Minor, Michel Blavet; and Sonata in D Minor, Anne Danican-Philidor. In the opinion of many Rampal is the world's premier flutist. (Playing time about 45 minutes)
                           Monaural HCR 5238 **$2.00**
                           Stereo HCR ST 7001 **$2.00**

SCHUMANN: NOVELLETTEN (Opus 21), Beveridge Webster, Piano. Brilliantly played in this original recording by one of America's foremost keyboard performers. Connected Romantic pieces. Long a piano favorite. (Playing time about 45 minutes)
                           Monaural HCR 5239 **$2.00**
                           Stereo HCR ST 7002 **$2.30**

New Books

101 PATCHWORK PATTERNS, Ruby Short McKim. With no more ability than the fundamentals of ordinary sewing, you will learn to make over 100 beautiful quilts: flowers, rainbows, Irish chains, fish and bird designs, leaf designs, unusual geometric patterns, many others. Cutting designs carefully diagrammed and described, suggestions for materials, yardage estimates, step-by-step instructions, plus entertaining stories of origins of quilt names, other folklore. Revised 1962. 101 full-sized patterns. 140 illustrations. Index. 128pp. 7⅞ x 10¾.
T773 Paperbound **$1.85**

ESSENTIAL GRAMMAR SERIES
By concentrating on the essential core of material that constitutes the semantically most important forms and areas of a language and by stressing explanation (often bringing parallel English forms into the discussion) rather than rote memory, this new series of grammar books is among the handiest language aids ever devised. Designed by linguists and teachers for adults with limited learning objectives and learning time, these books omit nothing important, yet they teach more usable language material and do it more quickly and permanently than any other self-study material. Clear and rigidly economical, they concentrate upon immediately usable language material, logically organized so that related material is always presented together. Any reader of typical capability can use them to refresh his grasp of language, to supplement self-study language records or conventional grammars used in schools, or to begin language study on his own. Now available:

ESSENTIAL GERMAN GRAMMAR, Dr. Guy Stern & E. F. Bleiler. Index. Glossary of terms. 128pp. 5⅜ x 8.
T422 Paperbound **$1.00**

ESSENTIAL FRENCH GRAMMAR, Dr. Seymour Resnick. Index. Cognate list. Glossary. 159pp. 5⅜ x 8.
T419 Paperbound **$1.00**

ESSENTIAL ITALIAN GRAMMAR, Dr. Olga Ragusa. Index. Glossary. 111pp. 5⅜ x 8.
T779 Paperbound · **$1.00**

ESSENTIAL SPANISH GRAMMAR, Dr. Seymour Resnick. Index. 50-page cognate list. Glossary. 138pp. 5⅜ x 8.
T780 Paperbound **$1.00**

PHILOSOPHIES OF MUSIC HISTORY: A Study of General Histories of Music, 1600-1960, Warren D. Allen. Unquestionably one of the most significant documents yet to appear in musicology, this thorough survey covers the entire field of historical research in music. An influential masterpiece of scholarship, it includes early music histories; theories on the ethos of music; lexicons, dictionaries and encyclopedias of music; musical historiography through the centuries; philosophies of music history; scores of related topics. Copiously documented. New preface brings work up to 1960. Index. 317-item bibliography. 9 illustrations; 3 full-page plates. 5⅜ x 8½. xxxiv + 382pp.
T282 Paperbound **$2.00**

MR. DOOLEY ON IVRYTHING AND IVRYBODY, Finley Peter Dunne. The largest collection in print of hilarious utterances by the irrepressible Irishman of Archey Street, one of the most vital characters in American fiction. Gathered from the half dozen books that appeared during the height of Mr. Dooley's popularity, these 102 pieces are all unaltered and uncut, and they are all remarkably fresh and pertinent even today. Selected and edited by Robert Hutchinson. 5⅜ x 8½. xii + 244pp.
T626 Paperbound **$1.00**

TREATISE ON PHYSIOLOGICAL OPTICS, Hermann von Helmholtz. Despite new investigations, this important work will probably remain preeminent. Contains everything known about physiological optics up to 1925, covering scores of topics under the general headings of dioptrics of the eye, sensations of vision, and perecptions of vision. Von Helmholtz's voluminous data are all included, as are extensive supplementary matter incorporated into the third German edition, new material prepared for 1925 English edition, and copious textual annotations by J. P. C. Southall. The most exhaustive treatise ever prepared on the subject, it has behind it a list of contributors that will never again be duplicated. Translated and edited by J. P. C. Southall. Bibliography. Indexes. 312 illustrations. 3 volumes bound as 2. Total of 1749pp. 5⅜ x 8.
S15-16 Two volume set, Clothbound **$15.00**

THE ARTISTIC ANATOMY OF TREES, Rex Vicat Cole. Even the novice with but an elementary knowledge of drawing and none of the structure of trees can learn to draw, paint trees from this systematic, lucid instruction book. Copiously illustrated with the author's own sketches, diagrams, and 50 paintings from the early Renaissance to today, it covers composition; structure of twigs, boughs, buds, branch systems; outline forms of major species; how leaf is set on twig; flowers and fruit and their arrangement; etc. 500 illustrations. Bibliography. Indexes. 347pp. 5⅜ x 8.
T1016 Clothbound **$4.50**

HOW PLANTS GET THEIR NAMES, L. H. Bailey. In this basic introduction to botanical nomenclature, a famed expert on plants and plant life reveals the confusion that can result from misleading common names of plants and points out the fun and advantage of using a sound, scientific approach. Covers every aspect of the subject, including an historical survey beginning before Linnaeus systematized nomenclature, the literal meaning of scores of Latin names, their English equivalents, etc. Enthusiastically written and easy to follow, this handbook for gardeners, amateur horticulturalists, and beginning botany students is knowledgeable, accurate and useful. 11 illustrations. Lists of Latin, English botanical names. 192pp. 5⅜ x 8½. T796 Paperbound **$1.15**

PIERRE CURIE, Marie Curie. Nobel Prize winner creates a memorable portrait of her equally famous husband in a fine scientific biography. Recounting his childhood, his haphazard education, and his experimental research (with his brother) in the physics of crystals, Mme. Curie brings to life the strong, determined personality of a great scientist at work and discusses, in clear, straightforward terms, her husband's and her own work with radium and radioactivity. A great book about two very great founders of modern science. Includes Mme. Curie's autobiographical notes. Translated by Charlotte and Vernon Kellogg. viii + 120pp. 5⅜ x 8½. T199 Paperbound **$1.00**

STYLES IN PAINTING: A Comparative Study, Paul Zucker. Professor of Art History at Cooper Union presents an important work of art-understanding that will guide you to a fuller, deeper appreciation of masterpieces of art and at the same time add to your understanding of how they fit into the evolution of style from the earliest times to this century. Discusses general principles of historical method and aesthetics, history of styles, then illustrates with more than 230 great paintings organized by subject matter so you can see at a glance how styles have changed through the centuries. 236 beautiful halftones. xiv + 338pp. 5⅝ x 8½. T760 Paperbound **$2.00**

NEW VARIORUM EDITION OF SHAKESPEARE

One of the monumental feats of Shakespeare scholarship is the famous New Variorum edition, containing full texts of the plays together with an entire reference library worth of historical and critical information: all the variant readings that appear in the quartos and folios; annotations by leading scholars from the earliest days of Shakespeare criticism to the date of publication; essays on meaning, background, productions by Johnson, Addison, Fielding, Lessing, Hazlitt, Coleridge, Ulrici, Swinburne, and other major Shakespeare critics; original sources of Shakespeare's inspiration. For the first time, this definitive edition of Shakespeare's plays, each printed in a separate volume, will be available in inexpensive editions to scholars, to teachers and students, and to every lover of Shakespeare and fine literature. Now ready:

KING LEAR, edited by Horace Howard Furness. Bibliography. List of editions collated in notes. viii + 503pp. 5⅜ x 8½. T1000 Paperbound **$2.25**

MACBETH, edited by Horace Howard Furness Jr. Bibliography. List of editions collated in notes. xvi + 562pp. 5⅜ x 8½. T1001 Paperbound **$2.25**

ROMEO AND JULIET, edited by Horace Howard Furness. Bibliography. List of editions collated in notes. xxvi + 480pp. 5⅜ x 8½. T1002 Paperbound **$2.25**

OTTHELLO, edited by Horace Howard Furness. Bibliography. List of editions collated in notes. x + 471pp. 5⅜ x 8½. T1003 Paperbound **$2.25**

HAMLET, edited by Horace Howard Furness. Bibliography. List of editions collated in notes. Total of 926pp. 5⅜ x 8½. T1004-1005 Two volume set, Paperbound **$4.50**

THE GARDENER'S YEAR, Karel Capek. The author of this refreshingly funny book is probably best known in U. S. as the author of "R. U. R.," a biting satire on the machine age. Here, his satiric genius finds expression in a wholly different vein: a warm, witty chronicle of the joys and trials of the amateur gardener as he watches over his plants, his soil and the weather from January to December. 59 drawings by Joseph Capek add an important second dimension to the fun. "Mr. Capek writes with sympathy, understanding and humor," NEW YORK TIMES. "Will delight the amateur gardener, and indeed everyone else," SATURDAY REVIEW. Translated by M. and R. Weatherall. 59 illustrations. 159pp. 4½ x 6½. T1014 Paperbound **$1.00**

THE ADVANCE OF THE FUNGI, E. C. Large. The dramatic story of the battle against fungi, from the year the potato blight hit Europe (1845) to 1940, and of men who fought and won it: Pasteur, Anton de Bary, Tulasne, Berkeley, Woronin, Jensen, many others. Combines remarkable grasp of facts and their significance with skill to write dramatic, exciting prose. "Philosophically witty, fundamentally thoughtful, always mature," NEW YORK HERALD TRIBUNE. "Highly entertaining, intelligent, penetrating," NEW YORKER. Bibliography. 64 illustrations. 6 full-page plates. 488pp. 5⅜ x 8½. T437 Paperbound **$2.25**

THE PAINTER'S METHODS AND MATERIALS, A. P. Laurie. Adviser to the British Royal Academy discusses the ills that paint is heir to and the methods most likely to counteract them. Examining 48 masterpieces by Fra Lippo Lippi, Millais, Boucher, Rembrandt, Romney, Van Eyck, Velazquez, Michaelangelo, Botticelli, Frans Hals, Turner, and others, he tries to discover how special and unique effects were achieved. Not conjectural information, but certain and authoritative. Beautiful, sharp reproductions, plus textual illustrations of apparatus and the results of experiments with pigments and media. 63 illustrations and diagrams. Index. 250pp. 5⅜ x 8. T1019 Clothbound **$3.75**

CHANCE, LUCK AND STATISTICS, H. C. Levinson. The theory of chance, or probability, and the science of statistics presented in simple, non-technical language. Covers fundamentals by analyzing games of chance, then applies those fundamentals to immigration and birth rates, operations research, stock speculation, insurance rates, advertising, and other fields. Excellent course supplement and a delightful introduction for non-mathematicians. Formerly "The Science of Chance." Index. xiv + 356pp. 5⅜ x 8. T1007 Paperbound **$1.85**

THROUGH THE ALIMENTARY CANAL WITH GUN AND CAMERA: A Fascinating Trip to the Interior, George S. Chappell. An intrepid explorer, better known as a major American humorist, accompanied by imaginary camera-man and botanist, conducts this unforgettably hilarious journey to the human interior. Wildly imaginative, his account satirizes academic pomposity, parodies cliché-ridden travel literature, and cleverly uses facts of physiology for comic purposes. All the original line drawings by Otto Soglow are included to add to the merriment. Preface by Robert Benchley. 17 illustrations. xii + 116pp. 5⅜ x 8½. T376 Paperbound **$1.00**

TALKS TO TEACHERS ON PSYCHOLOGY and to Students on Some of Life's Ideals, William James. America's greatest psychologist invests these lectures with immense personal charm, invaluable insights, and superb literary style. 15 Harvard lectures, 3 lectures delivered to students in New England touch upon psychology and the teaching of art, stream of consciousness, the child as a behaving organism, education and behavior, association of ideas, the gospel of relaxation, what makes life significant, and other related topics. Interesting, and still vital pedagogy. x + 146pp. 5⅜ x 8½. T261 Paperbound **$1.00**

A WHIMSEY ANTHOLOGY, collected by Carolyn Wells. Delightful verse on the lighter side: logical whimsies, poems shaped like decanters and flagons, lipograms and acrostics, alliterative verse, enigmas and charades, anagrams, linguistic and dialectic verse, tongue twisters, limericks, travesties, and just about very other kind of whimsical poetry ever written. Works by Edward Lear, Gelett Burgess, Poe, Lewis Carroll, Henley, Robert Herrick, Christina Rossetti, scores of other poets will entertain and amuse you for hours. Index. xiv + 221pp. 5⅜ x 8½. T1020 Paperbound **$1.25**

LANDSCAPE PAINTING, R. O. Dunlop. A distinguished modern artist is a perfect guide to the aspiring landscape painter. This practical book imparts to even the uninitiated valuable methods and techniques. Useful advice is interwoven throughout a fascinating illustrated history of landscape painting, from Ma Yüan to Picasso. 60 half-tone reproductions of works by Giotto, Giovanni Bellini, Piero della Francesca, Tintoretto, Giorgione, Raphael, Van Ruisdael, Poussin, Gainsborough, Monet, Cezanne, Seurat, Picasso, many others. Total of 71 illustrations, 4 in color. Index. 192pp. 7⅜ x 10. T1018 Clothbound **$6.00**

PRACTICAL LANDSCAPE PAINTING, Adrian Stokes. A complete course in landscape painting that trains the senses to perceive as well as the hand to apply the principles underlying the pictorial aspect of nature. Author fully explains tools, value and nature of various colors, and instructs beginners in clear, simple terms how to apply them. Places strong emphasis on drawing and composition, foundations often neglected in painting texts. Includes pictorial-textual survey of the art from Ancient China to the present, with helpful critical comments and numerous diagrams illustrating every stage. 93 illustrations. Index. 256pp. 5⅜ x 8. T1017 Clothbound **$3.75**

PELLUCIDAR, THREE NOVELS: AT THE EARTH'S CORE, PELLUCIDAR, TANAR OF PELLUCIDAR, Edgar Rice Burroughs. The first three novels of adventure in the thrill-filled world within the hollow interior of the earth. David Innes's mechanical mole drills through the outer crust and precipitates him into an astonishing world. Among Burroughs's most popular work. Illustrations by J. Allan St. John. 5⅜ x 8½. T1051 Paperbound **$2.00**
T1050 Clothbound **$3.75**

JOE MILLER'S JESTS OR, THE WITS VADE-MECUM. Facsimile of the first edition of famous 18th century collection of repartees, bons mots, puns and jokes, the father of the humor anthology. A first-hand look at the taste of fashionable London in the Age of Pope. 247 entertaining anecdotes, many involving well-known personages such as Colley Cibber, Sir Thomas More, Rabelais, rich in humor, historic interest. New introduction contains biographical information on Joe Miller, fascinating history of his enduring collection, bibliographical information on collections of comic material. Introduction by Robert Hutchinson. 96pp. 5⅜ x 8½.
Paperbound **$1.00**

THE HUMOROUS WORLD OF JEROME K. JEROME. Complete essays and extensive passages from nine out-of-print books ("Three Men on Wheels," "Novel Notes," "Told After Supper," "Sketches in Lavender, Blue and Green," "American Wives and Others," 4 more) by a highly original humorist, author of the novel "Three Men in a Boat." Human nature is JKJ's subject: the problems of husbands, of wives, of tourists, of the human animal trapped in the drawing room. His sympathetic acceptance of the shortcomings of his race and his ability to see humor in almost any situation make this a treasure for those who know his work and a pleasant surprise for those who don't. Edited and with an introduction by Robert Hutchinson. xii + 260pp. 5⅜ x 8½. T58 Paperbound **$1.00**

CATALOGUE OF DOVER BOOKS

GEOMETRY OF FOUR DIMENSIONS, H. P. Manning. Unique in English as a clear, concise intro- duction to this fascinating subject. Treatment is primarily synthetic and Euclidean, although hyperplanes and hyperspheres at infinity are considered by non-Euclidean forms. Historical introduction and foundations of 4-dimensional geometry; perpendicularity; simple angles; angles of planes; higher order; symmetry; order, motion; hyperpyramids, hypercones, hyper- spheres; figures with parallel elements; volume, hypervolume in space; regular polyhedroids. Glossary of terms. 74 illustrations. ix + 348pp. 5⅜ x 8. S182 Paperbound **$2.00**

PAPER FOLDING FOR BEGINNERS, W. D. Murray and F. J. Rigney. A delightful introduction to the varied and entertaining Japanese art of origami (paper folding), with a full, crystal-clear text that anticipates every difficulty; over 275 clearly labeled diagrams of all important stages in creation. You get results at each stage, since complex figures are logically developed from simpler ones. 43 different pieces are explained: sailboats, frogs, roosters, etc. 6 photographic plates. 279 diagrams. 95pp. 5⅝ x 8⅜. T713 Paperbound **$1.00**

SATELLITES AND SCIENTIFIC RESEARCH, D. King-Hele. An up-to-the-minute non-technical ac- count of the man-made satellites and the discoveries they have yielded up to September of 1961. Brings together information hitherto published only in hard-to-get scientific journals. In- cludes the life history of a typical satellite, methods of tracking, new information on the shape of the earth, zones of radiation, etc. Over 60 diagrams and 6 photographs. Mathemati- cal appendix. Bibliography of over 100 items. Index. xii + 180pp. 5⅜ x 8½. T703 Paperbound **$2.00**

LOUIS PASTEUR, S. J. Holmes. A brief, very clear, and warmly understanding biography of the great French scientist by a former Professor of Zoology in the University of California. Traces his home life, the fortunate effects of his education, his early researches and first theses, and his constant struggle with superstition and institutionalism in his work on microorganisms, fermentation, anthrax, rabies, etc. New preface by the author. 159pp. 5⅜ x 8. T197 Paperbound **$1.00**

THE ENJOYMENT OF CHESS PROBLEMS, K. S. Howard. A classic treatise on this minor art by an internationally recognized authority that gives a basic knowledge of terms and themes for the everyday chess player as well as the problem fan: 7 chapters on the two-mover; 7 more on 3- and 4-move problems; a chapter on selfmates; and much more. "The most important one-volume contribution originating solely in the U.S.A.," Alain White. 200 diagrams. Index. Solutions, viii + 212pp. 5⅜ x 8. T742 Paperbound **$1.25**

SAM LOYD AND HIS CHESS PROBLEMS, Alain C. White. Loyd was (for all practical purposes) the father of the American chess problem and his protégé and successor presents here the diamonds of his production, chess problems embodying a whimsy and bizarre fancy entirely unique. More than 725 in all, ranging from two-move to extremely elaborate five-movers, including Loyd's contributions to chess oddities—problems in which pieces are arranged to form initials, figures, other by-paths of chess problem found nowhere else. Classified accord- ing to major concept, with full text analyzing problems, containing selections from Loyd's own writings. A classic to challenge your ingenuity, increase your skill. Corrected republica- tion of 1913 edition. Over 750 diagrams and illustrations. 744 problems with solutions. 471pp. 5⅜ x 8½. T928 Paperbound **$2.25**

FABLES IN SLANG & MORE FABLES IN SLANG, George Ade. 2 complete books of major American humorist in pungent colloquial tradition of Twain, Billings. 1st reprinting in over 30 years includes "The Two Mandolin Players and the Willing Performer," "The Base Ball Fan Who Took the Only Known Cure," "The Slim Girl Who Tried to Keep a Date that was Never Made," 42 other tales of eccentric, perverse, but always funny characters. "Touch of genius," H. L. Mencken. New introduction by E. F. Bleiler. 86 illus. 208pp. 5⅜ x 8. T533 Paperbound **$1.00**

Prices subject to change without notice.

Dover publishes books on art, music, philosophy, literature, languages, history, social sciences, psychology, handcrafts, orientalia, puzzles and entertainments, chess, pets and gardens, books explaining science, intermediate and higher mathematics, math- ematical physics, engineering, biological sciences, earth sciences, classics of science, etc. Write to:

Dept. catrr.
Dover Publications, Inc.
180 Varick Street, N.Y. 14, N.Y.